THE SEARCH FOR SPEED UNDER SAIL

THE SEARCH FOR SPEED UNDER SAIL

1700 - 1855

BY HOWARD I. CHAPELLE

BONANZA BOOKS • NEW YORK

Contents

Illustrations

Plates

Text Plates

PLATES

PLATES

PLATES

Schooner, Packet, and Clipper Plates

Introduction

THE HISTORY OF THE DEVELOPMENT OF SAILING VESSEL DESIGN IN THE UNITED States is closely concerned with the so-called "clipper" ships. For many reasons, which will be discussed, speed under sail was widely sought and has become the standard by which most marine historians measure progress in American naval architecture during the period of sail.

Speed under sail has commonly been judged solely by "record passages" between ports and by record "day's runs." These take no account of the difference in the size of competing ships, nor of their loadings. Record passages were sometimes made when the fastest hour's run was at a relatively low speed. Such passages were often accountable to exceptionally favorable wind and weather and to good command, rather than to good ship design.

Such modes of judging the progress of American sailing ship design are obviously not accurate. There is need for an examination of what constitutes "speed" under sail; what it is in the design of a sailing vessel that decides the range of speed obtained, and under what conditions speed can be expected. This is not a matter of simple definition, for there are various determinations of what speeds are "fast" under specific conditions of weather, wind, and course. These factors must all be considered.

Speed comparisons of ships and vessels varying widely in size and construction date require a "dimensionless" analysis of each in order to establish an accurate evaluation of relative design excellence.

By applying modern projections and some elementary principles of naval architecture and hydrodynamics to plans of American-built sailing vessels, it is possible to explore the development of the art of fast sailing ship and vessel design in North America. The process will produce a more realistic evaluation of competing ship designs. This will require use of mathematics to establish the dimensionless factors necessary. Though this is not, perhaps, a glamorous treatment compared to the "fast" voyage or day's run, technically it is far more precise. What is lacking in thrilling description—of "hard-driving" skippers, desperate crews, and wild weather—is balanced by an interest in the exploration of the real areas of progress in American sailing ship design as an art and science. The relation of hull design and performance is one of the fascinating problems of the naval architect, but one rarely discussed from the historical, technical, and lay aspects. This will be attempted in order to obtain a better understanding and appreciation of the progress made in American naval architecture, from early colonial times to the final development of the clipper ship.

This report has been made not to support or to prove any theory of development in American sailing ship and vessel design, but to record the author's efforts to arrive at some sound conclusions as to exactly what American ship and vessel designers were capable of, in high-speed sailing hull-design during the great period of sail.

The plans used in this study were drawn as accurately as the original sources and skill of the author-draftsman permitted. Where the lines were interpreted in the drawings to any serious degree, the matter will be mentioned. In some instances deck arrangements and external details have been reconstructed from available data, in order that the plans might be used for future scale-model construction, for exhibition in the Hall of American Merchant Shipping, where the drawings will finally be deposited. These superficial additions, however, do not affect the validity of the hull analysis in any case, and they require no extensive description or explanation here. Most of the sail plans are necessarily redrawn from tables of spar dimensions, and therefore entail some reconstruction also.

Acknowledgments

THE AUTHOR DESIRES TO EXPRESS HIS THANKS FOR THE ASSISTANCE HE HAS RE-ceived in the long study of sailing ships incident to the preparation of this work. The staff of the National Maritime Museum, Greenwich, England, has been both patient and generous for many years in satisfying the author's curios-ity regarding ships' plans in the Admiralty Collection of Draughts. Every aid was given by Mr. Frank C. G. Carr, Mr. George Naish, Commander Arthur H. Waite, Mr. Michael Robinson, and Mr. Arthur Tucker. The Trustees of the museum have been most gracious. The staff of the Science Museum, London, England, was also most helpful.

Mr. William Salisbury and Mr. David MacGregor, authorities on ship-building history, have given much aid and pointed out many useful lines of inquiry. Lt. Col. M. E. S. Laws, in carrying out searches for information on American ships in the Public Records Office in London, has brought to light much valuable technical information from the Admiralty correspondence, surveys, and journals.

The staff of the Danish National Archives at Copenhagen, the staffs of the Swedish National Maritime Museum at Stockholm, and of the Swedish National Archives and the Director of the Bergens Sjøfarts Museum at Bergen, Norway, all gave generously of their time and knowledge.

The assistance received from the staffs of the Maritime Museum Prins Hendrik, Rotterdam, Holland, and of the Musée de la Marine, Paris, France, must also be acknowledged. I am deeply indebted to Commander José M. Martinez-Hidalgo, Director of the Museo Maritimo, Barcelona, Spain, for

ACKNOWLEDGMENTS

plans and other information concerning Spanish naval architecture in the period under study.

I am also indebted to the numerous American institutions—Portsmouth, N. H., Athenaeum; The Mariners' House, Boston; the Museum of Fine Arts, Boston; the Museum of History and Technology, Smithsonian Institution, Washington, D. C.; the Museum of the City of New York; the Mystic Seaport Marine Historical Association, Mystic, Conn.; the Mariners' Museum, Newport News, Va.; the Medford Historical Society, Medford, Mass.; the Peabody Marine Museum, Salem, Mass.; the Pratt Institute, M. I. T., Cambridge, Mass.; and the Webb Institute of Naval Architecture, Glen Cove, N. Y.—for making collections of plans, offsets, half-models, and documents available.

Individual collectors of material on naval architecture, both at home and abroad, have been most helpful: the late Ray Taft, Hingham, Mass.; Mr. D. Foster Taylor, Quincy, Mass.; Mr. William C. Kelley, Brainerd, Minn.; and Mr. John Stevens, Halifax, N.S. are among these.

The late Captain Harold E. Saunders, U.S.N.; Professor Cedric Ridgely-Nevitt; Mr. William A. Baker, N. A.; and Charles Wittholz, N. A.; have been of great assistance with their professional comments.

Acknowledgment must be made to Mr. Merritt Edson, Jr., Mr. William Earle Geoghegan, and Mr. James Knowles for their assistance with the drawings used in this study. Miss Mary E. Braunagel and Mr. Roger Pineau contributed much by their assistance with the text, both in preparation and editing. Dr. Philip K. Lundeberg, Curator in Charge, Division of Naval History, Department of Armed Forces History, Museum of History and Technology, Smithsonian Institution, and Dr. Melvin H. Jackson, of the Transportation Division, contributed research material.

Finally, I must thank the Museum of History and Technology, Smithsonian Institution, for the continuing opportunities for research that have been made possible during the study and its preparation for publication.

Howard I. Chapelle

THE SEARCH FOR SPEED UNDER SAIL

CHAPTER • ONE

The Status of Naval Architecture and Shipbuilding in the 18th Century

IN ALL FORMS OF TRANSPORTATION AN INCREASE IN SPEED OF MOVEMENT HAS been sought and has been accepted as a fundamental indication of progress. Even in the relatively slow movement of heavy bulk cargoes, on land or sea, an increase in speed is considered desirable, provided the inherent increase in cost can be made acceptable by existing or expected freight rates.

Throughout the ages when waterborne transportation was almost entirely in sailing craft, the desire for increased speed was as strong as it is today. If economic and other factors permitted, this desire was satisfied. In American merchant vessels of the colonial period, however, speed was not sought for its own sake alone. Fast sailing in a vessel became preferable to any commercial insurance policy, for speed under sail might not only preserve the vessel and cargo but might also save the liberties and even the lives of crew and passengers. The long wars at sea of this period and the lawlessness that characterized the short periods of peace made the trade routes unsafe for the colonial trader unless he had a "fleet and nimble" vessel. At the same time, the privateer, picaroon, or man-of-war needed speed to overtake a fleeing vessel or to escape from a too-powerful foe. In war the colonial shipbuilder would be asked to produce the fast privateer or the blockade-runner. In peace he would be asked to produce a fast carrier that could outrun a pirate. Or he might be asked to produce a fast smuggler.

The illegal trades of the American colonial merchant marine were not the mere expression of a group of lawless shipowners; they were the result of desperate efforts to supply the colonies with necessary products denied them by the mother country through restrictions on normal, legal trades, or by the closing of ports and coasts by European powers. The necessity that the colonial Americans obtain products from the West Indies and trade there in order to maintain even a limited economy, created what was probably the most important smuggling trade. It is now impossible to state with any accuracy the economic value of the illegal West Indian trades, for no intelligent merchant would keep any incriminating records, and government archives merely register the failures in these trades. But the British efforts to establish revenue agents and vessels in the colonies show that the trades were certainly active and probably highly profitable.

The American Revolution further increased the demand for speed under sail, for speed meant survival for the trader or privateer. After the war the young republic was weak, and for a time without the protection of a navy. Again, fast sailing was good insurance for any merchantman. With the outbreak of the French Revolution and throughout the Napoleonic wars until 1816, fast sailing vessels were in great demand. Privateer, coastal trader, blockade-runner and smuggler: all needed speed. Slow carriers that ventured out of American ports were too often the victims of a foreign man-of-war or privateer, which meant heavy financial losses for the owners.

The successful illegal trader, whether smuggler or blockade-runner, was usually designed for her business. Illegal trade is concerned with relatively expensive cargoes, for which there is greater demand than supply. Such cargoes retained their high value for long periods, unless the market somehow became glutted. Even with all possible precautions and the fastest vessel obtainable, the illegal trader always ran the great risk of capture and economic loss. Hence he usually operated with the practical minimum in capital risk. This could be done by building the smuggling vessel or blockade-runner as cheaply as possible, consistent with the need for speed. A small, cheap vessel not only required less capital risk, but her small cargo would not be apt to glut the market after a successful run.

Small vessels were therefore characteristic of the colonial smugglers and blockade-runners. They were usually sloops or schooners, and occasionally brigantines or brigs; all were built for speed, but were low in construction cost. During the French Revolution and Napoleonic wars, however, the widespread demand for the belligerent nations for large quantities of goods lessened the probability of glutting the market, and brought about the use of some large schooners and brigantines as illegal traders. Some of these were expensively built on the principle that "money makes the mare go." During this period blockade-running was so profitable that some owners could afford a few heavy capital risks—an exceptional condition in the illegal trades.

Even in the most profitable periods, however, sailing ships built as blockade-runners or illegal traders were usually under 110 feet in length. Such vessels would be "experimental" in the sense that speed under sail was of paramount importance, at the sacrifice or compromise of other normally desirable qualities. Large vessels in the dangerous illegal trades would attract too much attention because of mere size; and their capacity would make them conspicuous because of the unusual amount of activity entailed in the assembly of a cargo.

The sporting instincts in some of the more venturesome shipowners added to the demand for fast sailing vessels. Among the colonial traders and sailing-ship owners, some had a liking for fast vessels, just as many merchants of the times coveted fast horses. For the well-to-do sportsmen among the shipowners, a fast sailer had enough sporting or social prestige to compensate for its limited cargo capacity and earning power.

Before discussing the development of fast sailing vessels in America it is necessary to decide where to begin, and to establish the general state of ship design at that time. Records of the American colonial period are extremely limited in material suitable for technical analysis. This is due to the loss of many shipbuilding records, to the lack of plans, particularly of fast, experimental types; and to the general state of the art of ship design. The scarcity of suitable plans for the fast, progressive, small craft drawn before 1700 makes it impractical to analyze the individual designs before this date; and there is only a limited amount of useful material antedating 1760. Nevertheless, 1700 represents a convenient date for the beginning of this study, for it precedes the recorded appearance of any fast-sailing American type of vessel that in the light of present knowledge can be said to have been entirely distinctive in design.

The material employed for this examination of the design of American fast sailing vessels is necessarily contemporary and technical. Plans, design data, and competent testimony are required; and the contemporary books on naval architecture, written and published before 1851, are inadequate for this purpose. The known American collections of ship plans and shipbuilding papers contain no material of earlier date than the American Revolution and are not particularly useful until after 1794. Fortunately an interest in American-designed and -built vessels among European navies led to foreign collections of plans and other useful data. Much of this material has been preserved and is available for reference.

The Admiralty Collection of Draughts is the most prolific source of technical material on American-built vessels for the period prior to 1815. This great library of plans is now in the National Maritime Museum at Greenwich, England. It is basically a naval collection, extending back to 1675. However it contains plans of many purchased and captured vessels such as privateers, blockade-runners, and illegal traders, as well as merchant vessels occasionally purchased by the navy. In certain periods American-built vessels were taken into the service in great numbers by the Royal Navy and plans of some of these have been identified. This collection of ship plans is therefore a most important reference. As for documents other than plans, the Admiralty papers in the National Maritime Museum and in the Public Records Office in London are most useful sources. There are a few private collections of plans and documents, but in the main these are of limited value in this discussion.

On the Continent the naval archives of Denmark and Sweden are useful and a few plans of American-built vessels, some of very great value, are found there. A few such plans are in the marine museums of Norway, Holland, and France. The latter country must have had a great deal of American technical material in its naval records, but unfortunately the plans and related papers were maintained in the dockyards and local museums and many of these were destroyed during the First and Second World Wars. This is also true of Germany. The records of Spain, Portugal, and Italy have not yet been fully explored. It is probable that some material from these and other countries in southern Europe and in South America will eventually come to light, but it is doubtful that these sources would do more than supplement the plan material now available.

The plans obtained from these various sources consist of the lines plans showing the shape of the hull, and occasionally of details of the deck layout and outboard appearance. Spar dimensions are sometimes available, but the structural details are commonly omitted, before 1800 at least. Sail plans are relatively rare until after 1800 and rigging details are extremely rare throughout the whole period of sail. Documentary evidence such as contracts for the construction of new vessels, surveys of craft being purchased, and references to the quality of performance in individual vessels, is extremely spotty and often far from satisfactory. Nevertheless there is sufficient material available for most aspects of this discussion.

The paucity of published material on naval architecture dealing with actual design practices, before 1850, has been mentioned. It may be well to establish what works may have been available to American shipbuilders in this period, 1700 to 1850, before tracing the progress of the art of ship design up to the middle of the nineteenth century in America.

In the years before 1850, only one book on naval architecture originated in America: Lauchlan M'Kay's *The Practical Shipbuilder* (New York, Collins Keese and Company, 1839). It carried the subtitle "containing the best mechanical and philosophical principles for construction of different classes of vessels, and the practical adaption of their several parts, with the rules carefully detailed. The whole being plainly and comprehensively arranged for the instruction of the inexperienced." Lauchlan was the brother of Donald M'Kay, a noted designer and builder of clipper ships. Lauchlan M'Kay had been an Isaac Webb apprentice and was a naval architect, shipbuilder, and sea captain in his long and versatile career. Though obviously intended to explain the process of design, his book omits any important discussion of hull form for a given requirement, but as was usual, it shows variations in design in the plates.

No other American work on this subject appeared until John W. Griffiths began to publish his books and articles on ship design in 1851. However, a technical book was published at Pittsburgh in 1845—*The Shipwrights' Own Book* by George W. Rogers—which dealt with the projection of lines in drawings only; no design matters of moment were described in it.

It is possible that many English books on ship design were brought to America, though there are very few references to the possession of any of these books by an American shipbuilder. Among the more important publications that may have reached American hands are the following: John Hardingham's *The Accomplished Shipwright and Mariner* (London, John Thornton, 1706 and a 1709 reprint); William Sutherland's *The Shipbuilder's Assistant* (London, Thomas Page, W. and F. Mount, 1726; 2nd edition, London; Mount and Page, 1784); William Southerland's [*sic*] *Britain's Glory or Shipbuilding Unveiled* (London, A. Betteworth, 1729; 2nd edition, London, W. Mount and Thos. Page, 1740); Mungo Muray's *A Treatise on Shipbuilding and Navigation* (London, A. Millar, 1765); Marmaduke Stalkaart's *Naval Architecture or Rudiments and Rules of Shipbuilding* (London, author, 1781); Anonymous, *The Shipbuilder's Repository* (London, author, no date); Samuel Hutchinson's *A Treatise on Practical Seamanship and Naval Architecture* (Liverpool, author, 1787)—there were three editions of Hutchinson's book; Thomas Gordon's *Principles of Naval Architecture* (London, Thomas Evans, 1789); David Steel's *Naval Architecture* (London, C. Whittingham, 1805)—there were other editions of Steel's work in 1812 and 1822; English translation of Fredrik Henrik ap Chapman's Swedish work of 1775, *Tractat om Skepps-Byggeriet,* was published in 1820—this was the work of the Reverend James Inman, head of the Royal Navy's School of Naval Architecture. Various reports on studies of resistance and model tests were published, such as Beaufoy's and Gore's reports of 1799 and later, as well as the papers published by the Franklin Institute at Philadelphia and by the English Society for the Improvement of Naval Architecture in the 1830's.

It is known that Josiah Fox, the English naval architect who became a naval constructor in the United States Navy in 1794, had a copy of Steel's book and also owned Stalkaart's work. Steel's work was well-known to Quebec shipbuilders and there is reason to believe that Stalkaart's book was also known, as there were applications by a builder on the St. Lawrence in the early 1800's of the drop-keel, or centerboard, shown in Stalkaart's work.

The texts of these English books on naval architecture were limited to descriptions of the modes of drawing ship's lines; and the earlier books were limited to the use of tangent arcs in forming transverse sections of the hull and to simple calculations of displacement and of sail area, with extensive instructions for lofting, framing, and planking hulls. In general, the texts dealt with large ships. There was little reference in any of these books to the forming of hulls for speed and no useful, precise building instructions were given. On the evidence of contemporary plans, most of these books were obsolete, even at their individual dates of publication, so far as showing actual practices and ideas in design. The illustrations in the earlier books were crude. In later books the engravers often made mistakes in reproducing the lines. Some of the later books did show lines of some fast sailing vessels. Stalkaart showed lines of a large, fast frigate of sharp form designed by the American Tory Benjamin Thompson, and of a drop-keel cutter. Steel showed lines of an American schooner privateer and of a Norfolk pilot boat, as well as of a fast Bermuda schooner (now identified as H.M. schooner *Ant*). He also gave the offsets and specifications of a fast sailing schooner and of a cutter-brig (now identified as H.M. *Orestes*) taken from the Dutch.

In addition to plans and documents dated after 1800, there are collections of builder's half-models that are useful. As will be seen, these become very important in the study of vessels after about 1830. Collections in the United States National Museum, Smithsonian Institution, Washington, D. C., and in the Peabody Marine Museum, Salem, Massachusetts, are large and valuable. Other collections are in the Mystic Marine Museum, Mystic, Connecticut, and in the Portsmouth Athenaeum, Portsmouth, New Hampshire, the Maryland Historical Society in Baltimore, and the historical societies of many American ports and shipbuilding towns.

Before 1700 the colonies had few vessels other than coastal fishing boats— a small number of alongshore traders and a few transatlantic trading vessels— before the civil war in England in the mid-1600's cut them off from British shipping. The need for sugar and rum in the colonies and for food and lumber in the West Indies led to the creation of a colonial merchant marine. In New England there was a ready source of trade with the West Indian colonies— the fisheries off the coast. The first step was to build larger and more numerous fishing boats to supply fish that could be salted and sold or traded to the south. The salted fish could be also shipped in the larger fishing vessels, but this took them out of the fisheries for too long a period. Accordingly, a class of West Indian and intercolonial trading vessels was built.

A few large vessels were constructed in New England for the rather hazardous European trade. It took about four decades to create an active and prosperous New England trading marine. The other colonies were somewhat slower in building up their sea trades. In Maryland and Virginia the great tobacco ships were built on the Chesapeake.* But life in the tidewater sections

---

* Cerinda W. Evans, *Some Notes on Shipbuilding and Shipping in Colonial Virginia* (Williamsburg, Virginia, The Virginia 350th Anniversary Celebration Corporation, 1957). An excellent, though limited, account of Virginia and Chesapeake Bay shipbuilding and boatbuilding in the colonial period, by the Librarian Emeritus of The Mariners' Museum.

of the Chesapeake Bay required boats for everyday transportation, as this area consists of many "necks," creeks, bays, and rivers. Travel alongshore by land would require either constant ferrying or a roundabout trip around the headwaters of each creek, bay, or river. Boats were the answer, and the narrow winding channels of the waterways made a weatherly and handy boat desirable. Shipbuilding to meet these needs became active there sometime before 1648.

New York, New Jersey, Pennsylvania, Maryland, Virginia, and Delaware built large merchant vessels for English owners in the last quarter of the seventeenth century, as did New England. It is now difficult to identify all of the economic and political factors that created active shipbuilding industries in the English North American colonies. The loss of the greater part of the pre-Revolutionary War colonial port records prevents any extensive and thorough study of commercial and shipping conditions in this period, outside of New England and Pennsylvania. It is apparent, however, that shipbuilding rose gradually in importance in the colonies, and was well-established by the end of the first quarter of the eighteenth century. Construction for "foreign accounts"—mostly English, but also French and Spanish—seems to have accounted for many of the large-ship launchings, though merchant vessels of large size (for the eighteenth century) were built for local owners in all the colonies. It is incorrect to picture colonial vessels as small craft, or as cheaply built and primitively finished; it is equally incorrect to believe that almost all colonial shipbuilding was centered in New England.

In the seventeenth century many of the colonial vessels were rigged as sloops, shallops, and "catches." In hull they were of English model, built by English shipwrights and boatwrights, or by colonials who had been apprenticed to English masters. "Catches" became popular after 1650 in America and disappeared suddenly in the 1720's; hence there is a possible assumption that one variation of the "catch" was a primitive schooner. At any rate, the "scooner" suddenly replaced the "catch" in New England colonial records. Sloops were by far the most common rig from 1650 to about 1740. After 1680 the colonial sloop was often large, say 50 to 60 feet long on deck, and capable of transatlantic crossings. The shallop, a small vessel often having the schooner masting—but without jib or headsail, and therefore lacking a bowsprit—was confined to small craft under 50 feet in length. Some sharp-sterned "pinks" also appear in New England records; these were probably shallops in many cases. Brigantines became numerous after 1690.

In the last decade of the century the New England traders built a number of "runners" or "gallies." These were ships or brigantines (see Plate 1) built for speed under sail and to row well; they were employed almost entirely in the transatlantic trades. Such vessels—intended to operate without the convoy system—were really blockade-runners.

It was the custom to use "galley" as part of a ship's name—as *Adventure Galley*, for example—in both the British Navy and the English and colonial merchant marine. This was not done, however, with vessels rigged as sloops, schooners, or cutters, and rarely with brigs or with brigantines of the galley type. In the 1740's some 24-gun British Naval ship-galleys were rowed on both decks, and this was done in at least a few brigantine galleys.

The term "galley" came eventually to mean merely a "nimble" vessel, rather than one fitted and built to row well in addition to sailing fast. The term appears to have gone out of popular use in the 1750's.

The "scooner" rig seems to have first appeared in the Netherlands sometime before 1620 and was for a long period a small-boat rig. It was soon introduced into English waters and apparently was adopted by the Americans sometime before 1700. It first was utilized as a modified shallop rig, entirely fore-and-aft, but the American builders seem to have been the earliest to use the rig on relatively large seagoing vessels with square sails added. As the "scooner" rig had smaller individual sails and lighter spars than a sloop, in a hull of the same size, it required a smaller crew. It is not surprising then, to find in colonial records that the rig first appeared in coasting vessels. The term "scooner" may have been new in 1700–1720, but the rig was old and in a primitive form may have been known as the "catch." It is usual to identify the colonial catch with the Royal Navy's bomb-ketch rig of the late seventeenth century, which may be described as ship-rigged, with the foremast out. It is plain from the records, however, that the colonial catch was usually of a simple rig that could be used in relatively small craft with small crews.

Except for the possible development of the schooner rig for use in seagoing craft, there is as yet no evidence indicating the appearance of any distinctive American hull type or rig in the seventeenth or early eighteenth century. The sloop was a very popular colonial rig but it has yet to be established that American builders played any part in its early evolution. The large traders, brigantines, and ships built in the colonies seem to have been like their English-built counterparts in all respects of design.

The American colonies were, on the whole, well-supplied with most of the

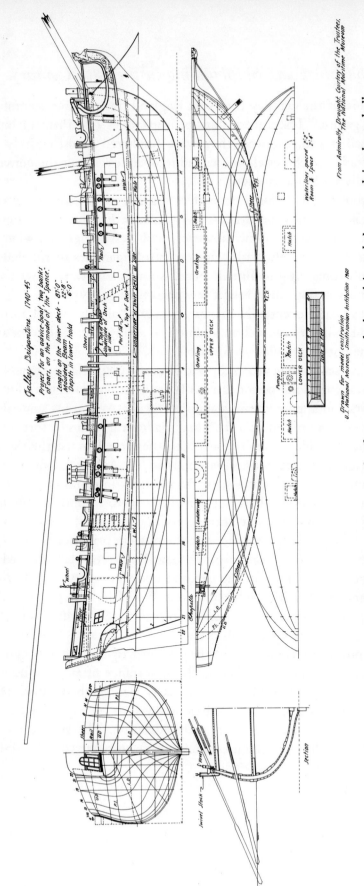

Galley Brigantine. 1740-45

Project for an advice-boat, two banks
of oars, on the model of the Spence.

Length on the lower deck - 87'.0"
Moulded Beam - - - - 22'.8"
Depth in lower hold - - - 6'.0"

From Admiralty Draught. Courtesy of the Trustees,
The National Maritime Museum

Drawn for model construction
U.S National Museum, Smithsonian Institution 1958

Plate 1. A design for a galley–brigantine of 1740–45, fitted to row on two decks and intended as an advice boat; hull
was to be a modification of that of the brigantine sloop; reputed a good sailer.

important materials required in shipbuilding. Timber was very plentiful. At first the colonial shipwrights had some difficulty in making proper selections, for there were American species of timber unknown to them. By 1700, however, the difficulties in selection had been almost entirely overcome. Because of low-cost materials, the colonial shipbuilders could build vessels more cheaply than the British. This enabled the colonies to build for English accounts and on speculation.* There was some complaint, however, that American-built vessels were short-lived. To some extent this criticism was true, for many builders lacked the capital required to store timber long enough for proper seasoning. Although Maine-built vessels having larch (hackmatack) frames and white cedar plank, and Chesapeake Bay vessels framed with mulberry or laurel, and planked with juniper would last thirty years, American-built vessels nevertheless had a reputation in England for being subject to early rot, particularly in the frame.

Sawmills were established in New England at least as early as 1628, and by 1660 there were over a hundred operating in the colonies. Most of these were operated by waterpower—a few by windmills—and the machinery consisted of a saw in an upright frame, in slides at the sides, driven by a pitman rod from a crank on the end of a waterwheel shaft. This was a "sash saw," producing from 2000 to 3000 feet of lumber a day. After 1660 "gang saws" came into use; these had several parallel saws in the frame and sawed only plank. The log was moved against the saw by hand or by a pawl and ratchet gear driven by the waterwheel in time with the saw strokes. While mills probably turned out much plank for shipbuilding, frames and heavy timbers were produced manually with the pit saw. Since shipyards in the colonies were rarely located near a source of waterpower, the number of shipyard sawmills was very small until steampower became available.

In the early years of colonial shipbuilding, ironwork was imported. By the end of the seventeenth century, however, a number of domestic furnaces were in operation. Early colonial smelting of bog ore produced a small supply and the opening of iron mines increased production so that by 1725 Maryland, Virginia, and Pennsylvania were exporting pig iron to England, and this continued almost until the Revolution.

---

* Colonial shipbuilding was carried on for foreign accounts, even though there was a depression in the colonial shipping trades. By 1690 the English colonies were becoming shipbuilding marts, supplying England's enemies with ships, as well as competing with English shipbuilders in the mother country.

Only a small quantity of ironwork was used in the construction of seventeenth- and early eighteenth-century vessels. It was limited to such items as stoves or hearth castings, chimneys, cooking utensils, cannon and ordnance fittings, anchors, chainplates, bolts, hooks, ring and eye bolts, rudder pintles and gudgeons, bands, spikes, nails, driving or "drift" bolts, straps, hinges, and latches or handles. Threaded bolts and nuts were rarely used in shipbuilding before 1800. Heavy fastenings were "drifts"—iron rods driven in holes of smaller diameter. If a through-bolt, its point might be "set up" over an iron plate or ring with a wedge driven through a slot in the end. Or if the fastening were not likely to require replacement during the life of the ship, the point might be "upset," or "headed," over a plate or ring; both the head and upset were formed on the rod by the driving hammer. Except for castings, sheet, or plate iron, all ships' ironwork was usually made by the local blacksmith. There was no lack of iron for colonial shipbuilding after 1675 and American-built vessels had as much or more ironwork in their structure and rig as contemporary British or Continental vessels.

In the late seventeenth century sailcloth was made in the colonies, usually of flax, and too loosely woven to stand well and wear long. The manufacture of cordage also began in the seventeenth century; species of hemp and jute were grown in some of the colonies for rope-making. The importation of sailcloth and rope from Europe, though intermittent, supplemented the local supply.

These supporting industries of shipbuilding were not much restricted by England, though she forbade the manufacture of ordnance and made some attempt to discourage ironmongery.* Steel was not employed in colonial ship-building, but it was needed for tools. Records show that sufficient steel was produced in the colonies for tool-making and that just before the Revolution small quantities of steel bars were being exported to England.

Jute, hemp, and sometimes animal hair were employed for caulking. Paint was rather expensive and tar, oil, and whitewash, the latter "set" with melted tallow, were popular substitutes for ships' bottom paint. Iron oxide paint or "barn red" was one of the cheaper and popular colored paints; earth pigments were generally available for topsides. Though some paint was made in the colonies, much was imported. Blue, red, and green, as well as yellow ochre,

---

* *Act to Encourage the Importation of Pig and Bar Iron from His Majesty's Colonies in America* (George II, 1750) was intended to prevent production of wrought iron, rolled or forged plate, or steel, in the colonies. This was the first restrictive law affecting colonial iron industries and does not appear to have been enforced because of disturbed political conditions in the colonies.

were the most popular colors. White was expensive and usually dried with a slight yellow tint. Fouling was a problem in fast vessels of these early days because there was no anti-fouling paint, or suitable sheathing for the bottom. Varnish and oil were used for topsides in the "bright strakes" until the 1830's.

The frequent arrival of English technicians in colonial ports provided a steady flow of well-trained workmen. This prevented any decadence in skill and ensured that the colonies had access to the latest practices and knowledge in the important trades and crafts.

Ship-design methods were well established at the end of the seventeenth century. Contrary to popular opinion, drawings were used in this period, not models. Surviving plans and manuscripts show that the planning of ship lines had been slowly developing in England from at least as early as the middle of the sixteenth century. Lacking any clear record of prior developments in marine drafting, it is permissible to speculate that methods of drawing ships' lines may have been in use far earlier. The engineering skill shown by the Greeks and Romans, and also by medieval builders, in the construction of buildings and fortifications, gives basis for an assumption that scale drawings were employed in their design; and there is good reason to assume that the same was true of ship design.

The records of English marine drafting begin with a manuscript* usually dated 1586. It is surely the work of more than one man, but the earliest and major part of it is assigned to Mathew Baker, one of Queen Elizabeth's master shipwrights. Authorities agree that this manuscript describes methods employed in Italian (probably Venetian) ship design that may have been introduced into England in the time of Henry VIII (or earlier), as well as methods —or at least material—of somewhat later date.

The manuscript describes a system of forming the hull by using tangent arcs for the transverse sections. After the midsection had been formed, the arcs were used to form the other sections, altering them in form by shifting the points of tangency along each arc. This was controlled by arbitrarily formed longitudinal curves; the sheer, maximum breadth line and width of floor in the plan elevation ("half-breadth plan") and by the sheer, height of breadth and rise of floor, along with the shape of the stem and stern, in the profile plan ("sheer elevation"). Over the midsection the form of the stern was usually drawn, showing the shape as viewed from dead astern, and this

* *Fragments of Ancient English Shipwrightry*, Cambridge, England, Magdalene College Library, Magdalene College, Pepys 2820.

became the "body plan" in later years. The midsection was usually placed a little forward of midlength of the keel. There were rules for shaping all the arcs and the crude scale could be corrected, in making the full-size patterns for the frames, by use of mathematics—plane geometry and trigonometry. Modern students have attempted to reconstruct lines of vessels by these rules and have found omissions that required them to "interpret" in order to obtain a workable plan. It seems apparent that this is inherent in the system and that each Elizabethan shipwright had modifications and interpretations of his own —the "secrets" of his profession. As time went on, modifications were made in the system to permit variation in the radii of the arcs for each transverse section, but by the time the system had been so developed it was decadent.

It does not appear to have been the practice in the sixteenth century, and well into the last half of the following century, to draw each frame individually by this system, but at least the "mould" stations (every third or fourth frame) were thus formed. These "mould" frames were set up in their proper positions on the keel and "ribbaned off" with battens reaching from bow to stern. These "faired" the mould frames, and "proved" the design by showing it could be planked. The intermediate frames, between each pair of mould frames, were then fitted to the inside of the battens. If all the frames were laid down by the system, there would be marked fullness or "snubbing" in the planking just abaft the stem near the forefoot, or where the lower planks met the stem, which at best would make a hull very difficult, and in some instances impossible, to plank.*

The Elizabethan system of designing lines remained in limited use in England until as late as 1727 and was employed in small-boat design even later. The system did not survive because it could not produce a fair form near the bow and stern. It also did not permit the change in curves of the transverse sections necessary to create wholly fair longitudinal or planking lines, nor did it allow for the numerous reverse curves required in the lower longitudinals to meet the bow and stern forms. The net effect was to require interpretations, and the results of this would prevent two builders working to the same design from producing identical vessels in form. By 1700 this method of producing lines of vessels had become known as "whole moulding."

The most complete and accurate discussion of whole moulding is by William A. Baker, in his "Early Seventeenth-Century Ship Design" (*American*

* *Wasa*, built in 1626–27 at Stockholm, shows a faired forefoot, which was evidently formed by use of mould frames and battens, as described above.

Neptune, October 1954, vol. 14, No. 4, pp. 262–77). This work should be consulted by readers interested in the Elizabethan system of design. Additional excellent contemporary source material may be found in:

(1) *Fragments of Ancient English Shipwrightry*, attributed to Mathew Baker, supposed to have been written in 1586, with later additions by others. (Mss., Pepys 2820, Magdalene College Library, Cambridge, England.)

(2) *Anthony Dean's Doctrine of Naval Architecture and Tables of Dimensions, Material, Furniture and Equipment appertaining thereto. Written in the year 1670 at the Instance of Samuel Pepys, Esq.* (Mss., Pepys 2910, Magdalene College Library, Cambridge, England.) Deals with modifications in the old system and shows increased use of visual fairing lines. Some of Dean's material was published in Sir Wescott Abell's *The Shipwright's Trade* (Cambridge, England, the University Press, 1948).

(3) *A Treatise on Shipbuilding, c.1620. From a manuscript in the Admiralty Library*, edited by William Salisbury, and *A Treatise on Rigging Written About 1620–1625*, edited by R. C. Anderson (London, The Society for Nautical Research, 1958). This is a useful reprint of two manuscripts by anonymous authors with notations.

(4) *A Most Excellent Mannor for the Building of Ships* or "*A most excellent briefe and easie treatise teaching the manner of building ships of all kinds and gallies by several proportions. Proportions for gallies, borde measure, timber measure, gauging of vessels and a table of synes.* (Anonymous mss., Scott Collection, Institution of Naval Architects, London, no date.) Ascribed to George Waymouth, *c.*1600–20.

(5) *The Accomplished Shipwright and Mariner*, by John Hardingham of Great Yarmouth (London, Richard Mount and Co., 1706 and 1709). This work mentions galleys, also fish-form hulls, and describes a system of drawing lines that was rapidly becoming obsolete at the time of its publication.

The hull forms produced by the Elizabethan and Jacobean systems of drawing lines were somewhat stereotyped. The keel was straight and relatively short compared to the overall length of the hull. The stem rabbet was formed with a long sweep or curve, sometimes with two or three tangent arcs. The sternpost was raking and the transom, of a "square tuck" form, overhung the head of the post with its lower portion immersed. The midsection was formed with a flat floor and apparently no deadrise or V in the midsection, from keel outward, was employed. In later designs the garboard was set at an angle to the floors or a small reverse arc was worked in from the keel outward, for a short distance, to form what is now known as the "hollow gar-board." The lower bilge had a rather small radius arc tangent to the floor, and from it, one of larger radius was formed that reached outward and up to a little below the height of greatest breadth, where there was a small radius arc. The "tumble home," or falling inboard, of the section above the arc at the height of greatest breadth was either a tangent straight line or a large radius arc in reverse, which made the tumble home take the so-called "line of beauty." No instance of a marked V-form in the floors of the midsection has yet been found in the surviving plans earlier than 1680, though *Wasa* of 1627 shows the garboard set at an angle to the floors. This negative evidence is insufficient, however, to support an assumption that such midsection forms did not exist before 1700 in some English vessels. Plate 2 is the plan of a small ship in the Danish Archives with an assigned date of 1665 (but 1695–1720 is more likely) showing rising straight floors.

In the common model, the use of the arcs of the midsection in forming the sections of the fore and after bodies produced a marked similarity in the form of entrance and run. Below the load waterline the entrance was often sharp and hollow, though at load line and above, the bow might be quite full. Like-wise, the run was hollow and very sharp below the load line or below the bottom of the transom stern. This appears to be a model that would sail well, and this form was used for some forty years after the old systems had become decadent, or were being rapidly modified out of useful existence.

Relatively little is known about the drawing instruments of Elizabethan days. A well-known drawing shows a shipwright and an apprentice of the time at a drafting table, the former using a large compass that probably served the dual purpose of compass and divider. An ivory or wooden scale rule and a drafting pen, or "right line pen," must have been used, since surviving plans of this period were done in ink. Plans were drawn on parchment, some with watercolor. Drawings were usually made on a scale of ¼ inch to the foot.

By 1690, drafting tools were well-developed and some special instruments employed only in marine drafting had come into use. Äke Classon Ralamb's *Skeps Byggerij eller Adelig Öfnings Tionde Tom* (Stockholm, 1691) (fac-simile printing, Stockholm, Sjohistoriska Museum, 1943) contains a plate show-ing marine drafting tools. These instruments include a right line or ruling pen, a graphic scale, a compass and divider (the compass fitted with pen and lead holder), and lead holders or handles to serve as pencils. Battens were in use; one is shown attached to the ends of a straightedge by stirrups. In the

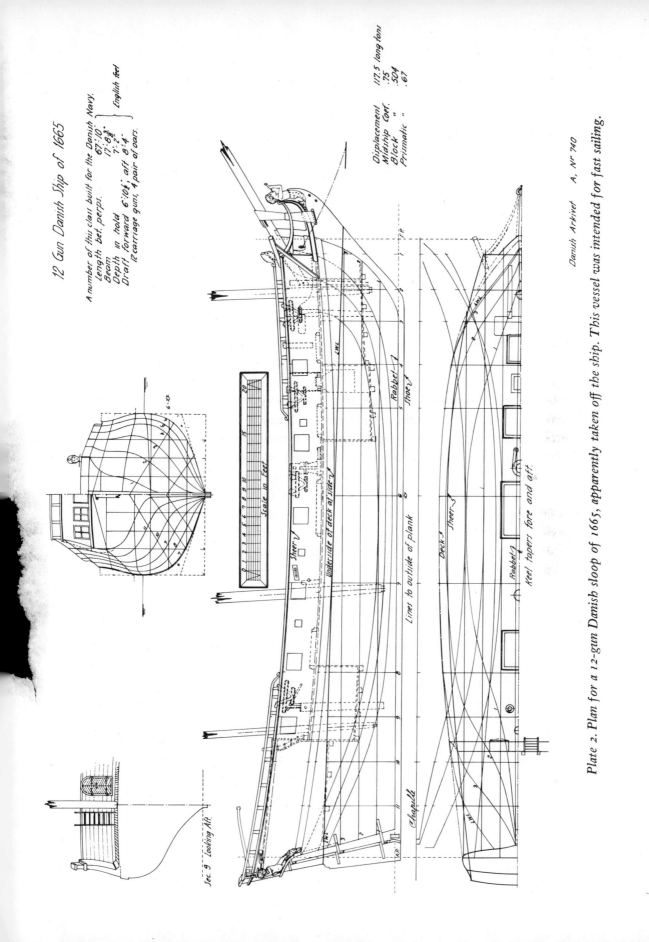

12 Gun Danish Ship of 1665

A number of this class built for the Danish Navy.

		English feet
Length bet. perp.	67'10".	
Beam	17'8⅜"	
Depth in hold	7'2"	
Draft forward 6'10⅞", aft 8'4".		

12 carriage guns, 1 pair of oars.

Displacement 117.5 long tons
Midship Coef. .75
Block " .504
Prismatic " .67

Danish Arkivet A. N° 740

Sec. 9 Looking Aft.

Scale in Feet

Underside of deck at side

Sheer

Rabbet

Lines to outside of plank

Sheer

Deck

Sheer

Rabbet

Keel tapers fore and aft.

Chapelle

Plate 2. Plan for a 12-gun Danish sloop of 1665, apparently taken off the ship. This vessel was intended for fast sailing.

straightedge were three long screw pegs with thumbscrew heads; by adjusting one or more of these, the batten could be sprung to varying curves or irregular sweeps. Another had one end of the batten embedded in a flat plank in which there was a violin peg, and the other end was held by a cord secured to this peg. By revolving the peg, the cord was wound up on the peg's shank and acted like a bowstring to bend and hold the batten to the desired sweep or curve.

Pencil lines were erased by rubbing the paper with fresh bread, and ink was erased by scraping the paper or parchment with a sharp knife. If this raised the fibers so that ink might run and blot, the rough surface was smoothed with the heel of a polished spoon, or with an ivory blade or "smoother."

After 1675, quality drawing paper appears to have become available and sheets of handmade paper were spliced to form the desired size. Parchment appears to have been favored even this late by some builders, but by the end of the seventeenth century the use of drawing paper was nearly universal.

In the later seventeenth century some ship designers began to use "sets of curves" or "patterns," instead of compass and battens. These "sets" were made up of "sweeps" formed on long, easy curves; small irregular curves made of boxwood or pearwood veneer were also used, as were parabolas and other mathematically formed curves. Most of these sets were made of thin wood by the ship designer to fit his individual requirements.

Lettering was done in script, first with quills, later with steel pens. Various inks were used, but gradually it was accepted that India or Chinese stick ink was best. The ink stick was ground in water in a china dish, sometimes with the addition of camphor or other substances. The ink could thus be made to any desired blackness and consistency.

The use of drawing-battens or "splines" for fairing sheer-lines and other longitudinal curves began late in the seventeenth century. These were held to the required curves on the drawing, first by pins, and later by special lead weights, or "ducks," that rested on both batten and drawing board. Wooden squares, or "gallows," were the counterparts of modern drafting triangles.

The draftsmen's scales (made of boxwood, pearwood, or ivory) were not on a standard calibration. As a result each draftsman drew his scale in graphic form on the plans. "Offsets," or measurements of the lines plan, could be lifted from the drawing by use of dividers and the resulting measurement (in feet, inches, and fractions) could be read by transferring the dividers' points to the plan's graphic scale, with a minimum possibility of scale error.

The graphic scale was made in various ways. Twelve equally spaced parallel lines would be crossed by evenly spaced vertical lines, each space respresenting a foot. The space to the left was divided by a diagonal leading from the upper right corner to the lower left. This would produce inch reading in the foot space thus divided, with fractions read by interpolation. Later six parallel evenly-spaced lines were used with the left foot space divided in half at the top or bottom and connected by lines to the opposite corners, M-shaped. Such a scale is used on drawings shown in this study. After 1600 the title, measurement, and particulars of the design, and the graphic scale were often part of an elaborate cartouche.

Drafting skill was relatively high and fine pen work is seen in many seventeenth-century plans. The drawings, however, were not precise in establishing the intended hull form. As late as at least 1760, because of incomplete projections and fairing, it was not possible to build true sister-ships, in different yards, from one design.

At the end of the seventeenth century, marine-draftsmen were still using the height and breadth of beam and the height and breadth of floor ends, with a main sheer line, as the longitudinal fairing lines. Some, however, were attempting to fair longitudinally the quarterdeck and forecastle deck rail sheers and were using the designed load waterline for fairing purposes as well. The complete projection of the stern and upper transom had not been developed, and would not be for almost another century. As a result, much was left to the interpretation of the builder and the longitudinal fairing of the transverse sections was far from being accurate or complete.

With the establishment of a mode for calculating the designed displacement in the seventeenth century, the use of mathematics in practical ship design really began. The mode was to calculate the areas of the individual transverse sections below the designed waterline. This was done in two ways; either by dividing each section into a series of small triangles whose areas could be calculated readily, or by use of a grid of one-foot squares drawn over each section. Along the curved outline of the section, the marginal triangles or squares were "averaged." The result gave at least practical accuracy, which was good, considering the difficulties inherent in the calculation of structural and other weights too great for weighing scales. The sections were treated in pairs, as ends of solid trapezoids; the ends from the last stations to stemposts and sternposts were considered as prisms, with longitudinal length "averaged." Having found the cubic-foot contents of the submerged portion of the hull, displacement was found by conversion to deadweight tons. In the early eighteenth century this was still somewhat complicated, as Hardingham's instructions show:

To find the Burthen reduce the contents in Feet into Liquid Measure allowing one Pint for a Pound (you may reduce it into Liquid Measure by dividing 1728, the inches in a Solid Foot, by 231, the Cubic Inches generally allowed in a Gallon of Wine measure), which will be found to be 7 gallons 48 parts, which Multiplied by the Content in Solid Feet will give you the Content in Gallons of Wine Measure, which multiplied by 8, the weight of a gallon, gives the Content of Weight in Pounds and that Divided by the Pounds in a Wine Tun (which is eighteen hundred Weight) namely 2016 will give you the Content in Tuns in the Whole Square. Wine Tuns Multiplied by 18 and divided by 20 will give the Content in Averdupois Tuns.

This illustrates the chances for error and the difficulties involved when material standards were lacking; today the displacement in cubic feet is divided by 35 to obtain long tons—salt water displacement.

The seventeenth century was a period of scientific interest in ship stability and the phenomena of resistance, particularly in France. Early attempts to calculate resistance factors created the use of mathematical science in theoretical ship design that now marks so much of the technical literature. Except for calculating displacement and the assembly of data on useful weights of structure and fittings, however, early attempts at scientific investigation produced little that was useful or that could be employed in practical ship design.

It is difficult to form conclusions as to the technical knowledge of early shipbuilders, particularly in the design of vessels built for speed, since relatively few ship plans have survived from the sixteenth and seventeenth centuries. The extant plans are all of naval ships and most of these are of large vessels. In all of these, speed had to be compromised for such other qualities as the ability to carry heavy armament and to stow supplies for a long cruise. Accordingly, one can observe only that Elizabethan builders recognized the disadvantages of high freeboard and lofty weights and knew the relation of sharp ends to speed in "race-built" or fast sailing vessels. Builders had certainly understood these factors when galleys were the only war vessels, but apparently the knowledge had been largely forgotten. Theoretically, the ideal ship form was supposed to be that of a fish; Baker in his 1586 manuscript suggests this by imposing the profile of a fish over the underbody of the profile of a ship in one of his drawings. But with the modes of drawing lines before 1700, it was not possible to visualize the longitudinal form of a vessel with sufficient accuracy in the plan to produce a predetermined hull form, in all aspects of design. Hence the fish form does not actually appear when early designs are reprojected in modern form for purposes of lines analysis.

The necessary step in constructing a ship from plans, or from a scale model, is the drawing in full size of the shape of the transverse sections and the ends of the ship—this is known as "laying down" or "lofting." This operation is a fundamental part of the development of marine drafting in the very nature of the use of small scale representations in drawing or in model. Lofting is no more than the repetition of the small scale drawing in full size, to produce the patterns for transverse frames and structural parts that would reproduce in the ship the form of the original small scale design. The advantage of the small scale drawing is that it allows accurate inspection and analysis of the whole shape and appearance of the ship during the process of design. Corrections or alternatives in the design, during drawing, could then be readily made before committing timber and much labor to building the ship. The more complete and accurate the fairing of the scale drawing, by use of longitudinals, the better the analysis of the design and the more accurate the lofting process. If precision were not obtained in making the design drawing, it could not be accurately reproduced in lofting. This would result in reshaping the timbers (when set up) in order to fair or plank the hull; the result would be that the ship, as built, would differ from the plans and lofting, so would not be as designed nor as predetermined in full. Such a condition might cause effects in sailing, stability, and handling that could not be accounted for by the designer, since he would have no accurate record of the departures from his original design. No matter what the performance of his vessel might be, he would have learned practically nothing from her that would aid in designing an improved ship.

Hence the mere reproduction of plans of vessels before 1700 does not permit a useful analysis of their lines or their maximum potential performance. Complete redrawing of these early plans in the modern methods of lines projection would be necessary, with much interpretation or reconstruction of the designer's intentions.

In any discussion of the performance of sailing vessels it is necessary to examine the elements of wind propulsion by means of sails. It must be recognized that sail power cannot be expressed in terms of effective horsepower, such as would apply in a discussion of the comparative efficiency of steamers or motor vessels today. The velocity of the wind is never constant for long;

it increases and decreases almost constantly over an appreciable range and at irregular intervals. With a given velocity and direction of wind at sea level, the velocity increases and the direction may vary somewhat as the height above the sea increases. There is no need to examine this complicated matter at great length; it is sufficient to state that it is quite impractical to attempt to place accurate numerical quantitative values on wind power applied to sails by means either of velocity or resulting pressure measurements.

Nor is the quantitative measurement of sail area a safe guide to the wind power available to drive a vessel. If there were but a single sail and if it were set so that the wind direction would be at right angles to the surface of the sail and if there were no distortion allowed in the surface or shape of the sail, then maximum wind power would be exerted. But in actual sailing, the rigs used in vessels above the size of small boats employ two or more sails. They must sail on points of the compass approximating 270 degrees in range, so that the wind impinges on the sails at various angles, rather than at 90 degrees alone. Under certain conditions and points of sailing the individual sails may be distorted by wind pressure or produce interference with each other, either by cutting off wind from another sail or by creating eddies that prevent some sail or sails from drawing. Aerodynamic forces, for the calculation of which there are no real constants, make the sailing rig of a vessel impossible to estimate in terms of comparative horsepower or in any other reasonably precise quantitative measurement. In terms of comparative area there is the problem of effectiveness of individual sails in the rig under a given set of conditions, or when sailing a given point or course. The selection of the individual sail to be carried is based upon the lack of interference its position indicates and the ability of the vessel to carry it, with the wind force existing on the course to be sailed. Then there is the inherent ability of a given sail to develop driving power on a given course because of its making or cutting.*

Quantitative measurements being practically impossible, it is apparent that comparison of the performance of two sailing vessels becomes extremely complex and can be simplified only by comparing two vessels under narrowly similar weather conditions, with due regard to size of hull and those parts of the rig that each can set in similar wind forces.

---

* The sail is not a simple airfoil, for its flexible qualities—under varying wind pressures and slight shifts in direction—cause an almost constant change in shape, and therefore in propulsive effect.

With regard to determining the potential maximum speed that can be obtained under a given set of practical restrictions, the design of sailing vessels is far more complex than the design of power vessels. The sailing-craft designer can work only in a field of assumption and speculation and must use his experience and observations of the type of vessel he is designing as guides, rather than theoretical assumptions or "scientific facts" of a quantitative nature. His judgment becomes the important factor in his success, and he often utilizes a series of generalities relating to power in the rig and resistance in the hull to formulate his design for a new vessel. These generalities are in fact no more than ideas that appear to work in practice. Some are readily supported by hydrodynamic theory but others are only the judgments of qualified designers, based on practical observation. These generalities are best illustrated in the analysis of designs where the plans give visual representation of the matters involved.

What is required in order to be able to call a sailing vessel "fast"? Sailing speds are relatively slow by mechanical standards. The only unqualified answer to this question seems to be that a fast vessel is one that in a given state of wind and weather can outsail her counterparts on at least two of the three basic points of sailing. "Counterparts" are vessels of the same type and approximate size and rig. The basic points of sailing are with wind dead astern, with the wind abeam, and with the wind ahead. As a sailing vessel cannot sail into the eye of the wind, she cannot sail over the 360-degree range; in practice her range is approximately 270 to 280 degrees. Therefore seamen consider "running" as being with the wind astern and within about 30 degrees on either side. "Quartering" or "broad reaching" is with the wind in excess of 30 degrees of dead astern but not over 75 degrees; "reaching" is with the wind abeam, say 10–15 degrees either way. "Close reaching" is with the wind slightly forward of the beam—perhaps 15 degrees, or a little more or less, forward of abeam. "Close-hauled" is sailing on a tack to windward, so that the vessel is sailing within 60 degrees of the wind direction. As a generality, fore-and-aft-rigged merchant vessels such as sloops, cutters, and perhaps a few schooners, could, if very efficient, point within 3½ compass points or about 40 degrees of the wind. Square-rigged vessels usually will not point much better than 5½ compass points, or 55 degrees. Large merchant vessels would not ordinarily point up quite so high as small craft in smooth water, but might equal them in heavy weather with a rough sea.

The lowest speed through the water, within the potential range of a vessel, is commonly close-hauled or "on the wind," as in beating to windward. From the low point, obtained when a vessel is pointed as high as she can be held and still move ahead, the speed usually increases steadily as she is allowed to fall off, until the maximum is reached somewhere about a position with the wind abeam or a little abaft that point. This high speed is usually maintained until the wind is on the quarter, but as the wind is brought nearly dead astern the speed declines, the amount depending upon the blanketing of sails in the vessel's rig. Most of these effects are accountable to conditions inherent in the rigs of sailing craft, but as will be seen, hull form may also be involved to some extent. In sailing with the wind abeam, from close reaching to broad off, every sail usually develops nearly full power and is little affected by wind eddies; this condition—reaching—provides the fastest course in sailing. With some vessels the highest speed is achieved on courses that bring the wind somewhat abaft the beam, or broad reaching. In many instances this is due to some peculiarity in the rig. Square-rigged vessels, for example, often sail fastest on broad reach, as long as all sails can be filled without one interfering with the wind of another. Fore-and-aft-rigged vessels often sail best on a reach or even when close reaching.

Another factor becomes apparent in sailing close-hauled—that is, side drift, or leeway. It is common to find that the closer a vessel is sailed to the wind, the greater her leeway becomes. This is related, primarily, to the speed that she can develop. If she has a good hull form for sailing to windward so that she can point well and maintain good speed, her speed produces forces of a hydrodynamic nature that increase her resistance to side drift. She is then called a "weatherly" vessel. In sailing close-hauled, a merchant sailing vessel of good normal form and rig would be able to make good a course from ¼ to 1 compass point, or from 3 to 11 degrees, to leeward of the course on which she is being steered. The practical seaman, however, never sails as close to the wind as possible—that is, pointing as high as the vessel can and still move—because this results in maximum leeway and lowest speed. This is called "pinching" and the vessel will not "fetch where she points," or "go where she looks." As sea and wind rise, pinching causes not only excessive leeway but also lack of steering control, and the vessel may finally become unmanageable due to loss of forward movement. The aim, then, is to point as high as possible and yet to maintain good speed through the water.

Weatherliness—the ability to sail close to the wind with little leeway—in a sailing merchant vessel was important for handiness and safety in narrow waters, as well as for fast voyages. If two vessels sail to windward at the same speed and making equal leeway, but with one vessel making good or pointing 4¼ points, while the other makes good only 5¼ points, the latter would be four minutes behind after sailing 20 miles.* As a result, on a long course to windward a weatherly vessel had a great practical superiority. The greatest range of courses available to the weatherly vessels, as compared to the less weatherly, gave greater ability to work up narrow channels and to handle in confined areas. In the illegal or dangerous trades the weatherly vessels could often use this quality to escape from a pursuer.

While it is logical to accept fore-and-aft-rigged vessels as more weatherly than square-rigged craft, there are some qualifications that must be noted. Though a seagoing colonial sloop might normally be much more weatherly than a brigantine when under "working" sails, this might not be true in all conditions and winds. The colonial seagoing fore-and-after usually employed some square sails. In some vessels there was not adequate area in the fore-and-aft sails to obtain maximum speed and square sails had to be set and used as long as possible, even to windward. After about 1720, ships and other square-riggers employed a number of staysails between the masts and some of the vessels had enough sail area to be quite fast on the wind in a gale. Such vessels might, in strong winds, become entirely fore-and-aft-rigged and the more weatherly.

Sailing vessels, because of hull proportions or rig qualities, usually sail their fastest on one, or at most two, points of sailing. As has been said, reaching is usually the point of sailing in which vessels sail the fastest, though exceptions occasionally do exist. The qualities of the more common rigs might be compared as follows: schooners normally sailed fast reaching, but were less weatherly than sloops and also slower with the wind dead astern; square-rigged vessels often sailed fast with the wind on the quarter, abaft the beam; some of the smaller square-rigged vessels sailed faster when reaching with the wind abeam or slightly forward of the beam. It is therefore apparent that potential sailing qualities vary with a number of design factors—the inherent effects of the rigs and those of the hull forms and proportions that gave maximum play to rig qualities.

* The value of weatherliness can be illustrated in another way. In beating dead to windward 20 miles, a vessel pointing 4½ points would travel 32 miles, one holding 4 points would travel 28.3 miles, and one working at 3 points would travel 26 miles, making no allowances for leeway or tide effects. The choice of course is determined by the vessel's ability to sail fast and point high.

It is true, of course, that wind pressure on the sails creates horsepower, though we cannot estimate the amount of power produced with any practical degree of accuracy. Generalizations may be made, however, in order to understand rig design problems. It is evident that the ranges of effective horsepower created in a rig depend upon the point of sailing. As shown by the relative speeds of sailing on each point, effective horsepower is low when sailing close to the wind and it increases as the wind comes abeam, or abaft the beam. It may also be stated that in all cases the useful amount of horsepower created is not very great. It depends upon effective sail area, of course, and there are physical limits to this, determined by the stability—capacity to carry sail—of the vessel in question.

The relatively small horsepower created in sails has a marked effect on hull design, in that the form must be one that drives easily with a low range of power. As will be seen, this produces a limited range of satisfactory hull forms and hull proportions. Finally, there is no one hull form—no ideal, lowest resistant model—that will accommodate the whole range of effective horsepower and the resulting range of potential speed under sail.

Some vessels have the quality of sailing at relatively high speed through the water, and are at their best when sailing on the points of greatest normal speed—reaching, or with the wind a little abaft the beam. They then achieve exceptionally high velocity. Such vessels are often long, narrow, and of relatively shallow draft. Owing to hull and rig feature, however, a vessel having a less high-speed potential may sail faster when close-hauled and pointing well, than a vessel with greater maximum speed potential. Such vessels are often relatively wide and of deep draft.

The points in which a new vessel performed best were important to know and could be learned only by sailing trials. This matter became very important in the illegal or dangerous occupations, for when a vessel was chased she could usually be maneuvered to sail on her best point. Sometimes, of course, this was not possible because the enemy might be faster in the prevailing weather, or because some peculiarity of position might cut the pursued vessel off from the courses on which she could sail fastest.

As stated previously, sailing vessels were considered fast if they performed well on two points of sailing, and preferably both under full sail and under shortened sail. Some American clipper schooners, for example, worked to windward very well under their fore-and-aft sails only, or under shortened sail, but also sailed fast with the wind on the quarter under both fore-and-aft and square sails.

Naval Architecture and Shipbuilding in the 18th Century

In establishing the potential maximum speed it is necessary to evaluate this by comparison with other vessels. It is reasonably accurate to state that large vessels can move through the water at higher speed than smaller vessels. This becomes more marked in strong winds and heavy sea, where the large vessel will usually have the advantage on nearly all points of sailing. In sailing vessels, an increase in size is accompanied by an increase in stability above that indicated by the increase in lineal dimensions.* This gives the greater power to carry sail and accounts for the usual superiority of the large sailing vessel over the smaller in strong winds. Careful observation of more than a hundred years of shipbuilding has shown that hull length influences the speed of a vessel. The effect of hull size on speed will be considered in subsequent pages.

In order to compare the technical excellence of two designs of ships of different length, using highest recorded speed of each, the difference in size must be taken into account. This is done by naval architects through the use of the "speed-length ratio," which is calculated by dividing the highest recorded speed of a ship in nautical miles per hour, or knots, by the square root of her waterline length, in feet. This produces a quantitative number, or "dimensionless" index number, for comparison. For example, an extreme case may be used to show the use of this quotient: a vessel 121 feet on the load waterline has recorded a run of 16 knots, while another vessel 240 feet on the load waterline ran 21 knots. Which of the two vessels had the faster design on the basis of speed-length? Calculating the speed-length ratio of each, it is found that the 121-foot vessel has a ratio of 1.455 while the ratio of the 240-foot vessel is 1.355. This indicates the 121-foot vessel is of the basically faster design.

The example is too extreme to be used in a practical design problem, but there are instances where the lengths of the vessels were close enough together and the difference in ratios so small, that the design of the smaller vessel with the higher ratio could be enlarged to the size of the larger vessel and thus produce a ship faster than the larger. This is rarely done in actual design, but mere statement of the theoretical possibility is sufficient to show that there is technical value to the speed-length ratio, besides its use merely as a basis of comparison.

In a judicial examination of the speed of sailing vessels of different sizes,

---

* Scale effect—an increase in size would increase stability as the fourth power, displacement as the third power, and sail area as the second power of the length; all other dimensions are assumed to be increased in proportion to that of the length.

types, and rigs, the speed-length ratio is of fundamental importance. It may be used to establish the expected speed of a vessel of given length that might be considered "fast sailing." Long and intensive observation shows that the highest service speed usually recorded in a seagoing sailing vessel of good design, with an efficient rig, is in the neighborhood of a speed-length ratio of 1.25–1.35. The highest recorded or claimed speed of a seagoing merchant sailing vessel showed a speed-length ratio of about 1.65. This rate of speed could be realized for a short period under exceptional weather conditions and in a very fast ship lightly loaded, or ballasted, and well-handled, with a strong, fair wind.

Taking 100 feet on the waterline as a basis for discussion, a speed-length ratio of 1.25 indicates a speed of 12½ knots. That this is reasonable is shown by the performances of the large fishing-schooner racers *Bluenose*, *Columbia*, *Puritan*, and *Mayflower*—all above 100 feet in waterline length, and none of which exceeded 12 knots in competition. These vessels were, nevertheless, very fast sailers with potential maximum speeds of nearly 15 knots or better.*

Observed maximum speed, which can be used in comparisons of vessels' designs, is the highest speed recorded in one hour of sailing on any point. Needless to say, the "fastest voyage" of a thousand miles of sea, such as the run from New York to San Francisco around Cape Horn, or the run from Hong Kong to London around the Cape of Good Hope, is of little service, for a record passage was often made with a ship that did not exceed a speed-length ratio of 1.0, or even much less. The best day's run is more useful, though not sufficiently precise. In a 24-hour run of 320 nautical miles, the average speed on an hourly basis is 13⅓ knots. Yet with normal variations in wind velocity, it is obvious that greater speeds, perhaps up to 14½ or 15 knots, must have been achieved in order to maintain the average. It is quite impossible, however, to establish any precise estimate of a proportion of increased speed obtained, over the average rate, that would be acceptable as the maximum speed of a ship, for comparison of her potential with that of another vessel.

There are a few instances in which the logs of fast vessels show not only the best 24-hour run made, but also the highest speed reached for one hour. This would allow a calculation of the relation of the "highest speed" to "average speed" percentage for use in analysis. However valid this may seem, it cannot

* Claims have been made for speeds up to 16½ knots for *Gertrude Thebaud* and *Oriole* but these claims may be exaggerations; at any rate they cannot be verified.

be used to establish another sailing vessel's potential speed by applying it to the average hourly run in the best day's run, for it is certain that no two ships would have the same variation in speed in relation to the hourly average.

Unfortunately, there are only a few sailing records, before the clipper ship period, on which to base comparisons. Occasionally the hourly speed of a vessel is mentioned earlier than this period, but usually in cases where the particulars of a vessel are imprecise or unavailable. The best day's run and the best passage cannot be used to calculate potential maximum speed of any sailing vessel. Hence the criterion for a given period in the comparison of the maximum speed of vessels is not wholly satisfactory. By an accumulation of design coefficients, however, it may be possible to establish basic criteria for comparisons that would be serviceable substitutes for use of the contemporary "best hour's run."

The characteristics of ship design that should produce very high rates of sailing speed are not necessarily those that would produce record-breaking passages in a prolonged voyage. Such fast voyages were most often the result of maintaining a constant, but moderate, rate of speed under varying conditions of wind and weather, rather than of bursts of very high speed in favorable conditions. Examination of logs of many very fast passages shows that the steady rate of speed maintained was often rather low and usually well within the scope of a reasonably good sailer of heavy burden. It should be stated that periods permitting a very fast ship to sail at her highest speed were commonly of extremely short duration and occur only infrequently during most passages. This matter will require more discussion from time to time as ship qualities are examined, with particular regard to specific design requirements for a given trade or service.

There remains one more matter of a general nature that ought to be examined at this time: the influence of foreign ship types on English, and hence on colonial American, ship designers. It has been the practice of maritime historians in the past to assume that any apparent documentary evidence of construction of a foreign type affected the whole range of contemporary British or American ship design. This line of reasoning also implied the "invention" or introduction of a type within a very limited period of time. The oft-used assumption that French ship designers influenced the design of American fast-sailing schooners of the late eighteenth century is an example. It is therefore desirable to examine this matter at some length in an effort to bring the subject to a proper level of judgment.

Research soon produces apparent evidence of foreign influence on British ship and rig design. Britain's naval position and the long wars prior to 1700 gave her shipwrights ample opportunity to study foreign-built ships, particularly prizes. It has been accepted that Baker, master shipwright in Queen Elizabeth's reign, used Venetian ship design and drafting methods in his manuscript (now called *Fragments of Ancient English Shipwrightry* and dated about 1586). It is claimed by some English authorities that the first English "frigate" was practically a copy of a Dunkirk privateer ship built in 1646, but there are other authorities who question this claim. The English did, however, adopt the square-sail ketch rig (or bomb-ketch rig) from a foreign source sometime before 1650.*

There was no reason why the English ship designers would not study very critically the foreign vessels that came into their hands. This was particularly true when the foreign vessel was an outstanding sailer. But this was also true of other nations, for the French, Dutch, Swedes, and others are known to have studied English ships and even to have imported English shipwrights when opportunity arose.

Ship design has never been entirely restricted to local or national sources. The constant search for improvement in a technical art in which there are so many mysteries, so much frustration, and so much competition as in ship design, made open-mindedness, active curiosity and critical judgment necessities for individual professional survival. Mere copying of any design was foolish, for it would not enable the copier to outdistance his competitors.

English, French, Swedish, Spanish, and other ship designers certainly adopted foreign ideas that were tested in the light of use-requirements and conditions. This cautious approach toward experimentation has been characteristic of sailing-vessel designers over the years. Radical departures are relatively rare. Sometimes the foreign design feature could be successfully applied; at other times it was soon dropped. Or a foreign idea might be incorporated into a design and then developed into a national and distinctive type. This was possibly the case with the English cutter, the French lugger,

---

* A very early English illustration of this rig is that of the *Roe*, a ketch built in 1655, shown in the etching of the fight of the *Mary Rose* (and the *Roe*) with seven Algerian ships, December 9, 1669, by Wenceslaus Hollar, in the Macpherson Collection, published in Frank C. Bowen's *The Sea, Its History and Romance* (London, Halton & Truscott Smith, Ltd., n.d., 4 Vols.), Vol. 1, page 287. The *Roe* is shown with mainmast nearly amidships, with course and topsail, and the mizzen rigged with lateen spanker and square topsail. No sails are shown on the bowsprit but the rigging indicates that a fore-staysail and jib may have been carried.

the American schooner, and the Algerian xebec, all of which became national, fast-sailing types, but all with some features "foreign" in appearance and possibly in origin, adapted to the type sometime during its development.

There are many examples in the shipbuilding histories of maritime nations, where foreign types and rigs were apparently reproduced, more or less completely, in a vessel or class of vessels, but once done, the development into a distinctly national variation began. The Spanish use of the Algerian xebec was an example of this process.

It must also be remembered that ships themselves are the best and most common means of conveying information on their design to a foreign area. The copying process thus began in ancient times—hundreds of years before ship-design records are available. It is quite impossible to determine how much real knowledge existed as to the design of fast sailing vessels at any given time before 1690. But there is some evidence that we have underestimated the knowledge of ship designers prior to 1800. How much of their knowledge can be credited to their inspection of foreign vessels is an unanswered question.

So far as America is concerned, ship design of a local and national type began very late, compared to Europe. The constant movement of English shipwrights into the American colonies in the colonial period brought the most advanced English ideas and design methods to the American shipyards. The colonial American ship designer also had ample opportunities to examine Spanish, French, Dutch, and other foreign ships, for large numbers of ships other than English traded in the colonies at times. American ship design was thus the natural heir to the well-developed ship design techniques of England and all of Europe. But everything in the design of an American colonial-built vessel was necessarily an adaptation or an experimental attempt to produce craft that would comply with colonial economic requirements, use colonial materials, fit colonial geographic limitations, and at the same time be useful in conditions in colonial foreign relations.

It has been the fashion to picture the colonial ship designer and builder as a primitive artisan, isolated from European developments and knowledge, dependent wholly on his natural intelligence, and required to develop hull forms and rigs from the most primitive and elementary beginnings. This is an entirely false view of American shipbuilding development.

The American ship-types were actually developed by a slow and lengthy process, in which many "foreign" ideas were seized upon, tested, and adapted or rejected. At times a basic design or model might be employed; luggers, lateeners, cutters, and other foreign rig-and-hull combinations were built in America during the Revolution and the War of 1812, for example. But these were experiments, built as the result of whims of the builders or owners. It is now possible to prove, by the evidence of available ship plans, that these reproductions of foreign types had no substantial influence on contemporary American design practices or theories. Indeed, with the difficulty in determining where certain hull characteristics really originated, it is impossible to decide which of two nations was the influencing factor.

The matter of influence will require more discussion when the relationships between American and European fast sailing vessels seem pertinent, due to apparent similarities in hull forms. There are certain facts, however, that should be kept in mind. No single detail of design can be accepted as sufficient evidence of influence. No national type of sailing vessel was the invention of a single designer or builder. No national type ever developed suddenly.

Individual national types commonly show one or more features that will be found in some other national types, and this was particularly true in Europe, and of course in America. The more developed the type, the more numerous are certain design elements that can be recognized, to a degree, in other types. Only in a few instances would this be difficult; Chinese junks have many common features as a class, but have only the most elementary relationship with western designs. But this is a relatively isolated situation. The development of national fast sailing types in Europe and America was a slow and lengthy process in all cases. These were each the product of much trial-and-error development, spurred by strong competition, in which the effects of hydrodynamics played a controlling part. In fast sailing types of vessels the restrictions imposed by hydrodynamics would be very marked. As a result, certain hull-form design elements might appear in two or more national types without there being any "influence" expressed through deliberate copying. Such design elements as sharp and even hollow waterlines, deadrise in midsection, and the profile of ends are very common characteristics in fast sailing types that may have been the result of the basic hydrodynamic factor rather than of "influence."

It is evident, then, that any claim of influence of foreign design upon a national type of sailing vessel must be treated with great caution and skepticism.

CHAPTER • TWO

1700 - 1760

ASIDE FROM A FEW SLOOPS, THE "GALLEY SHIP" OF THE LAST QUARTER OF THE
seventeenth century was the first type of cargo vessel designed primarily for
speed that was built extensively in the English colonies of North America.
This class of vessel, also known as a "runner," probably originated in the
Mediterranean in the sixteenth century. It had been introduced into England
as the "rambargo," or "ram-barge," of the rowing-sailing ship designs shown
in *Del Arcano Del Mare*, published in 1612–1620 and written by Sir Robert
Dudley, who styled himself the "Duke of Northumberland." Dudley's designs show the whole range of rowing-sailing ships—from the galley to the
galleon—but they are of more than common size. In the seventeenth century
there were numerous other types of rowing-sailing vessels, such as the French
"barque longue" or "corvette," all of which sought speed under sail and oar.

In the wars near the end of the seventeenth century the British Navy
could not furnish men-of-war to protect English traders. The resulting heavy
losses of merchant ships created a demand for swift-sailing cargo vessels—
blockade-runners—which led to the "runner" or merchant galley ship. She
was designed and built to sail fast, and yet with her shoal form and light
displacement, to be rowed easily in calms. This type was adapted by New

England shipbuilders in the 1690's when they, too, had demands from merchants for vessels to serve as runners.

There is no indication, in references to the colonial galley ship, that she differed in any way from her English prototype. The galley was usually ship-rigged but there were New England built brigantine-rigged merchant vessels of this type, which in basic design and in size were counterparts of the French corvette or barque longue.

No plans of American-built merchant galley-vessels have yet been found. There are, however, a number of plans of naval galleys in existence, from 1675 to 1750, and also a few plans of English merchant galley ships of 1700 to 1745. The Royal Navy built a class of 20- to 24-gun ships that were galley ships in design; apparently the result of experience with the galley frigates or ships of the *Charles Galley* class of 1675. The 20- to 24-gun ships rowed on either the gun deck, or after 1730, on the berth, or lower deck.

The plan of a small naval galley ship will serve to illustrate the important characteristics of the type, and as this vessel is about the size of many colonial merchant galleys, the design shows what some of them might have been in 1695–1710. The *Peregrine Galley* was built at the Deptford dockyard, on the river Thames, in 1700 as a naval cruiser. She was designed by, and built under the supervision of, the dockyard master shipwright William Lee. This handsome vessel gained the reputation of being a very fast sailer.

Her fine reputation and appearance led to her being converted, or "reduced," to a government yacht in 1716. Renamed *Carolina*, she was refitted above and below deck for the new service. In August 1720 her lines were "taken off" and a surviving "draught," or plan, was made. From this, and from the papers relating to her conversion, it has been possible to reconstruct her original form and appearance in a plan projected and faired in the modern manner (shown in Plate 3).

The history of this ship is of some interest. In 1733 she was rebuilt, and in the process her hull form was somewhat altered, particularly in the bow, changing her appearance. This work was done at the Deptford yard under the supervision of master shipwright Richard Stacey. With this rebuilding she was renamed *Royal Caroline*. In 1749 she was cut in two and a "parallel body" inserted, increasing her length by 3′9″. This was done by master shipwright Thomas Fellows at the Woolwich dockyard; and at that time she was restored as a 10-gun sloop of war or cruising ship and dubbed *Peregrine*. She sailed for Lisbon with dispatches on 28 December 1761, and was never

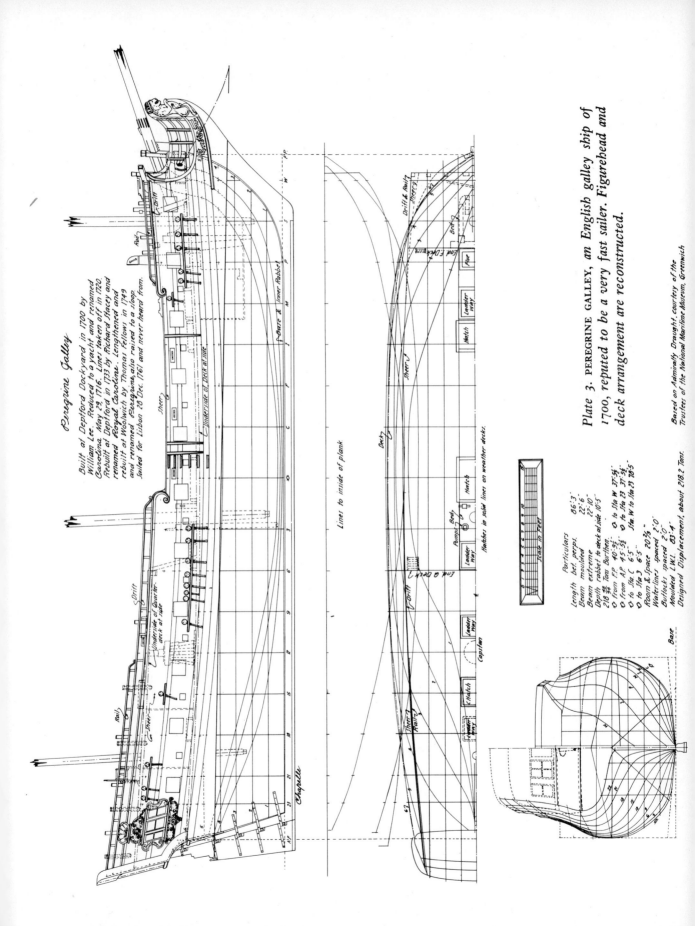

Peregrine Galley

Built at Deptford Dockyard in 1700 by
William Lee. Reduced to a yacht and renamed
Carolina, May 29, 1716. Lines taken off in 1720.
Rebuilt at Deptford in 1733 by Richard Stacey and
renamed *Royal Caroline*. Lengthened and
rebuilt at Woolwich by Thomas Fellows in 1749
and renamed *Peregrine*, also raised to a sloop.
Sailed for Lisbon 28 Dec. 1761 and never heard from.

Lines to inside of plank

Hatches in solid lines on weather decks.

Scale in Feet

Particulars

Length bet. perps.	86'·3"
Beam moulded	22'·6"
Beam extreme	22'·10"
Depth rabbet to deck at side	10'·5"
218 74/94 Tons Burthen.	
⊕ from FP 40'·9½"	⊕ to Sta W 37·5½"
⊕ from A.P. 45'·5½"	⊕ to Sta 23 37·5½"
⊕ to Sta C 6·5"	Sta W to Sta 23 10·5
⊕ to Sta 3 6·5"	
Room & space 20⅝"	
Waterlines spaced 2'·0	
Buttocks spaced 2'·0	
Moulded LWL 83'·4"	
Designed Displacement, about 218.2 Tons.	

Plate 3. PEREGRINE GALLEY, an English galley ship of
1700, reputed to be a very fast sailer. Figurehead and
deck arrangement are reconstructed.

Based on Admiralty Draught, courtesy of the
Trustees of the National Maritime Museum, Greenwich.

heard from again. It is probable that she foundered in the heavy gale that swept the Bay of Biscay in January 1762. No record has been found of her highest rate of speed, but throughout her six-decade career, this ship was considered an unusually fast sailer.

Since much of our record of eighteenth-century American ship design is derived by the taking off of lines, this process required explanation. There appears to be very little record of the practice of taking off in the Royal Navy. It is probable that crude attempts were made to measure and draw the form of fast vessels in the early seventeenth century. From the Admiralty Collection of Draughts, it is apparent that the mode of measuring hull forms and appearance of vessels was well established by 1700. Taking off usually produced very complete plans that often showed carving, deck arrangement, deck fittings, and occasionally some details of construction. Spar dimensions were given in a few instances. Taking off had to be done with sufficient precision to permit the making of an accurate scale drawing that would enable a duplicate ship to be built.

The British Admiralty appears to have become aware of the desirability of having plans of captured or purchased ships that had shown unusually good qualities in speed or other characteristics.

The earliest plan of a take-off that the author has seen is of the *Advice Prize* in The Admiralty Collection of Draughts taken from the French in 1704.* Detailed drawings made in this manner become increasingly numerous after 1738, and include both English and foreign vessels. The earliest date of taking off lines of vessels in England or on the Continent has not been established.

The take-off process required the vessel to be put in a drydock fitted for the work. The bottom of the dock was arranged so that the vessel's longitudinal centerline could be brought to an equivalent line on the floor of the dock. The hull was then shored and her vertical centerline was established and plumbed; the keel was supported above the dock floor on blocks and brought level and parallel to the floor. The positions of the desired number of cross sections of the hull were then decided and these were marked on the dock floor, at right angles to the longitudinal centerline. The dock was fitted with calibrated wooden battens, which were constructed to form large "squares," of the form of a carpenter's steel square, to send vertically on the dock floor and square to the longitudinal centerline at each transverse section location. By measuring in from the vertical arm and up from the horizontal

* Sold 10 April 1712 for £140 to a private owner.

38

arm (and square to each), the form of a section could be measured by "off-sets," in feet, inches, and fractions, so that the section could then be precisely plotted in the scale drawing. This method was also used to obtain the profile of bow and stern. As the measurements proceeded, they were plotted, and sections and end profiles drawn on paper marked in ¼-inch squares to check the work. The location of masts, stive or bowsprit, positions of all rails or mouldings, were carefully measured and sketched. Details of fittings, deck furniture, and carvings were often sketched and measured—all that would be necessary to produce an accurate plan. The take-off is the most desirable plan for analysis, as it records the hull form "as built" and in more complete detail than in the plans used to design these early ships. In building the vessel the design plan might not have been followed precisely, without any records of the departures made, hence the design plan might not be a truly accurate representation of the ship's actual form and appearance.

The degree of precision obtained in Admiralty take-offs increased steadily during the first half of the eighteenth century. By about 1745 the take-offs became reasonably accurate, though the extreme end sections close to the bow and stern were sometimes "out of fair" when checked by modern projection methods. Sometime after 1784 it was the rule of the British Admiralty that ships to be copper-sheathed, for which accurate plans were not available, were to be taken off and draughts prepared, so that precise estimates could be made of the required amount of costly copper sheathing. As a result there are plans of many purchased or captured ships that otherwise might never have been taken off and drawn.

When the lines of the *Carolina*, ex-*Peregrine Galley*, were taken off in 1720, the method used was not fully developed. As a result, the foremost and aftermost transverse sections were out of fair when checked. Apparently this was caused by misalignment in the measuring rules or staffs on the sectional stations in taking offsets where there was rapid change in form, or by errors in measuring from the base or dock floor to obtain heights. The interpretations in fairing these were not brought into question, however, since the remaining sections faired well and this condition established, within very small limits, what the end sectional forms would be to give a fair hull form, with the relationships established in the end profiles of the hull. In drawing the ship to the standard ¼-inch to foot scale small errors in measurements are cancelled out—one inch on the scale being little more than the width of a pencil line.

The modern projections of the lines of a vessel must be understood in order to follow an analysis of a design. In the lines plan, the vessel is shown as though she were a half-model. Only half of the hull is projected, since both sides will be alike. The profile, called "sheer elevation," or "sheer plan," shows the outboard profile of the hull with all outboard decoration and important detail. On this view the inboard profile, showing deck furniture and fittings, may also be shown, usually by broken lines. These are red lines in the old Admiralty draughts. The bow, in this view, is usually to the right, and the starboard side of the hull is represented, but this convention is not always followed.

To one side of the sheer plan, the forms of the various transverse sections are shown, and here the elevation of the transom or stern, viewed from astern, is also drawn. This view is the "body plan." The sections shown are outlines of the sections that would result if the half-model in the sheer plan were cut at each section station line, perpendicular to the back, or plane, of the hull's longitudinal and vertical centerlines. Horizontal straight lines appear on both sheer and body plans—these are the "waterlines" or "level lines" and are parallel to the base line in both views. In these drawings the base line is usually the line of the inside of the plank, at keel, or "inner rabbet line"; otherwise, it is an identified horizontal line near the keel. The transverse section lines on the sheer plan are perpendicular to the base.

Below or above the sheer plan is another view—this shows the form of each water or level line, and of the rail sheer and deck lines as if seen from above. This is the "half-breadth plan." The curves shown are the outlines of the sections that would result if the half-model shown in the sheer plan were cut along the water or level lines, perpendicular to the plane of the ship's longitudinal and vertical centerlines or to the flat back of the half-model.

The buttock-bow lines appear on the body plan as vertical straight lines parallel to the vertical centerline. On the half-breadth plan they are represented by straight lines parallel to the hull's centerline. If the half-model were cut longitudinally on these lines, the outlines of the resulting sections would be identical to the curves shown in the sheer elevation, extending from the rail down toward the keel and back again.

The diagonals in the lines plan are supplementary fairing lines that show, for example, that the hull could be properly planked. They are represented by straight lines at varying angles to the vertical centerline in the body plan. If the half-model were cut along these straight lines, the outlines of the sections would agree with the curves drawn over the half-breadth plan in reversed direction from a centerline just under the keel in the sheer plan.

The body plan shows the forms of the sections in the fore part of the hull (forebody) on one side of the centerline and the after part (afterbody), opposite. In a double-ended hull, having both ends alike in profile and form, as in a ferryboat, only the body plan sections of one half of the sheer elevation would need be shown.

Each of the curves shown in the lines indicates some element in the form of the hull, as will be explained later in the discussion of individual designs. The projections required to make a line plan, in designing a vessel, need not be discussed here.*

Plate 3, a modern drawing of the lines of *Peregrine Galley*, indicates some of the important design characteristics of the galley ships of her period. She will serve to illustrate the state of the art of fast-vessel design by English shipwrights in 1700.

The plan shows the galley ship to be slightly narrower and much shoaler than contemporary sailing ships of the same general size. The galley was somewhat sharper ended and relatively lighter in displacement. These features usually made a galley fast under sail and easy to row, compared to a normal sailing ship. *Peregrine Galley* had oar ports on her gun or main deck, between the gunports. Some galleys had two oar ports between each pair of gunports. Some of the larger galleys, such as many of the 20- to 24-gun ships, had the lower deck fitted for rowing, with a continuous row of oar ports in the sides broken only by a small entry port about amidships.† In these vessels the upper deck was armed and a few guns were sometimes mounted on the raised quarterdeck. Swivels were usually carried on the quarterdeck rails of merchant galleys.

Primarily, it was not entirely the number of oars or "sweeps" that distinguished the galley ship, though she usually carried more oars than a regular ship of her size; rather, it was the ease and speed with which she could be rowed due to the relatively light displacement and easy lines that had originally determined her classification. Galleys the size of the *Peregrine*

---

* For instructions on drawing lines in design of a boat or vessel see Howard I. Chapelle's *Yacht Designing and Planning* (New York, W. W. Norton & Company, Inc., 1936).

† In the 1740's the British Navy built a few 24-gun ships to row on both berth deck and gun deck, in two banks of sweeps on each side; for example, *Centaur*, 1745, Reg. No. 2814, Box 43, Admiralty Collection of Draughts, The National Maritime Museum, Greenwich, S.E.10, England. (Subsequent Admiralty draughts will be referred to by file and box numbers only.)

Galley used two or three men to a sweep; she had nine sweeps to a side.

The galley ships were rigged with the ship-rig of their period; square course, topsail, and topgallant sail on fore and main masts, and sometimes a royal pole and sail above the topgallant. On the mizzen there was a lateen spanker, commonly with a square topsail set above.

The galley-brigantines were square-rigged on the foremast—course, topsail, topgallant, and sometimes a royal. On the mainmast they carried a boomless gaff spanker, occasionally with a square topsail set above it. The lateen spanker does not appear to have been carried by Royal Navy brigantine "sloops" of the first half of the eighteenth century, nor does the limited evidence found indicate that it was carried by colonial brigs or brigantines. This matter will be referred to again.

A comparison of dimensions and proportions of the *Peregrine Galley* with a sailing ship will show how she differed from her sailing counterpart. The *Peregrine Galley* measured 86′3″ length on main deck or between perpendiculars, 22′6″ beam from outside of frame to outside of frame at midsection ("moulded beam"), and 10′5″ depth from rabbet to the keel to underside of deck at side of hull ("moulded depth"). Thus, she was almost four times her beam in length, or 3.83; her depth was slightly less than half of her beam, or 2.17; and she was a little over ⅛ of her length, or 8.28. The hull proportions are readily calculated from the draught dimensions and will be only occasionally used hereafter.

The *Advice Prize* was a French-built ship captured by the *Advice* and taken into the royal Navy in 1704; her draught in The Admiralty Collection of Draughts records her dimensions as 83 feet on the lower deck, 23′6″ moulded beam, and 12′4″ moulded depth. Her proportions are length to beam 3.53, beam to depth 1.91, and length to depth 6.73. The *Advice Prize* was a fast ship by reputation, and as her draught shows, sharp-ended compared to larger Royal Navy ships of her date.

The *Peregrine Galley* had a "moulded displacement" of about 218 long tons. Moulded displacement is that to outside of frames, without taking into account the displacement of the planking, external keel, stempost, sternpost, and rudder. In the commercial sailing vessel these might vary in a given size of hull, without apparent relation to hull form. Also, since the majority of plans to be considered were drawn to inside of plank, the moulded displacement will be used hereafter in comparisons of hull form; it has the advantage of a closer relationship to hull form alone than would the actual displacement in these old vessels.

The displacement of sailing vessels, commercial or naval, was not constant, except in such craft as pilot boats. The displacement varied with cargo, equipment, armament, and stores. Therefore comparisons must be based upon "designed" displacement, shown in plans as the "load waterline" displacement. This is another factor in sailing-ship speed records that makes precise comparisons impossible, for the actual displacement at the time of a record passage is never given. It must be recognized that the loading of a sailing vessel is always an important element controlling speed. This matter will be discussed later in more detail.

Proportions, such as those given for the *Peregrine Galley* and *Advice Prize*, are "dimensionless" in that they could establish the relationships of length, beam, and depth in any selected size. Similarly the "coefficients" are dimensionless, allowing comparisons to be made of vessels of markedly different size.

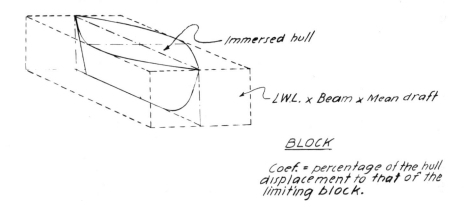

— *Immersed hull*

L.W.L. x Beam x Mean draft

BLOCK

Coef. = percentage of the hull displacement to that of the limiting block.

The "block coefficient" shows the relationship of the displacement of a hull to that of a block equal to the product of designed load waterline length times beam times mean draft of water, using "moulded" dimensions. In the *Peregrine Galley* the displacement is about 51 percent of the block. This would be in the range of such a coefficient for moderately fast, rather shoal modern steamers and motor vessels, 50 to 400 feet in length.* In itself, the block coefficient is not an indication of speed potential but does serve to indicate the displacement, capacity, or "bulk" relationship in comparisons of dissimilar vessels.

* George Simpson, *The Naval Constructor*, 4th ed. (New York, Van Nostrand Co., 1918), pp. 47–48.

The "midsection coefficient" is also an indication of capacity, to some extent. It is the proportion of the actual midsection area below the load waterline to the area of the rectangle formed by multiplying the waterline beam of

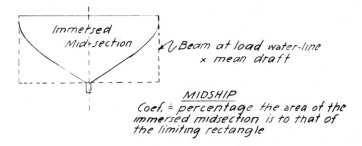

the midsection by the draft there—again moulded and so measured to the keel rabbet. In the *Peregrine Galley* the midsection coefficient is .81, indicating a moderately large midsection for the dimensions. No potential speed indication is obtained with this coefficient alone, though it is useful in a detailed comparison of hull forms.

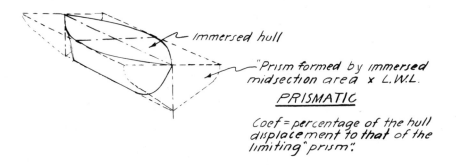

The "prismatic coefficient" is considered to be the most useful of the dimensionless proportions, as an indication of potential speed. It is the proportion of the hull displacement to that of the "prism" formed by the midsection area below the load waterline multiplied by the length of the load waterline— moulded as before. The prismatic coefficient indicates the fineness, or degree of sharpness, in the ends of the hull with due regard to the size of the immersed midsection. In the *Peregrine Galley* the prismatic coefficient is .65.

Sailing merchant vessels, due to the relatively low range of horsepower produced in their rigs under most conditions of wind and sea, are under certain limitations in prismatic coefficients. When sailing on the wind with relatively small effective power available, it appears that a low prismatic (.54 or less in a modern keel yacht with cutaway ends) may be desirable. On other points of sailing, however, where greater power is available, a much higher prismatic may be indicated, depending upon the maximum speed-length ratio obtained on each point of sailing. For the time being, no effort need be made to establish the relationship between sailing speeds and prismatics. This will appear as data on the recorded sailing speeds and hull characteristics of actual vessels, as such data are collected in this study.

Caution is required in comparing the hull forms of keel sailing yachts, which have very short keels and cutaway ends, with commercial sailing craft of the past. The prismatic of the modern keel yacht is lowered abnormally when the midsection used for prismatic calculation includes the area of the ballast keel, particularly when the keel is almost a fin. This may lead to a false conclusion as to the desirable low limit of prismatic in such yachts; some are said to have prismatics as low as .51. The extreme importance of windward sailing in yacht racing, combined with effects of measurement rules, may lead to such very low prismatics, rather than to the effect of hydrodynamic requirements alone. Probably very few sailing merchant vessels of any type had prismatic coefficients below .57.

The effectiveness of the prismatic coefficient as a criterion of the potential highest speed in a sailing vessel design seems to be influenced in some degree by the ratio of hull depth to length. It appears to be usually true, that in two hulls having the same prismatic, the one having the less camber in the buttock-bow lines, or the less depth of body, will have the potentially higher speed-length ratio. The camber of the buttock-bow lines can be averaged by using a line at, or very near to, one quarter of the load waterline beam (out from the longitudinal and vertical centerlines of the hull). Its effective and immersed length is the distance between the intersections of the buttock-bow line and the load line—in *Peregrine Galley* the proportion of camber in the length is $\frac{1}{10}$ the effective length or camber-to-length ratio 9.4, while in *Advice Prize* it is 12.9.

The lines of the *Peregrine Galley* show that the half-angle of the load waterline at the bow is about 46 degrees, which is blunt by modern standards. This would not create great resistance at speeds below, say, 5 knots but would normally become an adverse factor at higher speeds. The buttock-bow lines must also be considered at their forward intersections with the load waterline where in this case they cross at a relatively small angle—about 35 degrees—near the quarterbeam. The effect of this would reduce, in marked degree, the adverse influence of the full load waterline—the water passing under, instead of around, the entrance or forebody as the direction of least resistance. The angle at which the approximate quarterbeam buttock-bow line crosses the load line in the afterbody is probably of some importance at wave-making speeds, and in *Peregrine Galley* the angle is a very low 13 degrees. The relatively moderate camber of the buttock-bow line and its small angles of intersection with the load waterline indicate that *Peregrine Galley* might be easily driven at the normal range of sailing speed-length ratios, say 0.75 to 1.0. It should be stated, also, that the immersed transom increases the prismatic coefficient, but in the upper range of sailing speed has the apparent effect of increasing the effective waterline length. In some instances it may also reduce the camber-length ratio of the afterbody buttocks, which is helpful in the higher sailing speeds.

The buttock-bow lines, water or level lines, and shape of body-plan sections are the areas in design in which the draftsman tries to make the most of the hull proportions with which he has decided, or has been required, to work. The forms of the longitudinal curves in the lines plan have long been the subject of speculation on the assumption that these might somehow show the quantity of resistance to be met. Even in Elizabethan times, as we have seen, the idea of forming the longitudinal lines so as to produce a fish-shaped hull was prevalent. Writers on naval architecture referred to this theory until well into the nineteenth century, but without very definite instructions on the practical projections required.

Generally, designers have assumed that lines of flow to some degree followed the longitudinal curves in the lines plan, but there were differences of opinion as to where the bulk of the flow passed. Some believed most of the flow was around the hull, making the form of waterlines very important. Others considered the flow to be largely underneath the hull, making buttock-bow lines important. Another school of thought considered flow as following the diagonals, particularly those crossing the majority of the transverse sections at as nearly right angles to their outboard forms as their shape permitted.

While this matter of flow lines was undoubtedly considered by practical ship designers in the eighteenth century, there is little detailed discussion of it in any of the eighteenth-century works on naval architecture. In the nineteenth century, however, textbooks on naval architecture refer to this subject as though it were in regular use during the previous century. Chapman, a great Swedish naval architect of the eighteenth century, developed a theory of distribution of displacement that was controlled by a mathematically constructed parabolic curve. This was based upon analysis of satisfactory vessel designs to discover how far the areas of consecutive sections followed any regular law.*

In the middle of the next century Scott Russell developed the "Wave Line Theory" in which the water or level lines were to follow a curve of versed sines in the forebody and a trochoidal curve in the afterbody.†

Dixon Kemp proposed construction of a quarterbeam buttock in the afterbody on a parabolic curve, in his work on yacht designing in 1876.‡ This theory was based on analysis of at least nine successful sailing yachts of his time.

In 1852 Lord Robert Montague¶ had proposed the use of normal diagonals in drawing the lines, but offered no particular forms for these. There is no need to discuss these theories; it is sufficient to list them only to show how much thought and effort was expended in the long search for a hull form of "least resistance" using a variety of approaches in which the lines plan and calculations might be used.

Model testing has shown that there were elements of truth in all these theories. It is evident that proper distribution of displacement may be required to obtain a fast vessel, the distribution probably varying with the potential speed-length ratio sought. Present knowledge indicates, however, that this is a matter of having a distribution that corresponds with that of an easily-driven vessel of exactly the same hull proportions, rather than one with some ideal distribution that would insure low resistance for any given hull dimensions.§

The advantages of a long, sharp entrance, with the midsection slightly abaft midlength, have also been long established, particularly for the higher speed-length ratios. If shoulders or humps are not formed at the after end of the entrance, where the latter fairs into the midbody, the long, sharp entrance

---

* Application of Chapman's theory is explained in P. R. Marett's *Yachts and Yacht Building, a treatise on the construction of yachts and matters relating to yachting*, 2nd ed. (London-New York, E. & F. N. Spon, 1872).

† Dixon Kemp, *Yacht Designing* (London, "The Field Office," 1876); a treatise on the practical application of scientific principles upon which is based the art of designing yachts, showing application of wave-line theory in sailing-vessel design.

‡ *Ibid.*

¶ Lord Robert Montague, *Naval Architecture* (London, A. D. Mills, 1852); a treatise on shipbuilding and the rig of clippers with a new suggestion for laying down vessels.

§ Harold E. Saunders, *Hydrodynamics in Ship Design* (New York, The Society of Naval Architects and Marine Engineers, 1957), Vol. 1, page 84, col. 1.

seems to be a means of reducing wave-making in the high ranges of speed-length ratios in sailing vessels. It should be noted, however, that if high sailing speed is the aim, the forms of the buttock-bow lines in the forebody should probably be without marked humps also, because of the flow distribution that normally occurs in the forebody.

Model tests have shown that flow at the bow is only partly around the hull; much of the flow appears to pass downward and under the forebody at speeds where wave-making occurs. For this reason the turn of the bilges in the forebody sections of the body plan should be soft and easy so that the flow under the forebody is unhindered. Hence the need for very easy curves in the immersed buttock-bow lines in the forebody, as well, which normally produce easy sections forward.

It should be stated that "flow lines" do not in fact exist. The flow is in currents and eddies, of varying magnitudes and velocities, with ill-defined boundaries. Though flow lines are therefore an oversimplification, they are a necessary assumption in order to obtain some systematic understanding of the behavior of flow around a moving hull.

Studies of flow also indicate that some of it usually follows the normal diagonals, passing over the sections in the body plan at approximately right angles to their outline. The tests show, however, that accurate, quantitative flow lines cannot be readily assumed and plotted. It is apparent that flow under and around the forebody is affected in quantity by the relative degrees of fineness in the longitudinal curves—water or level lines, some diagonals, and the buttock-bow lines. Flow tests in models also seem to indicate that actual movement does not usually follow a truly continuous, normal diagonal—nor other longitudinal line—for any great length, but is absorbed by other flow movements and then changes direction. This seems to occur in the forebody, or in the vicinity of the midbody, and at the beginning of the run in the afterbody. Generally, the water near the keel and out to the bilge, in the forebody, appears to move under the hull, while that at the bilges follows a fairly normal diagonal, and that above the bilge moves around the sides of the hull.*

Where there are "hard curves," or humps, in any of the longitudinals, pressure is developed on the surface of the hull by the flow. This was well understood by some designers as early as the 1840's. The prominent yacht designer-builders of Poole, England, the Wanhills, made a practice of examining the copper-sheathed bottom of a new vessel at the end of its first season.

* *Hydrodynamics in Ship Design*, Vol. II, pp. 495, 515–16.

If any portion of the copper appeared to be burnished, or scoured, they considered it to be an area of high resistance and faired their next design accordingly, to ease the pressure and scour at such portions of the hull form.* Chapman seems to have been somewhat aware of the effects and appearance of pressure before 1800.

Separation of the flow from the hull occurs abaft points where pressure areas develop, or where there is an abrupt end in hull form below the line of flotation, as in a submerged transom stern. Though separation occurs to some degree at all speeds, the quantity of separation can be controlled by proper hull design for a given speed range. The importance of separation and pressure areas is that they are resistance-creating factors, producing waves alongside and astern of the hull. These waves increase in magnitude, change position, and absorb an increasingly large amount of propelling power, without a corresponding increase in speed, as the hull is driven beyond its proper speed-length ratio limitations.†

The flow in the afterbody is somewhat more regular than in the forebody. Here the general flow crosses the body-plan section outlines at right angles or "normal" to them. The water coming up from under the hull covers a greater area of surface in the sections of the body plan than is required by the flow around the sides.‡ It is this condition that makes buttock-bow lines of marked importance and supports Kemp's theory.¶ As Kemp stated, there is no apparent advantage in an exact parabolic curve in the quarterbeam buttock-bow line. As long as the quarterbeam buttock-bow line is straight for an indeterminate distance at its aftermost immersed end, the flow under the afterbody should not create waves and a disturbed wake. So far, however, there is no method available for determining the desirable length of the straight portion of the quarterbeam buttock-bow line for a given speed-length ratio. The effect of the amount of camber in this buttock is not mentioned by Kemp. Observations indicate that the higher the speed-length ratio, the longer the straight portion should be in the run and the less should be its angle of intersection with the load line. It is also probable that in the range of speed-length ratios of sailing vessels, the required length is not very great. The lines of most fast sailing vessels show this buttock line characteristic.§

It should be observed that the depth of camber in the quarterbeam buttock

* Letter from W. P. Stephens, February 6, 1936, to author.
† Saunders, *Hydrodynamics in Ship Design*, Vol. II, Chapter 46, pp. 133–39.
‡ Saunders, *Hydrodynamics in Ship Design*, Vol. II, pp. 594, 515–16.
¶ *Yacht Designing*, p. 82.
§ Saunders, *Hydrodynamics in Ship Design*, Vol. II, Chapter 46, pp. 133–136.

is closely related to the angle of its crossing with the load line, and the less the angle the less the camber indicated. This will have much greater effect on hull form than reference to the angle of crossing indicates, or the entrance and run angles of the load line would suggest.

Sailing vessels sail most of the time with an inconstant angle of heel that varies with wave action and the effects of changing wind velocity. Nevertheless, heel should be considered, since it obviously affects the flow. Again, there is little specific information on any mode of drawing the lines to meet this condition, particularly at large angles of heel. The use of a projected heeled load waterline is found as early as 1800, but aside from indicating the degree of nonsymmetrical form that develops in a well-heeled hull, there is very little to be extracted from any proposed analysis of this projection. It may be that quarterbeam buttock-bow lines, projected square to the heeled load line in the body plan and measured to the assumed waterline beam when heeled (for both sides), would assist in forming some opinion of the flows around the heeled hull. Analysis by this combination of projections, however, has not yet been attempted and therefore no guidance datum is available. It may be that small angles of heel do not greatly influence flow in most hulls, but once the heel is great enough to bring the edge of the deck, or the rail, under water, it seems obvious that the flow becomes obstructed and resistance increases sharply. Then the height of deck above water (freeboard) is of importance and should be great enough to allow necessary heel when sailing at approximately the vessel's maximum speed. Tests made in recent years have indicated that when carrying enough sail to produce the vessel's maximum speed on a reach, or close-hauled, sails begin to lose driving power as the hull angle of heel exceeds 15 to 17 degrees. Therefore the freeboard should be sufficient, theoretically, to allow at least 15 degrees of heel before putting the deck edge under. Except in this matter of freeboard, the lack of accumulated information on the desirable forms of heeled waterlines, and of their normal buttock-bow lines, makes projections of them useless for our purpose here. There is as yet no precise guidance datum for relating sail area to speed, other than in a comparison of like vessels; stability calculations do not at present give acceptable solutions of this problem.

Considering the relationship of fairing diagonals to lines of flow on normal diagonals, it is necessary to establish a mode of using them in order to analyze the lines. The diagonals having the greatest possibilities are those crossing the bilge in the body plan at the midsection. They should be drawn at angles to intersect the stemposts and sternposts near or at the load waterline level. The only established criterion by which they can be evaluated is that in fast sailing vessels such diagonals, when projected, will show no hard, quick curves in any portion of their lengths below the load waterline. Like much analytical material, the diagonals should be judged by comparison with those of a similar fast sailing vessel, rather than by relationship to some ideal form.

The *Peregrine Galley* shows good probable flow characteristics in most respects. The entrance is full, but not excessively so for common sailing conditions, since the buttock-bow lines at bow are well formed. The lower bilge diagonal is somewhat full forward. The quarterbeam buttock is satisfactory and the whole run is quite well designed. With the data established for this vessel it is possible to make comparisons with other vessels of varying sizes and types, as their data are accumulated.

A design for a smaller vessel from the Admiralty Collection of Draughts illustrates further the state of fast-sailing design in the early eighteenth century. By this time the sloop had become almost the "American Colonial rig," since sloops made up a greater proportion of the colonial traders than any other rig. These colonial sloops were used in the West Indian and coasting trade, and some in the transatlantic trades. Those used in long-distance runs were armed and often measured 60 to 66 feet on deck.

Sloops *Ferret* and *Sharke* were built at the Deptford dockyard, on the Thames, for the British Navy in 1711.* These sloops were intended for service in the English Channel, to carry 10 guns and 10 to 12 swivels. They were to be fast cruisers and carried relatively heavy armament; hence they would have to be of rather heavy displacement for their dimensions. To meet these requirements they were designed with full midsections combined with ends as fine as dimensions and displacement permitted.

The design, Plate 4, was for sloops measuring 65′ 7″ between perpendiculars, 20′ 6″ moulded beam, 62′ 3″ moulded waterline length, 10′ 2½″ moulded depth to underside of deck at side, 10′ 9″ draft at post in service trim, displacing 132.7 long tons, moulded. The proportion of length to beam is 3.23;

* Admiralty *Dimension Book B* (1660–1764) shows that the following were apparently built to the same design, though *Tryall* and *Jamaica* are open to question because of their date of build:

Ferrett—built at Deptford, 64′ 8″ x 50′ x 20′ 8″ x 9′ 1″, 113-55/94 tons, 1711
Sharke—built at Deptford, 64′ 8″ x 50′ x 20′ 8″ x 9′ 1″, 113-55/94 tons, 1711
Happy—built at Deptford, 64′ 8″ x 50′ x 20′ 8″ x 9′ 1″, 113-55/94 tons, 1711
Hazard—built at Woolwich, 64′ 8″ x 50′ x 20′ 8″ x 9′ 1″, 113-55/94 tons, 1711
Tryall—built at Deptford, 64′ 6″ x 50′ x 20′ 8″ x 9′ 7″, 113-55/94 tons, 1710
Jamaica—built at Deptford, 64′ 7″ x 50′ 1″ x 20′ 8″ x 9′ 1″, 113-73/95 tons, 1710

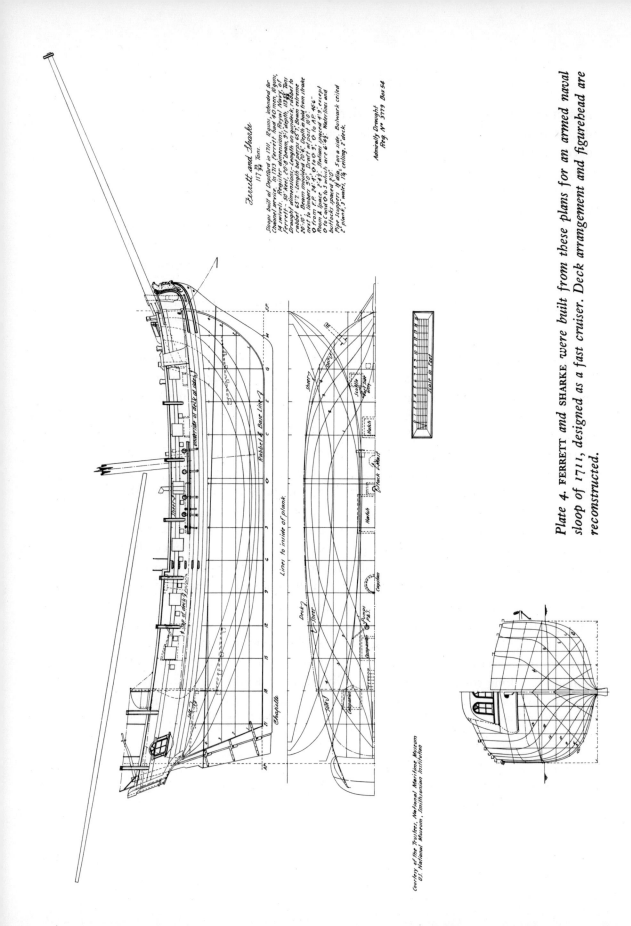

Plate 4. FERRETT and SHARKE were built from these plans for an armed naval sloop of 1711, designed as a fast cruiser. Deck arrangement and figurehead are reconstructed.

beam to depth is 1.97; and length to depth is 6.44. The block coefficient is .48; midship coefficient is .75; and the prismatic coefficient is .63. The buttock-bow line four feet out was selected for reference; its effective length was about 8½ times its greatest depth. The half angle of the entrance was about 45 degrees, but just abaft the stem there was a little hollow in the load line so the effective entrance was a little less. The half angle of the load line in the run was about 37 degrees. The reference buttock-bow line crosses the load line at 31 degrees forward and 20 degrees in the run.

Compared to *Peregrine Galley*, the sloops were proportionately wider and deeper, with smaller block coefficient, smaller midship coefficient, and smaller prismatic coefficient, but with deeper camber in the reference buttock-bow line. The hull is somewhat better formed for flow than that of *Peregrine Galley*, as both buttock-bow lines and diagonals are very easy. In spite of comparatively adverse proportions, the sloop design was probably a slight improvement in model over the older ship. It seems certain that the hull form and the sloop rig would produce a more weatherly vessel. No spar dimensions for these sloops have yet been found, but their rig probably differed little in proportions and in form from later sloops. *Ferret* was captured by surprise in Cadiz Bay by the Spaniards in 1728. She had been fitted with two masts in 1715–16. *Sharke* was rebuilt and then sold in 1732; *Happy*, sold 20 August 1735; *Hazard*, cast away 12 October 1714, off Boston, New England, all hands lost (this vessel may be the "Sloop off Boston Light," the well-known Burgis print published in 1720). *Tryall* was rebuilt and lengthened in 1714; her new measurements were 76 feet by 59′3″ by 21′3″ by 9′6″, 142–29/94 tons; she was broken up in 1731. *Jamaica* was wrecked on Grand Cayman, West Indies, 2 October 1715.

The sloops, like the galley ship, do not represent types in which the potential speed was of prime importance. They are examples of the age-old attempt to obtain primarily a required carrying capacity, and secondarily, speed. Fortunately a design of this period exists in which capacity was obviously sacrificed for speed.

In July 1736, the "scooner" *St. Ann* entered Portsmouth, England, with dispatches (a "packet") from Lisbon, flying the Portuguese flag. In August she was brought to the naval dockyard, her lines were taken off, and a British Admiralty draught or plan was made of her. Chapman* visited England three

---

* Frederik Henrik ap Chapman became the leading naval ship designer of the eighteenth century —his influence extending well into the nineteenth century. He was born to English parents in

times and probably obtained the draught sometime during one of these visits, possibly in 1753. This plan is now in his collection in the Statens Sjohistoriska Museum, Stockholm, Sweden. None of the available records show the date or manner of *St. Ann's* purchase, though she is reported to be mentioned in one Portuguese manuscript naval list as an American-built vessel. No reference to her has yet been found in the surviving Portsmouth dockyard papers, nor does Chapman appear to have recorded anything about her history. Probably her lines were taken off for the reason of her speed, just as the lines of the yacht *America* were taken off in the same dockyard about 125 years later. It seems possible that the *St. Ann* had been a yacht before she became a dispatch boat.

This schooner, shown in Plates 5 and 6, is the earliest vessel yet discovered having a very sharp rise of floor amidships and she is the earliest American-built craft whose plans have yet been found. This is no indication that she was a pioneering design in the use of sharp deadrise, but it points out clearly the limits of existing evidence. A somewhat similar underwater section appeared in Viking ships, but its use cannot be documented through the intervening centuries.

The schooner was very narrow and rather shoal for a sailing vessel of her day. She had a moderately sharp, convex entrance, with a trifle of hollow in the load waterline, just abaft the stem rabbet, but without a vestige of shoulder in the forebody, either in the load line or in the lower level lines. She was about as sharp as many twentieth-century cruising sailing yachts.

Her run was very long and fine; the quarterbeam buttock was practically straight for a short distance, where it crossed the load line aft. The camber in the buttock-bow lines was very small in proportion to length.

The midsection was formed with hollow near the keel rabbet at the garboards, with much additional rise outboard in the section and a well-rounded, easy bilge, developing into moderate tumble home in topsides.

Probably this vessel had cedar top timbers in her frame, as did later Amer-

---

Gothenburg, Sweden, September 9, 1721. His father was a captain in the Swedish Navy and Superintendent of the Dockyard at Gothenburg. Chapman visited London in 1741 and spent three years working in English yards. His next visit, in 1753, was to the Royal Navy dockyards at Deptford, Woolwich, and Chatham. At Deptford he was arrested for espionage but was at once released and his drawings (which had been seized) were returned to him. Chapman also spent much time in the Netherlands and in France and then returned to London, and finally to Stockholm. His studies and his large collection of plans, made him perhaps the best-informed ship designer of the century, and gave him the material for extensive analysis of hull form that is apparent in his published works.

ican schooners in the eighteenth century when on the "sharp" model. The British naval authorities considered them to be "slightly built," as will be seen when these vessels are examined.

The *St. Ann* was 58′ 2″ moulded length at rail, 54 feet on the moulded load waterline, 11′ 10″ moulded beam at load waterline. Her moulded depth from keel rabbet to underside of deck at side at ⚏ was 6′ 10¼″. She drew 5′ 2″ at post and 4′ 4″ forward. She was 12′ 1½″ beam over the wales. Stations were spaced 3′ 10″, J to K 1′ 11″, ⚏ to ⚏ 5″, ⚏ to A, and ⚏ to 1—3′ 5″. The original draught notes that her displacement was 956 cubic feet, or 30.59 short tons. It cannot be determined if this note, in English, is contemporary. With a faired plan and with planimeter, her displacement was calculated to be 967 cubic feet—30.94 short tons, or 27.63 long tons.

Her midship coefficient was .64, her block coefficient .40, and her prismatic .61. Considering her dimensions she was of small displacement, as shown by her block coefficient. Her prismatic is lower, to an effective degree, than in *Peregrine Galley* (.65) and *Ferrett* (.63) The effective length of the quarter-beam buttock would be about 46 feet and its camber about 2.7 feet, giving a length of about 17 times the depth. Her length to beam ratio was 4.89, or at load line 4.56 beam to depth 1.73, and length to depth 8.48.

Plate 5 shows her sail plan, reconstructed from the sail and spar dimensions given on the original draught. Lacking full information, the details of the rig, especially the shape of the fore square sails, are speculative. It is possible that the rig originally was to be fore-and-aft and that the topsails were added when she became a dispatch vessel making ocean voyages. Since the drawing was made, and a model started, it was found that the fore-topsail was drawn somewhat smaller than the sail area (specified in running yards). Hence, the course or foreyard should be lowered about three feet to give the topsail that much additional hoist. It seems probable that the topsail and topgallant yards are shown about 9 inches too high, so that the whole square-sail rig should be that much lower before altering the topsail. Also, as drawn, the fore course is about 1′ 6″ too high in the hoist.

It is apparent that by 1736 the schooner rig had long been in use and was well developed. The use of square sails with this rig is not shown in available seventeenth-century pictures. It is possible that one of the American contributions was in using the schooner rig for seagoing purposes, with square sails added.

The square sails were to supplement the fore-and-aft rig and were not

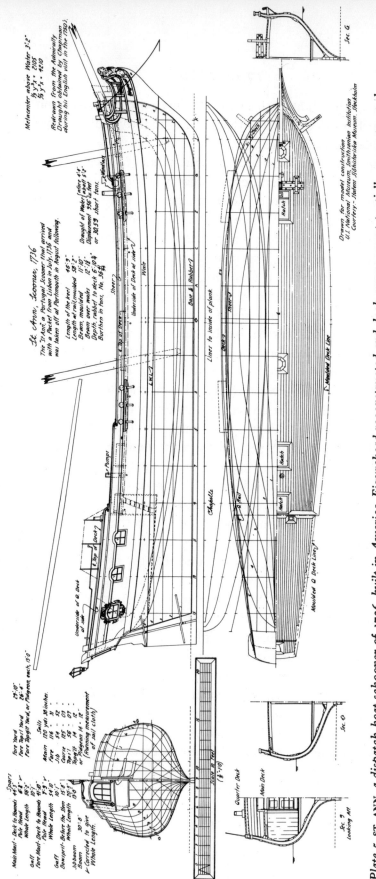

Plate 5. ST. ANN, a dispatch-boat schooner of 1736, built in America. Figurehead reconstructed and deck arrangement partially reconstructed.

normally required for windward work. They were, in fact, light-weather running sails. The weight of square sails furled on the yards aloft and their windage adversely affected the schooner's stability and her weatherliness. Therefore, the assumption is that the square sails and yards were brought to deck and stowed when not in use. This was particularly true in the case of the course. The schooner masting usually gave this sail great hoist and area, hence it would have to be hoisted to the fore yard, and could therefore be lowered for furling without lowering the yard. This permitted the fore yard, minus the bulk and weight of the furled course, to remain aloft to spread the

American-built schooner ST. ANN, *supposed to have been built about 1736 and sold to the Portuguese for a dispatch vessel. Model from plans taken off in Portsmouth Dockyard in 1739.*

foot of the topsail. The topsail and upper square sails—topgallant and royal, if carried—could be furled on their respective yards and then lowered. Hence the schooner rig, like that of the sloop, usually had square sails and yards fitted for lowering at sea when they were not used in beating to windward. Because of this limited use they were light in weight and simple in gear.

The fore yard was often a rather long heavy spar, and with the vessel rolling in a seaway it might get out of control in lowering and cause serious damage to the rigging and foremast, not to mention jeopardizing the crew. Careful control in lowering the yard was achieved by the use of a "horse," a hempen stay having an eye turned in at its head and a deadeye or heart in its foot. The horse was secured at the lower masthead by a lanyard, or lashing, in such a way that the eye of the horse was below and ahead of the heel of the topmast, the lashing usually passing over the fore spreader—or a false one—at the fore end of the trestletrees. The stay was set up on deck with deadeyes and lanyard close to the foreside of the mast, just clear of the wedges. The fore yard was probably secured to this horse, or stay, by a wooden thimble running on the stay. This had a tail, or lanyard, that passed over and around the center of the yard, and was turned in and secured. In addition, on each side, were two smaller thimbles. Around the foremast were parrals, the falls of which passed through these two small thimbles and thence to the deck, where they were belayed on the topsail bitts at the foot of the mast. The yard was hoisted by suitable halyards and had normal braces, lifts, and in large schooners, footropes. As the yard was lowered, it was guided down by the horse and the parral falls, leaving the parral hung over the fore gaff, or its jaws. This prevented the yard from taking charge in lowering. While sailing, the strain was taken off the horse by the parrals.

In the last years of the eighteenth century, the course had a short club in the middle of its head. In some vessels this was hoisted to the underside of the fore yard; in others it was hoisted to just under the forestay eye above the yard, to fill the topsail's gore in its foot. The course was spread by outhauls at the yard arms, led inboard to blocks under the yard, and thence to the deck. An alternate form consisted of a narrow course having at its head a shorter yard than the fore or "spread" yard; this sail and its yard were hoisted under the forestay forward of the spread yard to fill the gore. Another variation, popular in English cutters of 1770–1780, was to secure the head of the course to the fore or spread yard and fill the gore with a truncated triangular topsail set to a short yard.

At the foot of the course there was usually a light boom, secured to the sail only by the two sheets. It had single-part guys and might be secured to the mast by a parral, or it might be lashed to the bulwarks or timber heads, and canted to any angle required by the sail for a given point of sailing. The course was often furled on this boom and set athwartships on two crotches stepped in the waterways at the bulwarks. The boom also could be secured on end in the fore rigging and the sail stowed below.

The mainstay was in two legs, with an eye formed at the head and the lashing (as in the fore horse) was passed around the main-masthead. The stay might be set up with tackles to the inside of the knightheads, or more commonly, to the waterways at bulwarks in the bluff, or shoulders, of the bow. The lee stay was always slacked off, to permit the fore gaff sail to stand properly when sailing. By 1760, at least, some schooners had the mainstay, or triatic stay, set up to the fore-masthead cap, omitting the double mainstays set up on deck.

There probably were many various schooner rigging details, depending upon the size of the vessel and the sailing conveniences required in a given trade. Pictorial evidence indicates that the fore-and-aft rig of the schooner had become well developed by 1700. The foresail seems to have had the most important variations; it might be loose-footed and overlapping, or it might be boomed. The length of the gaffs also varied, apparently, though the short gaffs shown in Plate 6 certainly predominated in the first half of the eighteenth century. The lack of evidence of the use of square sails in schooners in this period is troublesome in the case of *St. Ann*. In the sail dimensions on the original draught, the "topgal't" or "Pidgeon" yards are given as 13 feet each, the sails as 14 yards 1 foot, as though two yards and two sails were indicated. In Plate 6 the normal topgallant sail is shown; the "Pidgeon" sail has not been found in any other eighteenth-century source. It should be noted that the plural "Pidgeon yards" might indicate a square topsail, or topgallant, on the mainmast; it has also been suggested that these yards may have been gaff topsail jack yards.

In examining this design, one must remember that *St. Ann* was built with no apparent consideration of cargo capacity. She probably represented her builder-designer's idea of a vessel in which speed, combined with reasonable seaworthiness, was the prime consideration. Yachts, pilot boats, mail packets, and governmental dispatch boats were usually the only types free from the restrictions imposed by cargo capacity in this period.

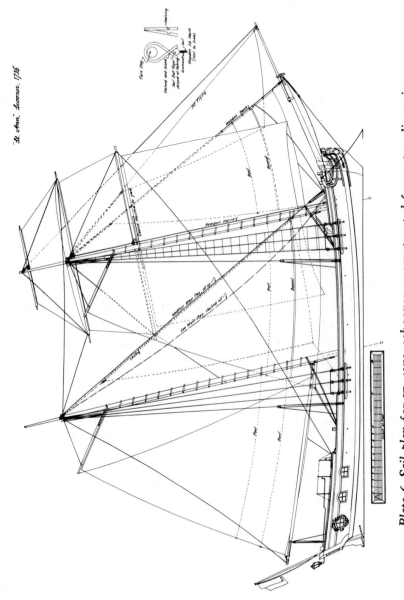

"St. Ann," Schooner, 1736

Fore Stay

Halyard and second Sail Gaff Royal Grommet's Seat joined at Halyard

Spanker Jib Halyard (not to scale)

Marking

Til Flying

Spanker Hawk

Brl.

Boom

Hempen Horse

Centre Hauling off Port

Weather Main Stay, all off

Brl.

Boom

Lee Main Stay, hauled all off

Brl.

Sailing

Brl.

Brl.

Brl.

Plate 6. Sail plan for ST. ANN, *schooner, reconstructed from spar dimensions.*

The narrow beam is evidence of her designer's effort to obtain speed. Experience, particularly with the various galley modifications, had shown that a narrow beam was one element that could produce speed, and a shoal body another. The combination of these two elements produced light displacement in a hull, which in turn led to the use of light construction. Designers of vessels of this description would find stability (the capacity for carrying sail) and weatherliness the two principal problems to be solved in order to obtain a fast sailer.

In *St. Ann* the solution was found in a hollow strake or garboard, which produced a hollow, fin-like structure in which ballast could be stowed effectively. Its flat side surfaces, added to the external keel, made an efficient lateral plane. While the development of this form is not fully recorded, surviving plans show that the use of a small amount of hollow garboard apparently became rather common in large English vessels in the last decade of the seventeenth century. The hollow garboard shown in these plans was not carried very far out from the keel, and the shape outboard of this was nearly flat, without much rise out to the turn of the bilge. There is no evidence of the use of the hollow garboard or of deadrise in very small vessels; the smallest so far available to show these features is the Danish 10- to 12-gun ship mentioned in Chapter One. This single example was about 66' 8" on range of deck. She had a straight deadrise of about 17 degrees from the horizontal, but without a hollow garboard, as is shown in the modern drawing of the ship in Plate 2. Unfortunately this vessel cannot be accurately dated and identified.

There is some evidence to indicate that hollow garboards may have been used to a far greater extent after the Viking age than the scant records show. At any rate, *St. Ann* also has some rise of bottom outboard of the hollow floor, which led to further reduced displacement within the underbody dimensions.

The ends of the hull were made moderately sharp, adhering to the basic model created earlier by "whole moulding." The flow lines were quite good, as far as can be judged without model tests, and the vessel would be easily driven in most of her range of probable sailing speeds.

The narrow beam would effect her power to carry sail and her ability to stand up with her sail in blowing weather. The hollow garboard midsection, and high bilge, with inside ballast would counteract some of the adverse effects of narrow beam, however, and they could be further reduced by lightening the topside weights through limiting any superstructure, and using light woods and small scantlings in the topside structure and deck.

The sail area was moderate and the spars were of small diameter and relatively light. Pole masts eliminated the need for doublings and crosstrees and further decreased weight aloft. If the sailcloth had been well made, *St. Ann's* fore-and-aft rig would probably have been quite efficient on all points of sailing, even by modern standards.

It seems probable, after careful examination of this design, that the schooner was at her best in moderate winds and sea; her best points of sailing were undoubtedly reaching and running, though she would by no means be deficient in windward work if properly ballasted. She probably had the highest speed-length potential of the vessels so far discussed. Her real advantage would be in her ability to reach a relatively high speed in a range of moderate wind velocities. This is often the characteristic of a vessel that does not have a form capable of the very highest potential speed-length ratio, due to lack of power to carry sail in strong winds, but rather is very well suited to a somewhat lower range of speed-length ratios. The model, or form, of hull best suited to the very highest sailing speed-length ratios may not be as easily driven at lower ranges. It is this fact that has prevented the appearance of the "low resistance" hull form that would perform equally well at all speeds with a selected range of driving power.

The designer-builder of *St. Ann* undoubtedly sought this ideal form, and though he failed, he certainly understood practical ways of producing a "fast sailer." He was fully aware of the inherent advantage of relatively light displacement for a given size of hull, when he could escape the rigid limitations of cargo capacity. *St. Ann* is clear evidence of a well-developed professional understanding of ship design for speed. Her rig design shows that there must have been a prolonged period of development before 1736.

The extent to which ship design had progressed in this period is further illustrated in the 24-gun ship *Lyme*, built under contract for the Royal Navy in 1739–40 by James Taylor on the Thames, at London. She is shown in Plate 7; a sixth rate; 106 feet between perpendiculars, or length on the range of the lower deck; 30 feet beam moulded; 9' 5" depth in hold. *Lyme* was a galley ship, with 18 sweeps a side on lower deck, pierced for 11 guns per side on the upper deck, two on the quarter deck, and two ballast or cargo ports on the lower deck not intended for guns. Details of her loss are unknown beyond that she foundered in the Atlantic sometime in 1745.

The importance of *Lyme* is that, superficially at least, she shows the basic hull form characteristic of later American schooners intended for fast sailing.

62

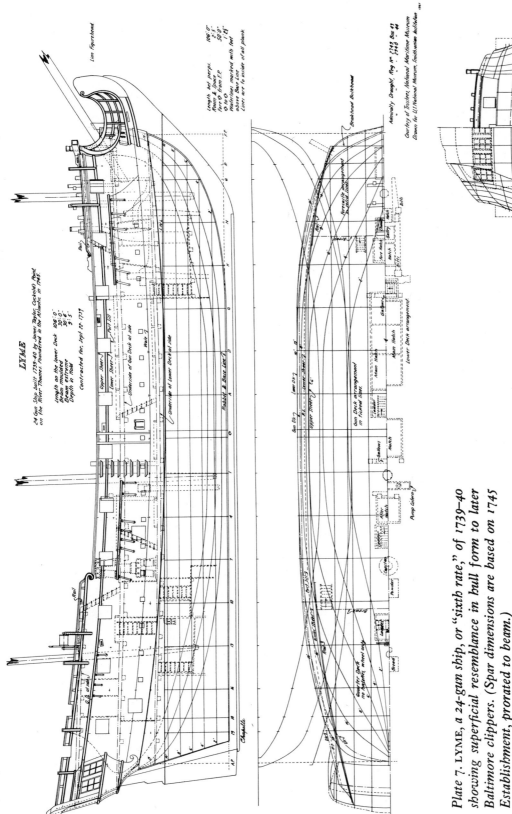
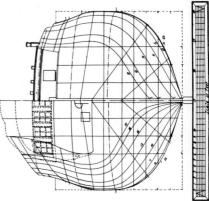

Plate 7. LYME, a 24-gun ship, or "sixth rate," of 1739–40 showing superficial resemblance in hull form to later Baltimore clippers. (Spar dimensions are based on 1745 Establishment, prorated to beam.)

It cannot be assumed, however, that *Lyme* was the first vessel to use this form, for it is probable that Jamaica and Bermuda sloops had employed it in even more extreme degree long before *Lyme* was built. This form of hull—with straight keel, raking sternpost rabbet, stem rabbet formed on a long sweep, midsection designed with rising straight floor from the keel, and a full, round bilge, with or without tumble home—will reappear many times in the design history of fast sailing vessels.

It should be noted, however, that surviving Admiralty draughts of this class, extensively built between 1727 and 1749, but beginning somewhere about, and with an example in, 1712, do not show this form. There was one exception, however, the *Boston*, built at Boston, Massachusetts, by Benjamin Hallowell, and launched 3 May 1748.* The *Boston* showed straight deadrise very much like that of *Lyme*.

Among the brigantines or "sloops" in the Admiralty Collection of Draughts, the *Cruizer*, built at Deptford in 1732–33, shows the same hull form, but with less sweep or rake in the stem rabbet. The brigantine *Peggy*—built for the Royal Navy in 1747 at Deptford—had a similar form, but with less rise of bottom. The evidence is sufficient, however, to show that this form—straight rise of floor and raking ends—was well known to English ship designers before 1750. The *Boston* is additional evidence that Colonial builders were also familiar with it.

Lyme, though a naval cruiser in which speed was very desirable, was a compromise in design, for she had to carry a large quantity of stores in addition to her armament. It was expected that such ships would be at sea for prolonged periods, and this was the case to a lesser degree with sloops *Ferrett* and *Sharke*. Though not an extreme example of this compromise in design requirements, the *Lyme* seems to have been satisfactory. She does not, however, appear to have been duplicated in the 20- to 24-gun class. Her hull form shows good lines of flow, retaining the buttock-bow lines of "whole moulding." As a result, the adverse effects of her full waterlines in the entrance are eased somewhat by the fine buttock-bow lines, giving her a scow-like forebody. The run is somewhat full, however, and this would prevent attainment of a high potential speed-length ratio. In light or moderate winds, nevertheless, this hull might be relatively "fast." Her second buttock has an effective

---

* *Boston* and *Cruizer*, see plans and descriptions in Howard I. Chapelle's *History of the American Sailing Navy: The Ships and Their Development* (New York, W. W. Norton & Company, Inc. 1949; reprint Bonanza Books, 1965); *Boston*, pp. 42–47, *Cruizer*, pp. 28–31.

length of 97′ 2″ camber 8′ 10″, or a camber-to-length ratio of 10.9.

She displaced 528.2 long tons on the designed load waterline, with a midship coefficient of .74, block coefficient .49, and a prismatic of .66; she was 115′ 3″ on the L.W.L. These particulars, which need no further discussion here, will be useful in later comparisons.

Though no plans of a Jamaica sloop of the late seventeenth or early eighteenth century have yet been found, her successor, the Bermuda sloop, was well recorded in the eighteenth century. One example is shown in engraved plans in *Architectura Navalis Mercatoria*, Plate LVII, Draught No. 15, published at Stockholm in 1768, by Swedish naval architect Fredrik Henrik ap Chapman. He apparently had obtained this plan during a visit to England. None of the ships in Chapman's book were dated, but one man-of-war shown was built in 1727, and others were built between 1720 and 1750, so the sloop was probably in this general period, a contemporary or predecessor of *Lyme*.

The history of the Bermuda sloop is somewhat obscure. Vessels of this rig were built at Jamaica early in the seventeenth century and appear to have had a reputation for fast sailing and good construction. In the last quarter of the seventeenth century, Bermuda had become a building center of sloops and these brought good prices, particularly when shipbuilding in Jamaica began to decline. In addition to sloops, the Bermudians during this period built small two-masted boats and a few brigantines.

As early as 1690, a large number of Bermuda sloops were sold to the mainland colonies. In the first half of the eighteenth century, the Bermuda sloop had become quite large and was purchased by English merchants for the West Indian and African trade. These sloops had a reputation for weatherliness and for fast sailing in light and moderate weather. They were built almost entirely of native cedar—a red cedar probably related to the Spanish cedar of Cuba. This wood was light and strong and resisted rot extremely well.

The Bermuda sloop was extensively employed by the American colonists during the Revolution. The French also purchased them as cruisers, and as a result, they came to be well known in Europe.

Few plans of the sloops exist, but as will be seen, the superficial characteristics of the Bermuda sloop of 1740–50 appear to be those that later marked the fast-sailing American schooner. The Bermuda sloop as a type continued to be built well into the nineteenth century, retaining its excellent earlier reputation.

Only published engravings show the lines and individual spar drawings. Plates 8 and 9 are redrawings partially reconstructed; the deck is taken from a Swedish draught, or copy, of the Bermuda sloop. The spar and sail drawing, Plate 9, is reconstructed from the spar drawings in the original engraving. The spars are identified by letters in the engraving, but no key to these was provided. A Swedish prospectus has been found, however, that gives the identity of each of the spars. The rig is nevertheless somewhat puzzling and the reconstruction (Plate 9) is only one possibility.

The Bermuda sloops had an international reputation throughout the last three quarters of the eighteenth century for good sailing qualities, particularly to windward. The *Maryland Gazette*, August 27, 1761, published an advertisement for the sale at Vienna, Maryland, of an 85-ton vessel, "very much on the Bermudas mould."* This indicates the reputation of the type in the colonies, and suggests differences from the usual colonial models. The hull form must have been known to many colonial builders for a long period before 1761, as trade between Bermuda, the Chesapeake, and New England was then of long standing. The model was but one of a variety that a colonial might select—all of English origin as far as he was concerned—each designed for a specific purpose.

Like *Ferrett* and *Sharke*, the Bermuda sloop was wide and deep; the entrance short, convex, and full; the run long and fine. She had moderate drag to the keel, much rake to the sternpost, and a well-rounded stem rabbet. The sheer was marked with a high-crowned roof over a stern cabin. The midsection—an important element in the model—was formed with a straight sharply-rising floor, high well-rounded bilge, and upright or slightly flaring topside. The midsection form eased the sweep of the buttock-bow lines, reducing the average cambers sharply over what a flat-floored midsection with the same relative length and depth of hull would require. This sloop hull had good flow lines for her proportions, being without sudden change in form or excessive fullness anywhere under water. She would sail well on the wind, as far as the cut and material of her sails would permit. However, the potential maximum speed, for her length, had been sacrificed in some degree to obtain an effective displacement in order to take on armament, cargo, and the necessary ballast to carry sail in a fresh breeze. These vessels were characterized by low freeboard to the main deck, which made them wet in blow-

---

* Howard I. Chapelle, *The History of American Sailing Ships* (New York, W. W. Norton & Company, Inc., 1935; reprint Bonanza Books, 1965), p. 82.

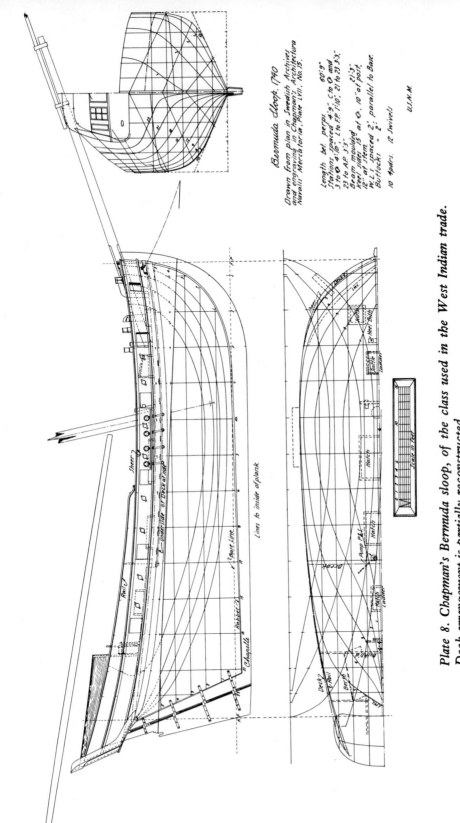

Bermuda Sloop. 1740

Drawn from plan in Swedish Archives
and engraving in Chapman's Architectura
Navalis Mercatoria, Plate LVII, No.15.

Length btl. perp..........60'9"
Stations .-spaced 4'.9", C to ○ and
  3 to ○; 4'.6", L to FP 110; 21 to 23 3'3".
23 to AP 3'3".
Beam moulded..........21'3".
Keel sided, 15" at ○, 10" at post.
12" at stem.
W.L., spaced 2'; parallel to Base.
Buttocks = 2'.

10 4pdrs. 12 Swivels

U.S.N.M.

*Plate 8. Chapman's Bermuda sloop, of the class used in the West Indian trade.
Deck arrangement is partially reconstructed.*

ing weather. To free the vessel rapidly of shipped water, the maindeck was given unusually heavy crown, as in Mediterranean galley vessels of low free-board. These short, heavy displacement sloops probably had a tendency to pitch deeply in a heavy head sea.

This sloop measured 60′ 9″ between perpendiculars, 58′ 8″ moulded load waterline length, 21′ 3″ moulded beam (21 feet at load line), 12′ 4″ draft at post, 10 feet draft forward, and was 9′ 5″ moulded depth amidships, rabbet to underside of deck at side. She was built of Bermuda's "pencil cedar," a name for red cedar. This wood produced a light hull structure, even with rather massive timbering, which gave increased capacity and also made ballast more effective.

Her moulded displacement to the load waterline was 129.3 long tons, her coefficients were midship .64, block .44, and prismatic .63. These show her to have been relatively less burdensome than *Ferrett* and *Sharke*, but with the same prismatic based on a smaller midship coefficient. These two sloops were longer than the Bermudian, drew less water, and probably had slightly more sail area. Yet by superimposing the Bermudian's lines over those of the English sloops, with load waterlines coinciding except for length, the forms of the quarterbeam buttock-bow lines could almost be made to coincide. Therefore there would probably be little difference in sailing performance on most points, the advantage of the English sloops' greater length being counteracted by the Bermudians' lighter displacement—unless the latter had markedly less sail power, which is unlikely. The camber-to-length ratio of the second buttock was 7.9 in this sloop.

The reconstructed sail plan, drawn by M. A. Edson, Jr., Plate 9, shows one of the rigs of an eighteenth-century sloop. The very long bowsprit and long main boom seem to have been very common. The fore-and-aft rig was powerful but not well proportioned by later standards of design.

The squaresail rig shown is that of a cutter of the period, with a crossjack yard. The crossjack yard spread the foot of the topsail and was secured to the mast by a vertical horse well below the gaff jaws, as in the fore course of a topsail schooner. A deep gore was thus formed in the square topsail foot. The fore course was bent to this yard. A variation of the rig had a spread yard located below the gaff jaws on the horse, to which the foot of the square topsail was secured. The course, in this variation, was bent to the crossjack yard, which was hoisted forward of and above the spread yard, so that the course would at least partly fill the gore in the topsail. The earliest illustration

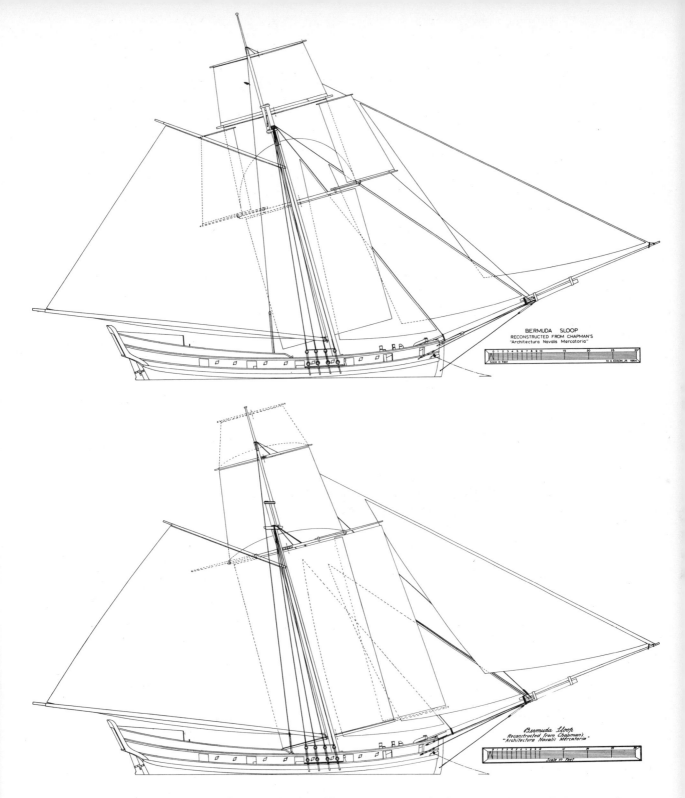

BERMUDA SLOOP
RECONSTRUCTED FROM CHAPMAN'S
"Architectura Navalis Mercatoria"

Bermuda Sloop
Reconstructed from Chapman's
"Architectura Navalis Mercatoria"

Plate 9. Two versions of the Sail plan of Chapman's Bermuda sloop reconstructed. Gore in the topsail in one may be excessive, but the drawings show a rig that was common from about 1720 to 1780 in large seagoing sloops.

of this rig found by the author is dated 1727.* There is enough pictorial evidence to show that these rigs were used by both sloops and cutters in the first half of the eighteenth century. The cutter had a running bowsprit, without stive, whereas the sloop had a well-stived fixed bowsprit; otherwise the rigs were alike, and as powerful and weatherly as their loosely-woven sailcloth would permit.

American sloop MEDIATOR, *built about 1741, taken into the Royal Navy in 1745, lost at Dunkirk the same year. Originally an American West India trader.*

An American-built sloop of 1741 is shown in Plates 10 and 11. This is the *Mediator,* "built in Virginia" according to Royal Navy records of the vessel's purchase in the West Indies early in 1745. She was then described as "about 4 years old." The *Mediator* was sunk at Ostend soon after her purchase, but not before her lines had been taken off in England.

* The Yactch or Yacht "Mary" and other vessels off Harwich 1727; engraving by P. C. Canot. Reproduced in Frank C. Bowen, *The Sea, Its History and Romance* (London, n.d., about 1927), Vol. 2, page 221.

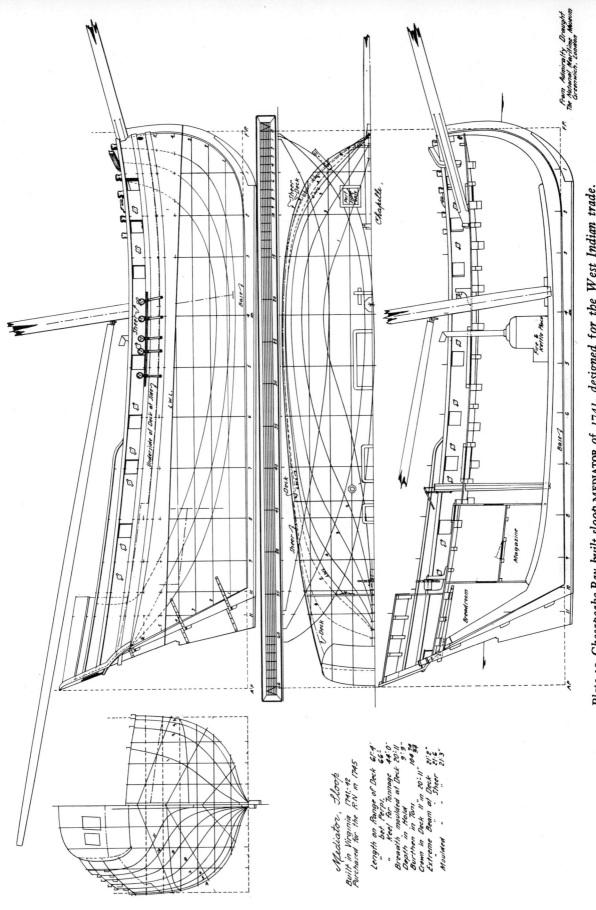

Mediator, Sloop
Built in Virginia, 1741-42
Purchased for the R.N. in 1745

Length on Range of Deck 61'.4"
    " bet. Perps., 66'."
    " Keel for Tonnage 44'.0"
Breadth, moulded at Deck 20'.11"
Depth in Hold 9'.9"
Burthen in Tons 104 ¾
Crown in Deck 11 in 20'.11"
Extreme Beam at Deck 21'.2"
Moulded " " Sheer 21'.6"
    " " Sheer 21'.3"

Plate 10. Chesapeake Bay built sloop MEDIATOR *of* 1741, *designed for the West Indian trade.*

From Admiralty Draught
The National Maritime Museum
Greenwich, London

The sloop was 61′ 4″ long on deck, or about 66 feet between perpendiculars, 20′ 11″ moulded beam at deck, 20′ 6″ moulded beam at load line, 27′ 4″ moulded beam at rail, 59′ 6″ moulded waterline length, and 9′ 9″ depth in hold. She drew 10′ 6″ at post, 9 feet forward.

It will be seen that in dimensions and proportions she was very close to *Ferrett*. *Mediator* had a moulded displacement of 124.36 long tons. Her midship coefficient was .71, block coefficient .44, and prismatic coefficient .62. Though larger than the Bermudian, she displaced less. Her prismatic coefficient was almost that of *St. Ann*, but she would have less potential speed due to her greater quarterbeam buttock-bow line camber. It is interesting to note that she has the same depth at quarterbeam buttock-bow line as *Ferrett*, but less length. The camber-length ratio was 7.7. The marked similarity in hull features relating to speed, as well as in proportions, of these three sloops, requires notice. It seems evident, from this, that a satisfactory model for the sloop rig had been developed before 1711. These sloops apparently sailed well and were not lacking in carrying capacity.

The rig shown in Plate 11 was reconstructed from *Mediator's* spar dimensions, recorded when she was surveyed and her lines taken off. Her square-sail rig is "squarer" than that of the Bermuda sloop, so that in proportion to her size, she had the more powerful rig. Her course was hoisted to the main yard, though this is not plainly indicated in the sail plan. The iron clamp holding the heel of the bowsprit appears in a number of draughts of Chesapeake Bay built craft of the eighteenth century and seems to have been characteristic of this area.

The Bermuda sloop's form of midsection, with straight, rising floor, seen in the 24-gun ship *Lyme* and in the Danish ship (Plate 2), appears now to have been widely accepted. Chapman shows a ship privateer of noted sailing qualities in his great plan album, *Architectura Navalis Mercatoria*, published in 1768. This is the *Neptunus*, Plate 12, built at Ostend, probably about 1720. She was 79′ 8″ between perpendiculars, 22′ 8″ moulded beam, 11′ 6″ draft at post, 9′ 6″ at stem, and armed with six 6-pounders and eight swivels. She had nine pairs of sweeps. Her midsection shows a moderately rising floor, much like that of the Danish ship in Plate 2. Fig. 1 shows original builder's draught, the above-water appearance of which Chapman altered for some reason in his published plan.*

---

* "Permission to copy plan obtained from an old Flemish shipwright named Petter Wiederleyne (who became Royal Shipwright at Gothenberg in 1724) in 1731, when I was 10 years old." Chapman; caption in Statens Sjohistoriska Museum.

Plate *11*. *Sail plan of* MEDIATOR, *reconstructed from spar dimensions.*

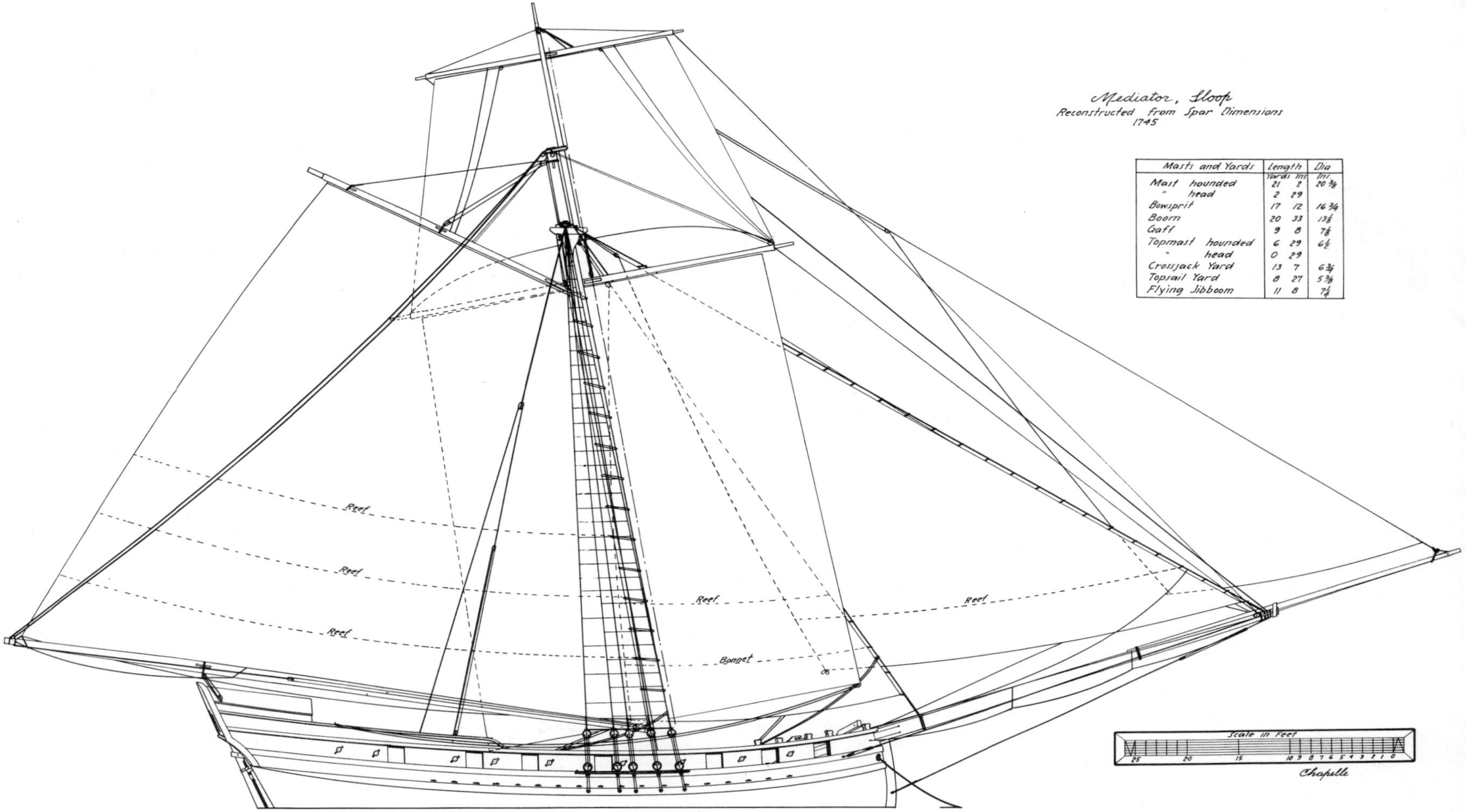
Mediator, Sloop
Reconstructed from Spar Dimensions
1745
Reef
Reef
Reef
Reef
Reef
Bonnet
Scale in Feet
25
20
15
10 9 8 7 6 5 4 3 2 1 0
Chapelle

Masts and Yards	Length Yards	Length Ins	Dia Ins.
Mast hounded	21	2	20 3/8
" head	2	29	
Bowsprit	17	12	16 3/4
Boom	20	33	13 1/8
Gaff	9	8	7 1/8
Topmast hounded	6	29	6 1/2
" head	0	29	
Crossjack Yard	13	7	6 3/4
Topsail Yard	8	27	5 3/8
Flying Jibboom	11	8	7 1/4

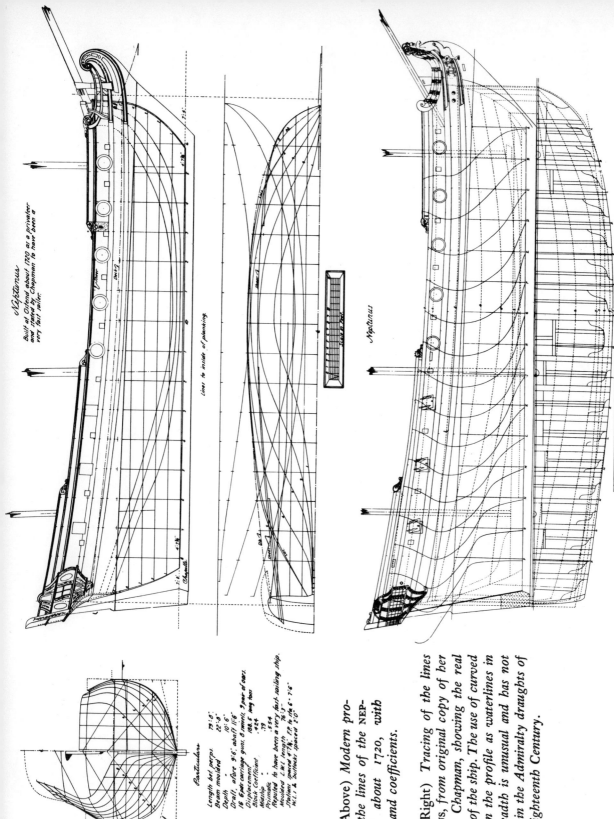

Neptunus

Built at Ostend about 1720 as a privateer and stated by Chapman to have been a very fast sailer.

Lines to inside of planking.

Neptunus

Particulars

Length bet. perps. 79'·0"
Beam moulded 22'·3"
Depth 10'·6"
Draft, afore 9'·6'; abaft 11'·6"
16 6-pdr carriage guns; 8 swivels 9 pair of oars.
Displacement 188.5 long tons
Block Coefficient .424
Midship .79
Prismatic .534
Reputed to have been a very fast-sailing ship.
Moulded L.W.L. length 76'·3"
Stations spaced 4'1¾"; F.P. to stn 6 · 7'·6"
W.L. 1' 2" Buttocks spaced 2'·0"

Plate 12. (Above) *Modern projection of the lines of the* NEPTUNUS, *of about 1720, with dimensions and coefficients.*

Plate 12a. (Right) *Tracing of the lines of* NEPTUNUS, *from original copy of her draught by Chapman, showing the real appearance of the ship. The use of curved level lines in the profile as waterlines in the half-breadth is unusual and has not been found in the Admiralty draughts of the early Eighteenth Century.*

The *Neptunus* displaced 188.5 long tons (moulded). Her block coefficient was .42, midship coefficient .79, and her prismatic coefficient .55. The very low prismatic is due to her extraordinarily fine and long run, as well as to very easy buttock-bow lines forward, combined with a large immersed midsection. The camber to length ratio of the second buttock was 8.4.

Chapman states this vessel went 16 knots. Varying estimates of the length of a nautical mile in 1720–30, however, made it probable that her real speed was about 13 knots, modern measurement. Even so, her speed-length ratio would be abnormally high for a waterline length of 76′ 3″, since 13 knots represents a ratio of about 1.49.

The English cutter must have been developed before 1727, since a picture of a cutter-rigged vessel at Harwich bears that date. In a letter dated 20 September 1745, Horace Walpole mentions the Royal Navy having "Folkestone Cutters," hired by Admiral Vernon. Draughts of cutters earlier than 1757 have not yet been found. But by this date their rig and hull form were well developed. The hulls were relatively short and broad, with little drag to the

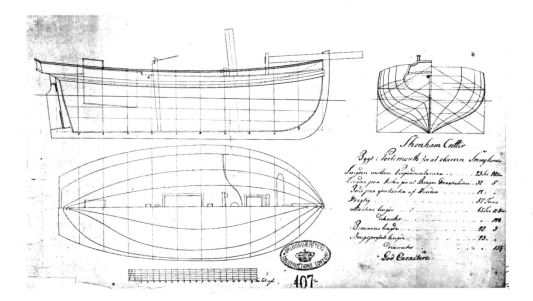

English merchant cutter of about 1765, of the type sometimes employed in cross-channel smuggling; this is a revenue cutter, however. Royal Danish Archives.

75

keel or rake in the ends. The midsection had hollow floors, with rise out to the turn of the bilge. Chapman shows a cutter, undated, having this form. Cutters were either clench-built or "lap-strake" planked. They were sharp-ended for their displacement, and very heavily sparred and ballasted. For example, a cutter of 43-foot length on deck, built in 1758, had a 66-foot mast-and-topmast, a 42-foot boom, and a 43-foot bowsprit. The fore-staysail set up to the stemhead, the jib was set flying on the bowsprit by use of a ring traveler and in-and-out haulers.

The cutter type seems to have originated as a smuggling vessel. Folkestone may have been the original home of the cutter, but by 1757 Dover and Shoreham were also active building centers. Cutters were built by the Admiralty beginning in 1764. A small number were built in colonial America, before the Revolution, but never became popular there, probably because the sloop served all purposes. After 1778, the British Admiralty had cutters whose deck length exceeded 74 feet.

The construction of vessels for the Royal Navy in the colonies has been referred to in the case of the 24-gun ship *Boston* of 1748. The first such vessel was *Faulkland*, a 5th rate, or 40- to 44-gun ship, built in "New Castle, New England" (now Newcastle, New Hampshire), by a colonial builder named Holland.* She was launched in 1694 or 1695. Her registered dimensions given in the Navy List were 128′ 6″ long on the lower deck, 109 feet on the keel, 33′ 2″ extreme beam, 13′ 9″ depth in hold, 637 71/94 tons. This vessel was "rebuilt without change" at Chatham in 1702, having developed "dry-rot."

Later, in 1699, Holland launched at Newcastle the 34-gun 6th rate *Bedford Galley* for the Royal Navy. Her registered dimensions were 103′ 3½″ long on the lower deck, 85′ 2″ on the keel, 28′ 8″ extreme beam, 10′ 7¾″ depth in hold, 372 tons. She appears to have been especially built as a man-of-war. This ship was reduced to a fireship in 1716, indicating weaknesses not worth repairing to retain her as a cruiser, but she continued as a fireship until 3

---

* The builder of *Faulkland* and *Bedford Galley* is listed in the Dimension Book only as "Holland." The correspondence of the Navy Board shows that these vessels were purchased from Mr. John Taylor, mast merchant. *Faulkland* appears to have been a mast ship. *Bedford Galley* is described as a sharp ship and a good sailer, but we know she was over-masted, as built, because her masts were later reduced. She is also described as built to the "dimensions of HMS *Sorlings*."

Newcastle, New Hampshire, adjoins Portsmouth on the seaward side of the New Hampshire shore of the harbor.

May 1725, when she was sunk to act as a breakwater at Sheerness dockyard.

No plans of these ships have been yet found (1967) in the Admiralty Collection of Draughts. There is no evidence to establish that the colonial builder Holland was responsible for the designs. *Faulkland* was short-lived, but *Bedford Galley* lasted as well as most of her English-built classmates.

No other seagoing naval vessels were built in North America until 1746, when Benjamin Hallowell, of Boston, was contracted to construct the 24-gun *Boston*. She was launched in 1748 and her dimensions, according to the draught made after her arrival in England, were 118 feet long on the lower deck, 97' 7½" on the keel, 32' 8½" moulded beam, 11' 1¾" depth in hold, 561 tons. The *Boston* was broken up in February 1752 after only about four years of service.

About the same time Nathaniel Messerve, of Portsmouth, New Hampshire, contracted to build a 44-gun 5th rate. She was laid down in 1747 and launched 4 May 1749. Her register dimensions were 139' 1" on the lower deck, 114' 2" on the keel, 37' 8½" extreme beam, 16-foot depth in hold, and 862 57/94 tons. She was named *America*, but in 1752 was renamed *Boston*. On 13 September 1757 she was sold as unserviceable for £367. Sir William Pepperell appears to have been sponsor for Messerve in this transaction.

While an Admiralty draught exists of the 24-gun ship *Boston*, none exists for the 44-gun *America*. A rather crude "Admiralty Model"—a contemporary scale model hull—is preserved, however, in the Athenaeum at Portsmouth, New Hampshire.

As in *Boston* and *Lyme*, *America* had straight rise of floor, with rather easy bilges. In design she appears to have been an enlarged *Prince Edward*,* 40 guns, built on the Thames in 1745 by Henry Bird.

These short-lived vessels ended interest in building of any large men-of-war in the colonies. No record has been found of the surveys held on these ships, but it is apparent that green timber used in their construction was primarily to blame for their short lives in the Royal Navy.†

However, some small American-built vessels were purchased for the Royal

---

* Admiralty Collection of Draughts, Reg. No. 1724, Box 32.

† The Admiralty had planned to build two 44's and two 24's in North America, but in letters dated 19 September and 10 October 1746, the Navy Board, referring to the *Faulkland*, claimed that North American timber was poor. The Board also complained about the difficulty of supervision and of supplying "King's equipment" at such a distance. As a result, the Admiralty authorized only two ships, sending Henry Wallace and Robert White to the Colonies as overseers in 1747.

Navy, but it is difficult to establish the identities of these before 1745. It is possible that two small vessels, probably sloops, purchased in the West Indies in 1702, the *Earl Galley* and *Harmon*, were American-built. They were not, however, registered in the Navy. The *Harmon* is noted as "sunk at Port Royal, Jamaica, in 1704—nobody would buy her"! A brigantine named *Mercury* bought at Antigua, West Indies, in 1744, may also have been American-built. She was purchased by order of Captain Warren, R.N., and registered by Admiralty order of 26 September 1744, carrying 16 six-pounders and 24 swivels. She was captured by the French, coming from Jamaica in 1745; neither draught nor the survey held on her have been found.

The earliest documented American-built vessel to be taken into the Royal Navy, therefore, is the sloop *Mediator*, represented by an Admiralty draught. She was registered in the Royal Navy by Admiralty order of 7 May 1745, to be armed with 10 carriage guns and 18 swivels.

St. Ann was not purchased by the Royal Navy. The first schooner to be registered in the Royal Navy seems to be *Barbadoes*, a Virginia-built vessel purchased at Antigua, West Indies, by Commodore Moore on 15 November 1757. A vessel named *Speaker* was presented to the Navy at Barbadoes by local merchants; this may have been an American-built schooner, but no records of her have yet been found, other than that she was commissioned 9 December 1756.

The Deptford yard shipwrights made an inspection of *Barbadoes*, as ordered by a Navy Board warrant of 10 November 1763. Their report showed that they examined her afloat, that she had been built in Virginia, and was "of uncertain age" and "very slightly put together"; timbers and beams were cedar, and very few knees were used in her structure. She had earlier undergone some minor repair at Portsmouth dockyard. She was rated as a sloop and her dimensions were given as 80 feet on deck, 52' 10" on the keel, 21' 6" extreme beam, depth in hold not given, 130 tons. She was considered a fast sailer, but no draught of the *Barbadoes* has been found. She was sold out of service on 15 March 1763 for £405.

An American-built ship named *Maryland Planter* was also purchased in 1757, on 26 January. She was converted the following March, at Deptford, to a fireship and named *Prosperpine*. Her register dimensions were 90' 9" on the lower deck, 75' 6½" on the keel, 25' 4½" extreme beam, 11' 6" in hold, and 253 tons. She was sold out of service 15 February 1763. No draught exists of this vessel.

During the French and Indian War a number of small naval craft were built on lakes Champlain and Ontario, none larger than a brig. Some of these were completely built on the lakes by colonial shipwrights, while two had timbers and frames prepared in England, shipped to a colonial port, and hauled overland to the lakes where they were assembled. The brigs *London* and *Halifax* were thus constructed by an Admiralty order of 5 May 1755, and erected on Lake Ontario. Both were taken or destroyed by the French at Oswego in August 1756. These brigs were 57 feet on deck, 46' 6" on the keel, 16 feet extreme beam, 7' 8" depth of hold, and 63 30/94 tons. No draught of these small vessels has yet been found.

Though draughts of American-built ships in the first 60 years of the eighteenth century are very few in number, all evidence shows that the colonial shipbuilder generally followed the English practices in design and construction, [except in the schooners]. This remained true, as will be seen, until well into the American Revolution. It therefore seems reasonable that the professional knowledge of the American shipbuilder-designer be assessed on the evidence of his English counterpart, insofar as they built vessels for similar purposes and of equal size. The American was not the only smuggler, of course; his British cousin was pretty active in the trade too. So there were markets on both sides of the Atlantic for fast sailers in this business.

Contrary to how it has often been represented, the first half of the eighteenth century was not a period of decadence in naval architecture. It was, in fact, a period of progressive activity, particularly in naval ship design. On 19 February 1732 (new calendar) a British experimental squadron of five recently built vessels, the 24-gun ship (galley) *Experiment* and the brigantine sloops *Wolf, Grampus, Otter, and Hawk* assembled 11 leagues southeast of the Lizard for sailing trials. These included five-hour trials, sailing on the wind in fresh breezes, east by north, during which it was found that *Wolf* went away from the rest. The difference between *Otter, Hawk,* and *Grampus* was slight, while *Experiment* fell astern of all. Then a trial of equal length was made before the wind during which *Wolf*, a galley-brigantine, led *Grampus* by a small margin; both led *Otter* and *Hawk* considerably; and all beat *Experiment* by far. During these trials the sea was smooth, the wind light to fresh.

The next day a trial was made with wind abeam, blowing very fresh. Again *Wolf* and *Grampus* went ahead very fast, but *Experiment* beat *Otter* and *Hawk*. The maximum rates of speed obtained are given in the reports:

Wolf made 10 knots, wind on the quarter, and 7 knots by the wind; *Grampus* 8½ knots, wind on the quarter, 7½ knots before the wind, and 6 knots on the wind. No attention appears to have been given these trials outside the Admiralty Surveyor's office. Plans exist in the Admiralty Collection of Draughts of *Experiment** (1727) and *Wolf* (1731). *Wolf*† was 87 feet on the lower deck, 86' 9" moulded L.W.L., 25 feet extreme beam, 6 feet in the hold, drawing 8' 4" at post. She had 34 oars. Americans were well acquainted with the Royal Navy brigantine sloop, for many of these served as colonial revenue vessels.

The value of length was slowly becoming appreciated; French naval ship designers seem to have been the first to make practical use of this design element in order to obtain speed. French frigates and corvettes of 1745–51 were longer and somewhat sharper than the British 20- and 24-gun ships. Rigs were improving and some fast-sailing small vessels were slowly evolving into distinctive types—the American schooner, the English cutter, and perhaps the French lugger.

So far as one may judge by the draughts as evidence of the knowledge used in practical ship design, the more skillful men had determined that the speed of any ship type or class could be improved—first, by an enlarged rig if the hull would carry it; secondly, by lightening the displacement by means of reduced beam, sharper ends, and/or increased deadrise; and finally, by increasing length, or by a complete increase in size. Ballast was necessary for sailing stability, but it was also deadweight that required an unprofitable displacement that supported neither cargo nor armament. By reducing topside weight of hull structures and fittings it was possible to reduce, somewhat, the proportion of ballast to displacement and to lighten the latter as well. Beginning in Elizabethan times, high sterns and forecastles had gradually been suppressed. The "rise in the deck" that had been six feet or over was now not over two feet. In American yards cedar was coming into use for top timbers and topside planking, and greater frame spacing was employed, producing what English naval shipwrights were to call "slightly built" vessels. The English cutter builders were engaged in similar efforts to reduce speed-retarding structural and ballast weights. This would allow an increase in sail area and a decrease in displacement, with sharper lines in the hull, for a given size of vessel.

* Admiralty Collection of Draughts, Reg. No. 3014, Box 45.
† Admiralty Collection of Draughts, Reg. No. 3312, Box 49.

A lack of sufficient precise information on the sailing speed of the individual vessels described in this and other chapters, makes it impractical to attempt comparative evaluation based on numerical coefficients. This can be done only after examining vessels of the nineteenth century, where reasonably precise data are available.

It will then be possible to form opinions on the comparative performances of vessels of varying types, sizes, and dates of build. Though comment is occasionally offered on the apparent qualities of individual vessels, it is important that the reader accept these as only tentative and confined to the generalities related to the discussion of the problems of speed-under-sail requirements in hydrodynamics, sail power, and basic sailing-vessel design practices.

CHAPTER · THREE

1760 - 1793

ENGLAND SUFFERED VERY HEAVY LOSSES OF COLONIAL AND BRITISH MERCHANT-men in her war with France (1757–1763), mostly through the activities of numerous and often powerful French privateers, as had occurred in the earlier wars with France and Spain. The Admiralty was unable to protect British trade and colonial shipping because it did not have enough fast, well-armed small cruisers. This situation led colonial merchants to resort once more to the construction of large, fast sailing craft. The change from slow to fast ships could not be quickly accomplished, nor did the convoy system offer sufficient protection, and losses mounted steadily from 1757 to 1762.

This, and other war problems, led to an increasing dissatisfaction among the American colonists with the British naval, military, and political administrations. Smuggling and other illegal trades increased rapidly, and by war's end in 1763 these activities of colonial merchants threatened huge losses in potential revenue to the British government, as well as great damage to British trade policies.

It was found necessary to strengthen the revenue service in the American colonies, and it was decided to employ naval ships and personnel for the purpose. However, not only did British naval officers dislike this duty, but the Royal Navy also lacked small vessels suitable for such service. Hence, naval officers were to be employed only in numbers sufficient to man such craft as could be purchased. Early in January 1764, the Admiralty began buying schooners for service mostly along the New England coast where smuggling was particularly active.

By 1755 there were two areas on the North American coast that were recognized as centers for the building of fast sailing vessels. One was the Chesapeake Bay area, as evidenced by contemporary references in Admiralty papers. The sloop *Mediator* and schooner *Barbadoes* were examples from this region. Bermuda is included in this area, because of the close relationship of its vessel types to those of the Chesapeake, as well as its geographic proximity and similar economic conditions.

The other area was Essex County, Massachusetts. The building of fishing schooners for the leading fishery port, Marblehead, had been carried on since at least 1721, when Marblehead owned 120 schooners engaged only in fishing. By 1741 this fleet had grown to 160. Massachusetts merchants also owned a large number of small traders—brigantines, schooners, and sloops—in the coasting and Atlantic trades.

The vessels of this fishing and trading fleet were attractive targets for eighteenth-century freebooters, for they could carry only small armaments and were usually lightly manned. Naval protection was not readily available for fishing vessels operating on the extensive North Atlantic banks nor for the widely scattered small traders. Therefore, in times of international disturbance, there was great demand for fast-sailing trading or fishing schooners, which gave rise to the "Marblehead" schooner that achieved such a reputation in northern colonies for speed.

Hence, the Admiralty ordered the Navy Board to obtain six "Marblehead schooners or sloops" to be named, upon purchase, *Chaleur*, *Gaspe*, *Hope*, *Magdalen*, *St. John*, and *St. Lawrence*. The Navy List shows these vessels to have been nearly alike in size: *Magdalen* was 90 3/94 tons; *Gaspe*, 102 44/94 tons; *Hope*, 105 40/94 tons; *St. John* and *St. Lawrence* (apparently sisterships purchased on the stocks) each 114 65/94 tons; and *Chaleur** (the only one whose draught exists) was 116 91/94 tons. Another vessel, *Grenville*, purchased for the Newfoundland station 7 August 1763, had been the *Sally*, built on Massachusetts Bay in 1754, and she too, was probably a Marblehead schooner.

* Admiralty Collection of Draughts, Reg. No. 4518, Box 64.

The *Chaleur*, according to her draught, was 70′ 9″ on the range of deck, 50 feet on the keel, 20′ 4″ moulded beam, 7′ 9½″ depth in hold, and 120 85/94 tons. It is doubtful that *Chaleur* was a fishing schooner, or even representative of the type, for her draught shows her to have been a burdensome vessel.

These purchases were followed by others. Snow *Egmont*, bought in 1764, was 62 feet on deck, 48′ ⅝″ on the keel, 19′ 7″ beam, 10′ 4″ depth in hold, and 99 57/94 tons. Schooner *Sultana*,* bought in 1768, was 50′ 6″ on deck, 38′ 5⅛″ on the keel, 16′ ¾″ beam, 8′ 4″ depth in hold, and 52 68/94 tons; according to her Admiralty draught, she was intended for a dispatch boat.

In 1767 two schooners for the Jamaica station were built at New York under the Supervision of Captain Kennedy, R.N. They were described by Rear Admiral William Parry, Commander-in-Chief of the Station, as "very fine 'compleat' vessels of about 72 tons or upwards" drawing 10 feet at the post and in need of coppering and equipment. The Admiral named them *Earl of Egmont* and *Sir Edward Hawke;* they were so registered in the Royal Navy on 22 May 1768. Each had a complement of 30 men and a lieutenant in command.

These vessels were classed as "armed schooners," and although their armament establishment has not been found, *Hawke* carried eight swivels and at one time also had eight carriage guns. These must have been very small guns—probably long three-pounders—for the gunports were only 18″ by 21″ and the bulwarks only 2′ 8″ high on the main deck, amidships.

The Admiralty draught on these schooners is a design plan. There is no way of determining whether its origin is American or Admiralty, but this drawing establishes the hull form of the type beyond any question. It is evident from the plan that the Essex County shipbuilders of this period employed the same basic English-Bermudian-Chesapeake hull form, or model, in their fast sailing vessels. We cannot now trace all possible migrations of the old Jamaica sloop—by way of Bermuda and the Chesapeake, to Massachusetts—but the New England and Chesapeake builders may well have been using the old English form brought directly from the mother country.

Like most design draughts in this age, the plan was incomplete, leaving a good deal to be interpreted by the builder. As in *Ferrett's* plan, this is particularly true of the aftermost portion of the hull. The shape of the transom is not projected and the two after sections require refairing, being much too

* Admiralty Collection of Draughts, Reg. No. 4521, Box 64.

full at and above the tuck to permit planking the round tuck stern shown. The underwater lines, however, could be developed with reasonable precision in redrawing, picking up the offsets by use of dividers and the graphic scale. Drawing scales were not yet standard in this period—at least the graphic scales on the draughts indicate this, for they are constantly short when measured with a modern architect's scale.

No other plan of a sharp Marblehead schooner has yet been found, nor is there any picture of one dated earlier than about 1790. But from numerous references to the type in the *Boston Gazette*, between 1760 and 1778, it is possible to obtain a general description. As a type they seem to have been at least moderately sharp, yet they could not be extreme models for they had to retain sufficient capacity to handle a paying cargo of salt fish. Thus their displacement was sufficient to accommodate armament for privateering. Some had bulwarks, as in *Egmont* and *Hawke;* but many had only a low rail on the main deck, the raised quarterdeck alone having bulwarks. Most of the fishermen seem to have been plainly finished, having either the plain curved stem shown in the draught, or a simple gammon-knee head. Traders built on this model were sometimes more ornate. Some of the schooners had painted decorations around the hawse holes; one is described as having painted sea-horses. Most were rigged as simple fore-and-afters, having three lower sails, with a main-topmast staysail and a jib topsail as light-weather sails. Large vessels of the type, and those fitted for privateering or the West Indian run, had a square fore course (or fore-topsail and course) added. Some set a square main-topsail as well. They are often described as having white bottoms, probably a mixture of whitewash and tallow, and multicolored topsides; the use of a combination of two or three colors—black, yellow, and red—was common. Some had "bright" strakes (varnished or oiled), and the transom was often painted with different colors than the topsides.

The plan of the *Egmont* and *Hawke* gives no measurements, so these must be picked off by dividers from the graphic scale. These measurements are 57′ 7″ on the range of deck (rabbet of stem to rabbet of post on projected main deck), 17′ 7″ moulded beam, or approximately 17′ 11″ beam over two-inch planking, and 7′ 4″ moulded depth at midsection. The Royal Navy registered dimensions of these schooners were 59 feet on deck, 17 feet extreme beam (over planking), 5′ 10″ depth in hold, and 78 69/94 tons. The register dimensions were not often the same as those obtained from the draught—design or take-off—for the register survey was rarely made in dock and was often intended primarily as a valuation for purchase by the Admiralty. The draught, however, was for an accurate technical record of the vessel, particularly when it was a take-off. The deck arrangement shown in Plate 13 is a reconstruction using, as a general guide, the other Admiralty draughts of New England schooners in 1764–77.

The "Marble Head Scooner" design, Plate 13, had a high, raised quarterdeck, strong sheer, straight keel with drag, curved stem, raking post, round tuck, and flat transom. The entrance was short, moderately sharp, and convex; the run was long and rather fine. The buttocks were not straight in any portion of their length. The midsection had straight, rising floor of very short length, faired into a well-rounded, slack bilge continued up to deck level, and then into marked tumble home. The masts raked sharply but spar dimensions have not been found. The freeboard to the main deck was very low; almost as low as in Chapman's Bermuda sloop. As a result the deck crown of the schooners was rather great. The last sailing Gloucestermen still retained the low freeboard that made the vessels wet when closehauled. A reconstructed rig for these schooners is shown in Plate 14, which shows their general appearance.

The proportion of length to beam was 3.23, beam to depth was 2.41, and length to depth was 7.67; using her 56-foot moulded length of waterline as the length. Her moulded displacement was about 91.21 long tons. Her midship coefficient was .69, her block coefficient .39, and her prismatic .70. Her quarterbeam buttock was about nine times its camber in effective length. Because of her great drag and the position of her designed midsection, her moulded draft at the midsection was 6' 6", though it was 6' 10" at one-half of her waterline length (56 feet), and the sectional area there was less than at midsection. As a result, this difference in measurements does not affect the validity of the calculations.

Though there have been no records found of maximum speeds reached by either of the two schooners, there is a statement on record that *Hawke* sailed very well on the wind and also in light and moderate winds. In other words she sailed "fast" when power was not great, but her maximum speed was not remarkably high. This characteristic is another important factor in the examination of speed under sail. In this example we are considering the design of a vessel that could reach a moderate rate of speed, or speed-length ratio, very easily with relatively little power being produced in the rig. Various sailing hull forms produce this ability and it is apparent that neither extremely

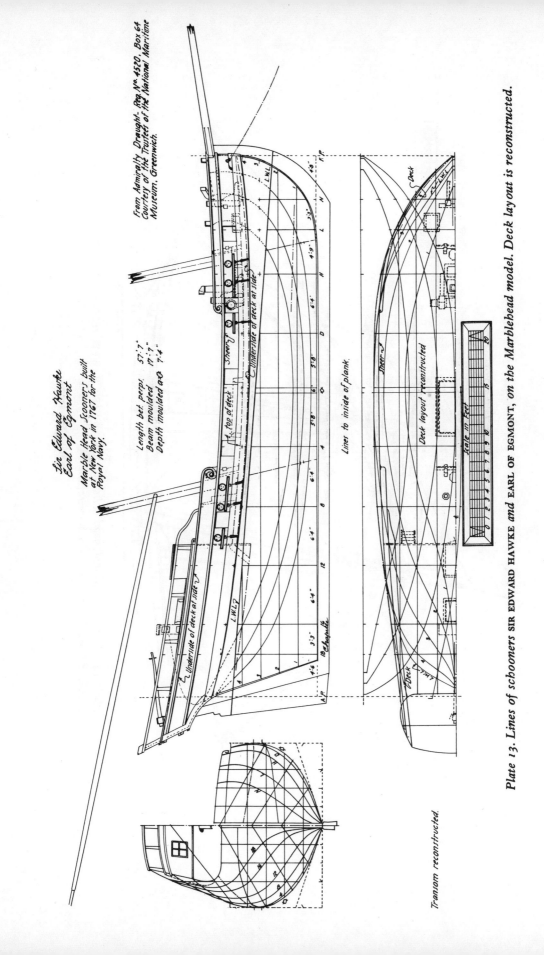

Sir Edward Hawke
Earl of Egmont

Marble Head Scooners built
at New York in 1767 for the
Royal Navy.

Length bet perp: 57'·7"
Beam moulded   17'·7"
Depth moulded a⊗ 7'·4"

From Aamiralty Draught. Reg. Nᵒ 4520, Box 64
Courtesy of the Trustees of the National Maritime
Museum, Greenwich.

Lines to inside of plank.

Scale in feet

Deck layout reconstructed

Transom reconstructed.

Plate 13. Lines of schooners SIR EDWARD HAWKE *and* EARL OF EGMONT, *on the Marblehead model. Deck layout is reconstructed.*

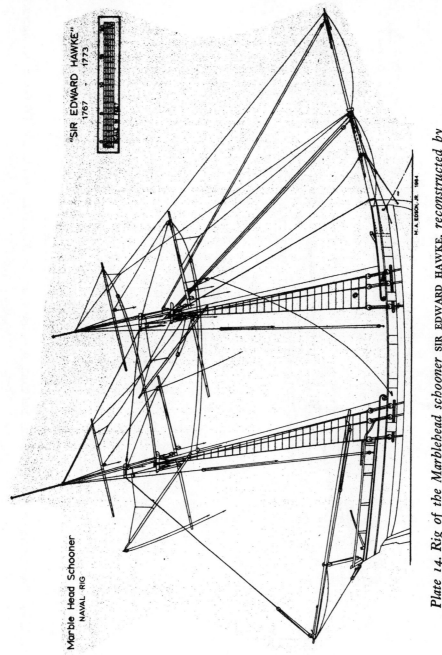

Marble Head Schooner
NAVAL RIG

"SIR EDWARD HAWKE"
1767 - 1773

M. A. EDSON, JR. 1964

Plate 14. Rig of the Marblehead schooner SIR EDWARD HAWKE, *reconstructed by M. A. Edson, Jr., for model construction.*

fine lines, nor very light displacement are wholly necessary. Weight is an advantage in that it produces momentum that once in motion, carries the vessel from puff to puff in light airs. Given the same hull form, a large rig produces greater momentum than a small one. Hull form, and perhaps proportions, must be proper, however, for the characteristic is primarily one of hull form, rather than rig design.

Study of the hull forms of vessels credited with outstanding performances in this kind of sailing has produced some general and preliminary information relating to their design. Some degree of deadrise—in the form of straight, rising floor—is helpful, when combined with a rather slack, or easy, bilge and gently curved, but not necessarily sharp, longitudinal lines. The lines of such vessels are almost invariably free of any hard, quick curves or hydrodynamic "pressure areas." These schooners' lines have this hull form; they are of some burden yet with easy curves in sections, waterlines, buttocks, and diagonals. Flowlines around such a hull encounter no marked pressure areas and produce no obvious wake disturbance or "turbulence" until reaching speed-length ratios in the vicinity of 0.75 or 0.80. These general comments, while reasonably accurate, are not comprehensive design guides, for there is a variation in the actual speed reached by designs having these characteristics, when in this limit of ratio and with equal power applied. This can be explained only by the emphasis, in each design, on some one element of the hull form at the expense of another.

When a vessel designed for moderate speed is driven beyond her limit, large waves form at bow and stern and in the wake. This "turbulence" increases with speed, absorbing more and more power until the sailing vessel goes out of control. This is often a very rapid process, and a vessel may cease to gain speed while the power in her rig is still increasing, because the increased power is only adding to the amount of turbulence in her wake. This turbulence may be caused by improper hull proportions for the speed the hull is being driven, by too large an entrance angle, or by excessive angles at intersections of the buttocks with the loadline at bow and stern, particularly in the run.

The practical advantages of designing to meet certain "average" weather conditions, rather than to meet unusual ones, will be increasingly apparent as this study progresses. At this stage it is desirable to say only that certain colonial trades, such as the summer coastwise and the West Indian trades, were carried on when the predominating winds were light to moderate. For such conditions the colonial builders produced a relatively fast sailer, having a profitable cargo-carrying capacity, which resulted in a hull having a moderate maximum-speed potential.

Since this problem is not discussed in colonial works on naval architecture, eighteenth-century solutions can be determined only by analytical examination of contemporary draughts showing actual design practices. The processes by which these design practices were established are speculative, but designers probably observed the forms of any vessels notably suited to a given trade and followed these forms—with only very cautious departures—when building a new vessel for this particular trade.

No methods of calculation, nor any wholly satisfactory design instructions, were available to insure the desired combination of capacity and speed until late in the nineteenth century. In modern practice this is achieved by model-testing. This proper combination is obviously important in a trading vessel and is the prime reason why few sailing merchantmen were ever produced for maximum-speed potential at any cost without some regard to cargo capacity and without consideration of the common weather conditions that would be met in their trades. The average winds to be met in a trade were important factors in determining whether a maximum-speed potential was worthwhile.

The Royal Navy continued purchasing American-built vessels as the American Revolution approached. Some were full-ended carriers for survey and storeship services, but most were small vessels required for coastal patrol work. Draughts of only two small schooners have yet been found. The *Sultana*, already mentioned, was built in 1766–67 by Benjamin Hallowell of Boston, Massachusetts. Hallowell, it will be remembered, had built the 24-gun ship *Boston* in 1748, but his connection with that short-lived ship must have been forgotten, or forgiven, because it was not held against him. Admiralty records show that a small sloop, the *Bird*, also built by Hallowell, had been purchased in England in 1764. She was 58′ 6″ on the range of deck, 17′ 7¾″ extreme beam, 8′ 1″ depth in hold, 75 20/94 tons, "said to be a good sailer" and "fit to take the ground." She was pole-masted, without topsails. *Bird* was not employed on the American coast.

The second draught is of *Halifax*, a New England schooner bought in 1775. She was full-built, 58′ 3″ on the range of deck, 18′ 3″ extreme beam, 8′ 10″ depth in hold, and 83 4/94 tons. Plans of *Sultana*, *Hallifax*, and *Chaleur* were published in the author's *The History of American Sailing Ships*. Sul-

tana and *Hallifax* were rather highly finished vessels in which no attempt was made for extreme speed. A second vessel, *St. Lawrence*, was purchased in 1775, along with another schooner and two brigs. Six more American-built schooners were purchased in 1776, as the American Revolution approached. No draughts of any of these have been found.

With the coming of the Revolution, American prizes were soon available for service in the Royal Navy. During this long war, a very large number of American-built prize vessels were purchased. These ranged from Continental frigates—such as *Confederacy*, *Virginia*, *Hancock*, and *Raleigh* whose draughts survive, as well as *Boston*, *Ranger*, *Providence*, and other national vessels whose draughts do not exist—down to privateers and trading vessels. The privateers taken into service included ships, brigs, brigantines, and schooners; many were well-built and finished vessels. The majority of the schooners, brigantines, and brigs, however, were cheaply built; they had to be fast-sailing but expendable. Of the many vessels purchased, very few were sloops; reference has been found to only two, and they were obtained on the West Indian station. One was a Bermudian; the origin of the other is uncertain, as the records conflict, but she was either an American or a Bermudian sloop named *Adriana*, renamed *Pelican*, and she was so large she was finally rerigged as a brig.

The draught of a fast, cheaply-built brig shows some of the extreme characteristics of a remarkable and interesting vessel, whose records are tantalizingly incomplete. The West Indian prize court records have not yet been found and the Admiralty records are fragmentary, so far as this brig is concerned. She was named *Badger* when in the Royal Navy and her draught was drawn at Portsmouth dockyard in June 1777.

The correspondence of the Admiral of the West Indian station shows a most confusing situation there regarding vessels named *Badger* in 1776–78. There had been an old brigantine of this name on the station, probably built at Hamble, England, in 1745 by M. Janvrin, as one of a class designed by the Royal Navy Surveyor Ackworth. She had been on the Iceland fisheries patrol in 1762, before being sent to the West Indies. By 1775 she was worn out and had to be replaced. A number of short-lived, purchased vessels, mostly prizes and each named *Badger*, followed her in quick succession.

The identity of the *Badger* represented by the Admiralty draught (redrawn in Plates 15, 16 and 17) can be established only in part. On 14 February 1776, the Admiralty ordered Vice Admiral C. Gayton, in command of the Jamaica station, to purchase three schooners and name them *Badger*, *Porcupine*, and *Racehorse*. On the 15th the Admiralty instructed the Navy Board to pay for these vessels when obtained. Vice Admiral Gayton's journal shows that he received the order on 23 May. On 25 June he ordered the purchase of "a brig of about 130 tons," and a week later he informed the Admiralty that he had bought a brig "a very fine vessel of about 130 tons" to be named *Badger*.* This vessel was commissioned at Port Royal on 26

Brig BADGER *of the Royal Navy, 1776. An American-built vessel, possibly the privateer* DEFENCE. *This vessel had a markedly hogged keel and other peculiarities of design.*

---

* The sequence in the list of purchased vessels, Account of Naval Storekeeper, Jamaica, Adm. 17/175, suggests that this may have been the brig *Defence*.

June under command of Lieutenant F. L. Le Montais, and in November her crew was increased and Lieutenant Everett took command.

On 14 April 1777, Admiral Gayton informed the Admiralty that he was sending *Badger*, "a fine-going vessel," to England with intercepted Franco-American correspondence. He mentioned that in two cruises *Badger* had captured 22 vessels. She mustered at Port Royal 20 April, arrived at Spithead 26 May, and was at Portsmouth from 5 to 30 June. While at Portsmouth the Admiralty ordered her into dock to be "cleaned and tallowed," and "leaks stopped." It was then, apparently, that the lines were taken off and the draught made. Her crew was again increased, this time to the number of 90. She left England 10 July and reached Port Royal 6 September 1777.

The *Badger*, carrying dispatches for the Windward Islands as well as Jamaica, called at Barbadoes before touching Antigua. On 7 September 1777, Vice Admiral Gayton wrote the Admiralty of her arrival and said she was "very leaky." On 25 October he reported that she had arrived in "very bad state" and that he "had been surprised how she ever reached this port." He doubted she could be refitted, but would have her surveyed. On 17 November he reported that she was "unfit for service" and that he had purchased a new vessel—"the rebel privateer that took Fraser's Highlanders in Nantasket Rode"—to be named *Badger* in her place.

Vice Admiral Gayton's reports and journal show an unusual frequency of replacement of small cruisers on his station and that with the exception of a few West Indies built vessels, he purchased prizes. The "fine going" 130-ton brig *Badger* was probably a prize, as there is circumstantial evidence that she had been built on the Chesapeake. Unfortunately Gayton's reports provide scant details concerning the vessels he purchased. In this case, however, evidence derived from the original Admiralty draught is presented in Plates 15–17, analyzed as follows:

The heavily crowned roof of the stern cabin appears on both Bermuda and Chesapeake Bay vessels built in the period 1740 to 1780, as do the cupid-bow-shaped scuppers shown on *Badger*. The deck cookhouse or "camboose" appears on American-built vessels employed in the West Indian trade, but not on European-built vessels of that century. Vessels built in the southern colonies in North America, and at Bermuda, as well as in the West Indies, of course, often had their galley hearth on deck, with or without a house. The heel of *Badger's* bowsprit rests on deck between two widely spaced bitts. As a result these could not be used to secure the heel, and the only substitute is a heel bolt through the deck and a deckbeam, or an iron strap bolted through a deck beam. The latter appears in *Mediator* and in some post-Revolutionary War schooners built in Chesapeake Bay. The heel bolt was often used on Chesapeake Bay built pilot schooners from 1785 on. The low, rather long, raised quarterdeck appears in *Mediator* and in some later Chesapeake Bay built schooners, arranged very much like *Badger* as to deck furniture.

The scantling dimensions given on the back of the Admiralty draught show the brig to have been lightly built and her frames irregularly spaced. This style of construction is commonly mentioned in dockyard surveys of American ships, particularly those built on the Chesapeake, from the time of the Revolution to around 1815 (see Plate 15).

Another piece of evidence is *Badger's* very thin planking, only 1¼ inches for both bottom and topside plank in the scantling dimensions. In the eighteenth century, Bermuda was building her vessels of red, or "pencil," cedar, which was described as a light, lasting, and rather brittle timber. Chesapeake builders used local white cedar (or juniper), timber which was somewhat heavier and stronger than Bermuda cedar. But the Chesapeake builders also planked with heartwood of the southern pine, oak, and other hard woods. Considering *Badger's* size, 1¼-inch plank is so very light that cedar would not appear to have been adequate. The thickness of plank for a vessel of such size would normally be about two inches; hence the unusually thin bottom indicates quite clearly that she must have been hardwood planked. Therefore, she was probably built somewhere on the Chesapeake as an illegal trader. It is evident that she was rather weakly built, as she was leaky soon after docking at Portsmouth, but her record of 22 vessels captured in two cruises shows that she was a very good sailer.

The brig's design, as shown in Plate 15, indicates that she was an experimental vessel with an intentionally hogged keel. The hog is too close to the sternpost to have been the result of weak construction, for here, as Plate 16 shows, the after deadwood is built up on top of the keel. Furthermore, the sheer lines are all fair, which could not be the case, with so much hog, were the latter caused by weakness. The intentionally hogged keel is rare; it appears in the old Indian pattamar and Bombay dinghy, but there the hog is forward, giving a deep gripe or forefoot. The builder's reason for using a hogged keel is, of course, unknown, but he may have seen vessels that sailed faster after becoming hogged, and decided to see if there were any virtues in this feature. Accidental hog might straighten the buttocks a little, but it probably did neither harm nor good, so far as modern experience can determine.

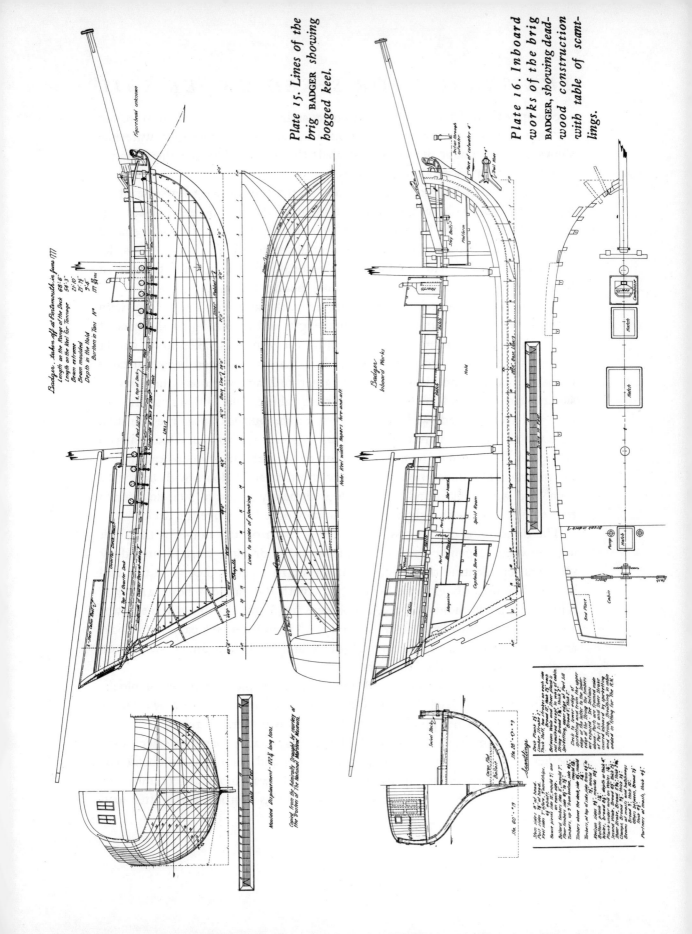

Plate 15. Lines of the brig BADGER showing hogged keel.

Plate 16. Inboard works of the brig BADGER, showing dead-wood construction with table of scantlings.

She appears to have been a good sailer, as her service record showed, for her bow-buttock lines are easy at both bow and stern. The load waterline shows a small amount of hollow just abaft the stern rabbet, but the entrance is full and short by modern standards.

The original Admiralty draught—one of the few drawn to a scale of ⅜ inch to one foot—shows an unusual amount of detail. There is evidence of care, in taking off the lines, to obtain precision by the use of closely spaced stations. This obvious effort to obtain an accurate record of the brig's design shows that she had stimulated professional interest, as much because of her sailing qualities, as because of her unorthodox design.

The brig was designed with moderate sheer, the keel with much drag, with a droop beginning a little abaft the midlength and increasing to the heel of the sternpost. The sternpost raked sharply; the stem was raked in an almost regular arc from keel to a little above deck height, and then became nearly upright. The entrance was short and rather full, and as noted, there was a slight hollow in the load line near the stem rabbet. The run was short, but easy and well-formed, with slight reverse in the buttocks near the transom. The vessel had a "square-tuck" or transom stern, the top of which curved aft in profile to permit the upper transom to be abaft the rudder head, in the old manner. The midsection shows very short, straight floors with little rise, combined with slack round bilge, made with nearly an arc of a circle, carried to the deck level, with a slight tumble home worked in above the deck.

The dimensions of the vessel were 68' 6" both on the range of the deck and between perpendiculars. The stations on the draught were identified by numbers representing their distances from the fore perpendicular in feet and inches. The breadth, extreme, was 21' 10", with the moulded beam 21' 7½". The depth in the hold was 9' 4". Tonnage by Admiralty measurement was 137 52/94 tons. She drew 11' 9" aft and 7' 5" forward as she came into dock, and had 12 four-pounders, carriage guns, and 12 half-pounder swivels on stocks secured inside the bulwarks.

She was built inexpensively and was—like any typical smuggler or blockade-runner—short-lived. Her cutwater may have carried a bust as shown, or a billet. Whatever her good qualities, beauty was not one of them.

The moulded displacement of the *Badger* was 122.3 long tons; her block coefficient was .73, her midship coefficient .74, and her prismatic coefficient .64. The camber in her quarterbeam buttock was moderate (camber to effective length is 8.7), and the straight line in this buttock at the after load line suggests a somewhat higher maximum-speed potential than in schooners *Hawke* and *Egmont*.

The rig of the *Badger*, as shown in Plate 17, was that of a brigantine, to which an improvised main course had been added. The main-topsail was sheeted to a spread yard, on a horse, as in a contemporary cutter's square top-sail. The course was laced to a crossjack of almost the same length as the spread yard. This yard was hoisted into the gored foot of the main-topsail, secured to the mast only with the yard's halyards. It is possible that no braces were fitted to this yard, as it could be controlled by those of the spread yard. The rig allowed the course and topsail to be lowered to the deck without interfering with the spanker. But lowering the crossjack and main course must have been troublesome in blowing weather and a heavy sea. This may have been a factor in the general acceptance of the snow's rig as that of a "brig" in the last quarter of the eighteenth century. In the snow the spanker gaff and hoops—and boom, if used—were on the trysail mast. This was a light mast located a few inches abaft the mainmast; its heel was either stepped on deck just clear of the mainmast wedges or on a "table," or chock, on the mainmast not quite as high above deck as the spanker tack or boom jaws. The head of the trysail mast was secured between the mainmast trestletrees by blocking and bolts. With the spanker set on the trysail mast, its gaff jaws and hoops were not fouled by the main yard parrels, as the yard was lowered. By the last quarter of the eighteenth century, brigs and snows were becoming so large that the main yard was too heavy for easy lowering and hoisting, with the result that it was rigged to be kept permanently aloft, and the snow rig ceased to be desirable. The trysail mast was also used in some sloops, as early as 1764, but the author has found no evidence of its employment in schooners, though such use would seem reasonable.

Some American marine historians believed that brigs and brigantines of the Revolution had lateen spankers, and models have been built with such a rig, but no contemporary plan, picture, or table of spar dimensions has yet been found to support this belief. On the contrary, available evidence shows that American and English brigs and brigantines had gaff spankers—sometimes without a boom.

There was, however, one rig that crossed a spanker yard. This was the "bilander," which had a lug-sail spanker. Chapman shows this rig, and so does a painting by J. Cleverly of 1752, in the Science Museum of London. An earlier grisaille by T. Boon shows the lug-spanker with a lug-topsail as

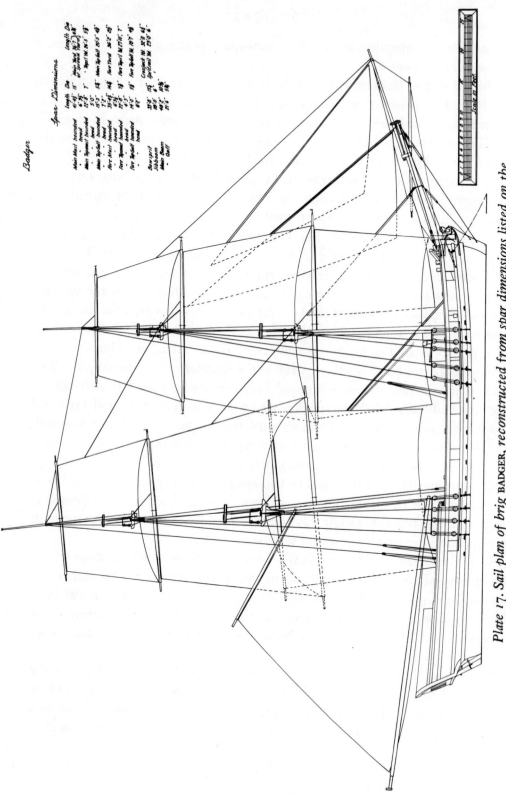

Badger

Spar Dimensions

	Length	Dia
Main Mast (deck to cap)	41'6"	15"
Main Topmast (Rigged)	25'6"	Y
Main Topgallant (Rigged)	25'0"	Y
Main Royal	13'3"	5"
Fore Mast (deck to cap)	40'0"	14½"
Fore Topmast (Rigged)	24'6"	9½"
Fore Topgallant (Rigged)	24'3"	7"
Fore Royal	13"	5"
Bowsprit	37'0"	19"
Jibboom	26'0"	9"
Main Boom	40'3"	10½"
Main Gaff	27'3"	8½"

Scale in Feet

Plate 17. Sail plan of brig BADGER, reconstructed from spar dimensions listed on the Admiralty draught.

A bilander; oil painting by J. Cleveley.

well. The Cleverly painting shows a square main-topsail with spread yard above a furled lug-sail spanker, but the yard of the latter is too short to be lateen-rigged.

The colonies are known to have used a few bilanders in the transatlantic trade, and one was fitted out for a privateer at Newport, Rhode Island, in 1742. Some of the vessels that brought German immigrants to the colonies in 1727–55 were colonial-owned bilanders, a few of which were certainly built in America.*

It should be noted that the colonial records do not confuse brigantines

* John Lyman, in *The Mariner's Mirror*, vol. 49, No. 2 (May 1962), pp. 142–43, discusses the colonial bilanders and brigantines.

or brigs with bilanders, showing that the latter was a distinctive type. The rig seems to have originated in the Baltic and it was employed by some English merchants. The bilander appears so rarely in any colonial records that it obviously was not a common American rig.

More than sixty American-built vessels were taken into the Royal Navy during the American Revolution, but thus far the plans of only four naval frigates, three Lake Champlain vessels, and nine privateers or merchant vessels, have been identified in the Admiralty Collection of Draughts. Of the fast sailing types, privateers, or blockade-runners, there are but one schooner, two brigs (of which *Badger* is one), and four ships. There are plans of five full-built merchant ships; one was employed as a privateer, though not sharp-built. Two of the full-built merchantmen, however, are referred to as being good sailers.

Only two sloops of the late 1765–1783 period have been discovered in European naval archives; one built in Virginia and the other in Bermuda. In the American naval archives only one plan of a frigate and one of a rather sharp 74-gun ship have been found.

Published sources have produced only a plan for a very sharp frigate, designed by Benjamin Thompson (Count Rumford, 1753–1814, the noted American Tory and scientist). The design is shown in Stalkaart's *Naval Architecture*, 1784, Plate XIV. This appears to be the earliest design for a large frigate having very sharp deadrise, though smaller vessels having this feature, designed even earlier, will be examined later.

There is enough evidence in the available plans to fairly establish the state of the art of design of fast sailing vessels in America during the Revolution. There is, however, a lack of plans of sloops and schooners built during the war. This is lamentable, for it would be in schooners, and some sloops at least, that the most radical and experimental designs might normally be expected to appear. Hence, the developments in such craft during the Revolution must be interpolated.

Nevertheless it is possible to arrive at some conclusions as to what seems to have taken place during the war in small vessels by examination of the plans of H. M. brig *Swift* (Plates 18 and 19). An Admiralty manuscript list shows this vessel to have been American-built in 1778 and she is so described in correspondence regarding her sale out of service in 1783. In that year her draught was prepared in the Deptford dockyard and forwarded to the Admiralty on 3 December.

Because the records are incomplete, there is uncertainty as to her original name. Admiralty papers mention that the "armed brig *Middleton* now *Swift*" was purchased in 1778 from Samuel Kemble. This does not adequately establish her identification, since there apparently were two vessels named *Swift* in the British Navy in 1778, and available information does not show which is the American brig.

When she came into the Deptford dockyard she had been in service for some time and had a crew of 40 (including officers), one boat, 10 three-pounder carriage guns, and 18 tons of pig-iron ballast. The dockyard officers considered her "over-hatted"—or over-sparred—and proposed to establish her with a crew of 30, two boats, six three-pounder guns, and some swivels; to increase her ballast to nearly 30 tons; and to reduce her spars and sail area. Some spars were to be shortened as much as six feet.

The *Swift*, Plate 18, was originally designed for a fast sailing vessel, as is obvious in her plans. She had fine ends, much drag to the keel, a very raking curved-stem rabbet, raking post, square-tuck transom stern, and moderate sheer. Her midsection was formed by sharply rising, straight floor, and a high and easy bilge carried up to the sheer to form some tumble home. Her quarterback buttock became straight as it approached its intersection with the after load line, then slightly reversed as it approached the transom. The load line, just abaft the stem rabbet, showed a slight hollow, when projected, in the half-breadth plan.

This vessel was very well built and finished. On her stern she had a carved panel showing three fleur-de-lis and two partial wreaths. Her quarter badges had false windows and formal carvings. The figurehead was omitted in the Admiralty draught and that shown in the plates is purely speculative.

The *Swift* was 75′ 6″ between perpendiculars, 20′ 10″ extreme beam, 20′ 5″ moulded beam, 7′ 9″ depth in hold, and she drew 9′ 9″ aft and 6′ 7½″ forward when she came into dock. Her moulded waterline was then 70′ 11″. Her plans, as redrawn, are shown in Plates 18 and 19; the latter was reconstructed from her spar dimensions, as taken off at Deptford. The original Admiralty draught shows a spar table, notated for the dockyard's proposed reduction.

The rig, Plate 19, was actually that of a brigantine, being without a main course. Though large for the relatively light-displacement hull that carried it, the rig was well-proportioned—the great drop in the topsails is noticeable. Her original spar dimensions as surveyed are as follows:

Spar	Length	Dia.	Yard	Length	Dia.
Mainmast	52' 7"	14"	Main Yard	35' 2"	6¾"
Main-topmast	24' 1"	7"	Main Tops'l Yard	25' 11"	4⅞"
Main Topgal't Mast	19' 6"	4⅞"	Main Topgal't Yard	19' 0"	4"
Foremast	42' 5½"	13¾"	Fore Yard	37' 7"	7"
Fore-Topmast	26' 0"	7⅜"	Fore Tops'l Yard	27' 3"	5¾"
Fore Topgal't Mast	18' 1"	5⅛"	Fore Topgat'l Yard	19' 6"	4⅜"
Main Boom	48' 5"	9⅜"			
Main Gaff				24' 4"	6⅛"
Bowsprit	31' 2"	13⅞"			
Jib boom	19' 7"	6¼"			
Spritsail Yard				27' 3"	5¾"

The hull form of this vessel may be said to have been a refinement of that shown in the *Lyme,* and in Chapman's example of a Bermuda sloop. The *Swift* was, in fact, a long stride toward the model or hull form that later characterized the fast American schooners. It is probable, then, that there may have been a steady refinement in hull design before the Revolution, of which we have no actual record in plans or text.

The *Swift* was of light displacement, about 87.8 long tons. Her block coefficient was only .37, her midship coefficient .64. Due to her sharp ends and the rake in her stem and post, she had a rather low prismatic coefficient of .60. Her second buttock out from the centerline had a camber of 4' 1½" in an effective length of about 58' 4"; camber to length was 14.2. She should have been a fast sailer, at least in light and moderate weather when she could carry sail.

In a vessel of *Swift's* dimensions and small displacement, the power to carry sail becomes a critical matter. Unless the vessel is very lightly built (as *Swift* was reported to be) and lightly burdened, there may not be adequate displacement for sufficient ballast. It is relatively rare to find such conditions in a merchant vessel. *Swift's* finish, and light displacement, suggest she had not been intended for a freighter; possibly she had been a mail packet. At any rate, it is evident that the British dockyard officials attempted to increase sail-carrying power by increasing the amount of ballast and reducing the armament, while also reducing power, or sail area. Unfortunately we do not know what the alterations did to the vessel's trim and performance.

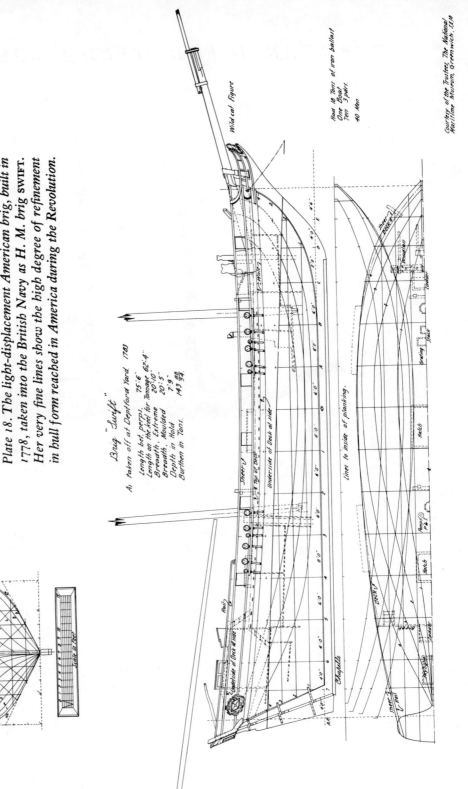

Plate 18. *The light-displacement American brig, built in 1778, taken into the British Navy as H. M. brig* SWIFT. *Her very fine lines show the high degree of refinement in hull form reached in America during the Revolution.*

Brig "Swift"

As taken off at Deptford Yard. 1783

Length bet. perps. 75'-6"
Length on the keel for Tonnage 62'-4"
Breadth. Extreme 20'-10"
Breadth. Moulded 20'-5"
Depth in Hold 7'-9"
Burthen in Tons. 143 $\frac{86}{94}$

Wild cat Figure

Head 18 Tons of iron ballast
One Boat
Ten 3 pdr.
40 Men

Underside of Deck at side

Lines to inside of planking.

Chapelle

Three Fleur de Lys in wreaths

Scale in Feet

Brigantine SWIFT, *built in America in 1778. Her very light displacement and rather ornate finish suggest she may have been intended for a mail packet.*

This was an inherent problem of design in the very sharp, light-displacement, sailing vessel for naval use or privateering. Stores, ammunition, and armament required in a cruiser combined to create a burden that often overloaded the vessel. Such was the case in H. M. sloop *Porto*, shown in Plate 20. This ship appears to have been an American-built vessel purchased by the French as a mail packet in the West Indies under the name *Harlequin*, and captured by H.M.S. *Cerebus* on 6 June 1780, near Martinique. She was a

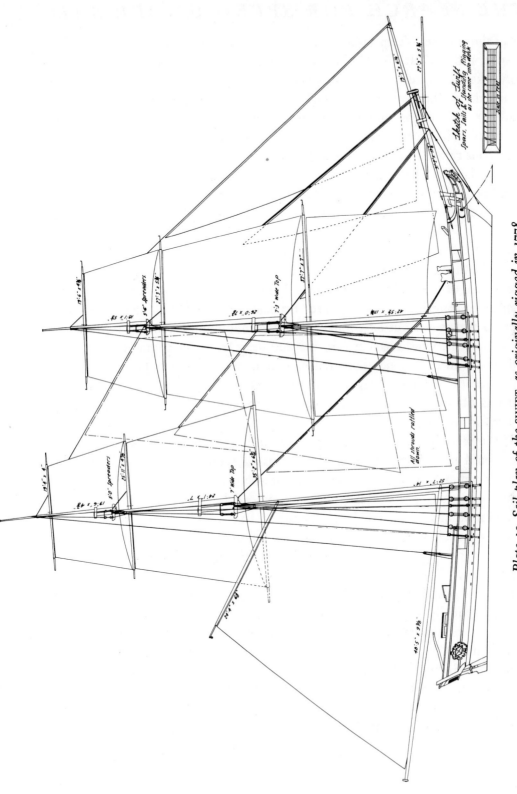

Plate 19. Sail plan of the SWIFT, *as originally rigged in 1778.*

small ship of the "sharp-built" model, 80′ 1″ long on deck, 20′ 5″ beam (extreme), and 9′ 3″ depth in hold. This ship had a short raised quarterdeck with bulwarks. Her sheer was moderate and she had a straight keel with some drag, small rake in the post, and curved rake in stem becoming upright above the load line. Midsection showed a straight, sharply rising floor, very slack bilge, and tumble-home topsides. She had a square-tuck stern. Her entrance was sharp, but rather short; her run was long and very fine.

Her plan, in Plate 20, has two load lines drawn on the sheer. The upper load line is that shown in the Admiralty draught, as she came into drydock at Portsmouth in July 1781 fitted for naval service. She then drew 11′ 9″ aft, 9′ 2″ forward, giving her a moulded L.W.L. length of 76′ 7″ and a moulded L.W.L. beam of 20′ 1″. In this trim she displaced 197.9 long tons; she had a block coefficient of .46, a midship coefficient of .68, and a prismatic coefficient of .68. The second buttock line out from the centerline had a camber to length ratio of 9.5. Her transom was deeply immersed; its submerged area was about 8.64 square feet. Her minimum freeboard to deck was 11 inches. She would have a very marked drag from her submerged transom, which would reduce her potential maximum speed. When she heeled under sail to even a moderate degree, her deck would begin to flood. In this trim she was obviously overloaded, because of the stores and armament assigned to her for man-of-war service.

If she were lightened to trim at 10′ 7″ draft at post and at 8′ 1″ forward, she would have displaced 154.5 long tons (a reduction of 43.41 tons), her block coefficient would have been .45, midship coefficient .68, and the prismatic coefficient .63. In this trim, her moulded L.W.L. length would be 76′ 4″ and moulded beam at L.W.L. would be 19′ 10″. Her minimum freeboard to top of deck would have then been 24 inches. The second buttock out from the centerline would have changed in camber-to-length ratio from 9.5 to 10.1.

It is obvious that a faster vessel would result if the load were lightened; but it is equally obvious that the difference of 43.41 tons in displacement would have been so great that she could carry only a small armament and limited stores, making the vessel unfit for naval service. Therefore a trim somewhere between the two extremes, giving only moderate submergence of the transom, would have been a preferred alteration for a naval cruiser.

That the *Harlequin* had been sailed in proper trim when in French hands is shown by Commodore George Johnston's letter of 5 July 1780 justifying

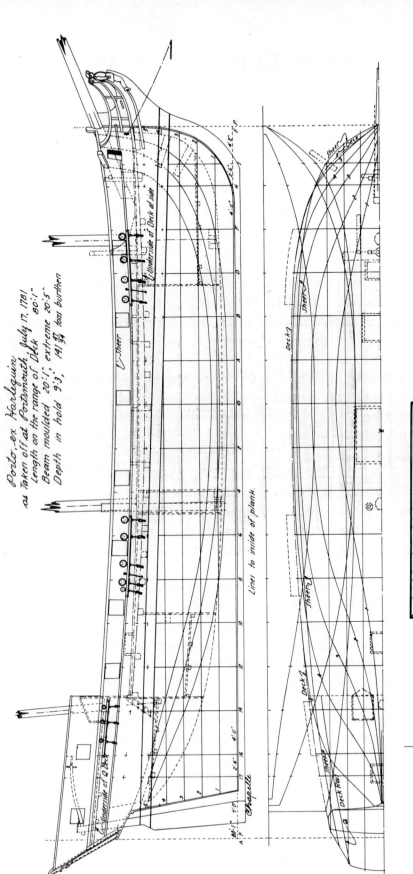

Porto, ex Harlequin
as Taken off at Portsmouth July 17, 1781
Length on the range of Deck 80·1·"
Beam moulded 20·1·"; extreme 20·5·"
Depth in hold 9·3·, 141 47/94 tons burthen

Lines to inside of plank.

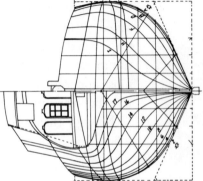

Courtesy of the Trustees of the
National Maritime Museum, Greenwich { Reg No. 3495
Porto
Box 51 }

Plate 20. Lines of the American ship HARLEQUIN; the two load waterlines are
shown to illustrate the effect of overloading a sharp-built sailing vessel.

his purchase of the vessel for use on the coast of Portugal. He stated she then drew nine feet abaft and 7' 6" forward. His glowing description of the purchase was perhaps partly based on the vessel's behavior in this trim and partly on the necessity of explaining an unauthorized purchase and addition to his squadron.

At any rate, he wrote that "she was built for sailing . . . goes and works remarkably well, . . . a perfect model of her kind, easily managed, sailing very swift and will sustain any sea, . . . superior to any other" and finally, "if we had searched the whole world I do not believe so fit a vessel could have been found."

If she were all that was claimed for her at the time of purchase, overloading by the naval authorities must have changed *Porto's* performance markedly. At any rate, Their Lordships directed that hereafter the Commodore was to consult the Admiralty before buying any more vessels, and indicated their displeasure; the vessel was sold out in 1782.

If a vessel were very heavily built and modeled for fast sailing, the displacement might be inadequate for much cargo or for heavy armament. In such a vessel the power to carry sail was controlled in large part by the proportion of structural weights, and weights of cargo, stores, and armament, to displacement. In a fast sailing vessel of heavy construction little would be left for ballast and therefore, if heavily loaded, the stability was affected. The *Wasa*, lost in Stockholm harbor in 1628 and raised in 1961, seems to have been such a vessel. But American sharp-built vessels usually were designed and built with this danger in mind, for the British dockyard surveys almost invariably refer to them as having been "slightly-built," that is, light in frame, and relatively light in structural weight.

The example of *Porto*, in overloading, shows the effect of cargo loads on a sailing merchant ship, for the coefficients change sharply between light and load waterlines, and similarly, the propulsion requirements also change. In full-rigged ships the spars and rigging were often heavy. If these were lost, and a light, small jury-rig set up, it was not unusual to find that the vessel sailed surprisingly well with the resulting small sail area. This is explained by the reduced displacement owing to the loss of heavy spars and gear, and the marked changes in the resulting coefficients. The result of this might be most apparent in a vessel having a full entrance and run at her normal load line, but very fine below.

Though the "full-built" American merchant vessel has been referred to, no example has thus far been examined. A vessel of this class is well represented in H.M. armed ship *Cherokee,* ex-*Codrington.* Sometime before 30 August 1774, the Admiralty decided to purchase a ship for the use of the Surveyor General of the Southern District of North America. On that date the Navy Board ordered the Deptford yard to survey four ships that had been tendered for this service. These were two-year-old *Nonpareil* built on the Piscataqua; *Codrington* built at Newbury ten months earlier; *Leeds Merchant* built in Rhode Island, nine years old; and *Lady Tyrconnel* of uncertain age. The last was judged unfit for consideration and was not surveyed. *Codrington,* then lying off the Stone Stairs in the Thames, was considered "a good sound ship" in initial inspection. It was decided to survey *Codrington* and *Nonpareil* fully, both being of about equal size, and on 7 September the yard reported that *Codrington* was much the better ship in all respects.

Codrington was then purchased and renamed *Cherokee;* her draught was made at Deptford. On 31 October 1774 she was ordered to be fitted for service in North America, armed with six three-pounder carriage guns and eight swivels, and manned with a crew of 30 men.

In 1777 she was renamed *Dispatch.* The records of this ship after 1777 have not been found. Her spar dimensions exist, as does a somewhat detailed inventory.

Codrington does not appear to have had any distinctively American design features, resembling in a general way the full-built British merchant vessels of her size and class, of which some plans survive. Her drawings show features of small merchant ships described in the few existing American contracts of the Revolutionary period, indicating plainly that the English model was used in colonial America.

The ship, whose lines are illustrated in Plate 21, had very moderate sheer, straight keel (shown in the lines without drag, but probably the ship was trimmed, when ready for sea, with about a foot more draft astern), curved-stem rabbet becoming straight and upright above her 12' 6" waterline, moderately-raking sternpost, square stern, and round tuck with upper-and-lower transoms. The run was short but well-formed; her entrance was short, full, and convex. The midsection shows slightly rising straight floor, low, easy turn of the bilge, topsides straight and upright until a few feet below the deck, where marked tumble home begins. She was, in general, a short, deep vessel intended primarily as a good carrier, having two complete decks, with short fore and after platforms in the hold. She was said to have handled well after

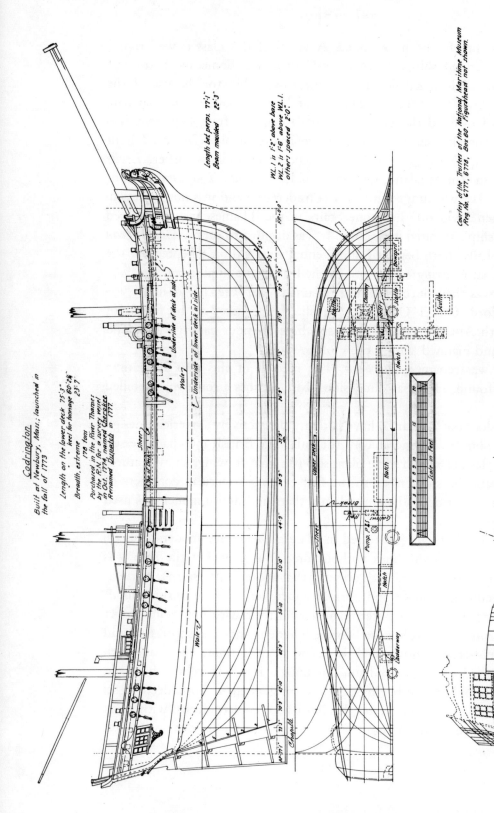

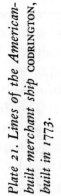

Codrington

Built at Newbury, Mass., launched in the fall of 1773

Length on the lower deck 75'3"; keel for tonnage 60'24"; Breadth, extreme 23'7

178 tons

Purchased in the River Thames by the R.N. for a survey vessel in Oct. 1774, named *Chevaux* Renamed *Despatch* in 1777.

Length bet. perps. 77'1"

Beam moulded 22'3"

W.L. 1 is 1'2" above base
W.L. 2 is 1'6" above W.L.1
others spaced 2'0".

Courtesy of the Trustee of the National Maritime Museum
Reg. No. 6777, 6778, Box 60. Figurehead not shown.

Plate 21. Lines of the American-built merchant ship CODRINGTON, *built in 1773.*

her mainmast had been shifted two feet forward of where it is shown in the draught.

The plans show that her upper deck had a break 13 inches high at 42' 1" from the fore perpendicular. On her quarterdeck she had open stanchion rails with low bulwarks forward of the quarterdeck. It will be noted that the deck drops, near the bow, to allow the hawse holes to be lower than could otherwise be the case.

This ship was 77' 1" between perpendiculars, 74 feet on the moulded waterline (as laid down in the Admiralty draught), moulded beam 23' 3" (maximum and waterline), 23' 7" extreme beam, and 17 feet from rabbet to underside of deck at side. In the trim shown in the plans, 12' 6" draft, she had a moulded displacement of 313.7 long tons, with a block coefficient of .60, a midship coefficient of .87, and a prismatic coefficient of .71. Her quarter-beam buttock line had an effective length of 67' 8" at 12' 6" draft, the camber then being about 9' 5" and the ratio of camber to length 7.2.

The ship rig in the period of the American Revolution varied somewhat. Some American naval ships had the lateen spanker, but those merchant ships whose spar dimensions exist, had the standing or hoisting gaff spanker, usually without a boom. Plate 22 is a reconstruction, based on the survey spar dimensions, of the rig of this ship. The doublings and pole lengths are based upon proportions obtained from other contemporary spar dimensions, in which these lengths were given.

It will be noticed that the spar dimensions produce a lofty, powerful rig, with very light spars above the lower mastheads. It can be assumed that this was done in order to drive the ship at her maximum potential speed when necessary. The inventory of sails, while not complete, shows that she carried lower and topmast studding sails on her main, at least. It is probable that she had studding sails on her foremast as well. Her rig is circumstantial evidence of the importance placed on good sailing qualities, in even full-bodied carriers, by American ship-owners of the colonial period.

Ships of the Revolution need not be discussed in any particular order. In most instances, the records are inadequate to establish the exact dates of building, and available plans show a range of types, rather than the development of individual types in the period.

The sharp privateer ship was extensively built in colonial ports during the Revolution. Many of these fell into British hands with the result that some are represented by plans. The ship-sloop *Barbadoes* shown in Plate 23 was

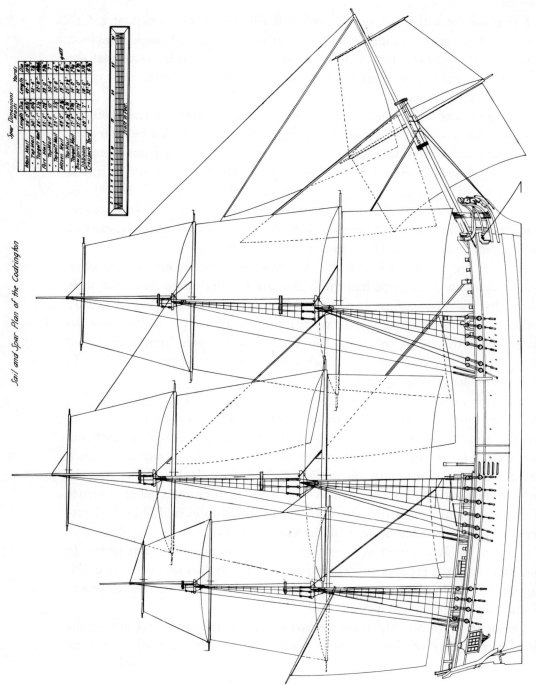

Sail and Spar Plan of the Codrington

Plate 22. Sail plan of the American-built merchant ship CODRINGTON, 1773, showing typical rig of a small American ship of the Revolutionary War period.

one of these; her original name was *Rhodes*, of Salem, Massachusetts. She had been captured in the West Indies by H.M.S. *Prothé* on 15 February 1782. The previous day *Prothé* had taken the Salem or Beverly ship privateer *Scourge*. Both were brought into the Royal Navy, and *Scourge* was renamed *Stormont*. This 80-foot ship was later taken by the French, but the *Barbadoes* (ex-*Rhodes*) survived, and was in the service until the war ended, when she was sold.

Admiralty Court records of the condemnation of the *Rhodes* have not been found, so the date and place of her building have not yet been established. It is probable, however, that she was built in Essex County, Massachusetts, about 1778–80.

Privateer ship RHODES, *a sharp New England built ship of the Revolution.*

As her plan (Plate 23) shows, she had a midsection formed with sharply rising straight floors, high, easy turn of the bilge, and strong tumble home in the topsides. She had much sheer, with breaks at the after end of her forecastle and at the fore end of quarterdeck. The quarterdeck was fitted with a light, open, stanchion rail. Her keel was straight, with moderate drag. The stem rabbet had a moderate curve, becoming nearly straight and upright above the load line. Her post had slight rake, with much more rake at the rabbet than on the face of the post. The entrance was short, convex, and rather full; the run was very long, but not extremely fine. The buttocks are somewhat rounded toward their intersections with the load line, in spite of a very long run for her length.

This ship was 97′ 7″ long between perpendiculars, 24′ 11¼″ extreme beam, 24′ 6¼″ moulded beam, and 10′ 7″ depth in hold. Her moulded waterline was 96′ 5″ long, moulded beam 24′ 5½″, and her mean moulded draft was 10′ 1″ at mid-length. In trim, the ship drew 10′ 11″ forward and 12′ 3½″ at post. She was described as a weatherly ship, but due to her relatively full ends it is probable that she was not capable of great speed when running free in strong winds.

This ship had a moulded displacement of 292.7 long tons; her block coefficient was .42, and her midship coefficient was .64. The prismatic coefficient was .65. The effective length of her quarterbeam buttocks was 83′ 7″ and the camber 7′ ½″. Ratio of camber to length was about 11.9.

The spar dimensions show that she had nothing above the topgallant masts on fore and main, and nothing above the topmast of the mizzen mast except very short poles or "stumps." She had a standing gaff spanker, with no boom. The gaff was shown opposite to the mizzenmast length, in the spar table, with the crossjack or mizzenyard at the bottom of the table, an unusual arrangement in Admiralty spar tables.

Her figurehead is not recorded, but may have been a Grecian warrior. The billet indicates a full-length figurehead. The most marked feature of this ship was her narrow stern, made more noticeable by the unusually long afterbody. This ship nearly approached the proposed ideal in the contemporary textbooks on naval architecture—"cod's head and mackerel's tail."

Another sharp-built privateer was the *Mohawk* (Plate 24). Her place of building has not been established, nor is her original name known. She began wages and sea victualing at New York, "in conformity to Admiral Pigot's Establishment" on 18 October 1782. On 8 September 1783, the Deptford

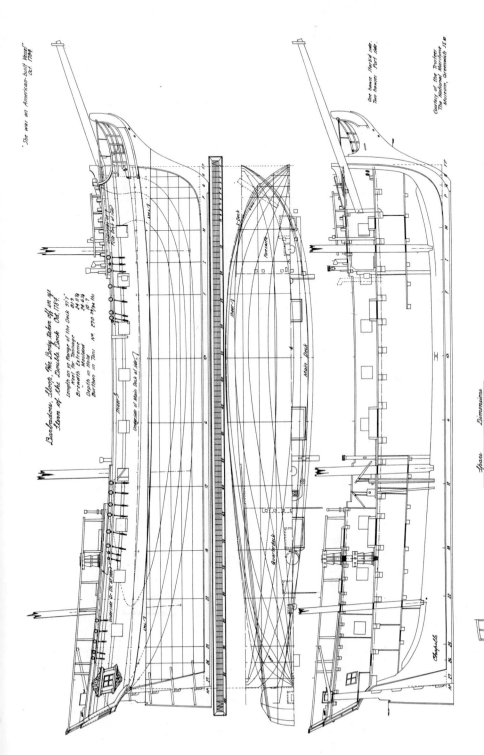
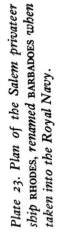

Plate 23. Plan of the Salem privateer ship RHODES, renamed BARBADOES when taken into the Royal Navy.

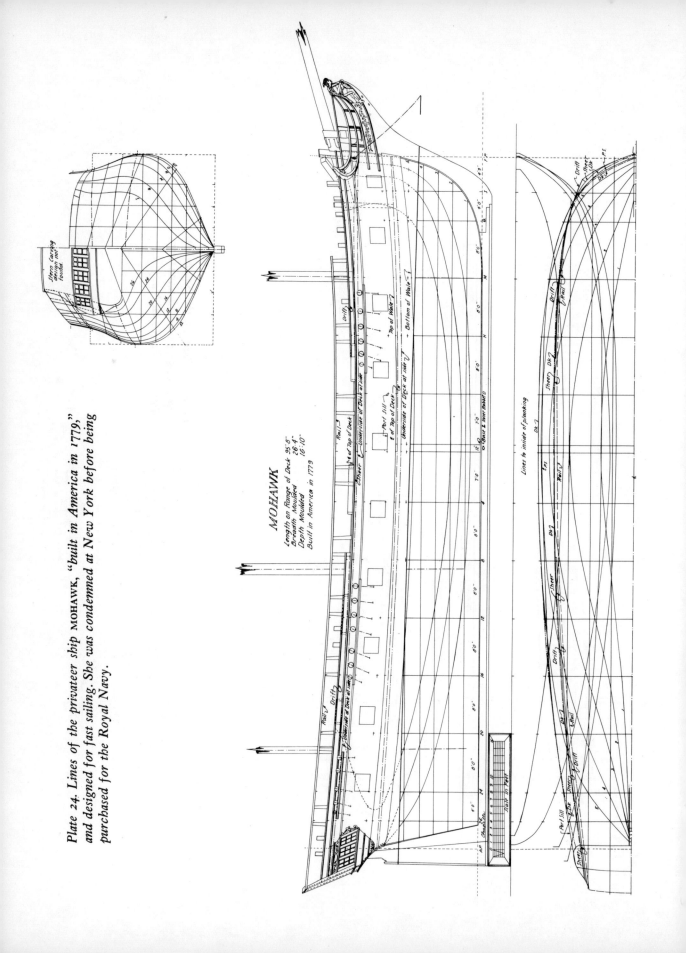

Plate 24. Lines of the privateer ship MOHAWK, *"built in America in 1779," and designed for fast sailing. She was condemned at New York before being purchased for the Royal Navy.*

MOHAWK

Length on Range of Deck 95'8"
Breadth Moulded   26'4"
Depth Moulded   16'10"
Built in America in 1779

yard reported she had been prepared for sale, that she was 284 86/94 tons, "had been built in America in 1779 and was copper sheathed." The British Admiralty Court records of New York during the Revolution have not yet been found.

This was a handsome double-decked ship, having a flush spar deck. Her lower or gun deck had ten gunports a side, including bridle port. Her spar deck, with light, open stanchion rail reaching a little past the foremast, was arranged for nine gunports a side. This vessel had the same general gunport arrangement that was to be used in many of the American frigates in 1796–1800.

The ship had an attractive, strong sheer, a straight keel with moderate drag (the vessel drew 12′ 3″ at post, 10′ 3″ forward), a curved-stem rabbet that became nearly upright above the load line, with a moderately-raking post. Her entrance was rather full and her run was long and easy, though somewhat rounded in the buttocks at the load line.

The midsection was formed with sharply rising floor, slightly hollow at the garboards; high, easy bilge, strong tumble home in the topsides. In lines she had some resemblance to *Rhodes*, but her run was slightly finer and her stern wider than in that ship.

The *Mohawk* was 95′ 8″ between perpendiculars, 26′ 4″ moulded beam, 16′ 10″ moulded depth, rabbet to underside of spar deck at side. Her moulded load line was 93′ 10″; her moulded beam at load line was 26′ 4″. Her moulded draft (at midsection ⚓) was 8′10″. Her moulded displacement was 274.7 long tons, block coefficient .40, midsection coefficient .65, and prismatic coefficient .61. Her quarterbeam buttock had an effective length of 83′ 8″ and camber 7′ 1½″; the camber-length ratio was 10.8.

Mohawk had the same downward turn of the upper deck at the hawse that was first noted in *Codrington*. She had hollow garboards, less extreme than shown in *St. Ann*. No spar dimensions nor deck arrangement for *Mohawk* have yet been found and her survey cannot be located.

A third ship-privateer was *Rattlesnake* whose plans were first published by the author in *The History of American Sailing Ships* in 1935. This vessel was probably built in Massachusetts; she was owned by Salem merchants. She was apparently built in 1779 or 1780, for her first commission was dated 12 June 1781. The Preble Papers, in the Massachusetts Historical Society, contain a statement that *Rattlesnake* was designed and built by John Peck, but no other authority for this has yet been found. At any rate, *Rattlesnake* was captured by H.M. ship *Assurance* in 1781 and taken into the Royal Navy as *Cormorant*. It was then discovered by the Admiralty that they already had a ship named *Cormorant* in service, so the vessel was renamed *Rattlesnake* and in 1784 she was ordered to be sold out of service.

Rattlesnake was 89' 3" between perpendiculars, 22 feet moulded beam, 8' 10½" depth in hold, and her naval register states she was of 198 70/94 tons burthen. This vessel was sharper in the entrance than *Mohawk* or *Rhodes*. She had strong sheer with a rise at the inboard ends of forecastle and quarterdeck. The latter had light, closed rail, but the forecastle had a light, open-stanchion rail. The keel was straight, with some drag, the stem rabbet strongly curved with much fore-rake but becoming nearly upright above the load line. The sternpost had moderate rake; the stern was formed with a round tuck and upper-and-lower transoms. The entrance was of moderate length, convex, and somewhat full. The run was not very long; the quarterbeam buttock became straight for only a very short distance at the after load line, balancing the entrance. The midsection showed straight, rising floor with high and well-rounded bilge carried up and inboard to the main-sheer.

The ship had an unusual amount of camber in the forecastle and quarter-deck and had light, narrow, removable gangways along the sides, connecting the forecastle and quarterdeck. Her spar dimensions produced a large rig, with the fore and main topgallant masts ending in short poles. The mizzen topmast ended in a long pole, on which no topgallant sail was indicated. The spanker had a long boom.

Her plans as redrawn are reproduced in Plate 25. There was a proposal to build a sloop on her lines, enlarged, but this was canceled by the Admiralty.

Rattlesnake's moulded displacement was 221.3 long tons, the block coefficient .50, the midship coefficient .71, and the prismatic coefficient .60. The moulded load waterline was 87' 7½", moulded beam at load waterline was 21' 11", and the mean draft, moulded, was 8' 1½". The effective length of the quarterbeam buttock was 76 feet, the camber 6' 2", and the camber-to-length ratio was 12.2.

Another full-built American merchant ship is shown in Plates 26 and 27. This is *London*, built at New York in 1770 or 1771; she was surveyed at Deptford in 1776 with the view of purchasing her for use as an armed ship; after the purchase she was renamed *Grasshopper*. This ship was said to have been a good sailer, and as the plans show, she was sharper in the ends than

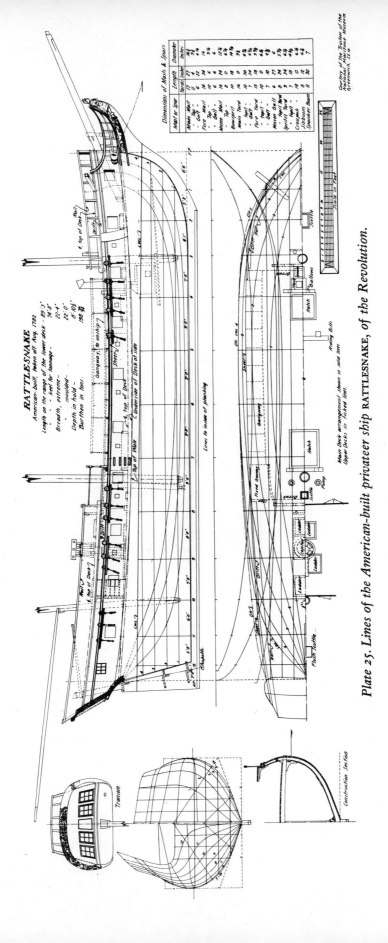

Plate 25. Lines of the American-built privateer ship RATTLESNAKE, of the Revolution.

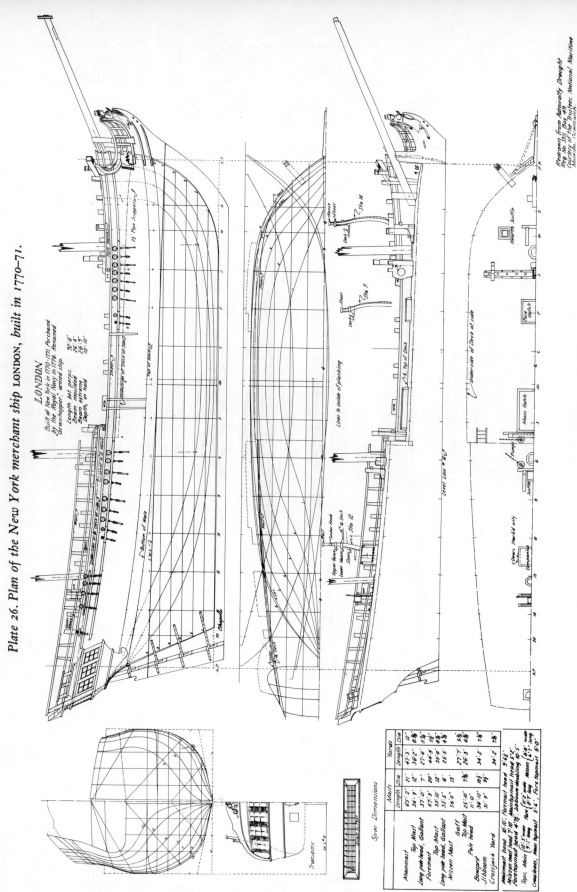

Plate 26. Plan of the New York merchant ship LONDON, built in 1770–71.

LONDON

Built at New York in 1770-1771. Purchased
by the Royal Navy in 1776. Renamed
"Grasshopper", armed ship.

Length bet. perps.   92'·6"
Beam moulded   26'·4"
Beam extreme   26'·9"
Depth in hold   10'·10"

Codrington. Constructed of oak and cedar, she was 92′ 6″ between perpendiculars or on the lower deck, 26′ 9″ extreme beam, 26′ 4″ moulded beam, 10′ 10″ depth in hold, and 282 44/94 tons burthen. To fit her as an armed ship, changes were made to her below-deck arrangement, gunports were formed in her rails, and swivel stocks were fitted.

This ship had a lively sheer, with a raised quarterdeck. Her upper deck was curved down sharply forward to allow low hawse holes. Her keel was short and straight; her stem rabbet was formed with a long sweep, coming upright well above the load line; her sternpost had much rake. Her entrance was short but much sharper than *Codrington's,* and she had marked shoulders about 11 feet abaft her stem rabbet. Her run was long and fine, with quarter-beam buttock becoming straight for a short distance as it approached the after load line. The midsection showed a short, straight, slightly rising floor; very slack, well-rounded bilge; and moderate tumble home in the topsides.

London had a moulded displacement of 362.8 long tons, on a moulded load line of 89′ 4″. Her block coefficient was .49 and her midship coefficient .81. The effective length of the quarterbeam buttock was 77′ 6″ and the camber 9′ 7″. The ratio of camber to length was 8.1, and the prismatic coefficient was .62.

The spar dimensions (with doublings reconstructed) produce a heavily canvassed rig. The original spar dimensions were slightly altered for naval service, and both are given in the sail plan. The mizzen—as in many other American ships of the period—had no sail above the topsail. It will be noticed that this vessel had a steering wheel; her tiller was under the quarterdeck.

The *London* is an example of a design in which an effort was made to produce a large carrier, for given dimensions, combined with good sailing and working qualities. This is a compromise that has always been most difficult to solve satisfactorily.

London appears to have been a Tory- or English-owned ship when purchased, since she had been hired as a transport for nearly a year (presumably to carry troops to America). In the winter of 1776, 37 American-built vessels had been offered to the Admiralty as transports, and *London* was one of these.

The last vessel of the Revolutionary War period to be examined is the schooner *Berbice.* This was an American-built vessel purchased in the West Indies by Admiral Rodney. The date of purchase has not been established, but it probably was late in 1780. She was employed as a tender and was condemned at Antigua, B. W. I., 12 September 1788. Two poorly-made

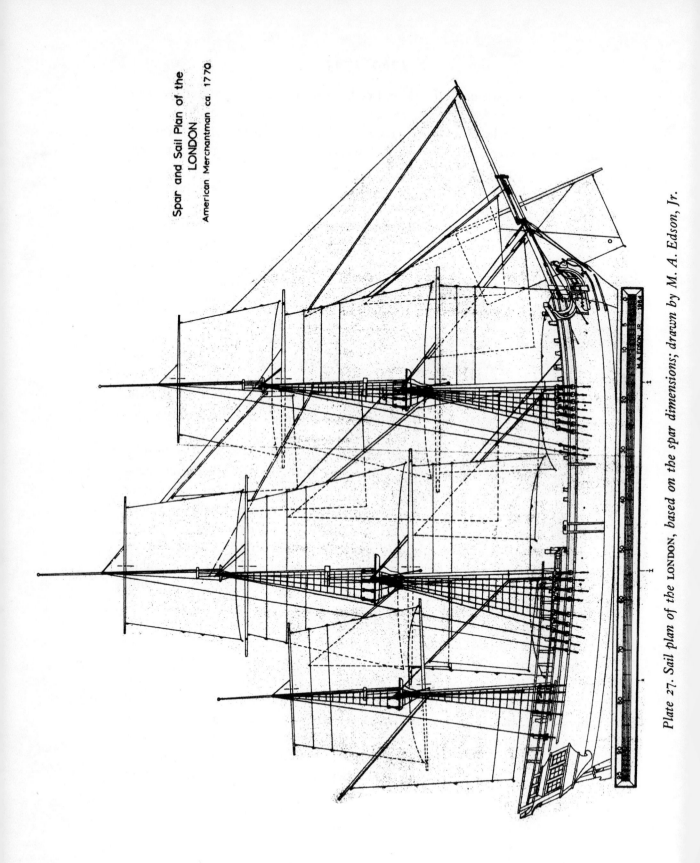

Spar and Sail Plan of the
LONDON
American Merchantman ca. 1770

Plate 27. Sail plan of the LONDON, *based on the spar dimensions; drawn by M. A. Edson, Jr.*

draughts of the vessel exist, one in the Admiralty Collection of Draughts and the other in private hands. Comparison of these show some variations in the aftermost stations and in minor fittings. Because of the variation in the after sections there is some doubt as to her real form, particularly in the buttocks near the stern.

Plates 28 and 29 show a reconstruction of this schooner. They are based on the two draughts, one of which gave incomplete spar dimensions, presumably those she carried when measured and drawn in the West Indies. The schooner was 72′ 9″ between perpendiculars, 20′ 2″ moulded beam, 7′ 6″ depth in hold, drawing 9′ 6″ at post and 6′ 6″ forward. At moulded load line her length was 66′ 8″, with a beam of 19′ 1″.

Berbice had slight sheer with a high, raised quarterdeck; straight keel with much drag; stem rabbet formed with a long sweep; very raking post; long, sharp, and slightly hollow entrance; long, fine run with a straight or somewhat hollow quarterbeam buttock close to the stern. The stern is formed with a square tuck, with upper and lower transoms above. The midsection shows straight, very rising floor, high easy bilge, with very slight tumble home in the topsides.

She had a moulded displacement of about 73.6 long tons; the L.W.L. was 66′ 9″. Her coefficients were: block .35, midsection .62, and prismatic .57. The effective length of her quarterbeam buttock was about 47′ 3″ and the camber 3′ 11″. The camber-length ratio was about 12.1.

The lack of precision in the sources for these drawings somewhat reduces the value of this vessel as evidence of design practices.

The sail plan (Plate 29) shows how she may have been sparred and rigged. She undoubtedly was heavily sparred and the draughts agree enough at least to indicate that *Berbice* was built for fast sailing.

There remain two schooners that may have been built toward the end of the American Revolution, or within ten years of its end. These are shown or described in David Steel's *Naval Architecture*, 1805. The first to be examined is *A Virginia-Built Boat Fitted for a Privateer*, Plate XXIII, in Steel. This plate has numerous engraver's errors—the location of the foremast is too far aft, as is obvious by the fore chains, and there is a mistake in the aftermost section affecting the form of the run. The engraved plan was probably copied from an Admiralty draught, now lost, but the schooner cannot be identified in the Royal Navy manuscript lists by her dimensions.

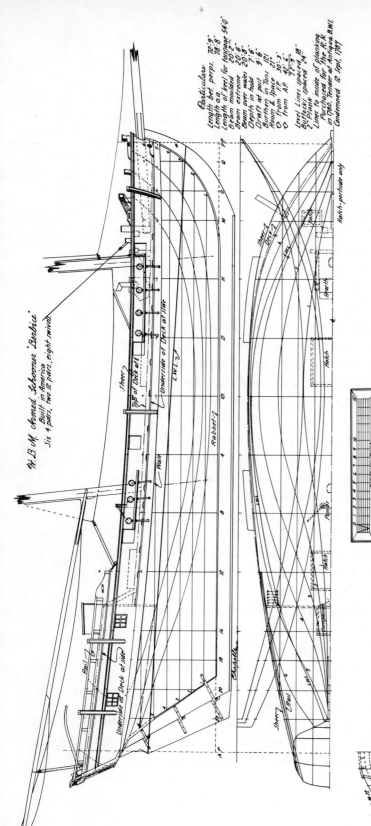

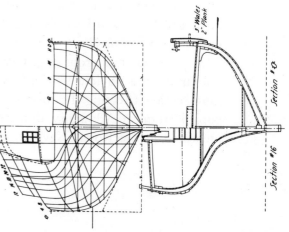

H.B.M. Armed Schooner "Berbice"

Built in America
Six 4 pdrs, two 12 pdrs., eight swivels

Particulars

Length bet. perps. 72'-9"
Length o.a. 78'-8"
Length of keel for tonnage 54'-0"
Beam extreme 20'-6"
Beam moulded 20'-8"
Draft over water 7'-6"
Depth in hold 9'-6"
Draft at port 21
Burthen in Tons 121
Room & Space 21"
⊗ from F.P. 30'-3"
⊗ from A.P. 42'-6"
⊗ Plank 72'-3"

Level Lines spaced 18"
Buttocks spaced 24"
2" Plank

Lines to inside of planking
Purchased for the R.N.
in 1780. Tender at Antigua B.W.I.
Condemned 12 Sept. 1789

Drawn for model construction 1959.
U.S. National Museum
Smithsonian Institution

Plate 28. Lines of the American-built schooner H.M. BERBICE showing an extremely sharp vessel.

Schooner BERBICE, *an American vessel seized in the West Indies by the British in 1780. Employed as an armed tender, she was a very fast sailer, probably built for illegal trading.*

This schooner was 81′ 4″ on deck, 21′ 10″ moulded beam, 8′ 6″ depth in hold, and 158 11/94 tons burthen (English measurement). She drew about 12′ 9″ at post, 8′ 4″ forward, and her assumed load line had a moulded length of 74′ 7″.

The schooner had a strong, flush sheer; the keel was straight with strong

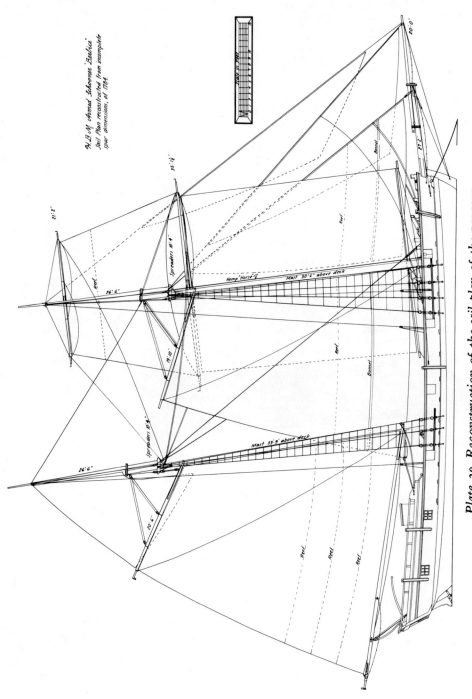

H.B.M. Armed Schooner 'Berbice'
Sail Plan reconstructed from incomplete
spar dimensions, of 1784.

Plate 29. Reconstruction of the sail plan of the BERBICE.

drag; the stem rabbet was on a long sweep; and the vessel had a gammon-knee head. The post raked a good deal; the stern was square tuck with upper-and-lower transoms. The entrance was of moderate length, convex and sharp. The run was long and fine, and the buttocks were slightly hollow near the transom. This schooner had a low raised quarterdeck. She may have had square sails on her main, as well as on the fore, judging by the number of chain plates, Plate 30.

There is no certain method of dating this vessel, since Steel gives no building date for most of the vessels shown in his plates. The reference to the Virginia-built boat "as fitted for a privateer" and her raised quarterdeck suggest a vessel designed before 1793 and possibly a captured American vessel of the Revolution, or she may date from the first years of the French Revolution.

Using the assumed load line, the "Virginia-Built Boat" had a moulded displacement of 155.7 long tons, block coefficient of .41, midsection coefficient of .66, and a prismatic of .61. The quarterbeam buttock had an effective length of 58′ 5″, the camber 5′ 9″, and the camber-to-length ratio was 10.2.

This schooner must have been a good sailer if properly rigged and this was probably the reason for her selection by Steel. As Steel's plan shows the waterline as she came into dock to have her lines taken, and as this is obviously a light line, her true sailing load line can be only guessed. As in *Berbice*, the vessel is not a completely satisfactory example of design practices at the time of her probable period of construction in the 1780's or 1790's.

The other schooner to be examined is shown in Plate 31. This drawing is from offsets and specifications given by Steel for "A Fast Sailing Schooner of 133 6/94 tons." Though well-detailed, the specifications include dimensions that cannot be interpreted and thus seem to have been the result of typographical or transcribing errors. Nevertheless, the offsets established the schooner's lines with satisfactory precision, and at least were sufficient to permit reconstruction of her general appearance. Her name and date and place of launch have not as yet been established. The hull form is certainly American in style and it is at least possible that she was built before 1790. It is probable that the material Steel published on this vessel also came from the Admiralty and had been taken from a vessel passing through naval dockyard hands. At any rate, the offsets produced the lines of an extreme and sharp schooner intended to sail very fast. The open rails and light construction, combined with much deadrise and fine ends, make the objective of her designer-builder obvious.

127

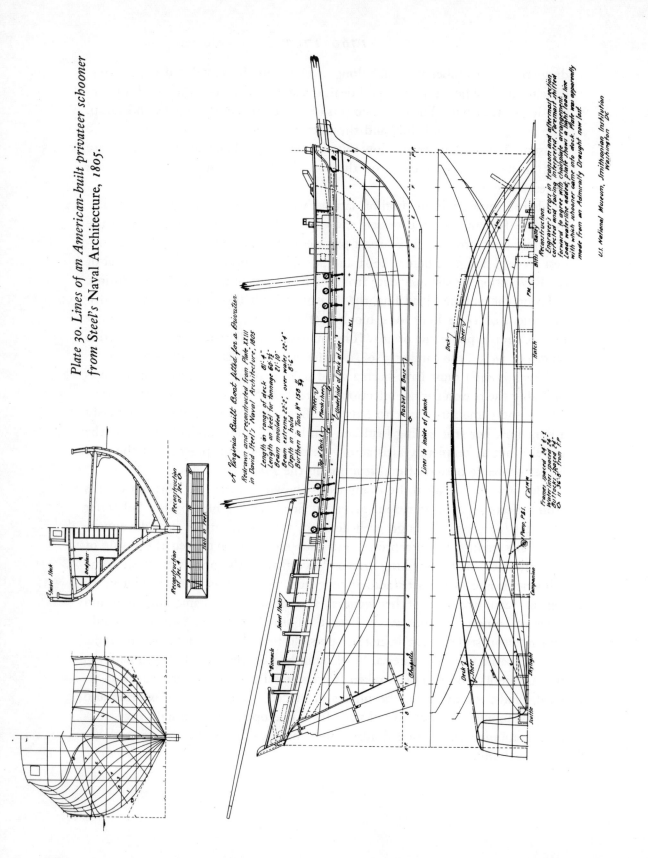

Plate 30. Lines of an American-built privateer schooner
from Steel's Naval Architecture, 1805.

A Virginia Built Boat fitted for a Privateer

Redrawn and reconstructed from Plate XXIII
in David Steel's Naval Architecture, 1805

Length on range of deck   81'.4".
Length on keel for tonnage 60'4½".
Beam moulded   21'.10".
Beam extreme 22'.2", over wales 22'.4".
Depth in hold   8'.2".
Burthen in Tons, N° 158 ¾.

Reconstruction

Reconstruction: errors, in trapezium and aftermost section
corrected and fairing interpreted. Foremast shifted
forward to agree with chainplate arrangement.
Load waterline added, plate shows a light load line
with which schooner came onto deck. Plate was apparently
made from an Admiralty Draught now lost.

U.S. National Museum, Smithsonian Institution
Washington, D.C.

The schooner was 77 feet long on deck with a moulded beam of 20′ 2″. She was 7′ 11½″ depth in hold and drew 9′ 3″ at the post and 6′ 3″ forward. The moulded length of her load line was 72′ 1″. She was a large schooner for her period.

The vessel had a small amount of sheer; the main deck was heavily crowned, with a low break for the raised quarterdeck. The keel was short for the length of the hull and straight with marked drag. The stem rabbet was on a long sweep, and raked forward above the load line. The sternpost raked sharply, with square tuck and upper-and-lower transoms above. The entrance was relatively long, sharp, and somewhat hollow just abaft the stem, up to the load line. The run was long, and very fine, the quarterbeam buttock becoming straight before intersecting the after load line.

While the true midsection was forward of the centerline, marked ⚍ in offsets and plan, it was somewhat farther aft than is commonly shown in draughts of the period. The midsection was formed with sharply rising floor having a slight hollow in the garboards. The bilge was rather slack and no tumble home was formed in the topsides; indeed, the open stanchion rail flared outboard slightly.

This schooner probably crossed topsail yards on both fore and main, as the number of chain plates seems to indicate. It is possible that this vessel was built as a merchant vessel and later converted to a letter-of-marque. At any rate, the title given to the offsets and specifications is sufficient to establish her quality and the reason why Steel selected the vessel for publication.

The schooner had a moulded displacement of 110.5 long tons; her block coefficient was .47, her midsection coefficient .67, and her prismatic .62. The effective length of the quarterbeam buttock was 56′ 4″ and the camber 4′ 11″. The ratio of camber to length was 11.5. This schooner illustrates one of the trends in hull design that came to mark the Chesapeake Bay built, fast sailing schooners of a later time.

The period of 1700 to 1785, and up to the beginning of the French Revolution in 1793, in fact, had produced many types of fast sailing craft, and for some of these, plans survive. The Jamaica-Bermuda-Chesapeake sloop and the early American schooner have been discussed. But other types should at least be noticed and recognized as contributions to the art of design of fast sailing vessels.

The English cutter was a particularly noted type by the time of the American Revolution. By 1778, there were British cutters of over 74 feet length

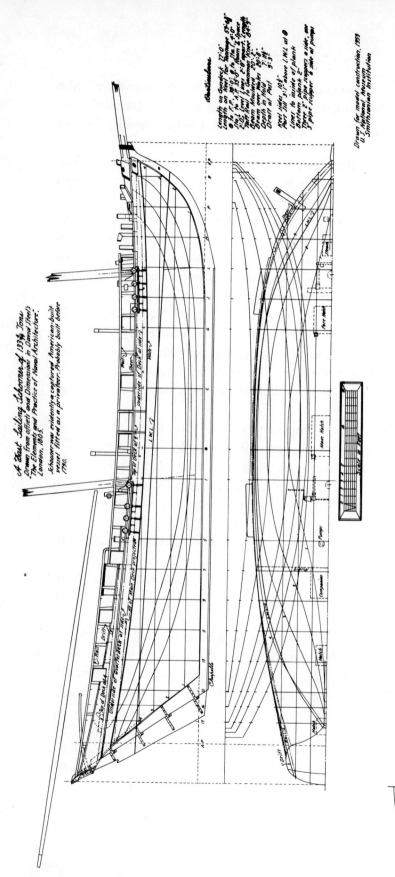

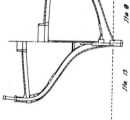
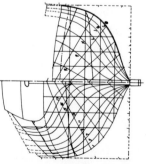

Plate 31. *A fast sailing schooner, armed and of American build; probably launched sometime between 1780 and 1795.*

on deck, sharp in model, and smart sailers. A few of these were employed by Americans in the Revolution. The lugger was also well-known and highly developed by 1785. This type was used extensively by both England and France, and two are known to have been used by Americans in the Revolution. These two types, the cutter and the lugger, probably developed into distinctive hull-and-rig combinations early in the eighteenth century, but their history remains obscure in this period.

The xebec was another notable type of fast sailing vessel. This type was developed late in the seventeenth century by the Algerine corsairs. The xebec was a sailing-rowing vessel apparently related to the earlier caravels and to the galleys. It was first rigged with three large lateens by the Algerines. An excellent drawing of a 127-foot Algerine xebec is shown in Plate LVII by

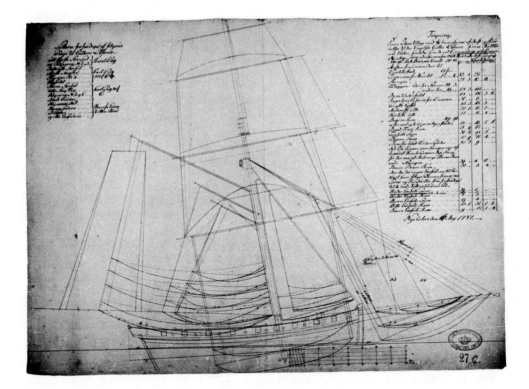

English cutter sail plan, 1787. Royal Archives, Copenhagen.

Chapman (*Architectura Navalis Mercatoria*). When the xebec was adopted by Spain, France, and other Mediterranean powers, the rig became various combinations of lateen and square sails. The xebec seems to have reached its greatest popularity as a fighting vessel by 1760, but was employed in the merchant service until about the middle of the nineteenth century.

The xebec was a relatively shoal hull, usually with rockered keel and very fine lines; the entrance and run were often very hollow. The midsection was like that of a Mediterranean galley, rather flat-floored, with easy, round bilge and flaring topside. When the Spaniards adapted the xebec for naval service, some of them had frigate midsections. Majorca was a building center for

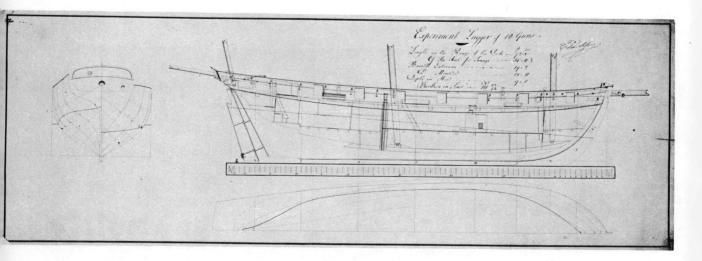

Royal Navy lugger EXPERIMENT, *contract-built about 1793.*

xebecs in Spain. Long, low, and rather narrow, the xebec was usually a very fast sailer reaching and running. In working to windward the lateen-rigged xebecs wore instead of tacked. Xebecs were built by the Americans during the Revolution and one was built at Baltimore as a privateer in the War of 1812. It is doubtful, however, that these were wholly like the Mediterranean xebecs. The xebec was transplanted to the Baltic, in the last half of the eighteenth century, and was used by the Danes and other Scandinavian powers, with various modifications.

Another type in use during the last half of the eighteenth century was the Spanish felucca. This was originally a square-sterned hull having a midsection much like the xebec. It was rigged with a very large lateen sail forward and a small one aft as a jigger, sheeted to a boomkin over the stern, and a running bowsprit with a large jib set flying. The Spaniards developed this type into vessels about 60 to 70 feet overall, having more draft than the original feluccas. The later Spanish feluccas had a midsection somewhat like an American sharp schooner; straight, rising floor; high, firm turn of the bilge; and upright

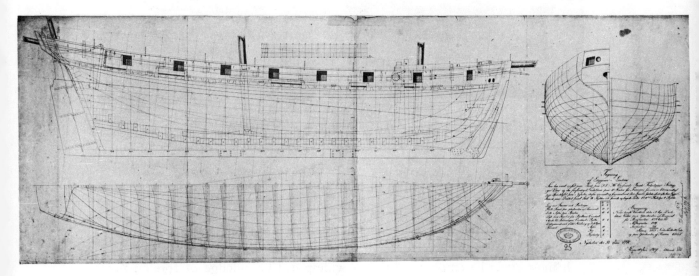

LARK, *an English lugger taken into Danish Navy as* LARKEN *in 1790. Royal Archives, Copenhagen.*

or slightly flaring topsides. The Spanish felucca was for a long period employed in the Spanish revenue service and in illegal trades. At least one felucca sailed from Spain to Mexico, to serve in the revenue service. This type seems to have reached its final development early in the nineteenth century. Other types of feluccas were used in the Mediterranean by the French, Italians, and the Barbary powers; most of them were three-masted and lateen-rigged. These were often closely related to the xebec.

HURRICANE, *Spanish felucca of the seagoing type, 1824. Taken by the steamer* Growler *while in slave trade. Museo Maritimo, Barcelona, Spain.*

The two Mediterranean types had heavily crowned decks, which were also to be seen in many American- and Bermuda-built sloops and schooners of the eighteenth century.

It must again be emphasized that a widespread knowledge of foreign fast sailing craft existed in America, and this occasionally produced experimental or trial duplications of an imported type. Such a vessel was merely an example of the availability of technical knowledge and an expression of the constant search for improvement, even if the result was nothing more than a transposed detail of design or construction.

There are numerous cases in which an American-built ship showed foreign ideas, but these had no noticeable effect on the design of American vessels generally. For example, the ship *Belisarius* was reputedly designed by John Peck of Boston during the Revolution. The body plan of this ship* was preserved in a notebook of Joshua Humphreys, American shipbuilder and naval constructor.

The midsection of this vessel had a very short, straight, rising floor, outboard of which there was a short hard turn of lower bilge (made angular in the drawing), then a long gentle sweep upward and outward to the load line, and an easy sweep to the height of greatest beam, above which there was marked tumble home. This is a form of midsection closely approximating a shape extensively employed by the French in 1725–1815. *Belisarius* was a vessel 93′ 8″ on the keel for tonnage, 30′ 6″ beam, and 15′ 6″ depth in hold

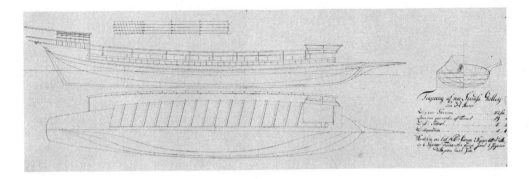

Mid-eighteenth-century Swedish galley of exceptionally fine lines. Royal Archives, Copenhagen.

to gun deck, according to Humphreys. This ship was taken by the British Navy, which registered her as being 104 feet in length on lower deck, 91′ 3½″ on keel, a beam of 27′ 6″, and depth in hold of 10′ 3″. Humphreys called her "one of the fastest sailing ships that swam the seas."[*] The English were not quite so enthusiastic. Vice Admiral Charles Stirling, R. N., described her[†] as having a sharp entrance, a large gripe, a great deal of deadwood, no hollow in the waterlines, and "a circular piece to the rudder, no hance." She sailed well, was stiff in a moderate breeze, "but did not answer all that was expected." Unfortunately, her faults were not listed.

There was an earlier case where the French hull form was employed in

---

[*] Published in Carl C. Cutler's *Greyhounds of the Seas* (New York, G. P. Putnam's Sons and Halcyon House, 1930; reprinted U.S. Naval Institute).
[†] Vice Admiral Charles Stirling, R.N., *Letters on Professional Topics* (London, 1825), p. 75.

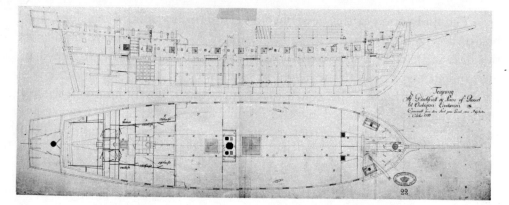

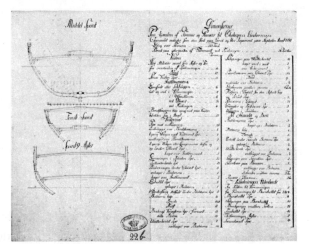

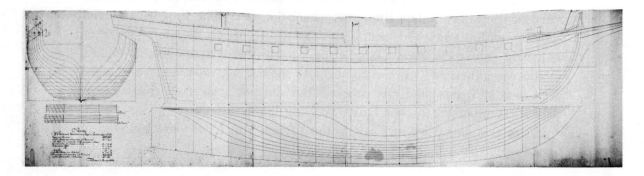

Danish naval xebec LINDORMEN, *built at Toulon in 1771. Royal Archives,* Copenhagen.

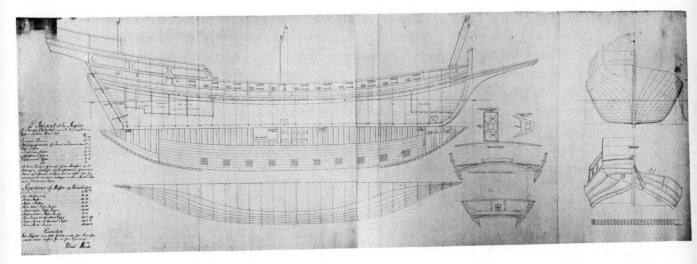

French xebec LE REQUIN, *built at Toulon in 1752. Royal Archives, Copenhagen.*

an American-built ship. This was in a French 38-gun ship of 946 tons taken by the British in 1757, named *À Bien Acquis* (or *Bon Acquis* in English documents), taken into the Royal Navy as H.M.S. *Aurora*. Referred to as a very fast sailer and unusually well-armed, the Admiralty draught is a take-off sketch, shown in Plate 32. It was found in Admiralty papers that she had

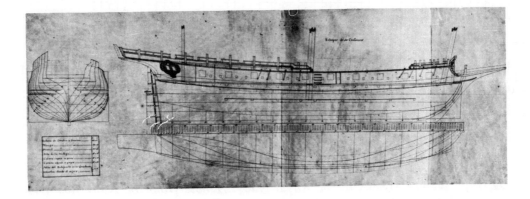

Seagoing Spanish xebec, about 1765–70, 30 guns. Museo Maritimo, Barcelona, Spain.

been built "after the French fashion in North America." The stations in the body plan are marked with their distance from the face of the cutwater and are to outside of plank. She was about 153 feet on the lower deck and about 39 feet extreme beam. The upper and lower bilges may be seen in her body plan, which is less abnormal in the after sections than in *Belisarius*. No American record of the building of this ship has been found. It would seem reasonable that she had been built as a large privateer. She may have been built in French Canada, but no records of French Canadian shipbuilding at this date have yet been found.

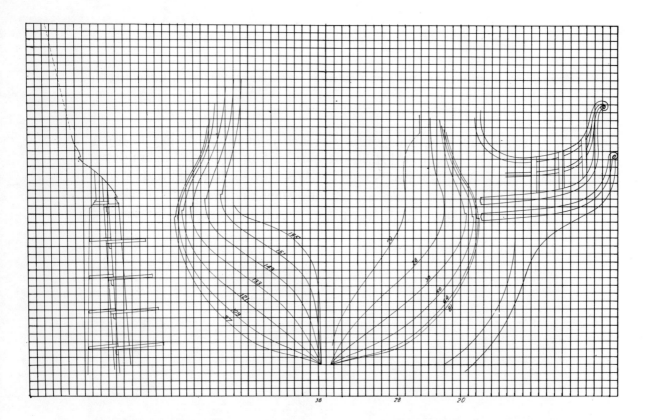

Plate 32. French 38-gun ship à BIEN ACQUIS, *taken by H.M.S.* CHICHESTER *November 24, 1757. Named* AURORA *in the Royal Navy. A note from the Navy Board to Secretary of the Admiralty, June 14, 1758, states "she was American-built," "after the French fashion," and "new." Portsmouth dockyard take-off sketch, lines to outside of the planking plotted on a drawn grid; 1/4-inch squares.*

The use of the French form of midsection, as shown in *À Bien Acquis* and in *Belisarius*, was apparent in the American frigates of *Constitution* and *Constellation* classes, as well as in some later frigates. The lower knuckle or bilge, however, had become less marked by 1794. Such a midsection form does not appear in American merchant vessels during or after the Revolution and it is evident that neither of the two ships, *À Bien Acquis* or the *Belisarius*, had any real influence on American ship design generally. The French form of midsection was also employed in many English frigate designs—with the prominence of the lower knuckles much diminished. Though frigates with single turn-of-bilge were extensively built by all the naval powers, the modified form of French midsection could well be taken as the usual "frigate-form," as late as 1820.

The development of the French midsection form cannot yet be traced. Available plans of French men-of-war, built between 1690 and 1700, do not show this form of midsection. Rather, the midsection was formed with slightly-rising straight floor and a full, rounded bilge fairing into tumble home topsides. This was the form employed at that period in English ships, though sometimes the floor might show hollow at garboard.

The advantages of the two-knuckle French section were large capacity for ballast just above the keel and therefore low enough to be very effective, a wide hull at the load line that gave initial stability, and a full section, which if accompanied by a fine entrance and run, produced a low prismatic co-efficient.

The form certainly developed out of the compass-formed midsections of the sixteenth century. Yet it does not seem possible to trace this section through the whole of the following century, using the evidence available at this time. Perhaps the French section was primarily a naval design and not useful in merchant vessels, for because of its very light condition, the vessel would be tender and unstable. The ability to sail on a light load line would have been a desirable characteristic in a merchant vessel but not important in a man-of-war.

There is a design for a sharp-built frigate having straight floor combined with great deadrise in the midsection, of American origin and of the period of the American Revolution. This plan of a large 38-gun frigate (Plate XIV) is shown in *Naval Architecture or Rudiments and Rules of Shipbuilding*, by Marmaduke Stalkaart (published by the author in London, 1781). The design was made by an American, Benjamin Thompson(Count Rumford)—Tory, soldier, and scientist. The vessel was to be 148′ 2″ between perpendiculars, 39′ 6″ beam over the three-inch planking, and 1000 5/94 tons burthen. The draught shows a frigate whose midsection is formed with a straight floor having marked deadrise, a high, easy turn of the bilge, and slight tumble home in topside. The entrance was convex and moderately full, the run long and fine. The quarterbeam buttock was almost straight where it approached the load line and the buttock-bow lines were fairly easy. The vessel would probably have been a good sailer if properly rigged, but she was never built. The arrival of peace put a stop to the building of Royal Navy ships and the large size of Thompson's 38, combined with increased cost, probably discouraged any interest by the Admiralty, in spite of the fact that the design had the recommendations of prominent naval officers and competent English shipbuilders.

The period between 1700 and 1793 thus produced a number of types of fast sailing craft and many individual vessels of great speed for their length. One vessel worthy of mentioning here was the 32-gun frigate *Hancock** of the American Continental Navy, built at Newbury in 1776. She was 136′ 7″ on the lower deck and about 136 feet on the waterline, 35′ 2″ extreme beam, 110′ ½″ depth in hold, drawing about 17 feet at post. After her capture it was reported that "she went, though foul, thirteen knots and could have carried much more sail than she had out."

Considering the size of each vessel that has been described, it is obvious that there were some that were very fast sailers, built on designs that were of very high quality. This will become more apparent when later vessels and their performances are discussed and comparisons made.

The interim between the end of the American Revolution and the formation of the federal government was a period of decline in building merchant vessels. Few vessels over 85 feet in length on deck were laid down, and some shipbuilding areas suffered severe depression.

A gradual revival in shipbuilding, particularly of fast sailing vessels, began with the outbreak of war at sea in the French Revolution, in 1793. As the tide of war swept over Europe, the seaborne trade of the United States increased rapidly and the construction of new vessels became increasingly

---

* Plan published in Chapelle's *The History of American Sailing Ships* (W. W. Norton & Company, Inc., New York, 1935), Plate 1, opp. page 62; and in Chapelle's *History of the American Sailing Navy* (W. W. Norton & Company, Inc., New York, 1949), Plate 4, opp. page 73.

profitable. In American shipbuilding development, the year 1793 marks the end of the eighteenth-century development and the beginning of the nineteenth-century development. The coming of a great European war affected all of the then-known globe to some degree, and the demand mounted rapidly for fast vessels for use in blockade-running and privateering, as well as for naval cruisers and dispatch carriers. Designers and builders now had economic reasons for production of extremely fast sailers of steadily increasing size and of improved design, construction, and fitting. A new era of great shipbuilding and design activity began; perhaps one of the most productive in American maritime history.

CHAPTER · FOUR

1793 - 1812

THE SHIPBUILDING COMMUNITIES ON THE SHORES OF THE CHESAPEAKE BEGAN
to benefit from the French Revolution soon after the start of hostilities. The
products of the Chesapeake shipyards were now low-cost, fast sailing craft
of moderate size for the period, whose qualities had become familiar to all
of the European naval powers during the American Revolution. Baltimore,
the metropolis of the Chesapeake area, had been settled in 1730. By 1752
there were only two seagoing vessels owned in the village, a brig and a sloop,
but shipbuilding was then being carried on in Baltimore and vicinity. It was
not until the American Revolution that the port became an active and important ship-owning town; the population then had grown to about 6000.
During the war, Baltimore benefited by the removal of many merchants and
shipowners from Philadelphia, brought about by the occupation of that city
by the British Army.

   After the outbreak of the French Revolution, Baltimore's merchant-ship-
owners increased in number and engaged extensively in blockade-running to
the warring nations or in smuggling with their colonies, as well as in the sale
of vessels to the belligerents. In 1790 the population of the port was 13,503;
ten years later it was 26,614.

In spite of its steady growth as a port and commercial center, Baltimore did not build the bulk of the vessels operated by her merchants after the beginning of the French Revolution. In fact after the American Revolution, from about 1785 on, the villages and towns on the shores of the Chesapeake (particularly on the eastern side of the Bay) continued to build most of the vessels registered in the area. Baltimore's shipyards built most of the large vessels, however, including some sharp-built, that were owned locally, as well as some large vessels for owners in other American seaports.

The Chesapeake Bay country was then particularly well-fitted for wooden shipbuilding. Timber was at hand in great quantity and was of good quality, particularly on the Eastern Shore. White oak, southern pine, juniper or "southern cedar," locust, and mulberry were well-suited for shipbuilding and were available along the shores of the numerous, and then deep, creeks and rivers opening into the Bay. Though the villages and towns in this area were not large, many of them could man two or three small shipyards, each capable of building vessels up to about 100 feet long on deck. Most of the vessels built were under 90 feet, however, and until about 1812 schooners under 80 feet were the most common type and size of vessel built in the area. Country shipyards kept local shipwrights so busy that the Baltimore yards sometimes suffered from a shortage of labor. This had happened during the Revolution and affected the city's shipyards on several occasions during the first half of the nineteenth century.

Labor in the country villages was cheap and not wholly dependent on the yards for a living. As in most colonial small towns and villages, the men partly sustained themselves through farming or fishing. Thus the workmen remained close to home when the yards were inactive, so that shipbuilding was not destroyed as a local industry in a time of economic depression. In New England traveling gangs of ship carpenters were common in colonial times, but there is little indication of these in Maryland records, though master shipwrights often set up vessels on the owner's property in a nearby county.

The skill of Chesapeake Bay ship designers can be judged only by what is known of the vessels they built, since few other records of the builders have survived. This is true of the early shipbuilders of nearly all American ports. It is quite evident from the available ship plans (most of which were taken off the finished vessels in England and on the Continent) that there was a rather large number of well-trained and skillful ship designers on the

Bay. It is not possible to document any particular reason for such a concentration of skill, since colonial ship registers of the Bay country before 1789 have been lost. But the records from 1789 on show that the Bay shipbuilders were relatively numerous and productive.

From the surviving evidence of their techniques in the few draughts that exist, it is apparent that the Bay shipbuilders, like most American builders of the time, employed plans (or draughts) in design. It also seems reasonable that some builders without drafting skill may have used the hawk-nest model to some extent, as was the case in New England, even though no models of this construction have yet been found in Maryland and Virginia. The history of the half-model will be discussed later.

The supporting industries of the shipbuilding trade were at hand in the Chesapeake country. Iron fastenings and fittings, flax sailcloth, blocks, caulking material, cordage, and tar could be had from nearby sources. By 1790, production was adequate and these supplies could be obtained quickly and at reasonable shipping expense. The area thus had every advantage for the construction of wooden sailing vessels.

When producing a fast sailer, the Chesapeake Bay ship designer and builder usually turned out an inexpensive vessel of very plain finish and usually lightly constructed, entirely devoid of carvings—a practical vessel of low initial cost. The frame timber employed was usually hard wood so that relatively small scantling was required to give necessary strength. The structural design had been so well established as to be almost standard—widely spaced "mould frames," made up of "futtocks" or sections joined and fastened together to form a timber or rib. These were drawn full size on a platform, or "scrieve-board," or in a mould loft, from measurements taken off of the scale drawing (the draught). At the whim of the builder, these "mould frames" might be regularly spaced and represented every third or fourth frame, or they might be irregularly placed to produce uneven frame spacing. To save weight, some builders spaced frames more widely in the ends of the hull than amidships and used cedar top-timbers. The ends of the deck beams were generally secured to the frames by numerous knees, or they might be joined to clamps—longitudinal stringers fastened to the inside of the frames—with only a few knees that were usually located at the mast partners.

When the mould frames were set up on the keel at the designed spacing, they were secured by battens or "ribbans," and between the mould frames, intermediate frames were fitted. These usually were "chunks" or futtocks, shaped to bear on the ribbans, but not always fastened together to make a rigid frame. The outside planking and the inside skin, or "ceiling" fastenings, would then secure the otherwise loose intermediate frame futtocks.

By 1796, the freeboard of fast sailing vessels built on the Chesapeake had become rather low, to deck level at least, when in sailing trim. The bulwarks were low and "light-built," sometimes a mere plank on edge or "log rail." Raised quarterdecks and quarterdeck rails were slowly going out of fashion, and a level, or "flush," deck and sheer were becoming popular.

The model of the vessels that came into use for war service as letters-of-marques owed much to the small pilot boats developed in such colonial ports as Savannah, Charleston, Norfolk, Philadelphia, and New York. These pilot-boat schooners will be examined in detail in later pages.

The emphasis that has been placed on fast sailing craft built on the Chesapeake can mislead one to the conclusion that only sharp-model vessels were built there, and that the Bay shipbuilders could not or would not produce a full-carrier or a combination carrier-fast-sailer. The fact is that the number of sharp-built vessels constructed on the Bay in any period was always smaller than the number of full-built carriers. The relation between the two depended entirely on the needs of the time and on the needs of the trades or occupations in which they were to be employed.

The Baltimore ship registers begin in 1789, and the registrations in that year amounted to 62, of which three were re-registrations in the district. Sixteen ship-rigged vessels were registered in this year, of which two were described as sharp-built; one was not described; and 13 were registered as full-built. Both sharp-built ships were constructed in Baltimore. One of the sharp-built ships was 106 feet long on deck, the other 94. The full-built ships ranged in size from 77 to 98 feet. Of 21 brigantines, five were sharp-built. One of these was built in North Carolina, one in Connecticut, one in Baltimore, and two elsewhere in Maryland. The brigantines ranged from 59½ to 84 feet in length; the largest of the sharp-built brigantines was 81 feet. Only one brig and one snow were registered. The brig was sharp-built, constructed at Philadelphia. Of 16 schooners registered, the smallest was 49 feet, the longest 80; eight were sharp-built, seven full-built, and one not described. Of the eight sharp-built schooners, one was built in North Carolina, two in Virginia, one in Massachusetts but rebuilt at Baltimore, and four in Maryland. There were six sloops registered, three were sharp-built, all were constructed in Maryland, and they ranged from 50 to 64 feet on deck.

The effects of the French Revolution on Bay shipbuilding can be seen in the number of Baltimore registrations.

1789	62
1790	66
1791	62
1792	88
1793	159
1794	228
1795	266
1796	239
1797	281
1798	240

While these totals include some re-registrations within the district and some vessels built outside the Bay, predominately the registrations were of vessels built in Maryland and Virginia. A large part of the Virginia shipbuilding in these years was on that state's Eastern Shore.

The registrations, up to 1798, the year in which the Quasi-War with France began, show that few schooners longer than 80 feet on deck were built (the largest was 93 feet, built in 1796) and that very few ships above 100 feet were registered; most of these were built outside the district. There was also active construction of sharp-built vessels outside the district; surviving registers of other ports of the same period indicate considerable building at Philadelphia, New York, Norfolk, Beaufort, North Carolina, and Charleston, South Carolina. During the Revolution many sharp-model vessels were built in New England, but though shipbuilding continued to be very active there, very few sharp vessels seem to have been produced in the postwar years.

The Bay's reputation for low-cost fast sailing schooners brought purchasing agents of the French Revolutionary government to the Chesapeake in August 1798.* The effectiveness of the British Navy had forced the French to divert much of their shipbuilding production to build replacements for their regular naval forces. As a result, there was a troublesome lack of small cruisers and privateers, and the French turned to the United States to supply such vessels. French representatives and merchants secretly purchased an undetermined number of fast sailing vessels at New York, Philadelphia, Norfolk, and particularly at Baltimore. Most of them seem to have been schooners and brigs, judging by subsequent British captures. Under French colors these

---

* *Naval Documents, Quasi-War with France, Operations (Feb. 1797–Oct. 1798)*, pp. 274–275.

vessels caused heavy losses to the British merchant fleet. Finally after the Royal Navy had captured a number of these American-built vessels, the British Government protested to the United States. The Federal Government then moved to stop the sale of fast vessels to the French, but public opinion and legalities prevented complete success. A device often resorted to was to send a fast-sailer loaded with cargo to a French port where both were sold, outside of American jurisdiction. A large number of fast American schooners were also sold to other European countries between 1795 and 1815.

The Quasi-War with France in 1798 was brought about by French seizures of American vessels, still another device by which the French acquired a few fast sailers. The British made very few purchases in America, but obtained their American-built cruisers by capturing them from the French. However obtained, American-built ships in British possession were usually taken off for Admiralty record purposes. This produced plans that can be used to judge how well some of the fast American schooners were designed. In fact the larger part of the surviving plan-records of these craft was found in European naval archives.

Of course the sharp-built pilot-boat type of construction was not entirely a product of the Chesapeake area. Southern New England, New York, and Philadelphia also produced very advanced designs of pilot boats as well as the larger, sharp-built vessels, both during the Revolution and afterward. Unfortunately the evidence is too limited to permit much design comparison; very few pertinent plans have survived from any of those building centers.

Until it was occupied by the British during the Revolution, Philadelphia had been an important colonial shipbuilding center, and builders along the Delaware had been notable for turning out well-built craft of superior design. The influence of Philadelphia builders was very great on both the Continental and Federal navies. John Wharton, though little known today, was apparently one of the leading colonial ship designers. He is believed to have been responsible for the designs of several Continental frigates and for the plan of a 74-gun ship. Construction of two or three of the latter was intended, but none were ever built. He also was the consultant to General Henry Knox, Washington's Secretary of War, when the designs of the first 36- and 44-gun frigates of the Federal Navy were being considered. There were other builders in colonial Philadelphia who were of at least local prominence. Though shipbuilding declined in Philadelphia during the Revolution, it recovered rapidly after the war.

Through the part played by some of her shipbuilders and designers, Philadelphia had a strong influence on the United States sailing navy until the Civil War. Chief among these was Samuel Humphreys, son of Joshua Humphreys, (John Wharton's one-time partner and protégé) who became Chief Naval Constructor in 1826. His associates included John Lenthall and Francis Grice, both Philadelphians and competent ship designers. In the years before Samuel Humphreys became Chief Constructor, William Doughty and Joshua Humphreys, both Philadelphians, had been employed in naval work. Josiah Fox, the English-born naval constructor, also lived and worked in Philadelphia for a time.

New York likewise had produced competent builders, and as early as 1693 John Marsh had become prominent locally as a designer of fast sailing vessels. William Walton, Joseph and Daniel Latham, and John Rivers were active New York shipbuilders before the American Revolution. But just prior to the Revolution, New York declined in shipbuilding, apparently because of labor shortages, and this was followed by the long occupation of the port by British troops during the Revolution. As in the case of Philadelphia, the shipyards in New York were inactive during most of the war. After the war New York again became active, and labor could be attracted to the city and vicinity by promise of steady employment and good pay, to supply the local growing demand for merchant vessels.

Among the more prominent New York shipbuilders and designers, between 1794 and 1812, were Thomas Cheeseman, his son Forman Cheeseman, Thomas Vail, Christian Bergh, Samuel Ackerly, Henry Eckford, Adam and Noah Brown, and William Vincent. The New York shipbuilders, like those of Philadelphia, produced well-built and highly finished vessels before and after the Revolution. The New York builders also turned out many fast sailing vessels and had a well-established reputation for building this type of craft.

Southern New England (Connecticut and Rhode Island) was a very active shipbuilding area long before the Revolution, standing second to Massachusetts (which then included New Hampshire and Maine) in tonnage launched between 1760 and 1770. Like the rest of New England, the Connecticut and Rhode Island shipbuilders produced moderately-priced vessels—usually full-carriers. The New England shipowners used these economical carriers as often as the conditions of the period allowed. New England builders could also turn out fast sailers when required, as the records show, particularly during the Revolution. It is therefore surprising that relatively few such vessels were built in New England during the Napoleonic Wars, when there must have been a market.

The industries necessary to shipbuilding were relatively convenient in this area, but by 1798 it had become necessary to ship in lumber, particularly shipbuilding timber, from increasingly greater distances, mostly by water, to southern New England as well as to New York and Philadelphia. The rising costs that resulted made these localities less attractive for the construction of ships and particularly the expendable types, until war requirements permitted large capital investments in such craft. The French Revolution soon produced this condition, and most of these areas again became active in shipbuilding, though not all produced swift sailers. Of these three areas New York seems to have produced most of the sharp-model craft, perhaps owing to the heavy New York interest in the risky West Indian trades and in European blockade-running, particularly after 1795.

Among the ship designers in all of these areas, there were some who had the knowledge required to produce outstanding vessels of great potential speed. On the Chesapeake, orders for fast sailers were numerous because here vessels could be built economically, and because the area was close to the Caribbean where the demand was steadily growing. But of greater importance was the fact that the Chesapeake Bay builders by the end of the Revolution had won an international reputation for producing very fast vessels. Though some very able southern builders were active—at Wilmington, North Carolina; Charleston, South Carolina; Savannah, Georgia; and after the Louisiana Purchase, at New Orleans—their production was relatively small, so that competition with the Chesapeake area was negligible.

The state of development in American naval architecture in this period can best be judged by the designs that have survived. No American ship designers of this period, other than Joshua Humphreys and Josiah Fox, have left much documentary evidence of their design theories and practices. Fox owned a number of books on naval architecture purchased in England.

The immigration of English trained shipwrights into the United States continued, but the number declined sharply after 1771, and was only a mere trickle after 1800. Nevertheless, the influence of the trained English shipwrights who came to America was often marked, as in the case of Fox, who was probably the first in America to loft the whole stern of a vessel in order to produce exactly what the design plan called for. The precision in loft work appears to have been one of the great improvements in this period, with the result that vessels were being built more nearly as designed; this led to increasingly careful projections in the draught, or lines plan. The use of longitudinal sections and buttock lines in the afterbody seems to have begun about 1794 in America and to have originated in England. Fox may also have introduced buttock-bow lines in the draught; at any rate the use of such projections in America can be seen on some plans of the period. The buttock lines were used at this stage primarily to fair the round tuck and establish the transom frames, rather than to shape the run.

The introduction of the half-model, carved from a solid block of wood, probably took place before 1700 in England. The framed half-model—the hawk-nest or "crow's nest" model—appeared sometime in the first half of the eighteenth century in England. This was a model formed with a backboard, either shaped to the hull profile or with the sheer elevation of the hull scribed into it, with solid, plank cross sections secured to it at suitable intervals representing the mould frames. Design by use of this type of model called for about as much skill in judging hull form as was required to draw a lines plan.

About 1794–96 the "lift" half-model appeared. In this the model was formed with "lifts" or planks whose thicknesses represented the spacing of the water or level lines in the sheer profile of a draught. In early models these lifts were temporarily fastened together with wooden toggles and wedges, or with gun-stock iron screws; later dowels or common screws were used. The block thus formed was shaped into the desired model. The lines were taken off by first marking the model with the required frame spacing; then by tracing the profile on a piece of paper or plank, with lift and frame spacings transferred from the model; then by disassembling the block and tracing the outlines of the lifts at the proper level line in the profile. Measurements could then be taken of the half-breadths for each mould frame at the level lines (at each scribed frame on the model) to form the "body plan" or drawing of the cross sections (mould frames).

This form of model, if carefully made and drawn, gave satisfactory results. The hull form could be seen in three dimensions, and therefore required less skill to form than in the case of the draught. As a result, the half-model gradually became popular in small shipyards during the first half of the nineteenth century. The "invention" of the "lift" half-model is claimed by two Massachusetts towns: at Salem, on behalf of Enos Briggs—whose half-model survives in the Peabody Marine Museum, identified as used to build the *Eliza*, a fast sailing ketch, in 1795; and at Newburyport, with claims for Orlando B. Merrill—the model survives in the New York Historical Society, identified (incorrectly) as the model of the U. S. sloop of war *Wasp* of 1815, but claimed to have been made in 1794. These models have few lifts, showing the hull forms to the underside of the main deck only.

The use of half-models of this type began in New England, spreading to New York about 1820 (where Isaac Webb was credited with introducing the lift half-model) and to the Chesapeake Bay somewhat later. Some builders first prepared a draught, then built a half-model to "prove" the lines. But generally the builders made the model, and then made a draught from the model. The more primitive yards often took the offsets from mould stations marked on the lifts directly to the mould-loft, omitting the draught altogether. This subject will receive further discussion in a later chapter.

Primitive model testing in tanks was proposed in 1721 by Swedenborg and put into practice by Bird in 1756, Benjamin Franklin in 1764, and by d'Alembert, Condorcet, and Bossut in 1775. Chapman also tank-tested models in the last quarter of the eighteenth century in Sweden. Only Chapman appears to have used models as an aid to design; the others merely theorized.*

Between 1790 and 1810 there were many experiments in Europe in the field of resistance. In 1790 a "Society for the Improvement of Naval Architecture" was formed in Great Britain, and from 1793 to 1798 tank tests were made by Beaufoy on which he published a report in 1799. Charles Gore continued these experiments and reported upon the effect of length in proportion to beam on resistance. Gore designed a very long, narrow, three-masted lugger to illustrate the effect of his findings on design. At intervals the Society had published proposals for improvements in design (among which were sharper entrances by filling on each side of the projecting cutwater), but on the whole the society had limited influence, as its members were non-professionals. Nevertheless some of the more literate shipbuilders and designers were interested in these publications. The influence of Gore's theories seems to appear in designs by the Royal Navy Surveyor Henry Peake, who turned out a number of cutters, schooners, and brigs of rather small beam for their length.

The last decade of the eighteenth century saw many experimental designs

* In 1758 the English Society of Arts offered prizes for "ships' blocks," or models, for testing resistance and seakindliness. In 1761 models of four 32-gun frigates and two 74's were tank-tested in Peerless Pool, London—suitable models having been obtained by this offer. However, it is now known that model-tests were made in England as early as 1670.

for vessels in the British Navy; in 1793 a contract-built, three-masted lugger, 72′ 8″ on deck and 18′ 11″ moulded beam, named *Experiment*, was launched at Cawsand. This vessel had extreme rise of floor, very high and slack bilges, a short convex entrance, and a long and rather fine run.

In 1796, Samuel Bentham designed and had built for the Admiralty two ships with drop keels, four schooners, and a waterboat. These also were of experimental design and construction. Two of the schooners—the sisters *Redbridge* and *Eling*, 80 feet length, 21 feet moulded beam, and 11′ 6″ in depth—had very rising, straight floors, flaring topsides above an extremely slack turn of the bilge, iron windlass and winches, geared steering, outside iron ballast in short sections, and eight diagonally planked bulkheads.

These examples are sufficient to show that departures in design from traditional forms were being built at the end of the eighteenth century and that new ideas in hull form, fittings, and construction were being introduced. It is likely that information on these experimental vessels reached America, for many of the experimental Royal Navy vessels cruised in areas frequented by American merchantmen and naval forces—the coasts of Spain and Gibraltar, and in the Western Mediterranean. Nor, as will be seen, were the Americans themselves backward in producing radical ideas in design.

The interest in experimental vessels was commonly greater in the merchant marine than in the navies, but only a small proportion of the private experiments of this period has survived in plans. Their survival usually depended upon naval interest to create a record in official archives.

So standard had become the general model of a fast sailing schooner by 1800, that it was somewhat difficult to judge by plans alone where a sharp-built vessel had been constructed. The New England built fast sailing craft usually had little rake in the stem above water, as may be seen in the Marblehead schooners, the *Rhodes*, and other examples. This characteristic did not usually appear in the fast sailing craft built in the other areas; most retained the heavy rake in the ends that marked the Chesapeake-built craft. There were departures from local characteristics in all areas, however, as would be expected, considering the opportunities of builders and owners to see and use the features of vessels built outside their home localities.

Chesapeake-built vessels visited New England and other building centers and were sometimes owned by local merchants, just as the New England built vessels were well-known on the Chesapeake, many being owned there. There was no isolation so far as the shipbuilding art in America was concerned; a builder could readily turn out a vessel designed on a foreign model or one from another building area, if the owner's whim required.

Hence, the distinctions that might have identified a vessel's place of build were often very obscure. In fact, this had also become common in the fast schooners built in Europe on American models. So expert were some of the European designers that they could produce what was, in all physical characteristics, an American schooner.

The development of the very sharp-built fast sailer, after the American Revolution, seems to have been paced to some extent by the evolution of the small pilot boats, as mentioned earlier. The surviving plans of early pilot boats are all of craft built in the last quarter of the eighteenth century. These, with some from the first decade of the nineteenth century, show that there were

American schooner off the coast of Virginia; water color, 1794. National Maritime Museum.

variations in the model, but all were of "small boat" design. The pilot-boat services in this period did not require cruising long distances from the home port, so until about 1800 the vessels were commonly under 60 feet on deck. Very little is known about earlier colonial pilot boats; the *Virginia Gazette* of 22 July 1737 advertised for a pilot boat, stolen or gone adrift, measuring 24 feet keel, nine feet beam, two masts and sails, hull painted red—apparently a shallop of about 32 to 35 feet on deck, without bowsprit and jib.

Three plans of American pilot-boat schooners built before 1800 are now known. One of these was built at New York. This vessel, named *Coureuse* (Plate 33), was captured by H. M. frigate *Pomone*, about two leagues west of Isle Groix, on the coast of France, on 27 February 1795. She was then a "Conventional" schooner (French Republican Navy) eight days out of Brest, bound for L'Orient, convoying five merchant vessels. H.M. frigates *Artois* and *Galatea* and the lugger *Duke of York* took part in the capture of the schooner and her convoy, which included one brig and two luggers. The two remaining brigs were scuttled, being of little value. The prize court records show that *Coureuse* had been built at New York "about ten years ago" (or about 1785) and had "not had any other name." This might lead to the assumption that she had been built for the French navy before the French Revolution, for the name *Coureuse*, meaning runner or a person of light morals, is an unlikely name for an American-owned vessel of that period. At any rate she carried eight two-pounder guns, in addition to small arms. She had a French crew of 23, including officers. She was refitted at Plymouth dockyard under the direction of Sir Sidney Smith and manned with 36, apparently as a dispatch vessel on the Mediterranean Station. She paid off sometime in September 1796 and was probably sold. No other information regarding her career has yet been found.

The *Coureuse* was taken off at Plymouth dockyard in June 1795; she was 55' 10" from face of stemhead to after top edge of transom or taffrail, 15' 9" moulded beam, 16 feet extreme beam, and 6' 5" depth in the hold. Her Admiralty tonnage was 55 35/94 tons for register. Her midship section was 20 feet from the fore perpendicular. The straight keel rabbet was only about 38 feet long—from heel of post to beginning of fore-rake sweep.

The vessel was flush-decked, with a small trunk cabin abaft the mainmast. She had a rather straight, flush sheer, short straight keel with much drag, strongly raking post with raking transom above (square tuck), with an outside sternpost and rudderpost. The fore-rake was on a long compound sweep,

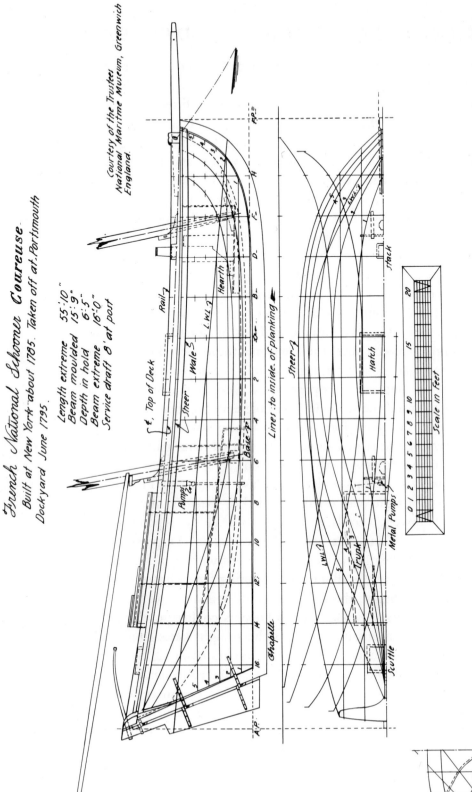

French National Schooner Coureuse.
Built at New York about 1785. Taken off at Portsmouth Dockyard June 1795.

Length extreme   55':10"
Beam moulded   15':9"
Depth in hold   6':5"
Beam extreme   16':0"
Service draft 8' at port

Courtesy of the Trustees National Maritime Museum, Greenwich England.

Lines: to inside of planking

Chapelle

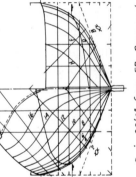

⊕ is 20':0" from F.P. Room and space 22¼" W.L.s spaced 12" Buttocks spaced 24".

Scale in feet

Plate 33. Reconstruction of the French national schooner COUREUSE as a New York pilot boat of 1783–85. (Rails and swivel stocks removed, channels and chain plates omitted.)

becoming nearly upright at stemhead. A low log rail served in place of bulwarks. A rather high, open stanchion rail running her full length had been added, possibly by the French, and six swivel stocks were fitted on each side. The plan shown here omits these, to show her as a pilot boat.

The entrance was convex, somewhat full, and rather short owing to the position of the midsection. The run was long, very fine, and nearly straight at the quarterbeam buttock and waterline intersection. The midsection showed a straight, rising floor, and a very slack bilge, its sweep being carried right up to deck, giving unusually flared topsides. The log rails stood vertical, as did the stanchion rail, which was secured inside them for naval service.

Her bowsprit had little stive; the heel was secured with an iron staple or strap to the foremost deck beam and a heel bolt in the next beam abaft. The usual rig of the American pilot schooner of before 1850 was a single headsail or jib, a lug foresail (overlapping the main), and a loose-footed boom mainsail. Fore and main had rather low peaked gaffs of moderate length. A pole or fidded main-topmast placed abaft the lower masthead served only to set a main-topmast staysail that had a short, vertical luff. When these small schooners were employed on long ocean voyages they were rigged with a square fore course set flying; and if the schooner were big enough, there was a fidded fore-topmast on which a square fore-topsail was also set. It is possible that some pilot schooners of the largest dimensions carried main gaff topsails, as this sail may have come into use shortly after 1700.

The pilot schooner's sail area was large because of the rig. The addition of light sails in the pilot boats was usually limited to the main-topmast staysail. Hence the three lowers were large enough to drive the schooner fast in light and moderate winds, and as a result she would be overpowered in a strong breeze. Therefore the rig was balanced to work with two combinations of sail. In very strong winds, or in jilling about waiting for a chance to deliver a pilot, or when not in a hurry, the schooner could sail well and tack under her foresail alone. In moderate winds these schooners could also work under foresails and mainsails, or mainsail and jib, as the straight keels employed in these boats made them somewhat insensitive to variations in rig balance. In the short-keeled modern yachts this advantage is sacrifiiced to obtain speed in the time required to come about, or to tack. There was one more feature of the rig of the *Norfolk* and some other pilot schooners—they usually had masts unsupported by stays and shrouds. These schooners always carried a single working headsail, usually with one or two reef bands, or sometimes there was a bonnet on the jib. The foresail had a bonnet and two bands of reef points; the mainsail had three reef bands. The foot of the mainsail could be triced up by hoisting the tack with a single part line. In some of the Norfolk boats the mainmast was made with a long pole in lieu of a fidded topmast; these boats were cheaply and very simply rigged.

Some details of the pilot-boat rig of around 1800 can be obtained from the 1795 pictures of the Virginia boats by Captain George R. Tobin, R.N. The fore gaff was hoisted close to the masthead, with the peak-halyard block secured to one side of the small false trestletree placed close to the head. The throat-halyard masthead block was apparently on the other side of the false trestletree. The main-topmast was abaft the mainmasthead, the main-gaff peak-halyard masthead block was on one side of the masthead cap, the throat-halyard block on the other side. A single main topping lift was used, with a guntackle purchase at the mainboom end. Vangs were used on both gaffs. The main sheet was double, port and starboard. No lazy jacks were employed. The jib was not very large, its halyard block was a guntackle purchase, and the masthead block was supported by a block between the fore end of the false trestletrees. The main gaff jaws were hoisted very close to the main trestletrees. Usually the topmast was used only as a flagpole, the topmast stay-sail being used only in summer. Much of the time these boats were sailed without having the jib set.

In practical requirements, the pilot boat was much like a yacht, in that she sailed with selected trim and displacement nearly constant at all times. She could easily be tuned up to racing pitch without the need of repeated attention. She could be designed for speed by employing the minimum displacement to carry her hull structure, rig, stores, and pilots, with an allowance for the minimum ballast that would enable her to carry her rig under the usual requirements of pilotage of the day.

Coureuse was a rather large schooner for her period, for pilot-boat dimensions show that few exceeded a deck length of 50 feet before 1800. In some ports the minimum size for pilot boats was established by regulation. At Norfolk, Virginia, a law of 5 May 1783 stated that a pilot must have a boat "of 18 feet keel at least" under a penalty of £50 for every vessel he undertook to pilot.

After about 1800 some pilot boats 60 feet or more on deck were in use at New York and Philadelphia. With this increase in size it was not unusual for these vessels to be rigged with one or two shrouds on each side of the foremast, and one on the main. A forestay, mainstays, and bobstays were often fitted in these larger boats.

The plan of *Coureuse** is the earliest of an American pilot boat yet found. The chainplates and channels shown in the original Admiralty draught of *Coureuse* appear to have been added when she was in French hands, for her small size and very moderate initial stability would not require a total of five shrouds per side. They were therefore omitted in the plan shown here. This schooner shows the "small boat" appearance that marked these pilot boats.

The working displacement and coefficients of the *Coureuse* are in doubt, for she came into the dry dock stripped and drawing only 7′ 2″ at post and 3′ 6″ at fore gripe (Station D), producing too light a displacement for stability and for the intended services. The calculations are therefore taken on a load draft of eight feet at post and 4′ 8″ at fore gripe. Another matter is that the design midsection ⲭ is not the section of maximum area. This section is number 4 and hence the calculations are based on it as the true midsection. The assumed draft approximates her service draft as a pilot boat and would permit use of enough ballast to give adequate power to carry sail. At this draft, then, the moulded displacement is 32.2 long tons. The block coefficient is .38, the midship coefficient is .69, and the prismatic coefficient is .56. The quarterbeam buttock shows an effective length of 35′ 6″ with 2′ 8″ of camber, giving a ratio of camber-to-length of 13.3. The load waterline, moulded, was 50′ 8″ in length.

Little is known about the sailing qualities of *Coureuse* except that it took about 19 hours for the frigate *Pomone* to capture her, from the time she was sighted. Considering the size of the schooner compared to a frigate, it can be said at least that *Coureuse* was a fast sailer. And that both *Pomone* and *Artois* were reputed excellent sailers. Plate 33 shows the lines of *Coureuse*, and Plate 34 a sketch of her supposed pilot-boat rig, reconstructed on the spar dimensions of a boat of 12 years later date and of about the same beam and depth.

The second pilot-boat schooner to be examined is a boat built at Norfolk, Virginia. Her known history is short. On 8 May 1794, Captain George Oakes, R.N. (on half pay), wrote the Admiralty from Philadelphia that he had sailed from India, carrying dispatches, for England. The vessel on which he was a passenger had been captured by a French squadron and the pas-

* Admiralty Collection of Draughts Reg. No. 4526, Box 64.

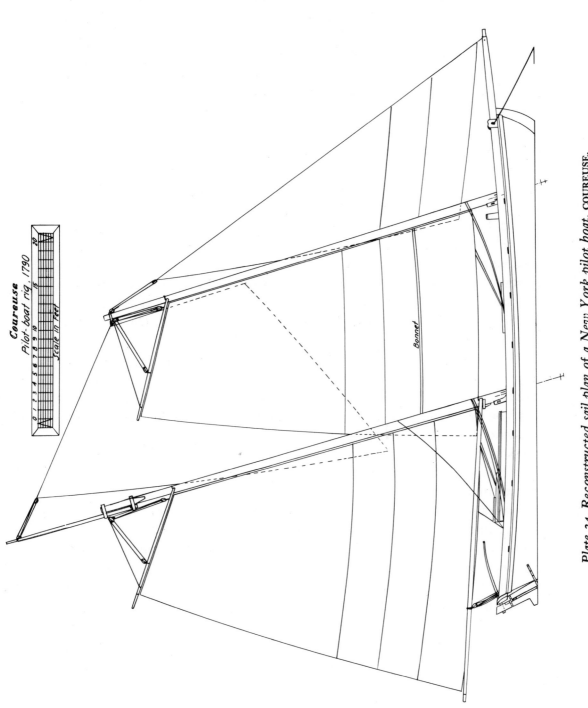

Coureuse
Pilot-boat rig, 1790

Scale in feet
0 1 2 3 4 5 6 7 8 9 10 15 20

Bonnet

Plate 34. Reconstructed sail plan of a New York pilot boat, COUREUSE.

sengers and crew had been landed at Norfolk, Virginia, where they were cared for by "Mr. Bond, British Consul to the Middle and Southern States of America." It is stated that Mr. Bond had purchased a pilot boat (he referred to her as *Swift* or *Swift Packet*) for 428 Spanish dollars, to carry dispatches to England. Oakes wrote that she had not been required for the original purpose, so the schooner was turned over to him. In her he carried the passengers and crew that had been in Bond's care to Cork, Ireland, arriving there 30 June 1794. Oakes had been forced into Cork by contrary winds. He left *Swift* there in the hands of the Admiral of the Cork station and proceeded to London to deliver both his Indian dispatches and those he was carrying from the British Minister or Consul General at Philadelphia.

The Admiral of the Cork station informed the Admiralty that *Swift* would be useful for the "impress service" there. Later he reported that she needed new sails and rigging and some repairs to her planking, and that she was not required for the impress service but would be useful for survey work. She next turns up, however, at Portsmouth dockyard where she was used by the commanding officer. A draught was made of her prior to 12 March 1803— the schooner had not then been registered in the Royal Navy. On 23 March she was ordered to be coppered and fitted for sea service.

The draught, redrawn, is shown in Plate 35, with her rig reconstructed. *Swift* was 49 feet on the range of deck, 15′ 7″ extreme beam, 15′ 4″ moulded beam, and 46 11/94 tons register. She drew 6′ 3″ aft and 4′ 3″ forward. Her length on the moulded load waterline was 44′ 5″. Again, the midsection is not the section of maximum area. In this case it is Station 2, used here for calculations as the midsection.

Her moulded displacement was 33.8 long tons; her block coefficient was .41, her midship coefficient .79, and her prismatic coefficient was .61. Her quarterbeam buttock-bow line had an effective length of 37′ 9″ with camber of three feet, giving her a ratio of camber to length of 12.7.

The schooner had a lively sheer, with the main deck heavily crowned. The deck did not follow the sheer and the bulwarks were very low. The keel was short and straight, with much drag. The sternpost was sharply raked, with the rudder and post outside the upper transom stern. She had a square-tuck stern, with upper, middle, and lower transoms. The stem rabbet was on a rather long sweep, giving the stem profile a somewhat modern appearance. The entrance was short, with some hollow in the loadline just abaft the stem. The run was quite short, with a rather steep, but straight,

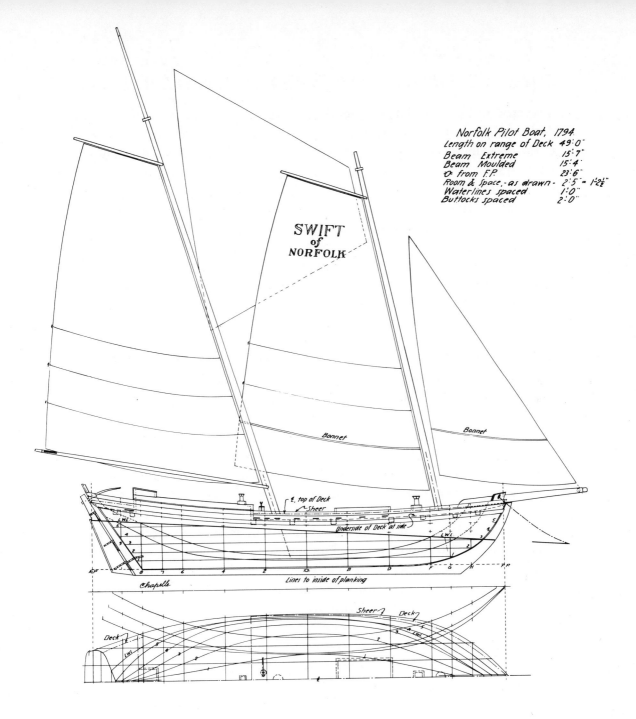

Norfolk Pilot Boat, 1794.
Length on range of Deck 49'·0"
Beam Extreme 15'·7"
Beam Moulded 15'·4"
D from F.P. 23'·6"
Room & Space, - as drawn - 2'·5" = 1'·2½"
Waterlines spaced 1'·0"
Buttocks spaced 2'·0"

SWIFT
of
NORFOLK

Bonnet

Bonnet

ℓ. top of Deck
Sheer

Underside of Deck at side

Chapelle

Lines to inside of planking

Sheer

Deck

Deck

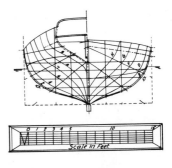

Scale in Feet

Plate 35. Small pilot-boat schooner SWIFT *built at Norfolk, Virginia, before 1794. This small schooner crossed the Atlantic from Norfolk to Cork.*

quarterbeam buttock. The buttock-bow lines were very easy forward. The deck arrangement showed that the heel of the bowsprit was through-bolted to the deck and deck beam, and that there was a rectangular hatch amidships, with a break in the deck abaft the mainmast to give a raised quarterdeck at the level of the topgallant log rail. At about 5′ 6″ forward of the transom the quarterdeck ended, and a "sunk poop" or cockpit deck was formed about 18 inches below quarterdeck level. A galley hearth was placed on the lower deck, or platform, with the chimney abaft the foremast. Most of these boats, however, appear to have had their hearths in the main hatch.

The midsection was formed with marked hollow at the garboards, no straight in the floor outboard, and a very slack bilge carried up to the deck so the topsides had marked flare outward; the transoms were small and together produced a slightly heart-shaped outline when viewed from astern. The fore sections showed a V-form, with some curvature. *Swift*, though without ornamentation, was a handsome little schooner. Her plan was somewhat carelessly drawn as to details, however; the wale was drawn lower aft than was practical with regard to the transom shape shown, and there were other minor errors. The interest of the Admiralty draftsman was apparently slight when a very small vessel was being drawn, judging by this draught.

The cabin for the pilots was under the raised quarterdeck, entered through a lift-hatch companionway. A small hatch or scuttle at the fore end of the cabin served for the chimney of a small hearth. Since the Norfolk pilot boats did not cruise far, the main hatch often served as a below-deck working space with a hearth standing in it. The apprentice and boat crew had bunks on the fore platform, access to which was through the main hatch. If it were necessary to keep to sea for many days, these small craft often became very uncomfortable because of their primitive accommodations.

When *Swift* was fitted by Captain Oakes to cross the Atlantic, she was given a fore course set flying on a rather short yard; the foot of the sail was wider than the head. The pilot-boat rig described earlier characterizes the rigging of *Swift*.

The Norfolk boats had a reputation for sailing very fast and for weatherliness. The flush deck became popular there after 1800, but the pilot-boat deck arrangement of *Swift* remained in use in most of the boats belonging to large ports.

Swift had the distinction of being used as a model for the design of a proposed class of Royal Navy dispatch boats. An Admiralty Order to the Navy

Board, dated 23 June 1803, directed the preparation of a draught based on *Swift* in conjunction with a contract for the building of 12 "advice boats" at Bermuda. The draught was forwarded to the Admiralty on 4 July. On the 14th, a copy was sent to Mr. Shedden (apparently the Bermuda Navy Agent), who sent a duplicate to Bermuda on the 3rd of November.

This design, though for larger boats than *Swift*, followed the hull form of that schooner very closely, and was to produce schooners 55′ 2″ on deck, 18 feet extreme beam, 17′ 9″ moulded beam, and 70 41/94 tons R.N. register. Plate 36 shows a tracing of this design. The effect of the changes in hull proportions from those of *Swift* are evident in the quarterbeam buttock shape and in a sharper entrance.

The Bermudians were not only turbulent politically but were considered independent to the point of contrariness in their dealings with the home government. In this case they did not belie their reputation. Upon receipt of the *Swift* draught, the contractors took exception to the design, with the result that in early 1804 the Admiralty informed the Navy Board that the revised *Swift* draught was not to be used; the builders were instead to construct the advice boats "from the most approved vessels for sailing usually built on Bermudian Islands." The Bermudians then sent a draught for a deeper schooner of 55′ 4″ length, and the Navy Board had an official draught made from this. But in 1804, when the first of the advice boats arrived in England, it was found that their hull form differed from the Bermudian draught, so the lines of this schooner were taken off—and used to build 12 more of these little craft in England! The same thing happened again in 1804. The Admiralty ordered 12 sloops or cutters to be built in Bermuda "similar to the *Lady Hamond*," a very handsome and fast Bermuda sloop. Again the builders balked, with the result that the vessels were constructed on a design that can be described only as an English cutter with a curved pilot-schooner stem! Judging by the existing draughts, the Bermudians did not select the better design either time.

The third example of a pilot schooner is in Steel's *Naval Architecture*, Plate XXV. Again there are a number of engraver's mistakes in the plate; the most important were that the knightheads are in an impossible position structurally and that the body plan does not fair unless alterations are made in two sections. Plate 37 is a redrawing that is an attempt to correct the errors of the original.

This schooner was of the same type as *Swift*, but probably of somewhat

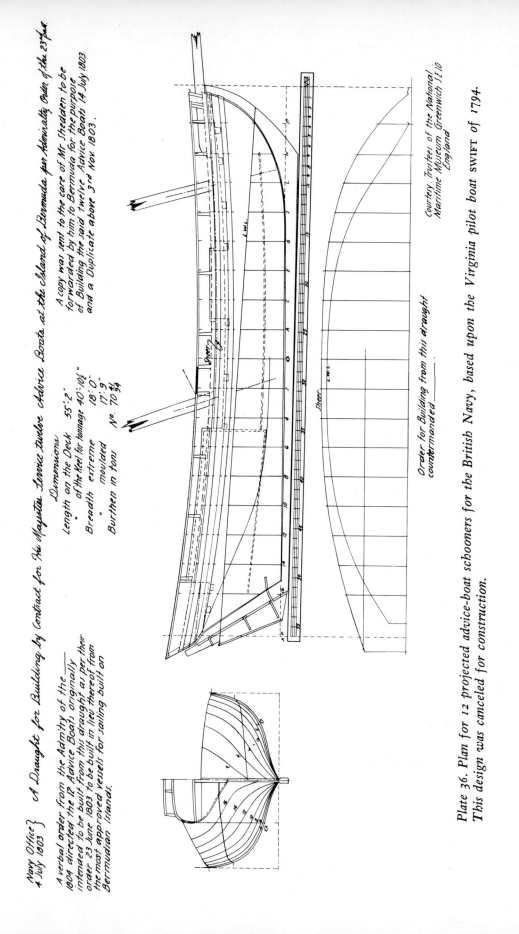

Navy Office } A Draught for Building by Contract for His Majesties Service twelve Advice Boats at the Island of Bermuda per Admiralty Order of the 23rd inst.
4 July 1803 }

A verbal order from the Admiralty of the
1804 directed the 12 Advice Boats originally
intended to be built from this draught as per their
order 23 June 1803 to be built in lieu thereof from
the most approved vessels for sailing built on
Bermudian Islands.

Dimensions
Length on the Deck   55'.2"
 " of the Keel for tonnage 40'.10½"
Breadth extreme   18'.0"
 " moulded   17'.9"
Burthen in tons   No. 70 41/94

A copy was sent to the care of Mr Shedden to be
forwarded by him to Bermuda for the purpose
of Building the said twelve Advice Boats 14 July 1803.
and a Duplicate above 3rd Nov. 1803.

Order for Building from this draught
countermanded

Plate 36. Plan for 12 projected advice-boat schooners for the British Navy, based upon the Virginia pilot boat SWIFT of 1794.
This design was canceled for construction.

later date, with the main deck carried flush from stem to "sunk" poop. She is shown in Steel's plate with block channels and with three shrouds per side for each mast. Like *A Virginia Boat Fitted as a Privateer*, the *Virginia Pilot Boat* was probably a vessel that had passed through Admiralty hands, where the lines were taken off, without her name being recorded by Steel. The *Virginia Pilot Boat* was larger than the *Swift*, being 55 feet (erroneously given as 56 feet in the engraving) in length on the range of deck, 15 feet moulded beam, 15′ 3″ extreme beam, and 52 83/94 tons register. She drew 7 feet aft and 4′ 5″ forward, and was 49′ 10″ moulded length on the load line.

In model she had a marked and handsome sheer, a heavy crown in the main deck, log bulwarks, straight keel with much drag, raking post, square tuck with upper, middle, and lower transoms, the middle transom curved in profile and overhanging a good deal so that the rudderpost head was inboard of the upper transom at deck. The stem rabbet was on a long sweep that did not become upright at the head. The entrance was short and convex, but with a slight hollow abaft the stem in the load line. The run was very long with slightly hollow buttocks, producing an abnormally fine run in so small a vessel.

The midsection was much like *Swift's*, with marked hollow in the garboards, no straight rise of floor, and slack bilge on a long compound sweep, producing flaring topsides. It appears that hollow garboards had a period of popularity in the Norfolk pilot boats during the last quarter of the eighteenth century, but shortly after 1800 the straight rise of floor in the midsection predominated. This boat was well-formed and was probably a very good sailer. It is likely that shrouds had been added after she left the hands of her American owner, hence she is shown here (Plate 37) without them.

While the lines of this schooner had to be refaired to some extent, the particulars to be used here are reasonably accurate. She had a moulded displacement of 31.0 long tons; her midship coefficient was .65, block coefficient .38, and prismatic coefficient .62. The effective length of her quarterbeam buttock was 35′ 4¾″ with 2′ 8½″ camber; the camber-length ratio was 12.7. No spar dimensions for this schooner have been found, nor is there record of her date or place of build, nor of her original name.

A larger pilot-boat model schooner is shown in Plates 38 and 39. This vessel was a three-masted schooner whose Admiralty drawings were unusually well detailed. This schooner was H.M. *Flying Fish*, of 10 guns, and her lines were taken off at Portsmouth dockyard in the fall of 1806. Her

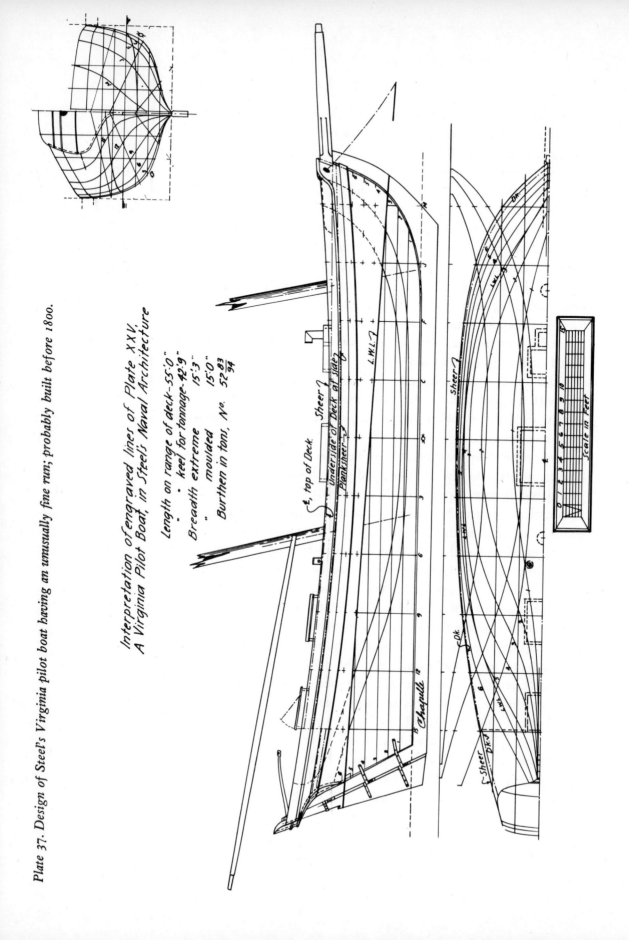

Plate 37. Design of Steel's Virginia pilot boat having an unusually fine run; probably built before 1800.

Interpretation of engraved lines of Plate XXV.
A Virginia Pilot Boat, in Steel's Naval Architecture

Length on range of deck—55'-0"
   "   "   keel for tonnage 42'9"
   Breadth extreme   15'3"
      "   moulded   15'0"
      "   Burthen in tons, N°. 52 83⁄94

ℓ, top of Deck.

Sheer

Underside of Deck at side
Plank sheer

L.W.L.

Sheer

ᴮChapelle 12

Scale in Feet

0 1 2 3 4 5 6 7 8 9 10

Dk.

L.W.L.

Sheer
Dk.

history was difficult to trace, owing to the large number of schooners bearing this name in the Royal Navy between 1803 and 1809. One schooner, about a year old, was captured in July 1803 off San Domingo by H.M.S. *Vanguard*, along with the very fine American-built schooner *La Supérieure* (of which more later), and both were taken into the Royal Navy.

The first schooner became *Flying Fish*. She was a national schooner of 130 72/94 tons, American-built, and armed with 12 guns. Another schooner, however, the American-built *Revenge*, was purchased and taken into the Royal Navy in the spring of 1806. This schooner was "uncommonly well built," a "remarkably fast sailer," and "about 6 months old." She could carry ten 9-pounder guns or 12-pounder carronades. In 1808 she was repaired at Portsmouth dockyard and surveyed. It was then reported she was 78' 8" on the range of deck, 60' 8⅛" on the keel for tonnage, 21' 7" extreme beam, 7' 10" depth in hold, and 150 32/94 tons burthen. She was planked with 1½-inch plank on her bottom. Her Admiralty draught, which as previously stated was made in 1806, shows identical dimensions, thus identifying her beyond question. On 9 March 1808, after the new survey had been received, the Admiralty ordered the Navy Board to purchase her on the basis of this survey, but the Navy Board replied that she had already been purchased by Admiralty order dated 12 November 1806!

The draught of *Flying Fish* made in September 1806 was used to build six schooners at Bermuda during 1807–08, in compliance with an Admiralty order of March 1807. These schooners were *Shamrock, Thistle, Mistletoe, Holly, Juniper*, and *Bramble*. For their construction it was necessary to take off very complete plans of *Flying Fish*. These plans were altered only by adding an overhanging transom to bring the rudderpost head inside the taffrail, and by increasing the stive of the bowsprit somewhat. There is a note on the draught that the "topsides, from the deck up, were added to her original build," but the date of this alteration cannot be determined. The Admiralty draught states that *Flying Fish* was built at Baltimore.* In her original form she undoubtedly had the low bulwarks of a pilot boat; these

---

* Baltimore ship registers show that *Revenge* was launched there early in 1805 and was built by William Flannigan, or Flannigain, for J. B. Salenave. She had three masts, 59' 6" on the keel, 21' 3" breadth, 8 feet depth, and 106 45/95 carpenter's measurement. She was reported "left at St. Thomas, Nov. 6, 1805."

Flannigan also built the three-masted schooner *Orestes* the same year. She measured 82' 2" on deck, 23' 3" beam, 7' 11" depth, and weighed 138–3/95 tons. She was sold to New York in 1806.

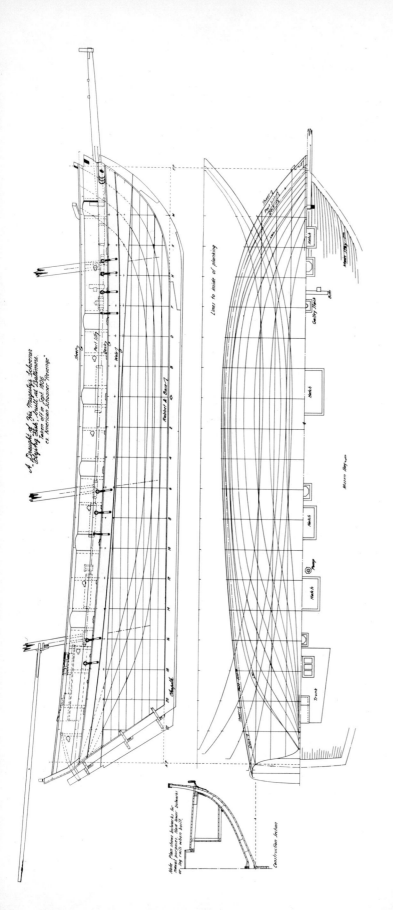

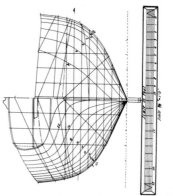

Plate 38. Baltimore-built three-masted schooner REVENGE, renamed FLYING FISH when taken into the Royal Navy. A "pilot-boat model," she originally had log rails of undetermined height, pilot-boat fashion.

Tern schooner REVENGE, *built at Baltimore in 1805. Taken into the Royal Navy as* FLYING FISH. *United States National Museum.*

were later raised to fit her arming. She was sold to the Royal Navy by her last American owner, N. W. Easton of Baltimore, in the West Indies. He had threatened to sell her to the French previously.

The three-masted schooner rig came into use during the latter half of the eighteenth century, perhaps as early as 1755. No mention of this rig has been found in the old works on naval architecture. In fact, the only references found so far are in naval reports, which mention a few such vessels. The American naval schooner *Experiment* was chased by a French three-masted schooner in 1800. A British three-masted schooner, also named *Experiment*, was reported to be cruising in the Caribbean in 1796. In *The Corsairs of France** there is an undocumented reference to "a three-masted schooner,

*By C. B. Norman (London, Sampson, Low and Co., 1887), p. 267.

the *Lincoln*," which had been captured by the French privateersman Thurot in 1759. Small pilot boats rigged as three-masted schooners seem to have become rather numerous after 1806. As a rule, the rig seems to have been confined to small, fast schooners throughout this period.

Another reference to a three-masted schooner was found in the 15 June 1796 issue of *City Gazette and Daily Advertiser* of Charleston, which reported the arrival at Philadelphia on 29 May of the schooner *Maria*, Wilson master, returning leaky after her departure on the 24th. She had been boarded by the French privateer *Pandour*. "The *Pandour* had been a three-masted schooner, but is now a brig, with yellow sides, low stern, no head, and her guns housed, of which she is said to have only six on board."

The *Flying Fish*, ex-*Revenge*, had a rather straight sheer, flush deck, straight keel, raking sternpost, square tuck with the rudder head outboard of the transom on the external sternpost, and a raking, curved stem. The

American three-masted schooner; lithograph by Rogers in 1825. National Maritime Museum.

entrance was moderately sharp and convex, the run long and fine; the buttock-bow lines were very easy forward and straight and soft in the run. The midsection showed sharply rising straight floor and a very slack, rounding bilge. The topside did not become upright until the sheer was reached.

Her dimensions have already been given; the moulded displacement was 109.2 long tons; the load waterline moulded was 74 feet. The block coefficient was .39, midship coefficient .60, and the prismatic was .65. The effective length of the quarterbeam buttock was 63′ 6″ and the camber 4′ 8½″, giving a camber-length ratio of 13.2. Admiralty records give actual displacement as 117 long tons, to outside of all plank and deadwood. Her service draft may have been greater than in her draught.

The sail plan, Plate 39, which shows how heavily rigged these fast schooners often were, is based upon the sail plan of *Flying Fish* that was sent to Bermuda. This is one of the few sail plans for the period around 1800 in the Admiralty Collection of Draughts.

The square sails shown, with the necessary yards, are fitted so that they could be lowered to the deck for stowing or furling. With either square sails or fore-and-afters, this schooner seems to have had the maximum rig. To carry this she was heavily ballasted with pig iron spread out over the middle third of her bottom. This and the light construction, employing much cedar, gave her sufficient power to carry the sail area that would be expected to produce her maximum potential speed under certain conditions of wind and sea. These appear to have been light to moderate conditions, judging by the sail area, rather shoal hull, slack bilges, moderate beam, and low freeboard.

A schooner of a different type is represented by *La Supérieure* (in official correspondence her name also appears as *Superieur*). This vessel was captured off Tortugas by H.M.S. *Thesus*, along with the schooner *Poisson Volant*, in July 1803, as mentioned earlier. Admiral Sir John Duckworth reported to the Admiralty, 14 July 1803, that both schooners "were coppered and very fine vessels, *La Supérieure* fully corresponding with her name." Her survey was enclosed—she was 86′ 4″ on the range of deck, 67 feet on the keel for tonnage, 23′ 6″ extreme breadth, 9′ 5″ depth in hold, and 196 76/94 tons. She was thought to be "about two years old, American-built, coppered and copper-fastened, and pierced for 16 guns." She was a national schooner and had a small supply of provisions on board when captured.

Plate 40 is a redrawing of *La Supérieure's* Admiralty draught. No dimensions or notes were given in the draught, but measuring of her lines shows that

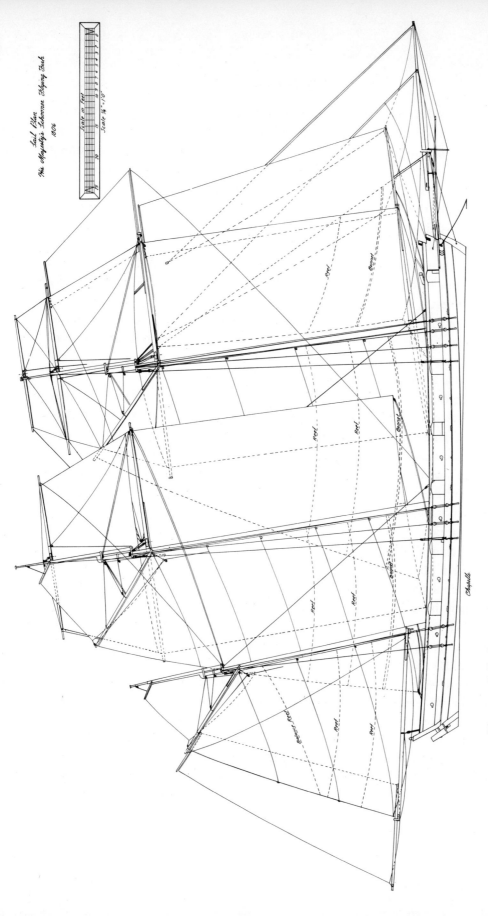

Chapelle

Plate 39. Sail plan of the Baltimore-built three-masted schooner FLYING FISH, launched about 1805.

she was actually 89' 6" moulded length at rail, 23' 2" moulded beam, and 10' 6" moulded depth. She originally was a fore-topsail schooner with flush deck. Her sheer was very slight; she had a straight keel with much drag, raking sternpost, round tuck, strongly-curved stem rabbet, gammon-knee head, sharp, convex entrance, and a long, fine run with hollow in the buttocks under the quarters. Her midsection was formed with sharply rising straight floor and high well-rounded bilge carried up to rail in marked tumble home. This schooner seems rather typical of the Chesapeake-built schooners of the period; she was constructed in 1801 in Maryland, according to French records. However, her original name is unknown so the American registry cannot be found.

Relatively deep with much deadrise, sharp convex entrance, fine run with hollow in the buttocks under the quarters, low freeboard, and very raking ends—all are features that slowly became standard characteristics in American fast, armed schooner design during the French Revolution.

The deck plan of this fine schooner, shown on Plate 40 in broken lines on the half-breadth plan, became nearly standard also for fast schooners between 75 and 90 feet on deck. The galley hatch was commonly forward as shown, or was placed just abaft the riding bitts. The iron heel strap securing the bowsprit went slowly out of fashion, and was replaced by double heel bitts. There were usually the main hatch and a scuttle (or small hatch) between the masts, though the scuttle was sometimes omitted. Abaft the mainmast there were usually a hatch and the pumps; the latter sometimes just abaft the mainmast. The trunk cabin was often used, as it gave a more comfortable accommodation than a cabin under a flush deck. Usually on the trunk, or on the flush deck, there was a companionway and a hatch, or skylight. A small scuttle just ahead of the rudder port gave access to the run. Steering was commonly with a wooden tiller, sometimes fitted with sheaves and pin, so that a steering tackle could be reeved off when required in heavy weather. Usually this was a single purchase on each side.

The absence of a windlass, or capstan, in many of the American schooners of this period requires explanation. The relatively large crews, particularly in privateers or letter-of-marques, could manhandle the cable and anchor by means of tackles stopped to the cable. The tackles were double or treble purchases laid out on deck on each side, one block secured aft and the other to the cable near the hawse. The tackles were worked alternately, and the running block was secured by strops (short pieces of rope) passed around

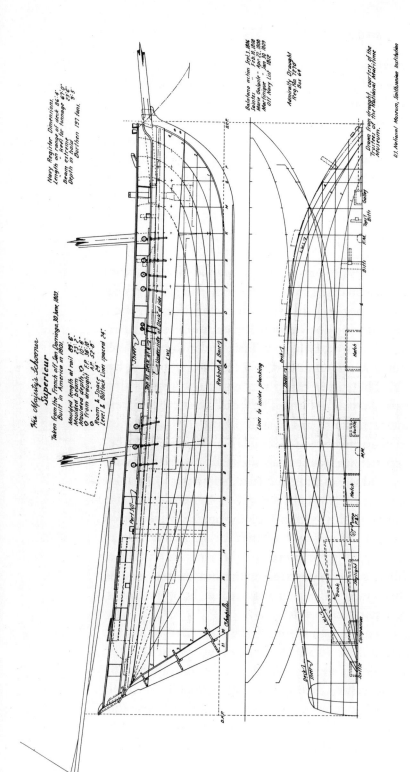
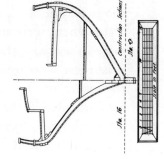
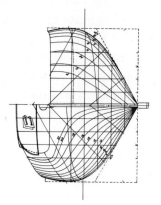

Plate 40. Fast American schooner LA SUPÉRIEURE, built in 1801 and sold to the French, from whom she was taken by the British Navy in 1803. She was eventually rerigged as a brigantine.

the hook or eye of the block and then around the cable. The strop was passed so that it jambed on the cable and could either be quickly thrown off or secured. Schooners of the larger sizes sometimes had a small iron winch on the mainmast, or mainmast bitts; this could be used to increase power on the tackles by bringing the falls to their heads. The winches often had long cranks, one end on the shaft of the winch and the other on an open bearing on the bulwarks or rails. These cranks unshipped, of course, and were then stowed inside the bulwarks on hooks or clips. The cranks enabled the tackles to be worked with fewer men than when unassisted by winches. Iron mast winches were employed in some American-built vessels as early as the 1760's, at least, but the date of their introduction has not yet been established. It should be noticed that the mast winches could also be employed in hoisting and trimming sail, and for other purposes.

The regular log windlass appeared only in merchant schooners and brigs that were intended to be manned by small crews. The capstan appears in naval vessels and the Admiralty draughts show many instances where one had been installed in an American schooner when she was being fitted for naval service. Some merchant ships, however, had capstans instead of windlasses. Pilot boats usually had no windlass until after 1810 when some were fitted with a small, low capstan called a "crab." This might be located amidships, or abaft the mainmast.

It should be noted that these vessels did not often use ground tackle, and when they did it was usually in shoal water. Some of these were privateers and pilot boats, who were almost constantly on the move. In port they might tie up in a slip or to a mooring or wharf. Hence, with ample manpower, there was no difficulty.

La Supérieure had no hawse holes; the cable passed over her rail, pilot-boat fashion, between timberheads. The rail cap at this point protected by sheet lead or copper, or by a hardwood wearing-piece. During this period all anchor cables used in these schooners were of hemp. Hawse holes were commonly lined with lead.

The schooner *La Supérieure* was 80 feet moulded length on the load line, and displaced 160.6 long tons. Her block coefficient was .39, midship coefficient .62, and prismatic .63. The effective length of her quarterbeam buttock was 60′ 6″ and the camber 4′ 8″, giving a camber-length ratio of 12.9. After a short service in the Royal Navy, she was rerigged as a brigantine or brig.

In examining the Admiralty Collection of Draughts, it was noticed from the surviving plans that the Admiralty began taking off the lines of French privateer vessels in 1745. These were sharp-ended craft having the French "pear-shaped" midsection described in discussing *À Bien Acquis* and the Revolutionary privateer ship *Belisarius* in the last chapter.

Vessels of this form of midsection, both ships and brigs, were taken from the French during the wars between the years 1745 and 1815; plans of a large number of these survive. But sometime about 1796 the British began to pick up large, flush-decked ship-privateers of an entirely different form. These had moderate or rather straight sheer, straight keel with moderate drag, raking post, round tuck, upper-and-lower transoms, and stem rabbet well raked and somewhat curved. The entrance was generally sharp and convex, though in some examples there was a slight hollow in the load line just abaft the rabbet and more in the lower waterlines or level lines. The run was often very fine and long, the quarterbeam buttock becoming straight or nearly so about where it crossed the load line. The midsection was formed with either sharply rising straight floor, or with slight hollow in the rise; the bilge was well-rounded and sometimes carried up in an easy sweep to form a slight tumble home in the bulwarks.

This description, it will be remembered, is very close to that of the fast-sailing American schooners. These ship-privateers included such vessels as *La Railleur* taken 1798, 89′ 6″ on the range of deck; *Le Confiance*, 1806, 117 feet on the range of deck; *L'Heureux*, 1800, built at Bordeaux, 127′ 8½″ on the range of deck; *La Vengeance* (*Scout* in the Royal Navy), 1800, 111 feet on the range of deck; *L'Huit Amis* (*Bonetta* in the Royal Navy), 1798, 103′ 1″ on the range of deck; *L'Audacieux* (*Voltigeur* in the Royal Navy), 1798, 114 feet on the range of deck; and *Bourdelois*, 1800, 138′ 6″ on the range of deck. Some of these vessels had the gammon-knee head that increased their resemblance to the American schooners. The majority of these vessels seem to have been built at Bordeaux. At least one very handsome privateer-frigate of this model was *Psyche*, captured by the British in the East Indies and lines taken off in 1813. She was 138′ 6″ on the range of the lower deck. Though her entrance was quite full, her run was very fine and she had the reputation of being very fast.

No documented explanation for the sudden appearance of this model of vessel in France has yet been found. There are a number of references to American merchants settling in France early in the French Revolution and operating privateers. A British naval officer mentioned in private correspond-

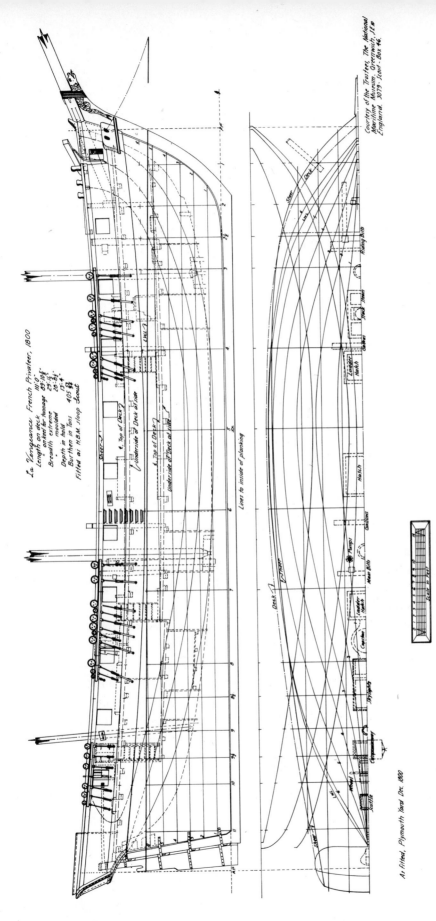

La Vengeance French Privateer, 1800

Length on deck .... 111'0"
Length on keel for tonnage 89'10⅝"
Breadth extreme .... 29'¼"
  "   moulded .... 28'8¼"
Depth in hold .... 13'4"
Burthen in Tons 405 75/94
Fitted as H.B.M. sloop Scout

Lines to inside of planking

As fitted, Plymouth Yard Dec. 1800

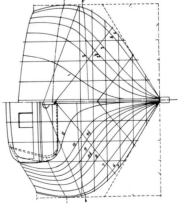

Plate 41. French privateer ship LA VENGEANCE, of a form resembling the American pilot boat model. This type appears to have been built almost entirely
in the period between 1795 and 1803. This model of vessel does not appear
in any earlier period in the Admiralty Collection of Draughts, where plans
of single-decked French ships date back to about 1745.

ence that an American shipbuilder was engaged in building privateers in France in 1796, but neither the name nor any official record of this builder has been found. It is mere speculation to advance any claim that these privateers were inspired by American designs or practices, however tempting this may be; yet it is difficult to account for these vessels otherwise.

Plate 41 is a redrawing of the Admiralty draught of one of these privateer ships, *La Vengeance*, captured by H.M.S. *Nereide* 28 February 1800 and taken into the Royal Navy as *Scout*. This is a beautiful example of the class, though not as extreme as some of the type whose plans survive. Since she answers to the general description given earlier, there is no need here for a repetition of the detailed description. She had a slight hollow in the load line forward and her quarterbeam buttock was straight for some distance before intersecting the load waterline aft, giving an exceptionally fine run.

This fine ship measured 111 feet on the range of the upper deck, 28′ 8½″ moulded beam, 29′ 1½″ extreme beam, 13′ 9″ in the hold, and she was reputed to have been a very fast-sailing vessel. There was a certain amount of prejudice against these flush-decked ships in the Royal Navy and some officers considered them unsafe. As a class they were undoubtedly very wet when driving into a heavy sea.

This ship was 105 feet on the moulded load line and displaced 330.4 long tons. Her block coefficient was .34, her midship coefficient .61, and her prismatic .56. The effective length of her quarterbeam buttock was 87′ 3″ and the camber 8′ 1¼″, giving a camber-length ratio of 10.8.

Though no plan of an American ship of this date and type is available, customhouse records and other documentary material show that sharp, ship-rigged vessels were built in the United States from 1794 to 1815 and some of these were certainly very similar to *La Vengeance*. It can be said only that, based on existing information, any claim that the Americans copied the French in this type is unfounded.

A brig built at Baltimore about 1801 is shown in Plates 42 and 43. This vessel, named *Numa*, was at New York in April 1808. She sailed that month, allegedly for "St. Barthelemy," but arrived at St. Pierre, Martinique, on 17 May 1808. There she was sold to a French merchant, renamed *Le Pierre Cézar* (also spelled *César* and *Czar*), armed with two six-pounder guns and four 18-pounder carronades (she was pierced for 18 guns), and was given a French letter-of-marque. Her Nantucket-born mate was William Marshall, who had sailed the month before from New York as a seaman. On 29 May 1808 she

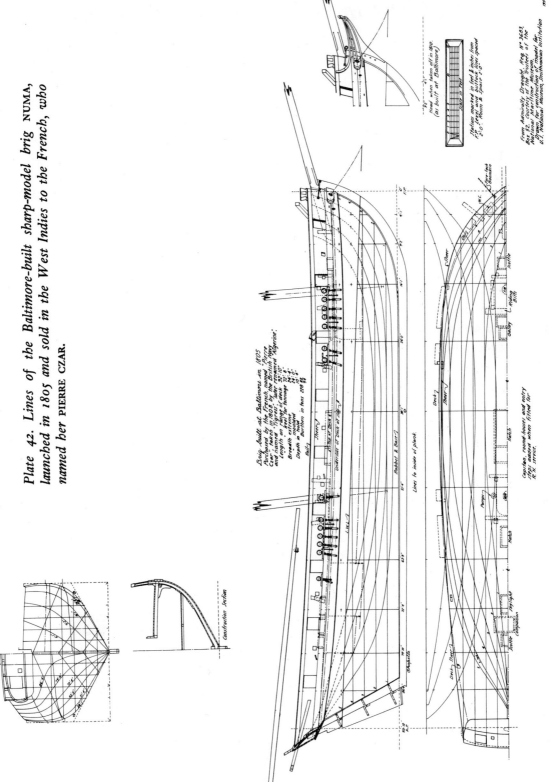

Plate 42. Lines of the Baltimore-built sharp-model brig NUMA, launched in 1805 and sold in the West Indies to the French, who named her PIERRE CZAR.

Construction Section

Brig built at Baltimore in 1805
Purchased by the French, named "Pierre
Czar," taken in 1808 by the British Navy
and named "Tigress," later renamed Magpie:
    length on range of deck .... 92'10"
    keel for tonnage .... 72'-8"
    Breadth extreme .... 24'-4"
    moulded .... 23'-10"
    Depth in hold .... 10'-9"
    Burthen in tons 298 75/94

Lines to inside of plank

Head when taken off in 1810
(as built at Baltimore)

Stations marked in feet & inches from
F.P. (keel and buttock lines spaced
2'-0". Room & Space 2'-0".

From Admiralty Draught, Reg. N° 3683,
Box 62. Courtesy of the Trustees of the
National Maritime Museum.
Drawn for construction of model for
U.S. National Museum, Smithsonian Institution

Capstan, round houses and entry
steps, added when fitted for
R.N. service.

sailed from St. Pierre for L'Orient, carrying sugar (80 hogsheads, two tierces), coffee (285 barrels and 190 bags), and 37 bales of cotton. Her officers and passengers also had small private ventures on board, mostly bags of coffee. On 29 June 1808 the brig was taken by H.M.S. *La Seine* after a four-hour-and-twenty-minute chase off the Spanish coast. On 30 October 1808, the Navy Board reported her purchase as ordered, for £2265/19/0. The Admiralty ordered her renamed *Tigress*, and armed her with fourteen 12-pounder carronades. A manuscript Navy List in the Admiralty Library states she was later renamed *Algerine*, but this cannot be verified in the Admiralty correspondence. As *Tigress* she served in the East Indies for a while, and was apparently sold out of service about 1812.

Numa was a fine-lined brig: 92' 10" on the range of deck, 24 feet moulded beam, 24' 4" extreme beam, and 10' 4" depth in hold. She had slight sheer, straight keel with marked drag, raking post, round tuck, upper-and-lower transoms, strongly curved stem rabbet, and a bust figurehead when built. She had a short, convex entrance with very easy bow lines, a fine run with straight buttocks near quarterbeam, and her midsection showed sharply rising straight floor and high slack bilge with sweep carried to rail to form slight tumble home. She was "privateer built," having gunports and bulwarks ceiled on the inside. A very fast sailer, her American mate claimed she would not have been captured had she not been much overloaded. Her figurehead was knocked off or removed sometime in her naval career, as she was once described as having "no head."

Plate 43 shows her rig, which was standard for the period and requires no extensive discussion. She had a spencer mast on the main, on which the spanker was set. The rig was high and narrow rather than square or wide. As usual in American vessels, the royals were set flying without royal yard braces. The royals were narrow on the head, wide on the foot, and with rather small hoist. Such sails could be trimmed by the topgallant yard braces in light weather, for which the royals were intended to be used.

The moulded load line was 86' 9" long. The moulded displacement was 189 long tons. The block coefficient was .42, the midship coefficient was .64, and the prismatic .64. The effective length of the quarterbeam buttock-bow line was 68 feet, the camber 4' 10¾", and the camber-length ratio was 14.2.

The pilot schooners used off the Delaware in 1800–10 were similar to those used off Sandy Hook. They were 50 to 60 feet between perpendiculars, broad of beam, and had fine runs. The pilot schooner *Nimble*, shown in

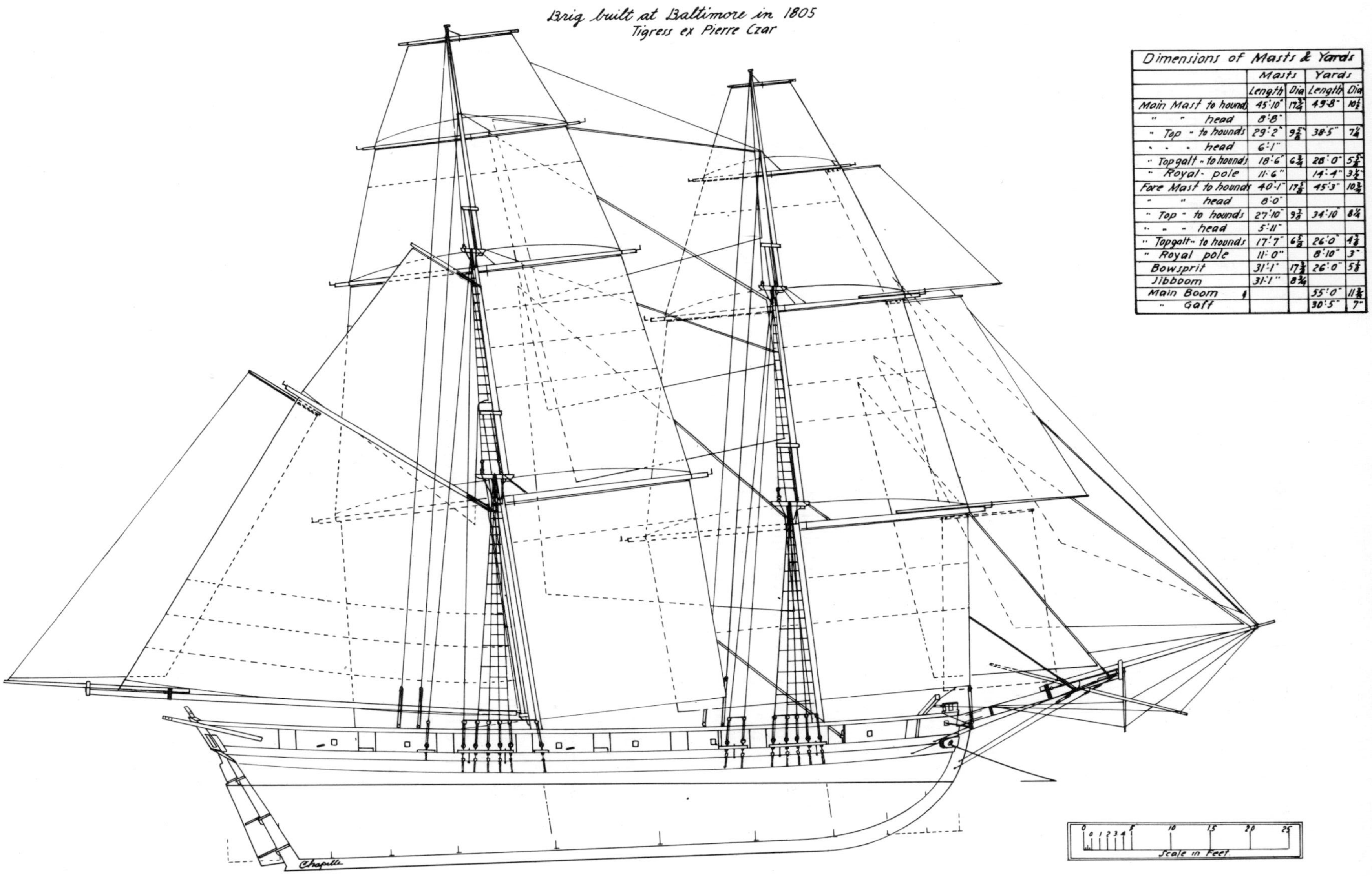
Brig built at Baltimore in 1805
Tigress ex Pierre Czar
Scale in Feet
0 1 2 3 4 5 10 15 20 25
Chapelle

Dimensions of Masts & Yards				
	Masts		Yards	
	Length	Dia	Length	Dia
Main Mast to hounds	45'10"	17¾	49'8"	10½
" " head	8'8"			
" Top " to hounds	29'2"	9⅝	38'5"	7¼
" " " head	6'1"			
" Topgalt " to hounds	18'6"	6¾	28'0"	5⅝
" Royal-pole	11'6"		14'4"	3½
Fore Mast to hounds	40'1"	17⅝	45'3"	10¾
" " head	8'0"			
" Top " to hounds	27'10"	9⅞	34'10"	8¼
" " " head	5'11"			
" Topgalt " to hounds	17'7"	6⅝	26'0"	4⅞
" Royal pole	11'0"		8'10"	3"
Bowsprit	31'1"	17¾	26'0"	5⅛
Jibboom	31'1"	8¾		
Main Boom			55'0"	11¾
" Gaff			30'5"	7"

Plate 43. Sail plan of the brig NUMA.

Plate 44, was built at Philadelphia from a design by Samuel Humphreys. This schooner had probably been built for Captain Robinson sometime in 1806 or 1807. In 1809 Humphreys prepared a modification of *Nimble's* design in which the length was increased 18 inches by shifting the after four stations, and the rake of the sternpost was increased—which lengthened her overall by another two feet. The schooner on the lengthened lines was built for Captain Thomas Turner and Otto Strawbridge in 1809.

Nimble was 55′ 6″ between perpendiculars, 45 feet on the keel rabbet, 16′ 6″ moulded beam, and 6 feet depth of hold. The extreme beam was 16′ 9″. She had a slight amount of sheer, straight keel, 1′ 6″ rake in the post, round tuck, sharply raking transom, and a curved fore-rake of nine feet. The entrance was rather short and full; the run, though quite long, had only a short length of straight line in the quarterbeam buttock. The midsection was formed with sharply rising straight floor; a high and rather soft bilge carried up to the rail to produce some tumble home. The schooner had bulwarks only about a foot high; the deck was flush to nine feet abaft the mainmast where it stepped up to the level of the main railcap for nearly the same distance, to form the cabin. Abaft this, the deck dropped a little below main-deck level to form a cockpit.

The schooner is a good example of the form of pilot boats that became popular during the first quarter of the nineteenth century: they were shallow and wide, of light displacement, with a fine run, and very low-sided. These boats carried a large rig and many were very fast and probably pretty wet when in a seaway.

The length on the moulded load line was 53 feet; the displacement 34.6 long tons. The block coefficient was .37, the midship .59, and the prismatic .63. The effective length of the quarterbeam buttock was 38 feet, the camber 2′ 2¾″, and the camber-length ratio 17.3. The particulars for the lengthened-lines design are not needed for present purposes. It should be noted, however, that in lengthening the design, Humphreys made some changes in sectional forms in the body plan. Samuel Humphreys was a very poor draftsman in this period, which may have been the cause of these changes, rather than an intentional alteration in hull form.

Another example of a pilot-boat schooner by the same designer is one identified only as *Schooner Yacht for Canton* (Plate 45) for Captain William Jones. No date is given, but she is of about the same period as *Nimble*. These "yachts" were really merchants' dispatch boats, used to pick up or deliver

182

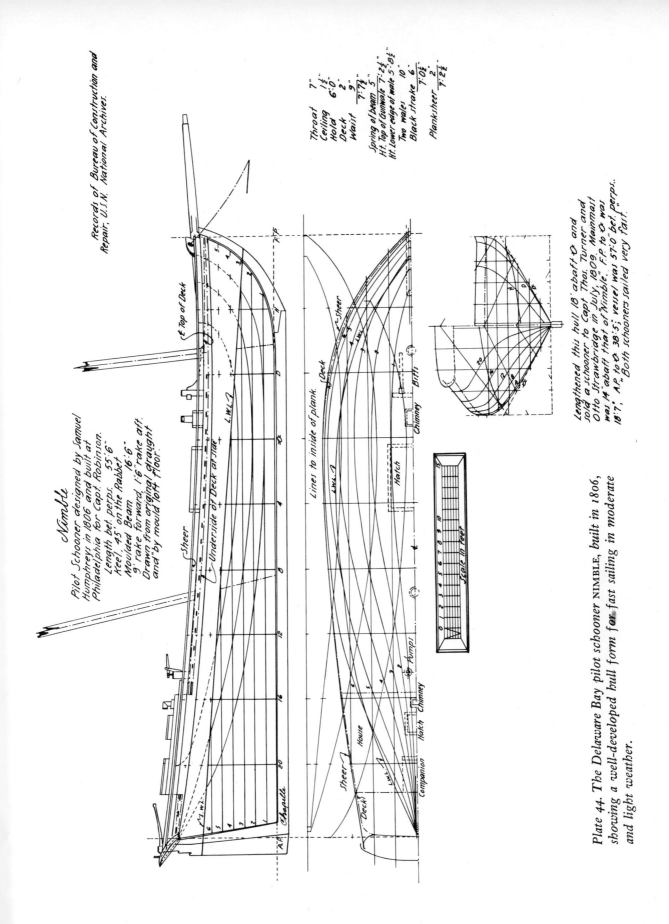

Nimble

Pilot Schooner designed by Samuel
Humphreys in 1806 and built at
Philadelphia for Capt. Robinson.
Length bet. perps.   55'-6"
Keel, 45" on the Rabbet
Moulded Beam   16'-6"
9' rake forward, 1'-6" rake aft.
Drawn from original draught
and by mould 'off floor.

Records of Bureau of Construction and
Repair, U.S.N. National Archives.

Throat   7"
Ceiling   1½"
Hold   6'-0"
Deck   2"
Waist   9"
                7'-7½"
Spring of beam 5"
Ht. Top of Gunwale 7'-2½"
Ht. Lower edge of wale 5'-8½"
Two wales   10"
Black strake   6"
                7'-0½"
Plank-sheer   2"
                7'-2½"

Lengthened this hull 18' abaft ⊕ and
sold a schooner to Capt. Thos. Turner and
Otto Strawbridge in July, 1809. Mainmast
was 14" abaft that of Nimble. F.P. to ⊕ was
18'7; A.P. to ⊕ 38'5; vessel was 57'-0" bet. perps.
18'7. Both schooners sailed very fair.

Lines to inside of plank.

Scale in feet

Plate 44. The Delaware Bay pilot schooner NIMBLE, built in 1806,
showing a well-developed hull form for fast sailing in moderate
and light weather.

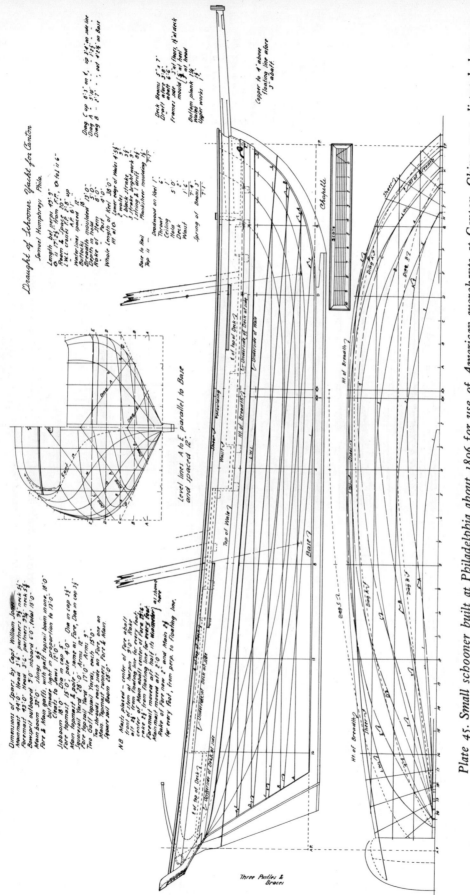

Plate 45. Small schooner built at Philadelphia about 1806 for use of American merchants at Canton, China, as a dispatch boat tender. Small dispatch vessels were known as "yachts" in China, since they could also be used for pleasure sailing.

messages and to operate between ships at a distant anchorage and the merchants' factories or establishments ashore. They served as inspection boats, and in fact did any work necessary. Never a luxurious pleasure craft, in later years they often engaged in opium and silver smuggling. In any case, the merchant demanded a fast sailer. Humphreys made a preliminary set of lines, but discarded these to draw a boat of lighter displacement. Both the preliminary and finished draughts survive.

Plates 45 and 46 show this "yacht"; a handsome little schooner, 49′ 9″ between perpendiculars, 13 feet moulded beam, and 5 feet depth of hold. Her planking was to be 1¼ inches thick, and she was to be coppered to above the waterline. The plates are drawn from the original draught, and the sail plan is reconstructed from the table of spar dimensions.

The boat had a rather straight, flush sheer; the keel was straight with much drag. The post raked sharply. She had a round tuck, with upper-and-lower transom above. The stern was well-curved with over eight feet fore-rake. The bulwarks were low. The deck stepped up 14 inches forward of the mainmast to six inches below the rail cap. This raised quarterdeck was carried aft to a little less than eight feet of the stern where it stepped down to main-deck level to form a "pilot-boat fashion" cockpit. The entrance was short, moderately full, and convex. The run was very long and fine with a short length of straight line in the quarterbeam buttock. The midsection shows a sharply-rising straight floor and a full round and high bilge with sweep carried to rail to form marked tumble home.

The lines plan shows that there was some trouble in the balance of rig and hull, for the masts were shifted—the dotted mast positions indicate those first drawn on the draught. The spar dimensions had been chosen by the owner, so Humphreys had an excuse for lack of balance.

This schooner was 46′ 2″ on the moulded load waterline and had a moulded displacement of 22.8 long tons. Her block coefficient was .32, midship .62, and prismatic .68. The effective length of the quarterbeam buttock was 39′ 8″ and the camber 2′ 8″; the camber-length ratio was 15.0. The rig, shown in Plate 46, had both of the fore yards fitted to lower so that the sails could be furled on deck, since the vessel was so small. The combination gaff and gaff-topsail boom in one is unusual.

The three-masted schooner rig was quite popular in Bermuda during the first decade of the nineteenth century, as well as in the Chesapeake country. An example of a Bermudian, the redrawing of the two schooner-waterboats,

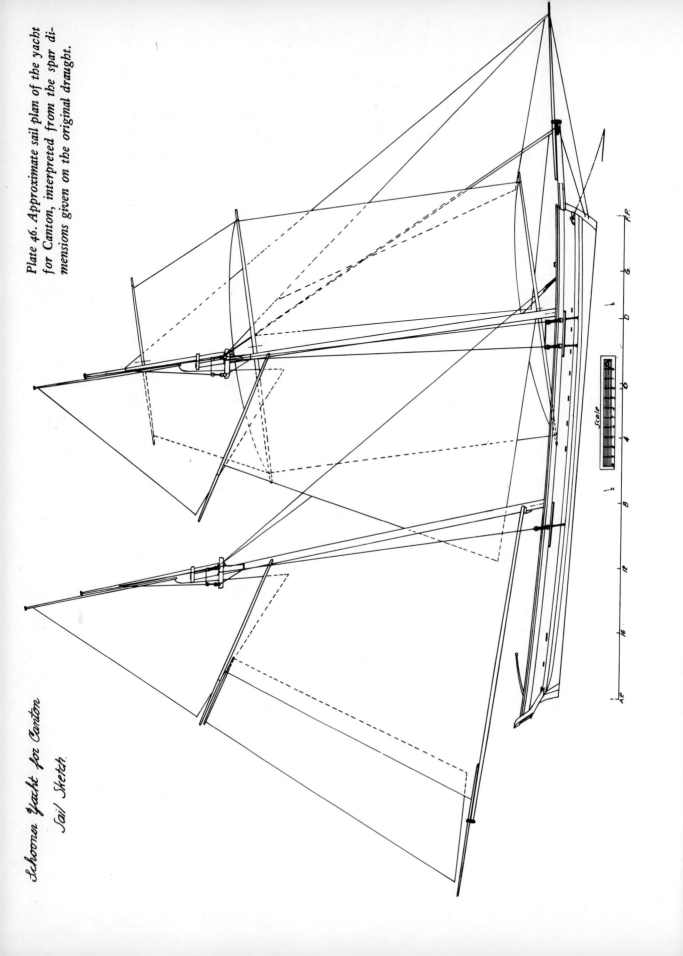

Plate 46. Approximate sail plan of the yacht for Canton, interpreted from the spar dimensions given on the original draught.

Schooner Yacht for Canton
Sail Sketch.

Scale

or "tanks," is exhibited in Plate 47. These schooners were designed in 1804 by Captain S. F. Evans, R.N., to the order of Admiral Sir John T. Duckworth; they were built under the inspection of Goodrich and Shedden and were intended for the Jamaican station. They were made of Bermuda cedar, copper-fastened. The vessels were 73 feet from face of sternpost to face of stem, 60 feet on the keel, 23 feet moulded beam, 9′ 6″ moulded depth, and 147 92/94 tons burthen. They carried lower masts rigged with three boomed gaff-sails and a small jib. The hold, 48 feet long between bulkheads and 8 feet deep, formed the water tank, which was divided by a single bulkhead athwartships at midlength and by a centerline bulkhead, giving four compartments; little or no ballast was carried. The vessels were fitted with a deck firebox or hearth and a windlass, and water was pumped through four wooden pump barrels. There were bilge pumps near the mizzen and three access or working hatches and a scuttle forward. The schooners had no accommodations, as they were intended for harbor and day service. They had very heavy guards to protect them from damage in coming alongside a vessel to supply water. The Royal Navy "tanks" appear often to have been designed to sail very well, in order to serve men-of-war outside the port quickly.

These vessels had a very flat sheer, and raking post outside the transom, with rudder hung outboard. The transom was heart-shaped. The stem was curved, with over eight feet fore-rake. The entrance was rather full and short, the run short but fine. The quarterbeam buttock was straight for a short distance, where it crossed the load line aft. The midsection had a moderate rise of straight floor; a round, slack bilge carried to the deck without becoming fully upright. The waterboats shown in Plate 47 represent one of the intermediate forms, between a sharp model and a carrier. They were named *Bermuda* and *Milford*.

The length on the moulded load line was 68′ 4″; the displacement was 136.4 long tons. The block coefficient was .48, the midship coefficient .72, and the prismatic .67. The effective length of the quarterbeam buttock was 56′ 3″, the camber 5′ 1″, giving a camber-length ratio of about 10.8.

These two water tanks were condemned 19 November 1825 and a new vessel was sent from England. The new vessel was found to be unsatisfactory, whereupon the Jamaica master-shipwright decided that *Bermuda* and *Milford* might be repaired. The Admiralty sharply cautioned him to be more careful about condemning vessels in the future. *Bermuda* and *Milford* continued in service until about 1830.

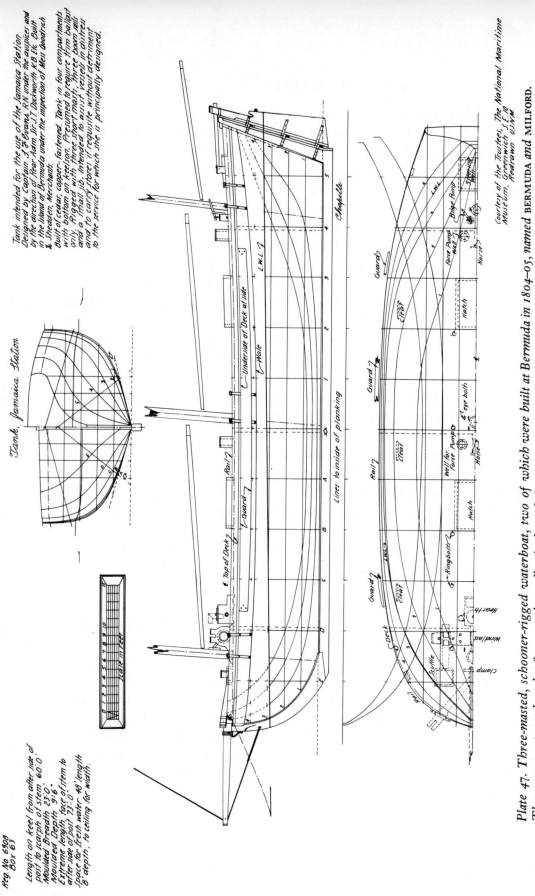

Length on keel from after side of
post to scarph of stem 60'0"
Moulded Breadth 23'0"
Moulded Depth 9'6"
Extreme length face of stem to
after side of post 73'0"
Space for fresh water 48' length
8' depth, to ceiling for width.

Tank, Jamaica Station

Tank intended for the use of the Jamaica Station
Designed by Captain J. F. Evans RN under the auspices and
by the direction of Rear-Adm. Sir J. T. Duckworth K.B. Etc. Built
in the Island of Bermuda under the inspection of Mess Goodrich
& Sheddan, Merchant.
Built of cedar, copper-fastened. Tank in four compartments
with bottom on keelson. Presumed to require trim ballast
only. Rigged with three short masts, three boom sails
and a trisail jib, intended to assist vessels in distress
and to carry stores, if requisite without detriment
to the service for which she is principally designed.

Underside of Deck at side

Lines to inside of planking

Chapelle

Courtesy of the Trustees, The National Maritime
Museum, Greenwich, S.E.10
Redrawn U.S.M.

Plate 47. Three-masted, schooner-rigged waterboat, two of which were built at Bermuda in 1804–05, named BERMUDA and MILFORD.
They were reported to be fine vessels, well-suited to their purposes.

An example of a small merchant ship, designed in 1804 by Christian Bergh and built at New York, is shown in Plates 48 and 49. The name of this vessel has not yet been discovered in the customhouse records but she is one of a numerous class of small, ship-rigged ocean freighters built in America between about 1790 and 1812. This ship, like many of her class, was designed to obtain a fair turn of speed and to be an economical carrier. In spite of their small size, ships like this one operated in the transatlantic trade and some were in the East Indies pepper trade.

This small ship had a moderate, flush sheer with an open stanchion rail above, carried nearly to the catheads. There was moderate rake in the sternpost and a curved fore-rake. The entrance was full and short but the run was rather long and fine. There was a small drag to the keel, and the buttock at about quarterbeam was rather easy forward and straight in the run as the load line was approached. One of the marked characteristics of these small ocean freighters was their great depth in proportion to length; this produced a slow sailer unless the ends were designed with care. Such vessels needed ballast when flying light, and unless properly loaded, they had a tendency to sail with an uncomfortable angle of heel.

The rig, shown in Plate 49, was rather large, and stuns'ls were carried on fore and main yards. Some of these small ships are shown in paintings with royals on fore and main set flying. Owing to the rig, and often to easy ends, these ships appear to have performed particularly well in moderate weather, but they did not have a high potential speed.

The vessel shown in Plate 48 was 83 feet on the upper deck, 23' 7" moulded beam, and 13' 5" moulded depth. Her length on the designed load line was 75' 10½", her moulded displacement then being 330.2 long tons. Her block coefficient was .59, midship coefficient .86, and prismatic .64. Her approximate quarterbeam buttock-bow line had an effective length of 68' 4", with a camber of 10 feet; the camber-length ratio was 6.8.

It has been pointed out that the American sharp seagoing schooner had become so well-known abroad by 1800 that European constructors were able to produce schooners on the American model. Plate 50 is an example. It is a design made in 1805 by an English shipwright apprentice named Henry Steer or Steers. This drawing differs from the original in not showing every frame and in not having the heeled load waterline projected. The original plan seems to have been drawn by Steers as a final examination on completing his apprenticeship. There is no indication that the plan was built from, and

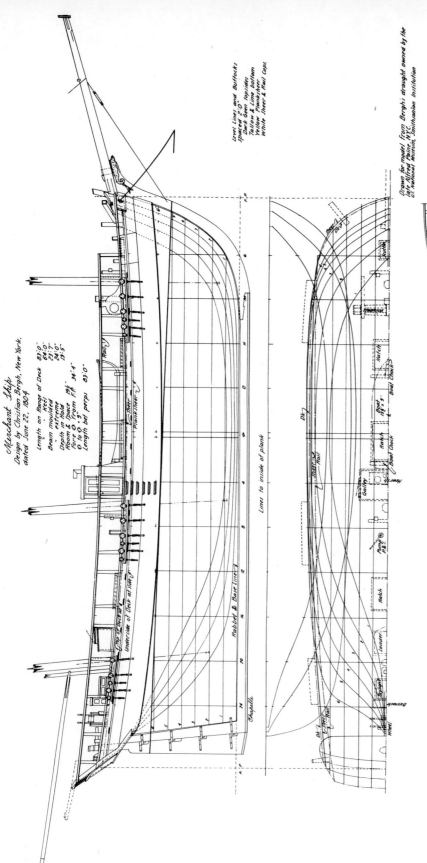

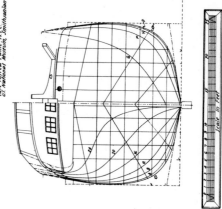

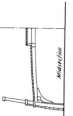

Merchant Ship

Design by Christian Bergh, New York,
dated June 22, 1804

Length on Range of Deck	83'·0"
Keel	64'·0"
Beam moulded	23'·7"
extreme	24'·0"
Depth in Hold	13'·5"
Room & Space	19½"
Fore O. from F.P.	34'·4"
O. to O·3'"	
Length bel perp.	83'·0"

Lines to inside of plank

Chapelle

Rabbet & Base line

Underside of Deck at side

Level Lines and Buttocks
Space and 2'·0"
Dark Green topsides
Tallow & Lime bottom
Yellow Planksheer
White Sheer & Rail caps.

Drawn for model from Bergh's draught owned by the
late Alfred Paine, N.Y.C.
US Nat'lonal Museum, Smithsonian Institution

Midsection

Scale in Feet

Plate 48. An American design of a typical small
ocean freighter of 1790–1812, capable of sailing
fairly well. Designed by Christian Bergh, she was
an economic and efficient carrier of this era.

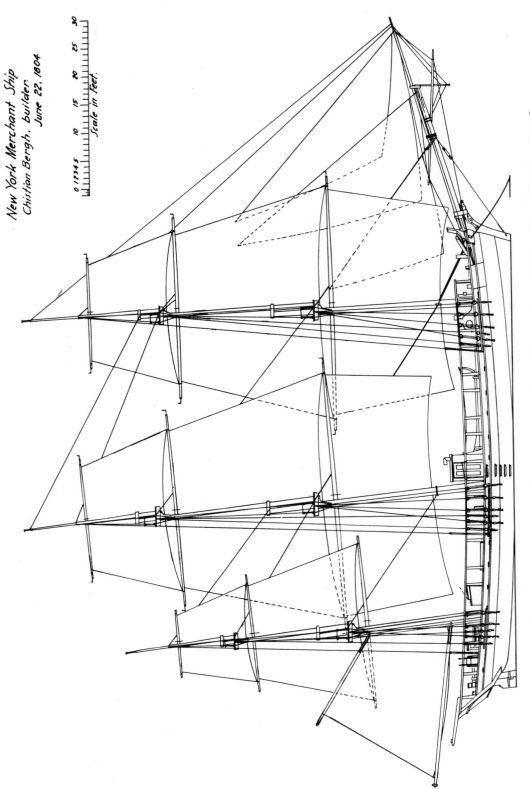

New York Merchant Ship
Christian Bergh, builder.
June 22. 1804

Scale in Feet.
0 1 2 3 4 5   10   15   20   25   30

Plate 49. Typical sail plan of a small American merchant ship of 1804, designed by Christian Bergh.

it was probably a project or a test of draftsmanship.

The plan (Plate 50) was for a large 12- or 14-gun schooner of the American model 90′ 10″ between design perpendiculars, 90′ 10″ on the upper deck, 23′ 2″ moulded beam, and 9′ 9″ depth in hold. The design is marked by heavy drag to the keel, strongly raking ends, strong sheer, a midsection formed with sharply rising straight floor, high and easy turn of the bilge, and with some tumble home in the topsides. The entrance is sharp, convex, and rather short. The run is long and very fine, with hollow in the buttocks under the quarters.

The projected schooner would have been 82′ 3″ long on the moulded load waterline, with a moulded displacement of 176.3 long tons. Her block coefficient was .36, her midship coefficient .60, and her prismatic coefficient .59. The effective length of the quarterbeam buttock was about 57′ 9″ and its camber 5′ 5″, giving a camber-length ratio of 10.7.

The apprentice designer of this schooner, Steers, came to America shortly after the end of the War of 1812, and was employed in the Washington Navy Yard. He later removed to New York, where he and an associate built the first marine railway in that area. He was the father of George Steers, who designed the schooner yacht *America* in 1850, and who was the constructor-designer of the Collins' liner *Adriatic* and of the steam man-of-war *Niagara*.

It is interesting to compare Steers' projected schooner with *Nonpareil*. This latter schooner was built by William Price at Baltimore for Thomas Tenant and launched in May 1807. She was captured in the morning of 4 February 1808 by H.M.S. *Diana* some 10 to 12 miles off the French coast near the approaches to Bordeaux, Cordovan Lighthouse bearing SE by E. The wind was very light and the schooner was taken by *Diana's* gig. She was unarmed and wholly dependent upon speed for safety. A report on her survey, dated 5 July 1808, was prepared at Plymouth dockyard. Her American register described her as 191 82/95 tons, length 91 feet, breadth 24 feet, depth in hold 9′ 11″, square stern, round tuck, no galleries, one deck, two masts, no figurehead. By her builder's certificate she was 64 feet keel, 23 feet beam, 9′ 10″ depth, and 155 64/95 tons. She had been built in three months.

The lines (Plate 51) show a schooner having a strong sheer, much drag to the keel, raking curved-stem rabbet, very raking sternpost, eight ports a side, round tuck, and midsection formed with sharply rising straight floor, a high easy bilge, and some tumble home in the topside. The entrance is

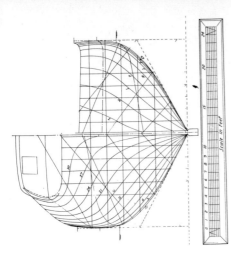

Plate 50. Plan of a fast American-type schooner designed by Henry Steers, father of George Steers (designer of the yacht AMERICA), when completing his apprenticeship as a shipwright in the Portsmouth dockyard, England. Original plan on 3/4-inch scale, showed all frame shapes, transom timbers, and the form of the load waterline when the vessel was heeled.

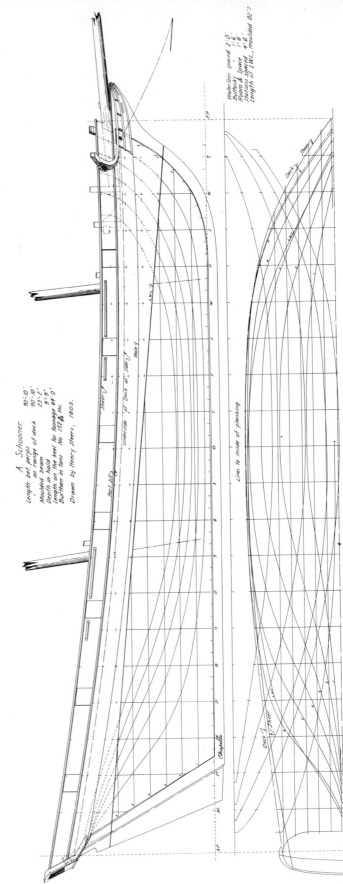

A Schooner

Length bet. perpr.	90'-10"
on range of deck	90'-10"
Moulded beam	23'-2"
Depth on hold	9'-9"
Length on the keel for tonnage	64'-0"
Burthen in tons	No 157 24/94 ths.

Drawn by Henry Steers, 1805.

Waterlines spaced 2'-0"
Buttocks   1'-6"
Room & Space   1'-6"
Stations spaced 4'-6"
Length of LWL., moulded 82'-3"

Line to inside of planking

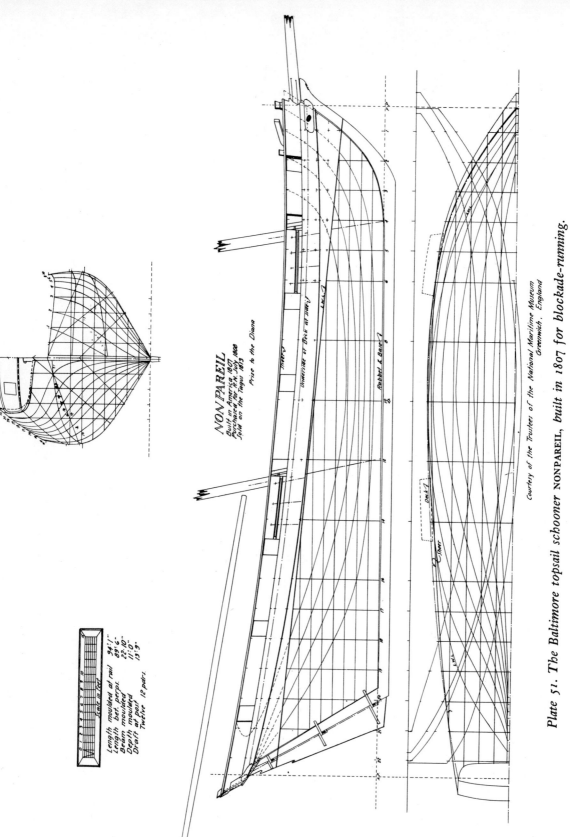

NONPAREIL
Built in America 1807
Purchased for R.N. July 1808
Sold on the Tagus 1813

Prize to the Diana

Waterline at Deck at Side

Rabbet of Keel

Scale in feet

Length moulded at rail   94'1"
Length bet. perp.   89'6"
Beam moulded   22'10"
Depth moulded   11'0"
Draft aft post   13'9"
Twelve 12 pairs.

Plate 51. The Baltimore topsail schooner NONPAREIL, built in 1807 for blockade-running.

rather short, but sharp and convex. The run is long and very fine. The buttocks are straight where they cross the after load waterline, and the outer buttocks are slightly hollow under the quarters. The lower transom has more than usual deadrise on its bottom or "cross seam."An Admiralty half-model of this schooner is in the National Maritime Museum at Greenwich, England.

The dimensions were 89′ 6″ between perpendiculars, 22′ 10″ moulded beam, 11 feet moulded depth, and the load draft was 13′ 10″ at post, as taken off. The length of the moulded load waterline was 82′ 6″, the moulded displacement 177.7 long tons, the block coefficient .32, the midship coefficient .59, the prismatic coefficient .59, the effective length of the quarterbeam buttock 58 feet, and camber 5 ′4½″, giving a camber-length ratio of 10.7.

Another American-built schooner captured while blockade-running and taken into the Royal Navy, was *Fly*, a more burdensome vessel than *Nonpareil*. *Fly* was taken by H.M. sloop-of-war *Scylla*, with cargo on board on 29 December 1811 while coming from Havre de Grace, France, bound for Bristol, Rhode Island. The capture took place some 43 miles off the Scilly Islands. Her cargo was French property and she carried some French passengers. She was apparently owned in Bristol but the register there for a *Fly*, dated 1811, gives no place of build nor any other particulars. She was ordered to be purchased 1 May 1812 by the Admiralty, and was renamed *Sea Lark* after being refitted at the Portsmouth dockyard.

Fly was a fore-topsail schooner 80′ 3″ on deck, 22′ 4″ moulded beam, and 9′ 10″ depth of hold. Her lines (Plate 52) show a vessel of moderate sheer and drag, with rather conservative rake in both stem and sternpost. This schooner had a round tuck, square stern, and gammon-knee head. Her entrance was short and convex, her run rather fine and long. She had sharply rising, straight floor at midsection, with slack bilges and a slight tumble home in the topside. Her length on the moulded load waterline was 76′ 8″; her moulded displacement was 142.4 long tons, block coefficient .31, midship coefficient .60, and prismatic coefficient .65. The effective length of her quarterbeam buttock was 63 feet, and the camber 5 feet; the camber-length ratio was 12.6.

The rig of *Fly* is shown in Plate 53 to be a conventional topsail schooner rig of the period. It is possible that *Fly* represents a southern New England version of the pilot-boat and schooner. Her spar dimensions given on Plate 52 show unusually large diameters for the lower masts and her plans also show more numerous shrouds than appear in the plans of Chesapeake and

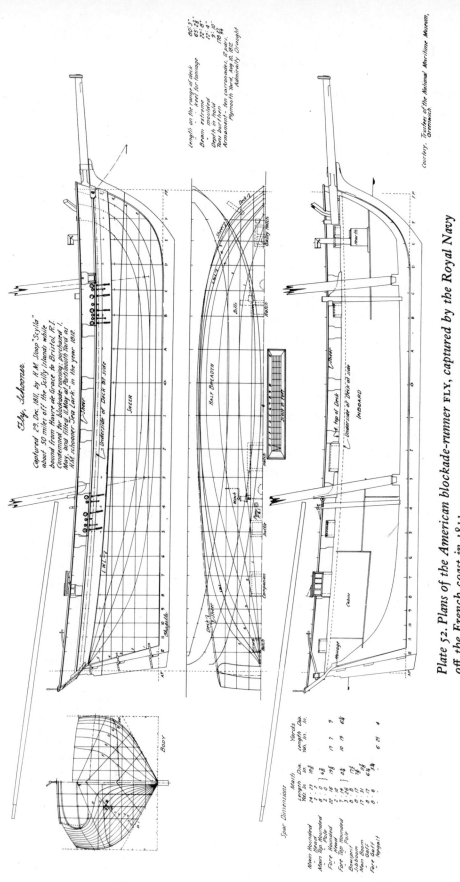

Fly, Schooner.

Captured 29, Dec. 1811, by H.M. Sloop "Scylla"
about 50 miles off the Scilly Islands while
bound from Havre de Grace to Bristol, R.I.
Condemned for blockade-running; purchased 1,
May, and fitted 11, May at Portsmouth Yard as
H.M. schooner "Sea Lark" in the year 1812

Length on the range of deck   80:3
keel for tonnage   65:2¾
Beam extreme   22:6"
moulded   22:0"
Depth in hold   9:10
Tons burthen   170 96⁄94
Armament - ten carronade, 12 pdr;
Plymouth Yard, Aug 10, 1812
Admiralty Draught

Plate 52. Plans of the American blockade-runner FLY, captured by the Royal Navy
off the French coast in 1811.

Schooner FLY, *1810, a blockade runner. United States National Museum.*

New York schooners, suggesting that she may not have been built in either of these areas. This, however, is speculation based on very limited evidence.

Dispatches from Vice Admiral Sir Alexander Cochrane, commander of the Leeward Islands station, to the Secretary of the Admiralty, dated "off Guadeloupe, 14 March 1810," announced the recent capture of a large letter-of-marque, the *Duc de Wagram*. He reported that he had the vessel surveyed at Antigua and that the report was so favorable that he had commissioned her, under the name *Dominica*, to take the place of a brig of that name that had foundered during the hurricane off Tortola in August 1809. The Admiralty ordered her sent to England, and acknowledging this order, Sir Alexander wrote that he considered her to be "so fine a vessel that he recommended her

197

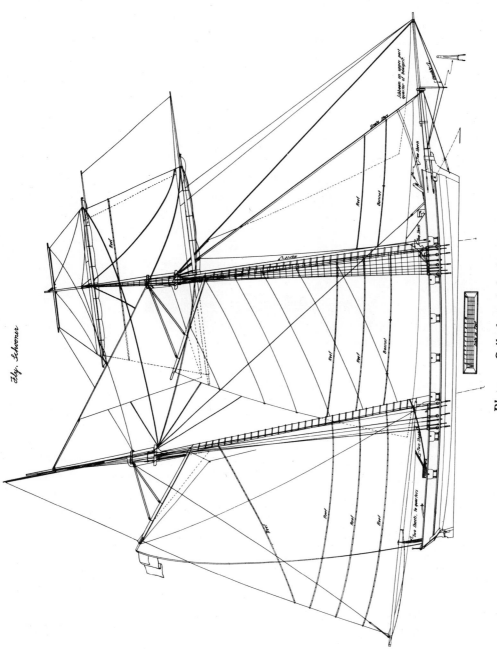

Fly. Schooner

Plate 53. Sail plan of the blockade-runner FLY.

lines be taken on arrival in England," and furthermore, he requested that she be ordered to return to him. She was purchased 23 May 1811 and her draught was completed 12 June 1811.

Dominica proved to be an excellent cruiser, capturing numerous French and American vessels in the West Indies. But early in the morning of 5 August 1812 *Dominica*, while escorting a mail packet, was sighted south of Bermuda by the American privateer schooner *Decatur* of Charleston, South Carolina. At 1:30 P.M. the schooners commenced action. This turned out to be one of the hardest fought small-vessel actions of the War of 1812. *Decatur* was the larger of the two schooners; when captured in 1814 by the British, it was reported that she had been built in the spring of 1812 at Charleston, South Carolina, coppered and copper-fastened, measuring 223 tons, 112 feet on deck, 90 feet on the keel, and 25' 4" extreme beam. Throughout her American ownership *Decatur* was commanded by Dominique Diron, a French privateer captain who had operated in the West Indies as commander of French privateers before the War of 1812.

The action resulted in the capture of *Dominica* and she was fitted out as an American privateer under the name of *Dominique*. She was retaken 22 May 1814, while bound from Charleston to St. Bartholomews, Tybee Light West 145 miles, by H.M. sloops-of-war *Doterel*, *Morgiana*, and the *Majestic* 74. Reinstated in the Royal Navy as *Dominica*, she was lost off Bermuda on 15 August 1815.

The incomplete Admiralty records of this schooner do not show that she was American-built, but official American references so state. In any case, almost without exception, the French privateer and naval schooners employed in the West Indies were vessels constructed in America and purchased by the French. Among the numerous French prizes taken in this area, only three schooners were French-built and two were Bermuda-built.

Dominica, as built, is illustrated in Plates 54 and 55. During the time she was in French hands and before she went into commission in the Royal Navy in 1811 she had an additional knee fitted outside her gammon-knee head, and false quarter galleries and roundhouses were added.

This schooner was 91 feet between perpendiculars, 89' 6½" long on range of deck, 22' 9" moulded beam, 9' 3¾" depth in hold, and 203 25/94 tons by Royal Navy measurement.

In lines she was a conservative design, having slight sheer, moderate drag to the keel, and rake in the ends. Her entrance was slightly hollow at the

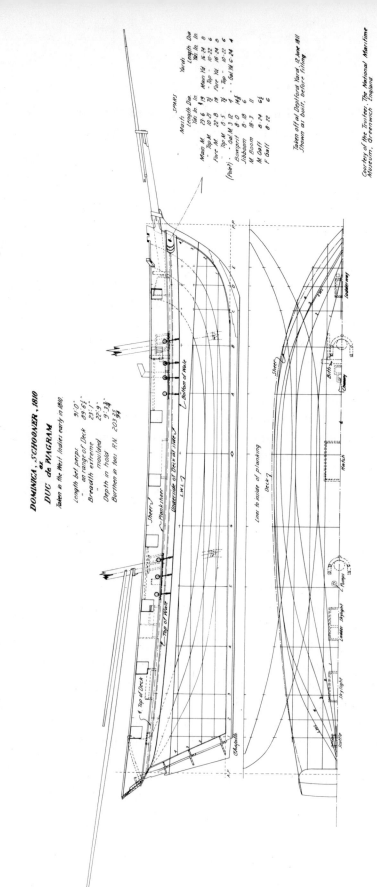
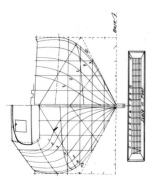

DOMINICA, SCHOONER, 1810
ex
DUC de WAGRAM

Taken in the West Indies early in 1810.

Length bet perpl	91'0"
" on range of Deck	89'6½"
Breadth extreme	23'1"
" moulded	22'9"
Depth in hold	9'3¾"
Burthen in tons RN	203 25⁄94

SPARS

Masts	Length	Dia		Yards	Length	Dia
	Yds	In	In			Yds	In	In
Main M.	25'6	1'9		Main Yd	14'24	8
" Top M.	10'2½	7½		" Top	10'22	6
Fore M.	22'8	1'9		Fore Yd	16'24	6
" Top M.	8'5	7½		" Top	10'22	6
(Fore) " Gaff M. 3'12	4		Gaff Yd 6'24	4
Bowsprit	8'0	1'4½
Jibboom	8'10	6
M. Boom	18'3	11
M. Gaff	8'24	6½
F. Gaff	8'22	6

Taken off at Deptford Yard, 12 June 1811
Shown as built, before fitting.

Courtesy of the Trustees, The National Maritime
Museum, Greenwich, England.

Plate 54. French letter-of-marque schooner DUC DE WAGRAM, said to
have been American-built. She was taken by the Royal Navy in the
West Indies in 1810. Retaken by the American privateer DECATUR in
1812. Fitted as a privateer under the name DOMINICA and again captured by the Royal Navy in 1814. Lost off Bermuda 15 August 1815.

load line; her run was long and rather fine, and the quarterbeam buttock was straight for a short distance at the after load line. Her midsection was of standard form—sharply rising straight floor, high and well-rounded bilge, with slight tumble home in the topside.

Her sail plan, Plate 55, shows her rig to have been somewhat more square than usual, and less lofty, but with very long square sail yards. This may have been the result of French ownership; however, unlike *Fly,* she was lightly rigged, in Chesapeake Bay fashion.

She was 84′ 6″ moulded length on the load line, displacing 141.8 long tons. Her coefficients were: block .38, midship .59, prismatic .64. The effective length on the quarterbeam buttock was 67′ 6″ and the camber 4′ 7½″, giving a camber-length ratio of 14.7.

A small, sharp, merchant schooner of this period named *Experiment* is shown in Plates I and 56. She is said to have been built on the Chesapeake. In 1812 this schooner, with Russian goods on board, arrived at Karlskrona, Sweden. The Swedish Admiral Puke saw her under sail; he later inspected her and as a result requested her purchase by the Swedish Royal Navy early in 1813. *Experiment* was then used as a model for four Swedish naval schooners, *Activ, L'Aigle, Puke,* and *Falk,* which were constructed sometime after her purchase. Throughout her career in the Swedish Navy *Experiment* had the reputation of being an extremely fast sailer; she was broken up in 1859.

Experiment was 71′ 6″ between perpendiculars, 22′ 9″ moulded beam, and 8′ 10″ moulded depth. She was rather wide for her length. Her sheer was slight and the drag of her keel great. The rake of the ends was marked, particularly in the sternpost. She had a gammon-knee head, with a well-curved stem rabbet; her square stern exhibited the usual upper-and-lower transom, but her tuck was square. At load very little of the square tuck was immersed. Her entrance was short, convex, and moderately sharp, with a slight hollow near the stem rabbet in the load line. Her midsection shows a hollow garboard and rising floor and a slack bilge carried to the deck line with a very slight tumble home in the bulwark. Her run was long and fine, with a straight quarterbeam buttock at the after load line.

Experiment was 71′ 4″ on the moulded load line, displacing 96.2 long tons, moulded, with the following coefficients: block .31, midship .51, prismatic .62. The effective length of quarterbeam buttock was 55′ 3″ and the camber 3′ 3″, giving a camber-length ratio of 14.7.

It should be observed that for a merchant schooner, and considering her

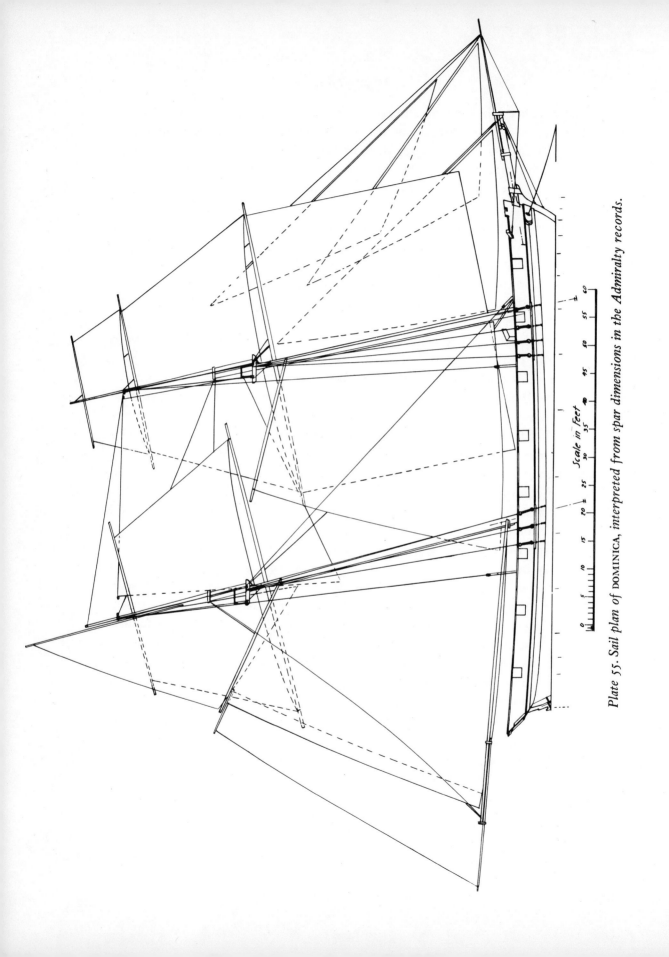

Plate 55. Sail plan of DOMINICA, interpreted from spar dimensions in the Admiralty records.

Scale in Feet

dimensions, *Experiment* had a small displacement. Her hull form, however, was such that she gained displacement very rapidly as her draft was increased. The general form of this schooner seems to indicate that she had been especially designed for blockade-running. Also the Baltimore district ship reg-

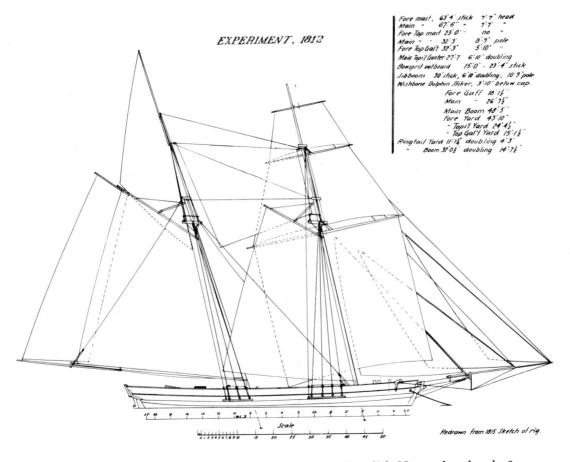

Plate 56. Sail plan of EXPERIMENT, *redrawn from Swedish Navy plan dated 1815. Lines are shown in Plate I.*

istration for the period 1810–25 show that such schooners as *Experiment* were very numerous, particularly in the West Indian and South American trades.

The rig of *Experiment*, Plate 56, shows that of the usual Chesapeake Bay fore-topsail schooner of the period, with its lofty lower mast, large mainsail and head rig, small square-sail yards giving a lofty, narrow square-sail rig. The plate is drawn from a Swedish draught made in 1815 and this may account for the gunter-pole fore-topgallant mast, stepped on the lower masthead and running up abaft the topmast. This is not shown in any sail plan of an American schooner known to the author, but does appear in schooners of this period built in Sweden and Denmark. Nevertheless, the gunter-type top-gallant shown here was duplicated in American ships in the skysail masts secured abaft the royal masts, and was used in American naval vessels during the War of 1812 and afterward.

The dolphin striker or martingale was used in American schooners in the 1790's but many of the Chesapeake Bay built schooners omitted this spar as late as 1825. Naval schooners and some large merchant schooners had the "wishbone" or two-armed dolphin striker, but most of the pilot-boat model schooners appear to have used the single martingale.

A large "sharp-built" American merchant ship is shown in Plate 57. This is the *Hannibal*, built at Baltimore, Maryland, in 1811.* The Admiralty record of this vessel is very unsatisfactory, as the Vice-Admiralty Court papers cannot be found. The Admiralty correspondence and other documents, however, show that the *Hannibal* was captured by H.M. frigate *Medusa*, H.M. frigate *Niemen* in company, with two British privateers in sight, on 31 January 1812 in the approaches to Bordeaux. It took the *Medusa* from 7:30 A.M. on 30 January to 2:30 P.M. on the 31st, to overtake the American ship. On 20 March 1812, the Admiralty referred to the Navy Board a tender, or offer, for the *Hannibal* for His Majesty's service. The survey report having been favorable, Admiralty orders were issued for her purchase on 23 May 1812. She was commissioned 26 October 1812 under the name *Andromeda*, and was sold out of service sometime in 1816. From scattered references to this vessel, she was considered a very good sailer and a well-built vessel.

Plate 57 shows a "half-clipper" by later standards, measuring 135' 6" on the range of deck, 36' 11¼" moulded beam, 10' 11" depth in hold, and the Royal Navy register shows her to have been 809 4/94 tons.

She was flush-decked, with slight sheer, about 4' 7" drag to the keel, strongly raking, curved-stem rabbet, billet head, moderately-raking post,

---

* Registered at Baltimore #186, 1811, "sharp built," two decks, three masts. 136'6" by 37'8", 850–61/95 tons, square stern, round tuck, no galleries, no figurehead (billet), built by William Price. Endorsed, "Captured by the British, 1812."

AMERICAN SCHOONER EXPERIMENT, 1812

Reputed to have been built on the Chesapeak and purchased for the Swedish Navy in 1813. Broken up in 1859.

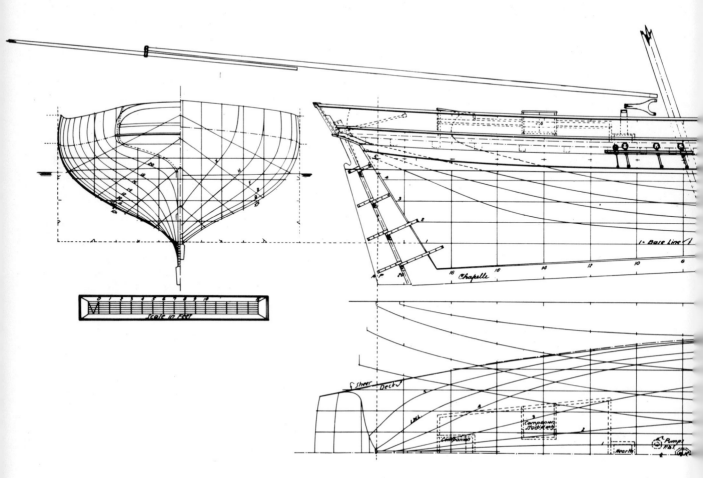

Scale in Feet

Sheer Deck

Base Line

Chapelle

This American merchant schooner, described as a very
fast sailer, arrived at Karlskrona, with Russian goods aboard,
in 1812. Her construction, rigging and sailing attracted the
attention of Admiral Puke who obtained permission to purchase
her for the Swedish Navy early in 1813. Her lines were carefully taken off and drawn, with some modifications in mouldings,
cutwater and appearance. It is uncertain that the "Experiment had
gunports originally; the earliest sail plan, 1815, does not
show any, but later ones show varying arrangements.
   The plans were used to build the naval schooners "Falk",
"Puke", "L'Aigle" and "Activ". They carried two 4 pdr.
carriage guns and six 12 pdr. carronades.
   The American register of this schooner has not been found.
Swedish record from Sjöhistoriska Museum, Archive Book.
Notes Nº 2, page 6, Nº ÖH 1052.

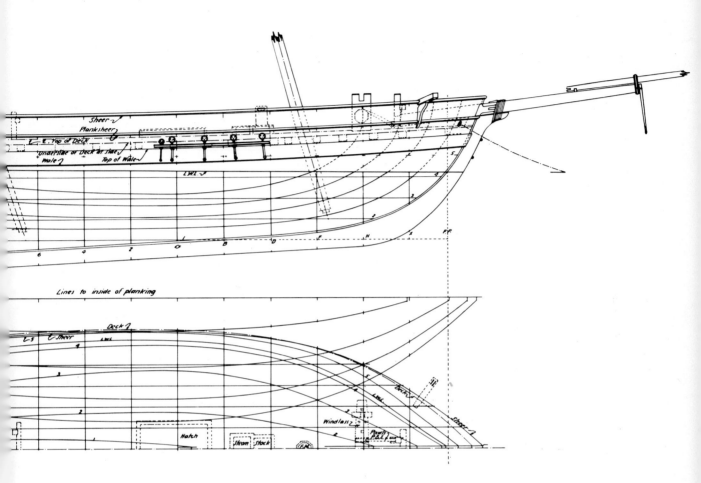

Length bet. perps. 71·6"
Beam moulded 22·9"
   "   extreme 23·1"
Depth, rabbet to deck at side, moulded, 8·10½"

3·6" F.P. to X, stations 4·4⅜"; 2·6" 20
to A.P. = 71·6" bet. perps..
W.L.'s and buttocks spaced 2·0:

Swedish Naval Archives

PLATE I. *The handsome merchant schooner* EXPERIMENT, *built on the Chesa-peake and purchased for the Swedish Navy in 1812.*

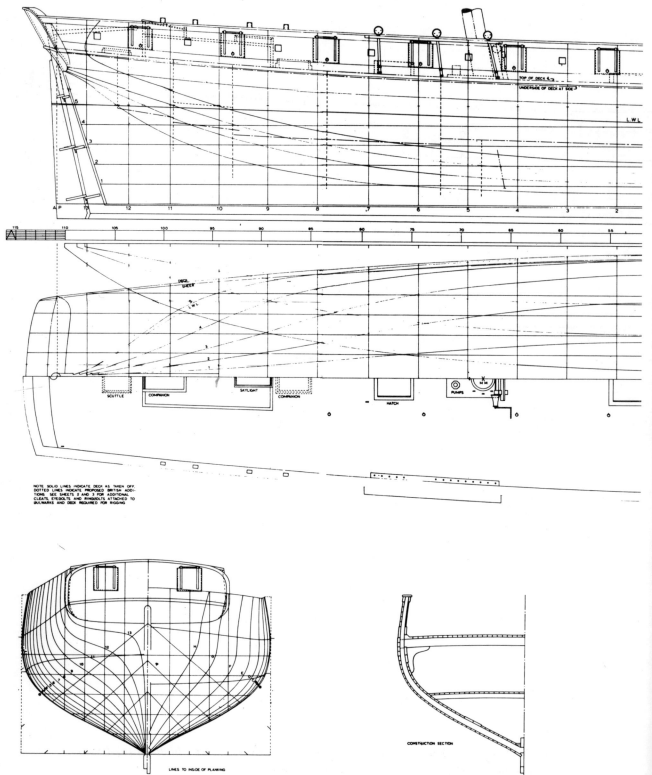

NOTE SOLID LINES INDICATE DECK AS TAKEN OFF.
DOTTED LINES INDICATE PROPOSED BRITISH ADDI-
TIONS. SEE SHEETS 2 AND 3 FOR ADDITIONAL
CLEATS, EYEBOLTS AND RINGBOLTS ATTACHED TO
BULWARKS AND DECK REQUIRED FOR RIGGING

SCUTTLE   COMPANION   SKYLIGHT   COMPANION   HATCH   PUMPS

TOP OF DECK
UNDERSIDE OF DECK AT SIDE
L.W.L.

DECK
SHEER
L W L

LINES TO INSIDE OF PLANKING

CONSTRUCTION SECTION

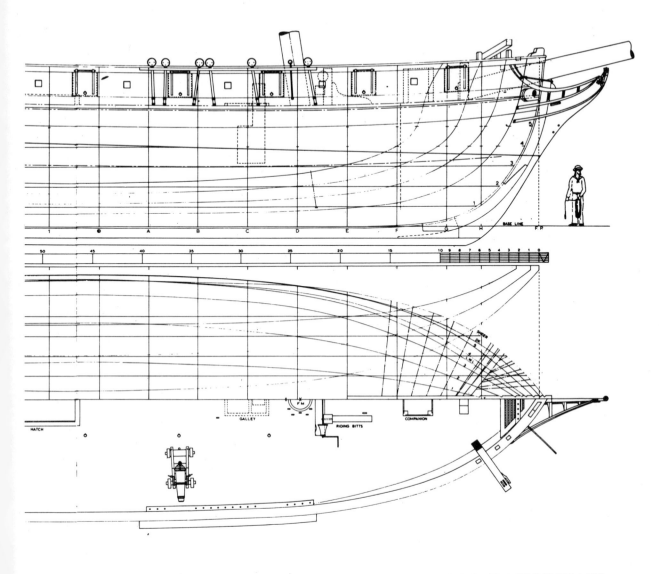

PRINCE de NEUFCHATEL - Privateer

Principal Dimensions

Length on the deck	110'-8"
" for measuring tonnage	93'-8¼"
Breadth extreme	25'-8"
" moulded	25'-4"
Burthen in tons	
English measure	328 ¹⁷/₉₄
American measure	319 ⁸⁸/₉₅
Probable armament	16-12pdr Carronades
	2- 6pdr Guns
Probable boats carried	26'-0" Launch
	20'-0" Cutter
	16'-0" Cutter
Copper sheathed	

PROBABLY BUILT AT NEW YORK IN 1812-13 BY ADAM & NOAH BROWN. INITIAL LETTER-OF-MARQUE ISSUED AT NEW YORK OCTOBER 28, 1813. UNTIL HER CAPTURE BY THE BRITISH, DECEMBER 26, 1814, THE NEUFCHATEL WAS AN ACTIVE AND SUCCESSFUL PRIVATEER.

REFERENCES: Admiralty draughts, Reg. Nos 6041/42, Box 46, courtesy of the Trustees of the National Maritime Museum; Deptford Yard Survey of March, 1815, courtesy of the Public Records Office; Steel, ELEMENTS OF RIGGING, London, 1794; Lever, SHEET ANCHOR, London, 1819; Chapelle, THE HISTORY OF AMERICAN SAILING SHIPS, New York, 1935.

Plan prepared for the SMITHSONIAN INSTITUTION, DIVISION OF NAVAL HISTORY by M. A. Edson, Jr. 1964

PLATE II. *Lines of the* PRINCE DE NEUFCHÂTEL, *a vessel noted for her sailing qualities, built at New York by Adam and Noah Brown in 1812–13. Admiralty take-off.*

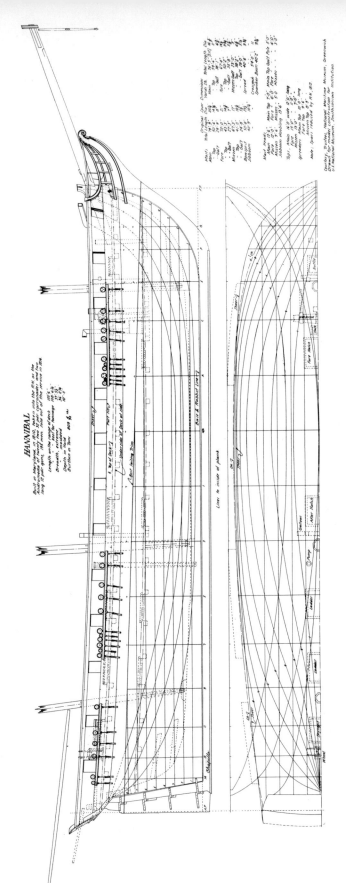

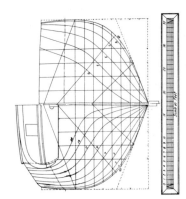

Plate 57. Large Maryland-built merchant ship HANNIBAL, launched in 1810. An attempt to combine good carrying qualities with fast sailing. Captured in 1812 and taken into the Royal Navy in 1812 as H.M.S. post ship ANDROMEDA.

short, convex, and rather full entrance; long, easy run, round-tuck square stern with upper-and-lower transom. The midsection shows moderately rising straight floor; slack, full bilge; and slight tumble home in topside.

She measured 129' 10" on the moulded load line and had a moulded displacement of 934.6 long tons. Her coefficients were: block .48, midship .68, prismatic .70. The effective length of her quarterbeam buttock was 116' 7", the camber was 10' 6", giving a camber-length ratio of 11.1.

It will be seen, when later vessels are examined, that *Hannibal* was large for an American merchantman in 1811. This ship proves that the Chesapeake Bay area was capable of turning out large vessels of good construction, and the registers of the Baltimore customhouse show that she was not the only one of this description.

In the period under examination, there are enough plans of fast-sailing, American-built vessels to show that a wide variety of hull forms, proportions, and general design features had been established. Future trends in pilot-boat models—whether ship, brig, brigantine, or schooner—would be limited to an increase in size and to certain refinements of hull and rig design.

The increasing length of wooden sailing vessels in this period produced longitudinal weakness and there were some complaints about hogging. These were very troublesome problems in armed ships, particularly naval vessels, because the weight of armament placed in their ends. American frigates, of the *Constitution* and *Constellation* classes, hogged severely within a few years of their launch. In England there had been numerous studies of the problem of longitudinal strength in large merchant ships and men-of-war, resulting in the addition of reinforcing timbers inside the ship, including such items as bracing stanchions, diagonal and iron knees, and additional longitudinals. It was also noted that a vessel's form, as well as her proportions, affected hog.*

In American vessels in this period, the expensive and heavy kneeing and internal timbering proposed in Europe were not utilized except in a few men-of-war, such as *President*. Americans had found that vessels designed with sharply rising straight floors and high bilge showed little tendency to hog, the planking in such vessels approaching the perpendicular enough to have the effect of a longitudinal bulkhead with its members locked by frame fastenings and by caulking. In fullbodied vessels, the American trend was

* John Fincham, *A History of Naval Architecture: to which is prefixed an Introductory Dissertation on the application of mathematical science to the art of naval construction* (London, Whittaker and Co., 1851), pp. 107–115.

toward nearly wall-sided hulls, where again the plank acted as a longitudinal strengthening bulkhead. The effect of caulking in obtaining longitudinal strength was recognized, for some American ship contract-specifications called for caulking the ceiling or inner plank, as well as the outer.

It should be noted here that a modern naval architect, in discussing wooden construction of fishing and commercial vessels, points out the advantage of deadrise with reference to longitudinal strength. In addition, the use of edge-fastening on part of the planking, such as in the thick plank or wales in some early Chesapeake vessels, is also recommended*

The advantage of great deadrise in producing longitudinal strength, and its acceptance as useful in producing good sailing qualities, were the reasons for retaining this characteristic, even though it was fully recognized in America that vessels with great deadrise were not economical carriers. Many attempts were made to combine marked, but not extreme, deadrise with cargo capacity. *Hannibal* might be considered such an experiment. The combination of fast-sailing qualities with large cargo capacity was always a difficult problem of design, for as long as the sharp deadrise model was most favored, and in fact afterward, the tendency was to sacrifice capacity for speed in the selection of hull form and design elements.

Some proposals were made for increasing the longitudinal strength of wooden hulls that did not increase structural weight or take up hold space. The most important of these was the use of diagonal planking, an innovation that became an important structural feature in American ships. The French, whose fast naval vessels had a midsection form that produced a hull having little resistence to hogging strains, had begun studies of the problem as early as 1746. During that year they built a vessel with diagonally planked ceiling, and in 1772 they built the diagonally planked frigate *L'Oiseau*.† This matter will again be discussed with regard to later developments.

In 1761 the British Navy tested the use of copper sheathing on the hull to protect it against the teredo worm and to delay fouling. On 18 October of that year the Admiralty ordered copper to be applied to the frigate *Alarm* 32 and she was sent to the West Indies station. On her return from that duty she was examined and found to be free of ship worms and her bottom was reasonably clean. But the underwater fastenings and iron fittings were

* H. C. Hanson, N. A., *Effect of Deadrise on Loadline Rules* (Seattle, Washington, privately printed by the author, undated).
† Fincham, *A History of Naval Architecture*, p. 198.

being destroyed. In the summer of 1769 the frigates *Aurora* and *Stag* were also sheathed. Canvas and other insulating materials were applied before coppering these ships, but their iron fastenings still failed after a few years of service. Coppering was continued, although in 1783 the Navy Board seriously considered abandoning it because of the damage to fastenings. It was decided to use copper alloy fastenings to reduce electrolysis, and these were ordered for new 44-gun ships and smaller cruisers in August 1783. Two months later this order was extended to all new ships.*

Because of the high cost of hand-wrought copper plates and alloyed fastenings, they came into use on vessels of the British merchant fleet very slowly. This was also true in America and it was not until the last decade of the eighteenth century that many merchant vessels were copper-sheathed, and then generally only large ships.† Rolled copper sheet began being produced in Maryland in 1782, and at Boston in 1794. As the war of the French Revolution progressed, however, coppering increased. The thin copper plates were tacked over felt, which was set with hot pine tar on both sides. Hence, until well into the second decade of the nineteenth century, American merchant vessels usually retained iron fastenings, protected from electrolysis by tar and felt. The wasting of the pure copper sheathing was rapid. It was not until the late 1820's that copper-alloy fastenings were commonly employed. The advantages of a clean bottom in a fast sailer were obvious, and many sharp American schooners were copper-sheathed and fastened after 1795, though this was expensive until after 1815. As late as 1822, however, the old lime-and-tallow, or "white-bottom," was still being extensively used in the United States.

In general, the American-built fast sailers carried little carving during this period. Busts and small figures of animals were used occasionally, but the majority of fast sailing schooners had either the simple curved stem of the pilot boat, with the bowsprit bolted athwartships through the knightheads, instead of gammoning, or the plain gammon-knee head.

The topsides of these schooners were commonly painted yellow or black, with one or more narrow colored stripes parallel to the rail and above the deck. Varnished pine topsides were common on the Chesapeake, often with a black stripe or band.

---

* Fincham, *A History of Naval Architecture*, pp. 95–97.
† American naval vessels were apparently all coppered and copper-fastened, beginning with the *Constitution* and *Constellation* classes of frigates.

The numerous Royal Navy surveys of American-built schooners that had been taken from the French or from blockade-runners captured from the Americans in this period, show important features in construction. Generally the British surveyors found them "slightly built," often with "irregular frame-spacing." The old practice of using mould frames, ribbaned-off, with intermediate frames inserted, made up of futtocks that were not fastened together, seems to have been rather common. The increase in spacing between frames toward the ends of the hull in order to save weight, did not appeal to the dock-yards of the Royal Navy, and judging by the survey reports, widely-spaced framing was considered unsafe. The planking of the schooners was often light, compared to British practice, and a lack of platforms in the hold, except for the after cabin floor, is noted occasionally. In a few instances comment appears regarding the lack of a windlass or capstan. The use of cedar for top timbers, oak futtocks, keel, deadwood, stempost, sternpost, and keelson was very common; pine plank with oak wales appeared often in the survey descriptions. The English master-shipwrights called southern yellow pine "fir" in dockyard surveys; the qualities of this timber apparently were unknown to them. From the survey reports it is obvious that there was some range in quality of workmanship but only three instances were found where the workmanship was stated to be poor.

The years between 1793 and 1812 saw the evolution of the sharp American schooner under war requirements, and the firm establishment of the pilot-boat model in America, as the preferred type for fast, ocean-going vessels.

CHAPTER • FIVE

1812 - 1820

MANY AMERICAN SHIPPING MERCHANTS AND SHIPBUILDERS REALIZED THAT THE United States was close to war with England in the fall of 1811. On the Chesapeake, at New York, and elsewhere, schooners, brigs, and brigantines on the sharp model and suited for letter-of-marques were set up on the stocks. These vessels were generally over 80 feet on deck; a few were 100 feet or more; and many had ceiled bulwarks that builders then described as "privateer-built." Foresighted merchants prepared to lay up slow-sailing carriers and to operate new swift-sailing blockade-runners and letter-of-marques in their place.

With war approaching, the builders and owners of new, fast vessels sought to fit them in the best manner for their purpose. In these vessels good sails were important and a great improvement had recently taken place in sail-cloth. Prior to 1811, sailcloth had been made of flax. These sails were soft, rather loose in weave, and did not hold their shape very well. It was necessary to wet them down to shrink the loose weave so that the sails would hold the wind in very light breezes when speed was sought. A mixed material, a combination of flax and cotton in sail duck, had been tried at Philadelphia and production of this sail duck had begun in Kentucky. In 1809 Seth Bemis began the manufacture of cotton sail duck at Watertown, Massachusetts, employing hand looms and a twisting machine that had 48 spindles. The price was then 65 cents a yard for No. 1 duck, and 58 cents for No. 2 duck. When the War of 1812 began, the price of No. 1 rose to nearly a dollar a yard. In 1812–13 the sale of canvas duck by one Baltimore dealer amounted to $20,000. Duck was transported to the Chesapeake, Philadelphia, and New York by wagons. Although the hand-woven cotton duck was made as hard as possible, power looms made sailcloth that was more closely woven, harder, more durable, and more uniform in texture.* Patented methods were also developed and the hard, close-woven sailcloth became standard in American sail-making between 1815 and 1831. During the war, privateers and blockade-runners using this cotton canvas were considered to sail much better on the wind than those using flax. The British Navy used flax throughout the war, as did the American Navy.

The problem of stability was one that developed in the sharp-model vessels early in the war. While the sharply rising floor and high bilge midsection produced adequate stability in these craft if they were properly ballasted, the addition of cannon on deck would certainly affect in some degree their power to carry sail. It was found that some of the small pilot boats, fitted out early in the war, were unable to carry even one gun in blowing weather. When a gale was expected, the gun and mount had to be stowed in the hold. Even large privateer schooners sometimes had trouble. Improper ballasting resulted, in some of these vessels at least, to over-gunning. In others, insufficient displacement caused the owner or captain to reduce ballast in order to float the guns high enough so that they would be effective in a seaway. There was over-sparring and over-canvassing in some of these craft also, of course, for sail power meant speed, and the additional displacement required by armament could slow down a vessel retaining her normal rig. By increasing the sail area this disadvantage might be overcome—but an overestimate of the vessel's power to carry sail could result in a very tender, or unstable, vessel.

The ballasting commonly used in these sharp vessels was pig iron,† for they usually had too little room over the keel to permit use of the more bulky

---

* J. Leander Bishop, *A History of American Manufactures from 1608 to 1860* (Philadelpia, E. Young & Co., 1864), Vol. 2, pp. 2, 139–40, 232, 272, and 274.
† The ballast stowage from H.B.M. schooner *Flying Fish*, ex-*Revenge*, shows she carried 13 tons 5 hundredweight of iron pigs (79 in number) and 3 tons of stone; 6 small pigs of iron were also carried stowed as required for trim. Pigs were 4½″ by 4½″ by 4′ 3″. The center of gravity of the ballast was a little abaft the middle of the L. W. L.

stone or gravel. The heart-shaped midsection had certain advantages, for its form usually placed the center of buoyancy high, close to the load waterline. The ballast, placed low, usually brought the center of gravity low. When upright, the center of gravity (like the center of buoyancy) would be on the vertical centerline of the hull, and preferably below the center of buoyancy. If the vessel were heeled, the center of gravity remained fixed on the vertical center line but the center of buoyancy, due to hull shape, would move toward the direction of heel. By calculation from the lines, the movement of this center can be established. Plotting its heeled location would show that the new location of the center of buoyancy would have an upward effect in righting and the center of gravity would have a downward effect. If vertical lines were drawn through each center, perpendicular respectively to the upright and heeled load waterlines, these verticals would intersect above the load waterline. This point of intersection is known as the "metacenter." The higher the metacenter above the center of gravity, the greater the righting moment or power. In the design stage, by plotting the position of the metacenter on a midship diagram at varying angles of heel, it can be seen what range of stability the vessel will have. This method of determining stability by calculation was used by Chapman and occasionally employed in the design of large naval sailing ships, but the center of gravity calculation was laborious and time-consuming, with the result that little calculated stability data are available for sailing merchant vessels.

In full-bodied vessels, having more or less flat floors, there was room for large quantities of ballast, but the center of buoyancy was low compared to its location in the heart-shaped midsection. In sailing ships of the flat-floored form, the metacentric height may not be great when loaded and sharply heeled, due to the relatively high center of gravity; on the other hand it may be great when not loaded and with small angles of heel. Generally, then, the flat-floored sailing vessel had marked initial stability when light, at small angles of heel, but had a limited range of stability. Such vessels could sail without much, or even any, ballast in some cases. This had economic advantages to the operators, when cargo was to be obtained at two or more ports in order to fill the vessel. But when light, such sailing vessels were often lacking in weatherliness, which accounted for numerous losses on lee shores in blowing weather. A flat-floored sailing vessel should be deep in the hold to obtain a marked range in stability when loaded, but this element did not help stability when sailing light.

Ballast for calculation would include cargo and stores for load-line stability conditions. Armament and stores would be included in load and stability calculations in men-of-war. The amount of permanent ballast, pig iron (kentledge), required in fitting out most small men-of-war—brigs, brigantines, schooners, and ship sloops—compared to the total load displacement was moderate, say from 8 percent to 14 percent or around 10 percent. Modern cruising yachts run from 20 percent to 38 percent; racers up to 80 percent.

A vessel having hollow garboards and hard bilges, combined with much depth in hold, had marked initial stability, and usually a large range. Those of comparative depth, having straight, rising floors, had somewhat less initial stability and usually a little less range. Stability of sailing vessels is a more complicated problem than the foregoing indicates, for sail area and weight of rig, location and weight of cargo, danger of flooding when heeled at extreme angles, the buoyancy of raised, closed-in quarterdecks and forecastles, effects of hull proportions and form, particularly the ratios of depth to beam and freeboard to beam, all become important factors in stability calculations.

A very important factor in the requirements of a sailing-vessel design is the range of stability. The ideal would be recovery up to 90 degrees heel from the perpendicular. Deep and well-ballasted vessels may have this range theoretically, but usually the hatches and deck openings are in the water before a 90-degree heel is reached. Since such an extreme would normally occur only in blowing weather when the sea would probably break open some of the hatches or companionways, swamping would result.

In practice, the maximum safe heel obtained seems to have been somewhere around 55 to 65 degrees from the perpendicular in many merchant sailing vessels; at this angle of heel the wind pressure in the sails was somewhat diminished, at least under normal conditions. It is also evident, however, that many sailing vessels could not safely be heeled beyond 45 to 50 degrees from the perpendicular, either because they were lacking in range or because of the possibility of flooding. Many of the privateer schooners of the War of 1812 were in this category, due to excessive armaments, as has been mentioned. Capsizing of merchant sailing vessels (knocking down and flooding), occurred all through the sailing-ship period. Very fast-sailing merchant vessels and privateers required careful handling in gale weather, as a general rule, because of these stability factors.

The use of rules for sparring vessels was common in the first third of the nineteenth century in America. The difficulty in using these rules for reconstructing spar plans, however, is that no two agree closely enough in results. The designer-builder or the captain used his judgment, or "eye," to determine the spar lengths. It seems to have been common practice to use multiples of the extreme beam to obtain spar lengths. On the Chesapeake, for example, the total length of the mainmast in a schooner was often 3.1 to 3.5 times the beam by rule. Some builders used three times the beam plus half, or the whole, depth of hull amidships. The foremast was a foot or two shorter, but of larger diameter, for it usually supported the largest part of the sail plan—the foresail, headsails, topsails, and course. The length of the main boom was commonly 2 to 2.5 times the beam. The bowsprit was around 1.2 times the beam. The other spars were made generally proportionate to these, but elaborate, detailed proportions were given in books on sparring and rigging. So far as can be judged, the builders rarely adhered exactly to their own rules, for these were for general "guidance" only. These sparring rules controlled the size and shape of the sails, which in turn had much effect on the balance of the rig and the hull. If trials showed that a new vessel steered poorly, it was the custom to move the masts or change the rake to correct this fault. In one class of Royal Navy schooners the positions of the masts were shifted twice.*

Many post-war accounts of American privateers of the War of 1812 mention "Long Toms" as part of their armament. This was often a heavy long gun on a four-wheel carriage that could be "shifted" to fire through any available gunport. Privateers as a rule showed many more ports than they had guns, so the shifting gun was common.

Some these Long Toms were pivoted guns, mounted on a sliding carriage that turned on a circular metal track in the deck, the carriage pivoting on a heavy bolt through the deck. Such guns were not uncommon in the low-bulwarked pilot-boat privateers, where the normal pivot mounting allowed the gun to fire at point-blank range over the very low rails or bulwarks.

In vessels having high bulwarks, a pivot gun had to be raised enough for its fire to clear the rails or have its traverse of fire limited to two, or at most, four ports on each side. The use of unusually large gunports, at the pivot, has not been indicated in any of the plans of sailing vessels of this period yet found.

A raised pivot created obvious structural objections for use with a heavy long gun. Hence, some vessels with such a pivot mounting substituted a large

* Calculations of centers of area and lateral plane were employed in the R.N. by the late 1830's, however.

carronade for a long gun as a pivot gun. Chapman had employed pivot mountings in Sweden before 1790; the American gunboats of the Jefferson era and some American naval vessels of the War of 1812 on the Great Lakes were armed entirely with pivot guns. French privateer schooners in the West Indies also had pivot guns before 1812, but these vessels all appear to have been American-built.

The mode of mounting one or more large pivot guns in a vessel having high bulwarks and a broadside battery remains a matter of speculation, except in a few cases where the guns were placed on a raised forecastle or quarter-deck.

A very fine example of a letter-of-marque built on the Chesapeake was the schooner *Lynx*, built at Baltimore in 1812 for James Williams, Amos Williams, and Levi Hollingsworth. Her American register dimensions were 97′ by 24′ 4″ by 10′ 8″ and 225 17/95 tons. The *Lynx*, along with Baltimore schooners *Arab*, *Racer*, and *Dolphin*, was captured 13 April 1813, while anchored in the Rappahannock River, by boats of Sir John Warren's squadron, consisting of the 74's *San Domingo* and *Marlborough*, the frigates *Maidstone* and *Statira*, and the brig-sloops *Fantôme* and *Mohawk*, and schooner *Highflyer*. The British attacked in 17 boats, and with strong resistance from only *Arab* and *Dolphin*, captured the American vessels. This bag of prizes brought three fine schooners into the Royal Navy, *Lynx* as *Mosquidobit* (a town in Nova Scotia), the *Racer* as *Shelburne* (also a Nova Scotia town), and *Dolphin* under her American name.

Lynx was a letter-of-marque carrying six guns. Of the four schooners, only *Dolphin* was on a privateering cruise; she carried 12 guns and had a complement of 100 men. *Lynx* with 40 men, *Racer* with 36, and *Arab* with 45 were carrying cargo; they were blockade-runners in fact. *Racer* was 99′ 6″ length on deck, 24′ 4″ beam, and 10′ 7″ depth of hold, built in 1811 in Talbot County, Maryland. *Arab* was 105 feet on deck, 27′ 6″ beam, and 13 feet depth in hold, built in Somerset County, Maryland, in 1812. *Dolphin* was a relatively small schooner of 161 tons; she was described as being both fast and well-built.

According to the British Admiralty draught made after her capture, *Lynx* was 94′ 7″ between perpendiculars, 23′ 8″ moulded beam, and 10′ 3″ depth in hold. A good example of her type, she had a marked sheer, almost four feet drag to the keel, strongly raking and curved-stem rabbet, gammon-knee head, marked rake in the sternpost, round tuck, upper-and-lower transoms, sharp, convex entrance with very easy bow lines, long, fine run with quarterbeam buttock straight near the waterline, with marked reverse curve as the transom was approached. The midsection shows rising, straight floor, carried well out, and rather quick high turn of bilge with slight tumble home in topside. Though privateer-built, she made no cruise as a privateer. Her lines are shown in Plate 58.

Her length, moulded, on the load line was 88 feet. She had 191.3 long tons moulded displacement. Her coefficients were: block .37, midship .63, and prismatic .59. The effective length of her quarterbeam buttock was 70 feet and the camber 6 feet, giving a camber-length ratio of 11.7.

LYNX, *an American letter-of-marque built at Baltimore in 1812. Taken into the Royal Navy as* MUSQUIDOBIT. *United States National Museum.*

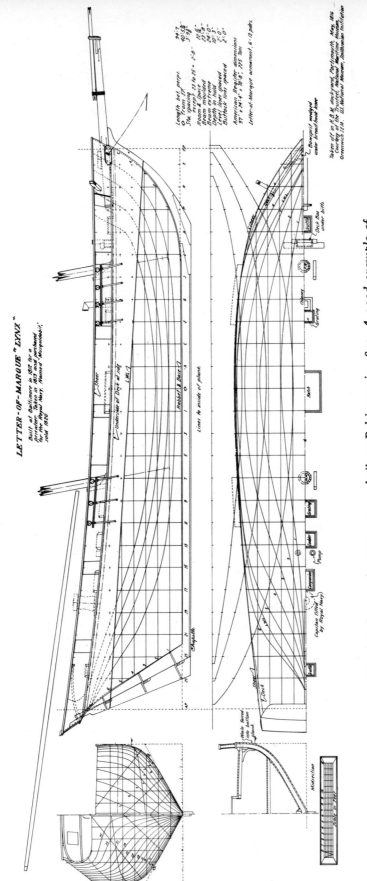

Plate 58. Letter-of-marque LYNX, built at Baltimore in 1812. A good example of a Chesapeake Bay model schooner of the War of 1812.

The sail plan of the *Lynx* is shown in Plate 59 and was not extreme. The base of the sail plan, from flying jib boom pole to end of ringtail boom, was very long, but the rig was not lofty. The upper spars were apparently light, but since no table of spar dimensions giving diameters has been found, this may be a matter of drafting.

A New York built letter-of-marque, *William Bayard*, is shown in Plate 60. The printed lists of the Royal Navy mistakenly identify this vessel as "*Alban*, formerly *James Madison*." The *Madison* was a Revenue Cutter of about 160 tons, built at Baltimore and taken by H.M.S. *Barbadoes*, 22 August 1812, near 31° 09′ N, 74° 35′ W. Extended search in Admiralty records has brought to light the fact that the *Alban*, whose plan survived, had been the New York letter-of-marque *William Bayard*. Built at New York in 1812 by Christian Bergh, her American register dimensions were length 97′ 6″, breadth 24′ 9″, depth 11′ 2″, and 241 16/95 tons. Her owners have been listed on her plan. She loaded at New York in January 1813 with a cargo of 1,861 bags of coffee and 50 boxes of brown sugar. With a crew of 31 she cleared customs 29 January 1813, and sailed on 8 February for Bordeaux. She had a letter-of-marque and was armed with four nine-pounders, four brass swivels, and small arms. H.M.S. *Warspite* and *Pheasant* took her on 12 March 1813, about 230 miles from Bordeaux, after a chase of seven hours and ten minutes in strong breezes. She was eventually purchased for the Royal Navy and renamed *Alban*.

The draught made for the Admiralty shows her to have been 94′ 4½″ on deck, 24′ 2⅝″ moulded beam, and 10′ 6″ in the hold. When she was surveyed, the Plymouth dockyard stated that her planking was 1⅞ inches thick, so when the purchase was ordered it was proposed that she be doubled with 1½-inch fir. Then it was discovered that an error had been made and that the *Bayard* was planked with 2¼-inch stock. The Admiralty indicated its displeasure with the dockyard officers for careless surveying.

The schooner had little sheer, about three feet drag in the keel, short fore rake with curved-stem rabbet, moderate rake to post, round tuck, and upper- and-lower transoms. The entrance was short, sharp, and convex, the run long and fine. The quarterbeam buttock is not straight until above the load line aft. The midsection shows rising, straight floor, carried well outboard, rather slack, high bilge, with slight tumble home in the topsides. The plan shows a capstan fitted when she was taken into the British Navy; she had neither cap- stan nor windlass when captured. Oarports are shown in the bulwarks.

The length on the moulded waterline was 91′ 8″; the moulded displacement

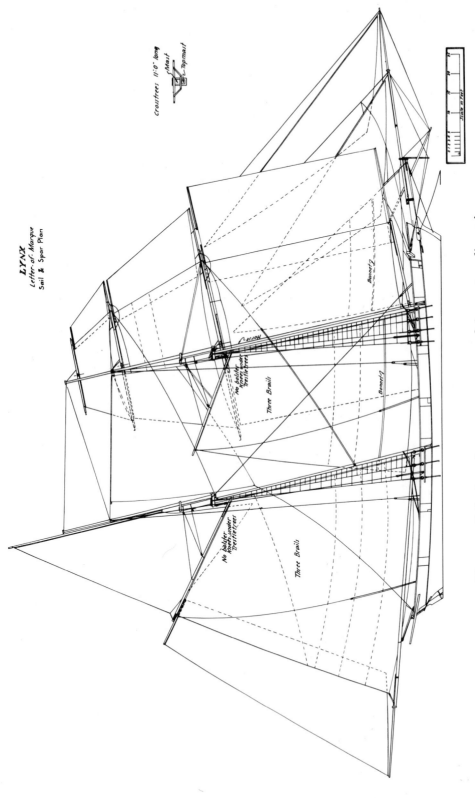

Plate 59. Sail plan of LYNX, reconstructed from spar dimensions.

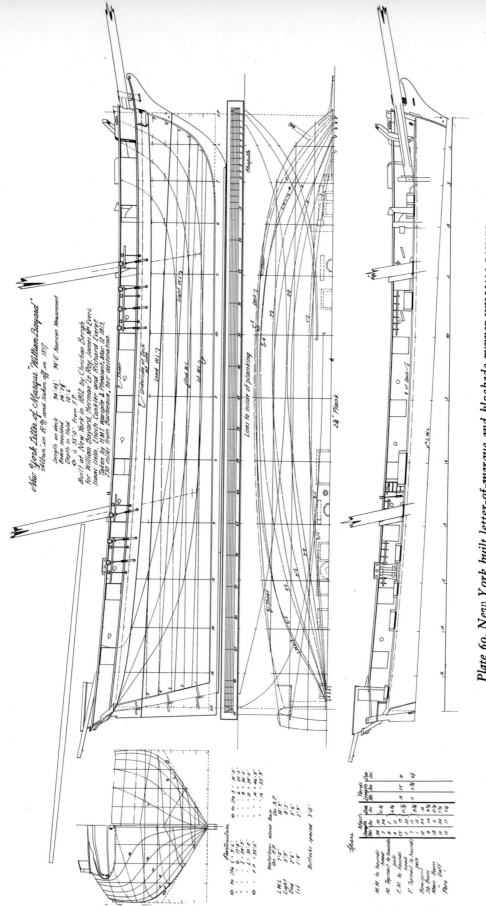

Plate 60. New York built letter-of-marque and blockade-runner WILLIAM BAYARD.

was 205.9 long tons. The coefficients were block .39, midsection .61, and prismatic .64. The effective length of the quarterbeam buttock was 72 feet, the camber 5′ 2″, giving a camber-length ratio of 14.1.

The table of spar dimensions shows her to have been a fore-topsail schooner, but apparently somewhat more heavily rigged than *Lynx*, the topmast being given more support by shrouds carried down to the channels.

The designer-builder of *Bayard*, Christian Bergh, who was born in New York in 1763, had built a number of fast sailing vessels prior to 1812. He later became one of the leading builders of packet ships, and was considered by his contemporaries to be a highly competent shipbuilder and a capable ship designer. He died in 1843, after having retired from business.

Grecian was a letter-of-marque schooner built at Baltimore by Thomas Kemp in 1812 for Isaac McKim of Baltimore. Her American register gives her dimensions as 99′ 6″ by 24′ 2″ by 10′ 7′ and 228 80/95 tons. According to the Captain's log of H.M.S. *Jaseur* in the Chesapeake on 1 May 1814, he received on board in the morning a negro from the shore who informed him that an armed vessel was in a nearby creek. *Jaseur's* boats were armed and sent off at sunset in search of this vessel. At daylight, 2 May, the boats returned with *Grecian*; she carried four guns, though "pierced for 20 [should be 18]." She carried 20 men, two mates, a captain, and a supercargo, and had a cargo of flour consigned to Cuba.

She was not immediately purchased for the Royal Navy, for on 10 January 1815, Rear Admiral Durham, Commander in Charge of the Leeward Islands station, wrote the Admiralty from Carlyle Bay, Barbados, that owing to recent losses of small craft on his station, and to the activities of swift privateers, he had purchased "a fine American schooner called the *Grecian*, a very fast-sailing vessel only 2 years old, coppered and copper-fastened, now the property of a merchant of this Island." The Admiralty ordered *Grecian* to be sent to England, and on 22 September 1815 the Navy Board was ordered to have her surveyed at Portsmouth. On 3 November 1815, the Navy Board reported her "fit for H.M.'s service," at a valuation of £9/5 per register ton; she measured 233 18/94 tons by survey. She was thereupon registered and provided with eight 18-pounder carronades, two six-pounder guns, and a crew of 60 men.

There is no explanation as to why this large, swift schooner* had been

* Adm. 1/506) Capt. G. E. Watts to Vice Admiral Sir A. Cochrane, May 2, 1814, reported f332) of the *Grecian* "one of the fleetest and most beautiful schooners in America," that she was coppered, copper-fastened, pierced for 20 guns, with only four mounted, with five brass swivels.

allowed to be sold to a private owner, prior to purchase by the Royal Navy. There can be no question as to the identity of this schooner, for the Admiralty draught agrees as well as could be expected with the American registry, and no other prize of this name can be traced. Obviously, she cost the service more by being allowed to pass through a second owner's hands.

The *Grecian*, shown in Plate 61, was of a rather extreme design. The arched gunports are difficult to account for, except so far as they might have represented a saving in weight. It is probable that the port lids were upper-and-lower halves, the lowers hinged and the uppers to lift out. The drag of the keel was very great for a schooner of this size. It can be presumed that in building *Grecian*, Kemp had attempted to produce a very fast schooner for blockade-running rather than a privateer.

This vessel was 95′ 1″ between perpendiculars, 23′ 5″ moulded beam, and 10′ 5″ depth in hold. Spar dimensions were not found. *Grecian* had a very slight sheer at the top of the bulwarks, projected through the arched port tops in a fair line, with a little more at the planksheer moulding below the gunports. It will be noticed that these ports had their lower portion closed by a washboard, apparently inserted in the ports. The vessel had strong drag to the keel, marked, curved fore rake and gammon knee, and also a marked rake to the sternpost. She had a round tuck, with upper-and-lower transom; her entrance was convex, sharp, and rather long for her date. The run was of moderate length, but fine; the quarterbeam buttock became straight before it crossed the after load line, and then showed hollow to a very marked degree as it approached the lower transom cross seam. *Grecian's* center of buoyancy was farther aft than was usual in 1812. The midsection was formed with sharply rising straight floor carried well out, a slack, high bilge with slight tumble home in topsides. *Grecian* had very flat quarters, and in a heavy sea must have pounded rather heavily.

She had a moulded displacement of 216.4 long tons, on a moulded load waterline of 89 feet. Her coefficients were: block .35, midsection .54, and prismatic .65. The effective quarterbeam buttock was 70 feet, the camber 5′ 4″, giving a camber-length ratio of 13.2.

Thomas Kemp, builder of the *Grecian*, was one of the leading shipbuilders in Maryland when the War of 1812 began. Of Quaker stock, he was born 28 February 1779 in Talbot County on the Eastern Shore of Maryland. It is not known where he learned the shipbuilding trade, but possibly it was at St. Michaels. He went to Baltimore in 1803, and sometime before June 1804

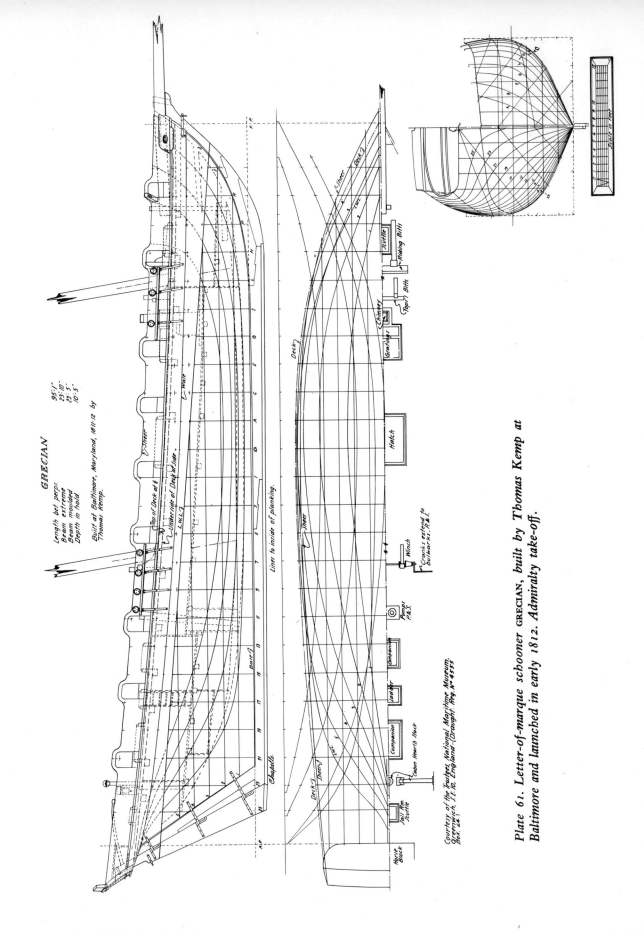

GRECIAN

Length bet. perps.	95'-1"
Beam extreme	23'-10"
Beam moulded	23'-5"
Depth in hold	10'-5"

Built at Baltimore, Maryland, 1811-12 by Thomas Kemp.

Courtesy of the Trustees, National Maritime Museum,
Greenwich, S.E.10, England.—(Draught. Reg. No 4555
Box. 24.1

Plate 61. Letter-of-marque schooner GRECIAN, built by Thomas Kemp at
Baltimore and launched in early 1812. Admiralty take-off.

he began business as a shipbuilder with his brother Joseph. He built the schooner *Thomas and Joseph* about this time, probably on leased ground. On 6 July 1805 he purchased property from his father-in-law at Fells Point, which was then as far up the harbor as a deep-draft ship could be launched, and set up his shipyard. During the early years most of his business was in the repair of vessels. In 1810, however, he built the ship *Wabash*, followed by *Marmion* in 1811. He also built the schooners *Comet* and *Charles* in 1810, and in 1812 he built the schooners *Patapsco*, *Chasseur*, *Grampus*, and *Cora;* most of these were notable privateers or letter-of-marques. Throughout the war he continued building large privateers and letter-of-marques, as well as repairing and refitting vessels. Early in the war he resparred some vessels, to increase their sail area and speed. He also built naval gunboats, as well as the sloops-of-war *Erie* and *Ontario*. He operated in partnership with a shipwright named Gardner in 1815–16, as Kemp & Gardner. But the postwar business depression was then affecting shipbuilding. Late in 1816 he moved to St. Michaels, where three years earlier he had purchased a farm. There he built only one or two small vessels and prepared plans for a third, before his death on 3 March 1824, at the age of forty-five. He was a very able designer and builder and a successful businessman as well.

Other active shipbuilders in Maryland during the War of 1812 were William Price, John Price, William Flannigan, William Parsons, Andrew Descande, and James Cordery in Baltimore; and James Montgomery, Noah Richardson, William Harrison, and James Stokes on the Eastern Shore. All of these built large privateers or letter-of-marques, as well as merchant vessels.

Returning to New York, the plan of a letter-of-marque built there is shown in Plate 62. This is the *Zebra*, built in 1812 by Adam and Noah Brown for James A. and William Dunlap. She was launched in November and sailed from New York shortly after 8 December 1812, loaded with cotton and bound for Bordeaux. Arriving safely and disposing of her cargo, she loaded brandy, drygoods, and seven passengers, including owner James Dunlap. *Zebra* sailed for New York on 11 April 1813, clearing from the river on the 19th. She was captured next day by H.M. frigate *Pyramus*, with H.M. frigates *Belle Poule* and *Andromach* in sight, after about six hours' chase. *Zebra* had her master and 37 men on board and carried 10 guns, 60 muskets, 16 pistols, 20 cutlasses, and 20 pikes.

Her American register stated she was 104′ 4″ long, 25′ 7″ beam, 10′ 2″ depth, and 243 4/95 tons. The orders relating to her purchase by the Admiralty have

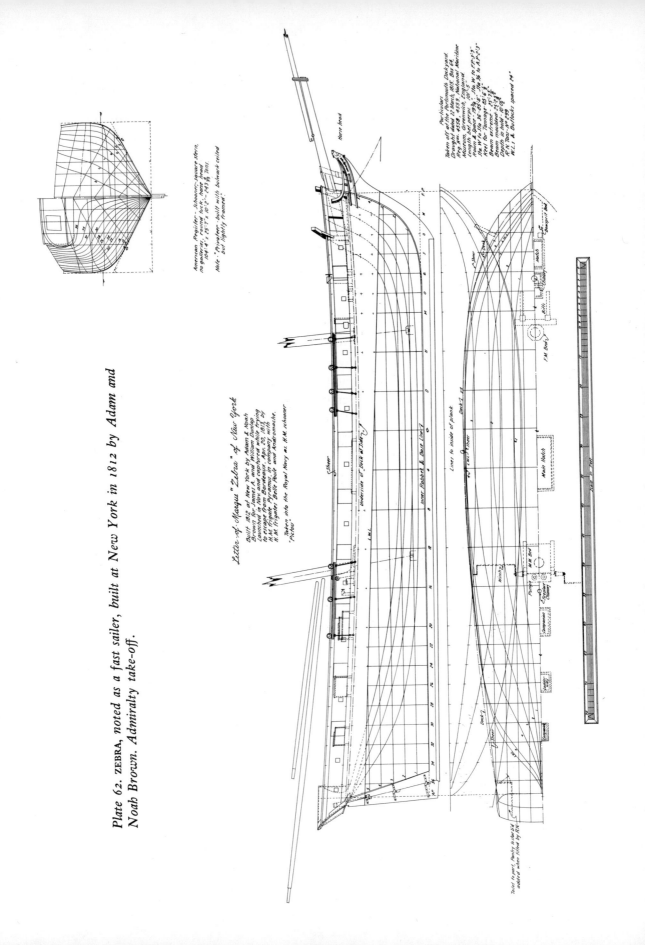

Plate 62. ZEBRA, *noted as a fast sailer, built at New York in 1812 by Adam and Noah Brown. Admiralty take-off.*

American Pepister – Schooner-square stern,
no galleries, round tuck, horse head
104' 4"; 25' 7"; 10' 2" – 243¾ Tons

Note "Privateer-built with bulwark ceiled
but lightly framed"

Letter-of-Marque "Zebra" of New York

Built 1812 at New York by Adam & Noah
Brown for James A. and William Dunlap
Launched in Nov. and captured while trying
to escape from Bordeaux. Apr. 20, 1815, by
H.M. Frigate Pyramus, in company with
H.M. Frigate Belle Poule and Andromache.

Taken into the Royal Navy as H.M. schooner
"Pictou"

Particulars
Taken off at the Portsmouth Dockyard
Draught dated 23 March, 1815. Box 64.
Reg. No. 4558. 4555. National Maritime
Museum, Greenwich. Registered
Length o/s perpend.: 90'6"
Room & Space: 19¾": No. W to FP 13
No. W to No. 36 · 85'8": No. 36 to A.P. 2·3
Keel for Tonnage: 85'6¼"
Beam extreme: 25'3½"
Beam moulded: 25'2⅝"
Depth in hold: 10'9¾"
R.N. Tons: No. 239
W.L. 1 & Bulkheads spaced 14"

not been found but her draught, made at Portsmouth, dated 22 March 1815,* shows she was taken into service as *Pictou*, to replace a schooner of this name that had previously been the American-built *Bonne Foi*.

Zebra is shown in her draught to have been 101′ 5″ between perpendiculars, 25′ 2⅝″ moulded beam, 10′ ½″ depth in hold, and 299 R. N. register tons. She had very moderate sheer, about four feet drag in her keel, a short fore rake with curved-stem rabbet, trail and headrails with a horsehead figurehead, raking sternpost, round tuck, upper-and-lower transoms, convex entrance was somewhat full, though the bow-buttock lines were rather easy. Her run was long and fine, the quarterbeam buttock coming straight close to the after load line. The midsection was formed with straight, sharply rising floor, carried well outboard, a high, firm bilge, and slight tumble home in topside. She was "privateer" built, with gunports and ceiled bulwarks and was fitted for sweeps in rowports between the gunports. *Zebra* was a well-finished schooner and is listed as one of the fast vessels of her period.†

Her moulded load waterline length was 98′ 5″, displacing 247.5 long tons moulded. Her coefficients were block .40, midsection .59, and prismatic .67. The effective length of the quarterbeam buttocks was 83 feet, camber 5′ 8″, and camber-length ratio was 15.6.

Noah Brown was born near Stamford, Connecticut, in 1770. Five years later the Brown family moved to Stamford, New York, where Indians captured his father and three older brothers. The father was killed, but the three brothers returned home after their captivity. There were two other brothers in the Continental Army, and one of them was killed near Philadelphia. After the Revolution, Noah's mother, with five small children, returned to Connecticut and Noah "learned the house carpenters' trade." In 1792 he moved to New York and remained there as a house builder until 1804. In that year he and Adam, a brother, went to the vicinity of Fort Niagara long enough to build a schooner for the fur trade, after which they both returned to New York and worked as ship carpenters in the Forman Cheesman yard on the East River. Then in 1805 they built a whaling ship at Sag Harbor on Long Island and in 1807 they were working in the George Peck shipyard at New York; later that year Noah went to North Carolina to cut live oak. The brothers next worked on the frigate *New York*, then building, but soon were in business for themselves, Noah apparently having thoroughly mastered the

* Admiralty Collection of Draughts, Reg. No.'s 4558 and 4559, Box 64.
† Cutler, *Greyhounds of the Sea*, p. 404.

shipbuilding trade. Adam may have been a trained shipwright. They built a gunboat for the Navy as well as a number of merchant vessels, and carried on a ship-repair business at the same time. In spite of Noah's not having served a shipbuilders' apprenticeship, they were competent enough to build privateers, letter-of-marques, and a naval vessel at New York during the War of 1812. On Lake Erie they built two brigs, three schooners, and a schooner-dispatch boat for Perry, in addition to constructing five buildings ashore. On Lake Champlain they built McDonough's ship-sloop, brig, and nine gunboats, and completed a schooner on the stocks, and they went to Lake Ontario with Eckford to build two 130-gun ships, which were not completed. Among privateers they built the 20-gun brig *Warrior* (which achieved a speed of 15½ knots, according to Noah*), and the schooners *General Armstrong, Paul Jones*, and the *Prince de Neufchâtel*, all notable vessels. They also cut down a merchant ship to a flush-decked privateer, named *Yorktown*. At the end of the war they were building Robert Fulton's *Steam Battery* and his torpedo-boat *Mute*.

Noah Brown ceased building in 1833 with the ferryboat *Sussex*. He and his brother had a spacious and well-equipped yard, and had been prominent New York shipbuilders since 1820.

Another example of an armed schooner is *Transfer*, shown in Plate 63. This plan was redrawn from an original builder's draught in the collection of plans belonging to U. S. Naval Constructor John Lenthall, deposited in the Franklin Institute, Philadelphia. This was one of two builder's draughts marked "Baltimore Schooners." The reverse of *Transfer's* draught is inscribed: "For Captain Charles Stewart Commanding United States Frigate Constitution off Boston, Massachusetts." Since Stewart took command of *Constitution* in early June 1813, and soon after sailed on a cruise, the draught was probably sent to him about that time. The vessel has not been found in the Baltimore registers. She may have hailed from Norfolk, as Stewart was there for some time, but that matter cannot be checked because many of the Norfolk records for this period were destroyed in 1861–64.

The draught, Plate 63, shows a schooner strongly resembling the Chesapeak type and finished plainly. She was 93′ 7″ between perpendiculars, 22′ 4″ moulded beam, and 10 feet moulded depth, inner rabbet to underside of deck

---

* Noah Brown's statement printed in the 1913 brochure *The Victory on Lake Erie*, prepared for the Battle of Lake Erie Centennial. *Warrior*, brig, built by Noah Brown in 1814, 120 feet by 31 feet by 12 feet, 397 5/95 tons (Reg. No. 265, New York).

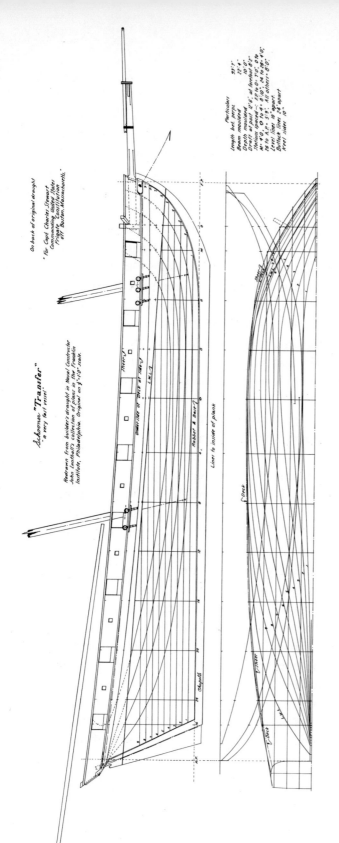

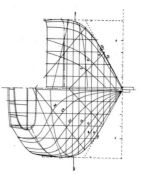

Schooner "Transfer"
"a very fast vessel"

Redrawn from builder's draught in Naval Constructor
John Lenthall's collection of plans in the Franklin
Institute, Philadelphia. Original on ¾"=1'0" scale.

On back of original draught

"For Capt. Charles Stewart
Commanding United States
Frigate Constitution
off Boston, Massachusetts."

Particulars:
Length bet. perp.   93'1"
Beam moulded   23' 4"
Depth moulded   10' 0"
Draft at paul 12'6"; at larbol 8'2"
Nations spaced 12'0" to 0'7'0", 0 to
N'4'0, 0 to 4 - 8'10"; 24 to 28 4'0";
28 to A.P. - 5'3". All others - 8'0";
Level lines 10' apart.
Buttock lines 24" apart.
Keel sides 10"

Liner to inside of plank

Plate 63. *Copy of a contemporary draught of an American schooner,* TRANSFER,
*of the letter-of-marque size and type built during the War of 1812. Customhouse
register not found.*

at side. She drew 12′ 6″ at the post and 8′ 2″ at forefoot. She was pierced for seven sweeps and eight gunports on each side. It is probable she was a fore-topsail schooner, rigged like *Lynx*, judging by the chainplate arrangement at her channels. On her draught is the notation, "a very fast vessel."

The schooner had little sheer and a straight keel with 4′ 4″ drag. The fore rake was long and much curved at the stem rabbet, and the post was strongly raking; she had a short and sharp but convex entrance, long and very fine run, with the quarterbeam buttock coming straight for a very short distance forward of its intersection with the after load line. The *Transfer* had a round tuck with upper-and-lower transom stern. The buttock-bow lines are somewhat full in the entrance.

She was 90 feet moulded length on the load line and had a moulded displacement of 176 long tons. Her block coefficient was .36, midship .60, and her prismatic was .61. The effective length of her quarterbeam buttock was 71 feet and the camber 4′ 9″, giving a camber-length ratio of 14.9.

Plates II, III, and IV show a famous New York privateer, *Prince de Neufchâtel*. Some accounts give Christian Bergh as her builder, but the customhouse records show beyond any question that she was designed and built in the winter of 1812–13 by Adam and Noah Brown. This is verified by the register carried on board her at the time she was captured by the British. In addition, Noah mentions her as one of the privateers he and Adam built. The Brown brothers appear to have designed the vessels they built, for on 6 September 1819 the Navy Board wrote to ask for the plans of all of the naval vessels they had built on the Great Lakes.

Neufchâtel was owned by Madame Flory Charreton, widow, an American citizen residing in New York City. Soon after completion, the vessel was armed and sailed to Cherbourg, France. While anchored in the outer roads she dragged her anchors and went ashore. It was blowing hard. As a result she beat her keel off and suffered other damage before she could be refloated. The vessel required very extensive repairs before she could leave Cherbourg. She had obtained a letter-of-marque at New York 28 October 1813, under Captain J. Ordronaux. She went to sea from Cherbourg the following March and took nine prizes in the English channel. Her owner died about this time and the vessel passed into the hands of the estate trustees. Operating out of France, she again went to sea in June and captured six prizes.

During the rest of the summer of 1814 she cruised in European waters, capturing a number of prizes. She was chased by seventeen English cruisers during her career, escaping each time through her sailing qualities. Late in September 1814, she entered Boston harbor and was refitted. She sailed on a cruise early in October and five days after leaving port she was attacked by the British frigate *Endymion*, who had tried to overtake her in very light winds without success. A calm having set in, *Endymion* sent five boats carrying between 111 and 120 men. In the attack on the privateer, *Endymion* lost between 70 and 93 men killed, wounded, and prisoners. *Neufchâtel* returned to Boston October 15th with a prize ship she had taken earlier. Here the schooner was sold by the trustees to Ordronaux and associates for $21,000.

A new letter-of-marque was obtained 12 December 1814 and in the evening of the 21st she went to sea under Captain Nicholas Millin, or Mellin, manned by 120 men, with 18 guns. On the 26th she ran into a gale and on the 28th, at daylight, she was sighted by a frigate squadron, under Commodore Sir George Ralph Collier, made up of frigates *Leander*, *Newcastle*, and *Acasta;* the first two were new and built to match the American 44-gun ships. All were reputed to be good sailers. Handicapped by a heavy sea and strong gale winds, *Neufchâtel* managed to keep clear until 4:20 P.M. at which time she hove to and surrendered. She had damage to her spars by this time, and in her effort to carry sail, was overpowered by sea and wind. According to British reports, credited to the officers of *Newcastle* (logs of Captains and Masters are now missing), the frigates ran at 13 knots for hours during the chase. Captain Kerr of *Acasta* called *Neufchâtel* an "hermaphrodite" in his log.

The reports of Collier and the others led the Admiralty to order that *Neufchâtel* be surveyed at Deptford, in a letter to the Navy Board dated 16 February 1815. This Admiralty order of 16 February 1815 specifically directed a survey be made of the *Neufchâtel* "with a view to ascertaining (the reason for) her remarkable sailing qualities." The Board returned a preliminary survey six days later. In view of the vessel's history, this report is interesting, for it shows the attitude of some dockyard officers toward American-built schooners. The yard reported the vessel to have been built "generally of yellow pine fir and American oak" but from the "imperfect and loose manner in which she appears to have been put together and the great expense necessary to fit her for H.M.'s Service," she was not considered suitable for purchase. Rough dimensions are given, but the report also gave her draft, ballasted, as 8′ 3″ forward and 11′ 6″ aft. It was remarked that she was copper-sheathed. On the 28th the yard reported it had not docked the schooner. On 5 April 1815 they sent her spar dimensions—"all caps are iron bound." On the 8th they got her into dock and on the 14th the yard sent her draught and spar plan to the Admiralty. The damage at Cherbourg was not discovered, apparently, in the survey, but this may have accounted for her "imperfect and loose manner" of build.

On the 10th of April the Admiralty ordered the Navy Board to prepare "a draught of a facsimile of the hull of the *Neufchâtel*." On 4 May 1815 the Board sent the draught with comment that they had added a platform deck for berthing the officers and men; the Americans had provided no separate storage for provisions nor accommodations for the crew. The provisions had been stowed "promiscously" over the vessel and the crew had slept on the cargo. They also observed that *Neufchâtel* had small scantling, with large openings (space between frames), and that her bottom plank was only two inches thick. For a vessel of almost 111 feet length and of 328 tons this was below the accepted margin of safety and inadequate for a cruise in the Channel, according to the dockyard officials, in spite of her survival in a long chase during a gale in the North Atlantic! The Board recommended that a facsimile schooner be built at Woolwich dockyard and be established with sixteen 12-pounder carronades, two six-pounder guns, and a crew of 75 men.

On 23 May the Admiralty informed the Navy Board that the construction of the facsimile was postponed. This was the end of that project. There is a report that *Neufchâtel* hung on the dock's gate sill in getting her out of dock and "broke her back," but no report or mention of this appeared in the official papers.* The further fate of *Neufchâtel* is unknown.

The survey shows she had frames sided 7 inches, moulded 6½ inches at the first futtock heads, moulded 5 inches at upper deck and 4 inches at gunwale. Wales were in four strakes, 3 inches thick, 10 inches broad. The sheer strake was 3 inches thick, 6 inches broad. The bottom was of 2-inch oak, copper-fastened. Waterways were 5½ inches thick and 10½ inches broad. Clamp was fir (pine) in two strakes 3 inches thick, 1' 7" broad each. Decking was 2½-inch pine. Beams, 4 of oak, 18 of fir (pine), sided 11 inches, moulded 10 inches, were at each end with one hanging and one lodging knee. Knees bolted with five iron bolts each. Frames spaced 2 feet on centers. Ceiling was of pine 2 inches thick, thick stuff at first futtock heads was 2 inches thick, in two strakes each 1' 11" broad. She had neither windlass nor capstan. Her riding bitts had 10½" by 10½" posts. Foremast had a light grating top; mainmast

---

* The origin of this story was probably a claim made by the prize-agent against the Admiralty, alleging damage while in the dockyard.

had no top. The lower edges of her wales were dubbed fair into the plank below.

The schooner measured, according to the Admiralty draught, 110′ 8″ on the range of deck, 25′ 4″ moulded beam, and 328 22/94 tons British, or 318 88/94 tons American, measurement.

She had little sheer, very moderate drag to her keel, short, curved rake at stem rabbet, coronal figurehead and stem fitted with trail knees and a single rail above, raking sternpost, round tuck, and upper- and-lower transom. Her entrance was convex, somewhat full, and long for her time. Her run was long and fine, particularly low, and the quarterbeam buttock came straight about five or six feet forward of its intersection with the after load line. Her midsection showed rising straight floor, a high and easy turn of the bilge, with slight tumble home in the bulwarks.

The rig shown in Plates III and IV was reconstructed from the spar dimensions and Admiralty plan and requires no special description. The yards were very "square" and the fore-and-aft rig rather lofty. This drawing, by Merritt A. Edson, Jr., was made for the construction of a ⅜-inch scale model for the United States National Museum.

Her moulded waterline length was 107′ 5″, and her moulded displacement was 253 long tons. Her coefficients were block .39, midsection .64, and prismatic .62; the effective length of her quarterbeam buttock was 87 feet and the camber 5′ 1½″, giving a camber-length ratio of 17.0.

A New England privateer is shown in Plate 64. This is the schooner *Dash* launched in early 1813. She was built by James Brewer on the Harrasecket River near Freeport, Maine, for Seward, Samuel, and William Porter, of Porter's Landing, Maine, from a hawk nest half-model now in the Bartol Public Library, Freeport, Maine. Her letter-of-marque was issued at Portland, Maine, on 30 August 1813, and her register dimensions were 103 feet length, 26′ 8½″ beam, 9 feet of hold and 22 24/95 tons. The model is to a nonstandard scale, but using the register dimensions as a guide, a proportional graphic scale produced the following dimensions: 103′ 7″ between perpendiculars, 26′ 6″ moulded beam, 10′ 1″ depth moulded, with a draft at sternpost of 11′ 5″.

This vessel was first rigged as a fore-topsail schooner and proved to be a fast sailer. Her maiden voyage was to Santo Domingo, during which she was chased once and sprung her foremast. She made a second voyage to the West Indies and again was chased, this time by a British "74," but by throwing

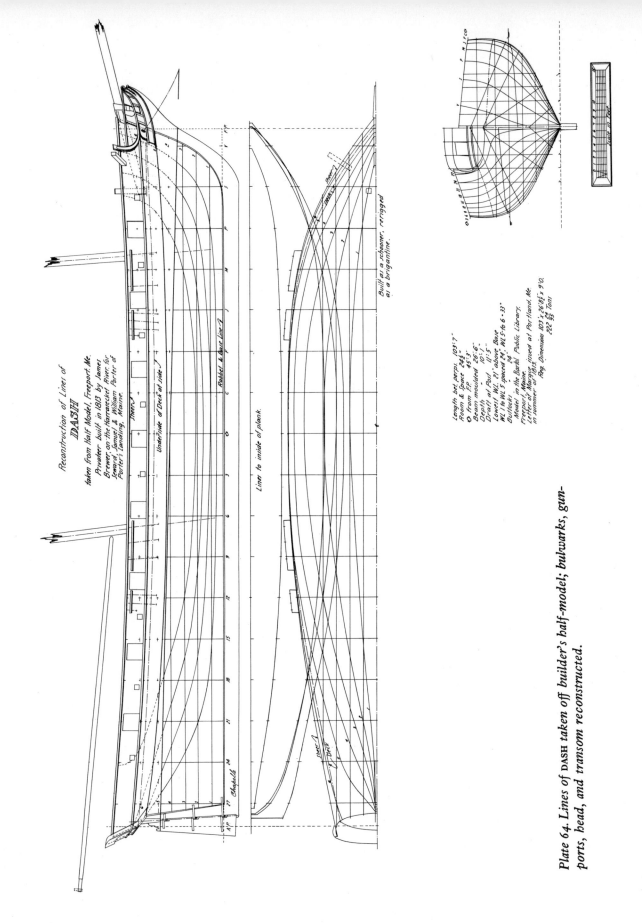

Reconstruction of Lines of

DASH

taken from half Model, Freeport, Me.

Privateer built in 1813 by James
Brewer, on the Harraseeket River, for
Seward, Samuel, & William Porter of
Porter's Landing, Maine.

Underside of Deck at side

Rabbet & Base line

Lines to inside of plank.

Built as a schooner, rerigged
as a brigantine.

Length bet. perpl. 103'-7"
Room & Space 24¾"
⊕ from F.P. 45'-3"
Beam moulded 26'-6"
Depth 10'-1"
Draft at Post 11'-5"
Lowest WL. 2' above Base
WL 1 to WL 5 spaced 24"; WL 5 to 6 · 33"
Buttocks 24"
Model in the Bartol Public Library,
Freeport, Maine.
Letter of Marque issued at Portland, Me
in summer of 1813.
Reg. Dimensions 110' x 26⅚ x 9'0:
222 ⁵³⁄₉₅ Tons

Chapelle

Plate 64. Lines of DASH taken off builder's half-model; bulwarks, gunports, head, and transom reconstructed.

overboard part of her deck load and two guns she got away from her pursuer.

On her return she was fitted out as a privateer and in her refit she was re-rigged as an hermaphrodite with a larger square-sail rig on the foremost mast than she had originally. She had a 32-pounder shifting gun with a couple of 18-pounder broadside guns. She made five successful cruises, taking 15 prizes in her short career. She left port about the middle of January 1815 and met the privateer *Champlain* of Portsmouth, New Hampshire. The two vessels headed south but ran into a heavy gale and separated. *Dash* disappeared with all hands; it is supposed she was overpowered and capsized on Georges Bank in the tremendous seas created by the gale and the shoal water there.

Dash seems to have been unusual in having a very narrow stern; she had moderate sheer, small drag to the keel, short, raking curved-stem rabbet, billet head, and a slightly raking sternpost, round tuck, and upper-and-lower transom. Her entrance was convex and moderately sharp but not long. Her run was also rather short but fine; the quarterbeam buttock was straight from a little forward of where it crossed the after load line. She was wide and shoal for a vessel of her size, rig, date, and type. She must have had a very limited range of stability with her heavy guns on deck.

Her length, moulded, on the load line was 99′ 7″, and her moulded displacement was about 220.5 long tons. Her coefficients were: block .38, midsection .60, and prismatic .63. The effective length of her quarterbeam buttock was 77 feet and the camber 5′ 1½″, giving a camber-length ratio of 15.1.

Another type of New England privateer is *Reindeer*, shown in Plate 65. This vessel had a sistership, *Avon*, and these sisters were enlargements of the hermaphrodite *Rambler*.* All were built by Calvin Turner of Medford, Massachusetts, in 1813–14. *Reindeer*, launched in 1814, was built for Benjamin Rich and others of Boston. She measured 118′ 9″ length, 30-foot beam, 12 feet in the hold, and 381 75/94 tons burthen. *Avon*, launched the same year for the same owners, measured 119′ 9″ for length, 30 feet beam, 12 feet in the hold, and was 388 24/94 burthen.

Avon was captured by H.M. sloops *Barbadoes* and *Columbia* on 8 March 1815 near St. Bartholomews, after short action. *Avon* carried eleven long nine-pounders and three long 24-pounders, the latter on pivots. She was described by her captors as coppered and copper-fastened, of stout build, and a fast sailer, "well adapted for H.M. service."

* See Chapelle's *The History of American Sailing Ships* (facing p. 142) for an excellent painting of *Rambler*, which will give an idea of the rig of the Medford-built vessels.

234

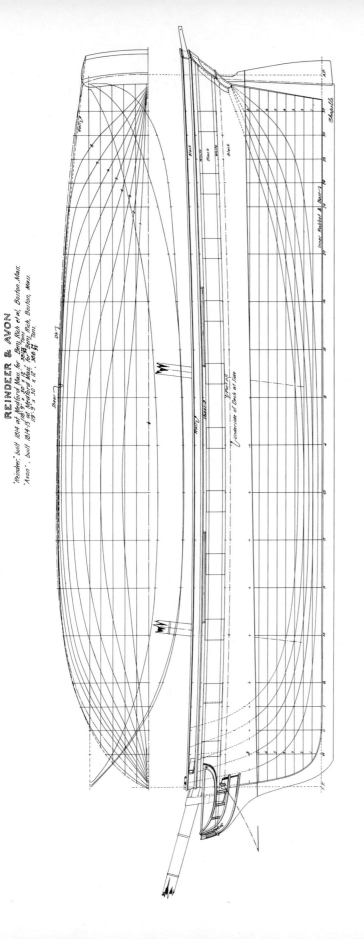

REINDEER & AVON

"Reindeer", built 1814 at Medford Mass. for Benj. Rich et al, Boston, Mass.
305 4/95 Tons
"Avon", built 1814-15 at Medford Mass. for Benj. Rich, Boston, Mass
119'-9" x 30' x 12', 306 95/95 Tons

Chapelle

Dimensions from Draught
Length bet. perp.   119'-6"
Beam moulded   30'-6"
Depth moulded   15'-3½"
Room & Space   24"
Keel, sided   12"
Wt. I, spaced   18"
Buttock   24"
O II 49'-3" from F.P.

Coppered, black topsides, two narrow white
stripes at top & bottom of port lists.
Shield figurehead. Brig or Hermaphrodite, rigged

Lines to inside of plank.

Lines from half-model in Medford Historical
Society, Medford, Mass. This is a duplicate
of Turner's half-model made in 1885 by
C.B. Johnson.

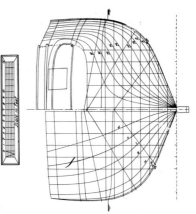

Plate 65. Lines for two New England letter-of-marque vessels, REINDEER *and* AVON, *built in 1814; fast carrier and man-of-war models. Designed and built by Turner at Medford, Massachusetts, in 1814.*

Sail plan of brig Spark.

The lines, Plate 65, were taken from a half-model in the Medford Historical Society Museum, Medford, Massachusetts. This model is a copy of an original now lost. It was made in 1885 by C. B. Johnson and is supported by another copy, in private hands, that coincides with the Medford copy. It therefore is assumed that the lines are reasonably accurate. The model produced the following dimensions: 119′ 6″ length between perpendiculars, 30′ 6″ moulded beam, 15′ 3½″ moulded depth.

The design showed very slight sheer, small drag to the keel, very slight rake in ends, sharp, short, convex entrance, and long and easy run, with some straightness in the quarterbeam buttock at the after load line. The stern had a round tuck, with upper-and-lower transoms. The midsection was formed

236

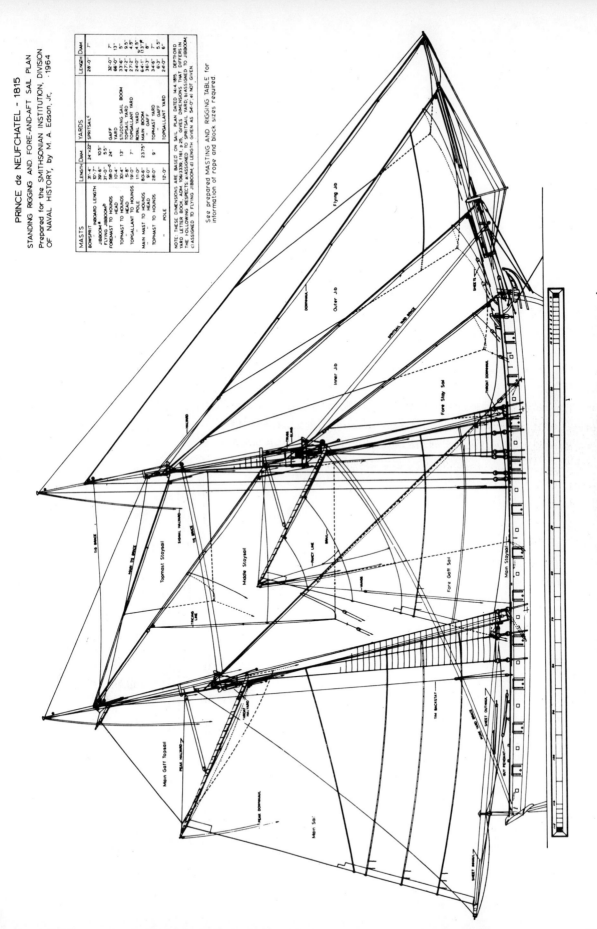

PLATE III. *Reconstruction of the rig of the* PRINCE DE NEUFCHÂTEL.

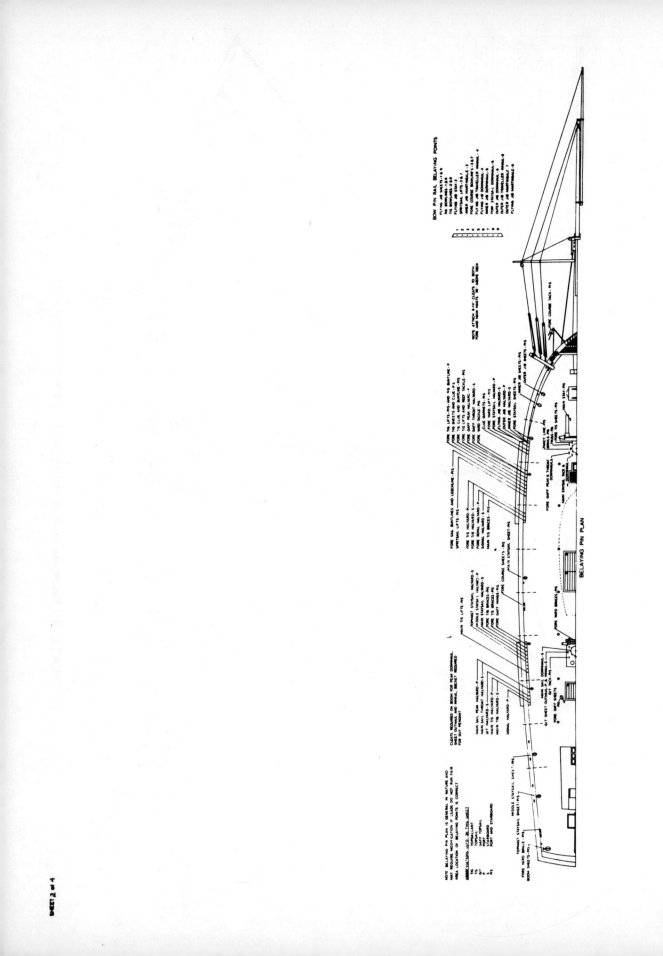

BELAYING PIN PLAN

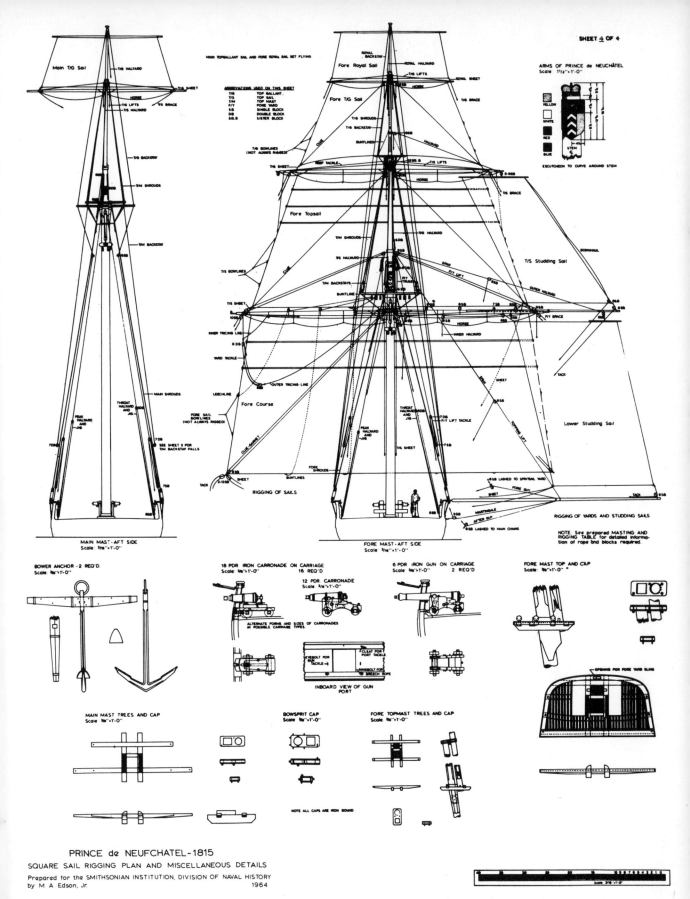

PRINCE de NEUFCHATEL – 1815
SQUARE SAIL RIGGING PLAN AND MISCELLANEOUS DETAILS

Prepared for the SMITHSONIAN INSTITUTION, DIVISION OF NAVAL HISTORY
by M A Edson, Jr.   1964

PLATE IV. *Details of the* PRINCE DE NEUFCHÂTEL *for construction of a model.*

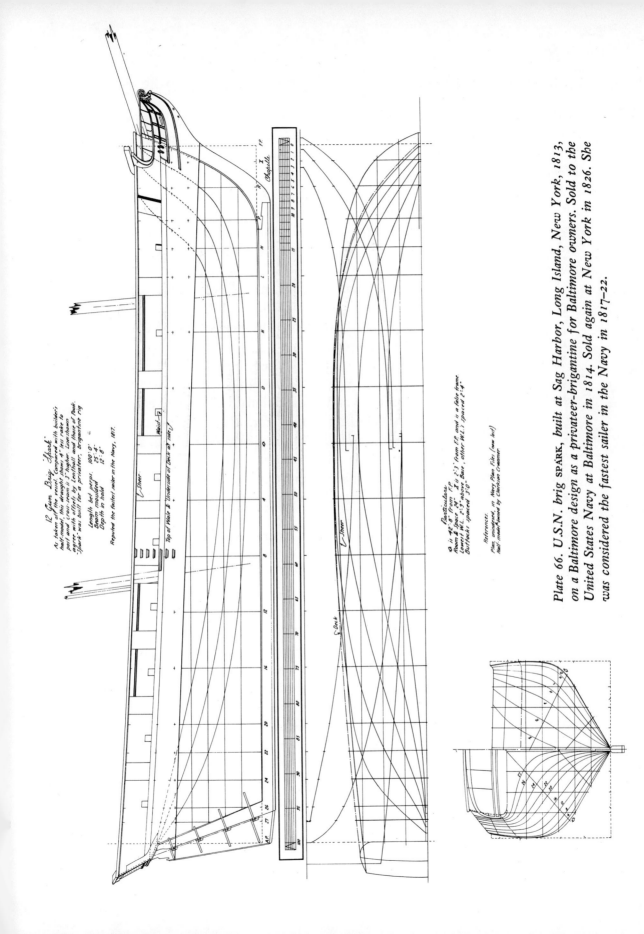

Plate 66. U.S.N. brig SPARK, built at Sag Harbor, Long Island, New York, 1813, on a Baltimore design as a privateer-brigantine for Baltimore owners. Sold to the United States Navy at Baltimore in 1814. Sold again at New York in 1826. She was considered the fastest sailer in the Navy in 1817–22.

with rising, straight floor carried well out, a full, round bilge with slight tumble home, compared to the vessels previously seen in this chapter; the displacement is heavy and the design is more closely related, in principle, to *Hannibal* shown in Plate 57.

The moulded waterline length of the model with 116′ 5″, and the moulded displacement was 580 long tons. The coefficients were: block .48, midsection .72, and prismatic .68. The effective length of the quarterbeam buttock, or 3rd out, was 104 feet, and the camber 9′ 6″, giving a camber-length ratio of about 10.9.

These Medford vessels were designed as fast carriers rather than out-and-out fast sailers. They were coppered, had black topsides, gilded headrail beading, two narrow white stripes through the top and bottom of the gunports, and American shields for figureheads.

Brigs and brigantines such as those just discussed required more displacement for a given size of hull in order to carry the heavier spars usually considered proper with those spar plans and the additional ballast they entail.

Another example of a fast sailing brig of the War of 1812, shown in Plate 66, was designed at Baltimore and built at Sag Harbor, Long Island, in 1813 as a privateer brigantine. By this year the Chesapeake had been blockaded by English cruisers and it was increasingly difficult to get American vessels to sea past the Virginia Capes. Some merchants therefore, usually furnishing a draught, had made contracts to build to the northward, where the outlook for running the British blockade was more favorable. The builder of this brig is not known. The vessel was launched 40 days after her keel was laid, but had not made a voyage in 1814; when the United States Navy purchased her from her Baltimore owners. Whether she was originally named *Spark* cannot now be determined, but she was registered in the Navy under that name and rigged as a brig. She came to be considered the fastest sailer in the Navy. She was obtained by the Navy for the purpose of joining a squadron of small fast schooners and brigs that was to raid British waters in the West Indies. But before the vessels were ready, the end of the war put a stop to this program. *Spark* was used on the West Indian station after the war and was sold out of service in 1826 at New York, reported to have become too rotten to be worth repairing. She had been armed with 14 guns when first commissioned, but this armament was reduced to 12, made up of ten 18-pounder carronades and two long 18-pounders.

Because of her excellent sailing qualities her lines were taken off so that a number of half-models could be made. Plate 66 agrees with the offsets taken off by Lenthall and Pook, naval constructors, but varies slightly at the stern from one of the models. The variation, however, will not affect the analysis of her lines, as the differences are chiefly concerned with the rake of her sternpost and the exact height of her cross seam and top of the round tuck.

The brig was 100 feet between perpendiculars, 25′ 4″ moulded beam, and 12′ 8″ depth of hold. In model, she had very little sheer, moderate drag to the keel, a somewhat small fore rake in the curved stem rabbet, billet head, marked rake in the sternpost, round tuck, and upper-and-lower transom. The entrance was short, convex, and somewhat full. The run was long and fine, with a straight quarterbeam buttock at its crossing of the after load line. The midsection was formed with strongly rising, straight floor carried well out, a high and rather hard turn of the bilge, and some tumble home above. Her sail plan was large in area.

She was 96′ 11″ on the moulded load waterline, displacing 293.6 long tons, moulded. Her block coefficient was .42, midship coefficient .63, and the prismatic coefficient was .66. The effective length of the quarterbeam buttock was 82 feet and the camber 6′ 4″, giving a camber-length ratio of 13. This vessel was said to have carried her sail well, and to have been very fast on all points of sailing.

While pilot boats are occasionally mentioned as engaging in privateering, their small size and their light displacement for even their small dimensions sharply circumscribed their general usefulness. Nevertheless, some were employed for military purposes and a few were quite successful in taking prizes, particularly early in the war.

Plates 67 and 68 show an American-built pilot boat of unknown antecedents. The very scant Royal Navy references show that she was purchased under the name *Achilles* in May 1813 from private owners, by request of Admiral Cochrane. It was specifically stated by Cochrane that she was not then a prize. It is probable, however, that she was at one time a prize and had been condemned and then sold to private owners. Her name was changed to *Anna Maria* and she was, for a time, tender to the *Tonnant*. On 19 June 1813, she was established as a dispatch vessel, under Lord Keith. By June 1815, she had been renamed *Express* and her lines were taken off in the Plymouth dockyard the following month. She was later attached to Lord Exmouth's fleet in the Mediterranean and was present at the bombardment of Algiers in August 1816. In 1829 she was sold out of the service at Malta.

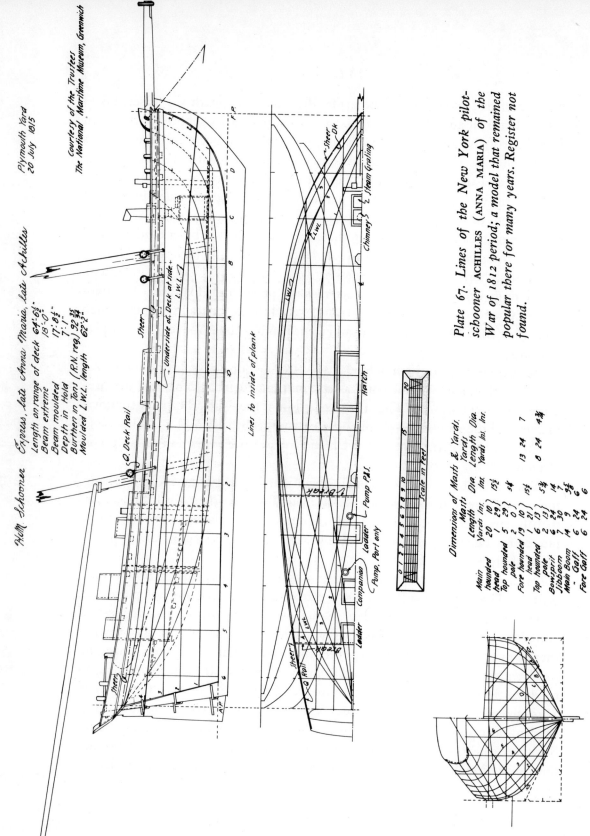

HM Schooner Express, Late Anna Maria, Late Achilles

Length on range of deck 64'-6½"
Beam extreme 18'-0"
Beam moulded 17'-8½"
Depth in Hold 7'-1"
Burthen in Tons (R.N. reg.) 92 35/94
Moulded L.W.L. length 62'-5"

Plymouth Yard
20 July 1815

Lines to inside of plank

Dimensions of Masts & Yards.

	Masts		Yards	
	Length	Dia.	Length	Dia.
	Yards Ins.	Ins.	Yards Ins.	Ins.
Main	20 10 }	15½		
rounded	29 }			
head				
Top rounded	5 29	5¼	13 24	7
pole	2 0 }			
Fore rounded	19 10 }	15¾	8 24	4¾
head	21 }			
Top rounded	6 13 }	5¾		
pole	1 21 }			
Bowsprit	6 24	14		
Jibboom	7 30	7		
Main Boom	14 9	9½		
Gaff	6 24	6		
Fore Gaff	6 24	6		

Scale in Feet

Plate 67. Lines of the New York pilot-schooner ACHILLES (ANNA MARIA) of the War of 1812 period; a model that remained popular there for many years. Register not found.

Nonofficial sources state she was built at New York, but her original name cannot be discovered and no *Achilles* has been found in the New York registers that agrees with this schooner. It is stated in official records that she was American-built, at least. She was a very fast sailer and a good seaboat, well suited to service as a dispatch vessel.

The schooner measured 64′ 6½″ length on the range of deck, 18 feet beam, 7′ 1″ depth of hold, and 92 35/94 tons English measurement. She drew 9 feet at the post and 5′ 8″ at the fore gripe.

She had a graceful sheer with a raised quarterdeck rail aft. The deck was raised, at a point about 9 feet abaft the fore-end of the raised quarterdeck rail, to the level of the quarterdeck rail. The cabin under this deck was about 16′ 3″ long. Here the raised deck ended and to the transom a "sunk poop," or cockpit, was formed, the floor of which was in the faired line of the main-deck projected to the transom, in height. The drag of the keel was great, and the fore-rake was long and strongly curved. She had a plain pilot-boat stem without knee or head. The sternpost raked strongly, with round tuck and upper-and-lower transom above. The entrance was convex but rather long and sharp; the run was very long and fine; the two outer buttock lines becoming straight close to and below the after load line in the manner that seems to appear often in the lines of fast sailing vessels. The midsection was formed with a strongly rising, straight floor carried well outboard, a high, slack bilge, and a slight tumble home topside. Like many American vessels with sharply rising straight floor, the schooner had a rather deep keel outside the rabbet with more depth forward than aft, and a large foregripe.

The length of the moulded load line was 62 feet and moulded displacement was 64.4 long tons. The block coefficient was .38, the midship coefficient .63, and the prismatic coefficient was .64. The effective length of the quarterbeam buttock was 52′ 3″ and the camber 3′ 7″, giving a camber-length ratio of 14.5.

The rig, shown in Plate 68, was reconstructed from spar dimensions recorded on the draught. It should be noted that as a pilot boat she would not have crossed yards, and probably would have no fore-topmast, as in the pilot boats described earlier.

Snap Dragon, shown in Plate 69, was a pilot-boat model schooner that was a very successful, medium-size privateer. She was purchased for $8000 at New York in 1812 by Captain Otway Burns, jointly with William Shepard, John H. Bryan, Isaac Taylor, James McKinley, John Harvey, and Edward Pasteur. It is said her original name was *Levere*, or *Le Vere*, but nothing re-

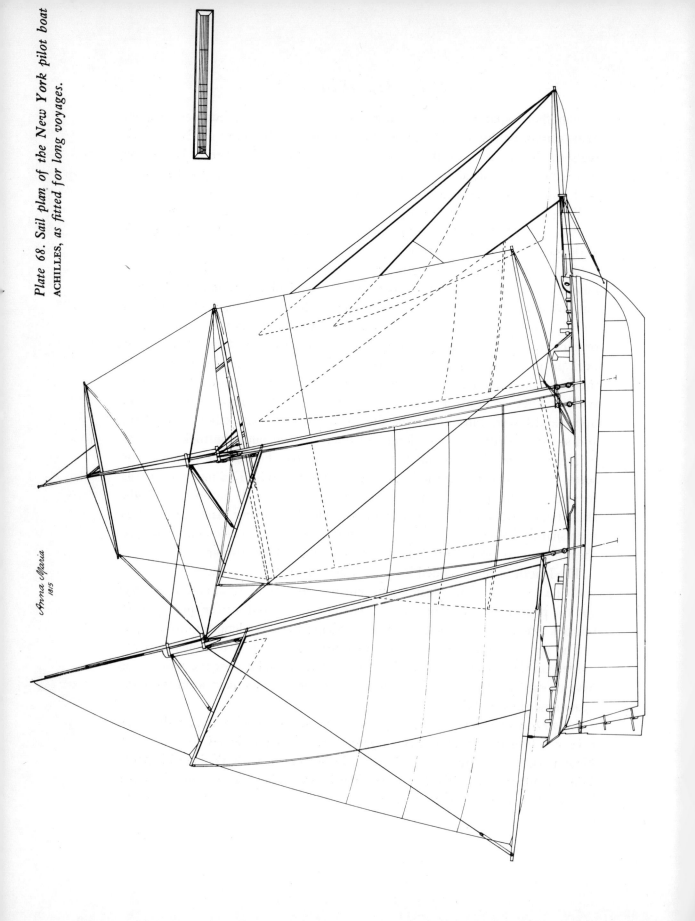

Plate 68. Sail plan of the New York pilot boat
ACHILLES, as fitted for long voyages.

Anna Maria
1815

sembling this name can be found in the New York ship registers. She was armed with six guns, and under Captains Pasteur, Burns, and Graham, she captured nine prizes—one with a cargo valued at half a million dollars.

In 1814 *Snap Dragon* was captured by H.M.S. sloop *Martin* and arrived 29 June 1814 at Halifax, where she was condemned in the Vice-Admiralty court. She was licensed at 140 tons and is stated to have had a crew of 80. Her letter-of-marque does not give her dimensions or place of build. Nevertheless, the court records indicate the licensed tonnage would be lower than measurement would have given.

The half-model of *Snap Dragon* was obtained by the Naval Historical Foundation from the descendants of one of the stockholders in the schooner and is on loan to the United States National Museum, Smithsonian Institution. This is now (1967) the oldest builder's model in the Museum's collection. This half-model is of the "block" type, that is, a solid block of wood, but in this case the sheer has been raised by an added "lift" of uneven depth. The model shows the hull to deck height. The scale is a half inch to one foot, apparently, producing a schooner 89′ 4½″ on deck and 24′ 9″ moulded beam. The moulded depth would be 10′ 1″, from rabbet of the keel to underside of deck at side. These dimensions appear proper for a sharp schooner carrying six guns and a crew of 80 men; certainly she could not have been much smaller. The various published sources concerning the history of this schooner are generally untrustworthy and the complete Admiralty Court proceedings on her condemnation at Halifax cannot be found. The career of the vessel under the United States flag as a privateer, however, is stated accurately in one reference.*

Snap Dragon was of somewhat light displacement for her dimensions. Plate 69 shows the lines of the half-model, with bulwarks, gunports, channels, head, and stern reconstructed. Her rig was probably that of a "two-topsail" or "fore-and-main topsail rig," for a reputed crew-member's journal refers to "furling topgallants," "single-reef topsails," and, incidentally, to a "bonnet in the foresail."

Snap Dragon had a rather straight sheer, straight keel with about 3′ 6″ drag, strongly curved and raking stem rabbet, very raking post, upper-and-lower transom, and round tuck. She had a sharp, convex entrance of moderate length and a long, easy run, the quarterbeam buttock coming straight

---

* Edgar S. Maclay, *A History of American Privateers*, 2nd ed. (New York and London, D. Appleton and Company, 1899, 1904), pp. 321–322.

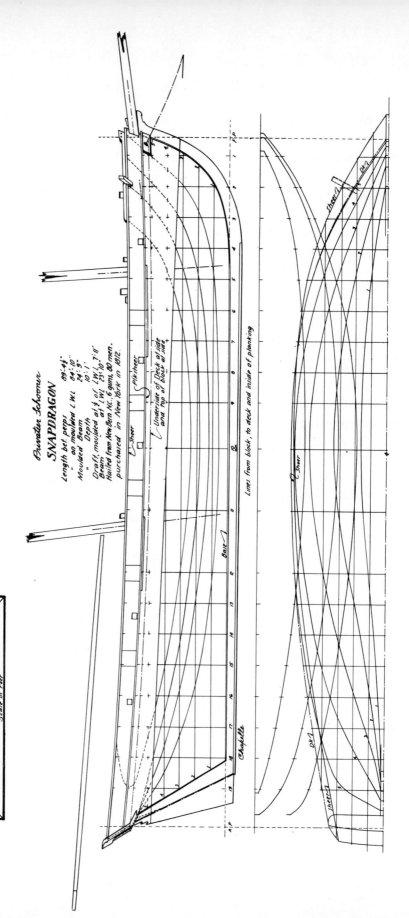

Plate 69. Lines of SNAP DRAGON *taken from half-model; bulwarks, gunports head, and transom reconstructed. Register not found.*

Privateer Schooner
SNAPDRAGON

Length bet. perps.   89:4½"
      on moulded L.W.L   84:10"
Moulded Beam   24:9"
      Moulded Depth   10:1"
Draft, moulded at ⅞ of L.W.L 7:11"
Beam   moulded at ½ L.W.L 23:10"
Hailed from New Bern N.C., 6 guns, 80 men.
purchased in New York in 1812.

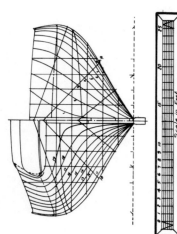

Scale in Feet

only a short distance from its intersection with the load line aft.

The length of the moulded waterline was 84' 10"; the moulded displacement was 157.7 long tons. The block coefficient was .34, midship coefficient .56, and prismatic coefficient .62. The effective length of the quarterbeam buttock was 67 feet and its camber 4' 2"; the camber-length ratio was 15.9.

Owing to the reputation of sharp-model American schooners, created during the Napoleonic period, many European naval powers utilized them as models for fast-sailing, light cruisers. In many instances—particularly in France—plans were obtained and placed in the national naval archives. As a result a number of interesting draughts were preserved. Some of this material, in dockyard files, was destroyed in World War II. Unfortunately, these draughts were not usually identified as to name and therefore there is the presumption that in many instances the plans might have represented proposed designs rather than actual vessels.

Plates 70 and 71 show plans of a large fore-and-main topsail privateer-schooner, identified only as built in Maryland about 1814. The original draught was brought to France from New York along with other draughts. The vessel was 89' 10" long on deck, 22' 2" moulded beam, and 9' 9" moulded depth. As drawn, her draft at the sternpost was 12' 7". She is shown loaded very deep and might have sailed best at less draft, say 11' 6". It is stated that the schooner had excellent qualities, which of course indicates that the draught was of a named vessel. It is not possible, however, to identify this schooner from the customhouse ship registers. In Plate 71 the sail plan certainly indicates an over-sparred and over-canvassed vessel. Nevertheless, this is an example of the type, and her coefficients have been calculated.

This vessel was 85 feet long on the moulded load line, the moulded displacement, to 12' 7" draft, was 193.6 long tons. (The French copy of the draught gives displacement as 207 tons.) The block coefficient was .48, the midship coefficient .76, and the prismatic coefficient .63. The effective length of the quarterbeam buttock was 68 feet, the camber 5' 6"; the camber-length ratio was 12.0.

Another example is shown in Plate 72. The original draught of this schooner, reportedly destroyed in World War II, had been obtained in America by a French naval officer after the War of 1812, but no other identification was made. The draught shows a deeply laden sharp schooner. This vessel was of the larger dimensions in her class, of the general size of *Flight, Tom, Expedition, Cashier, Revenge, Leo, Transit,* and *Chesapeake.* The registers show no

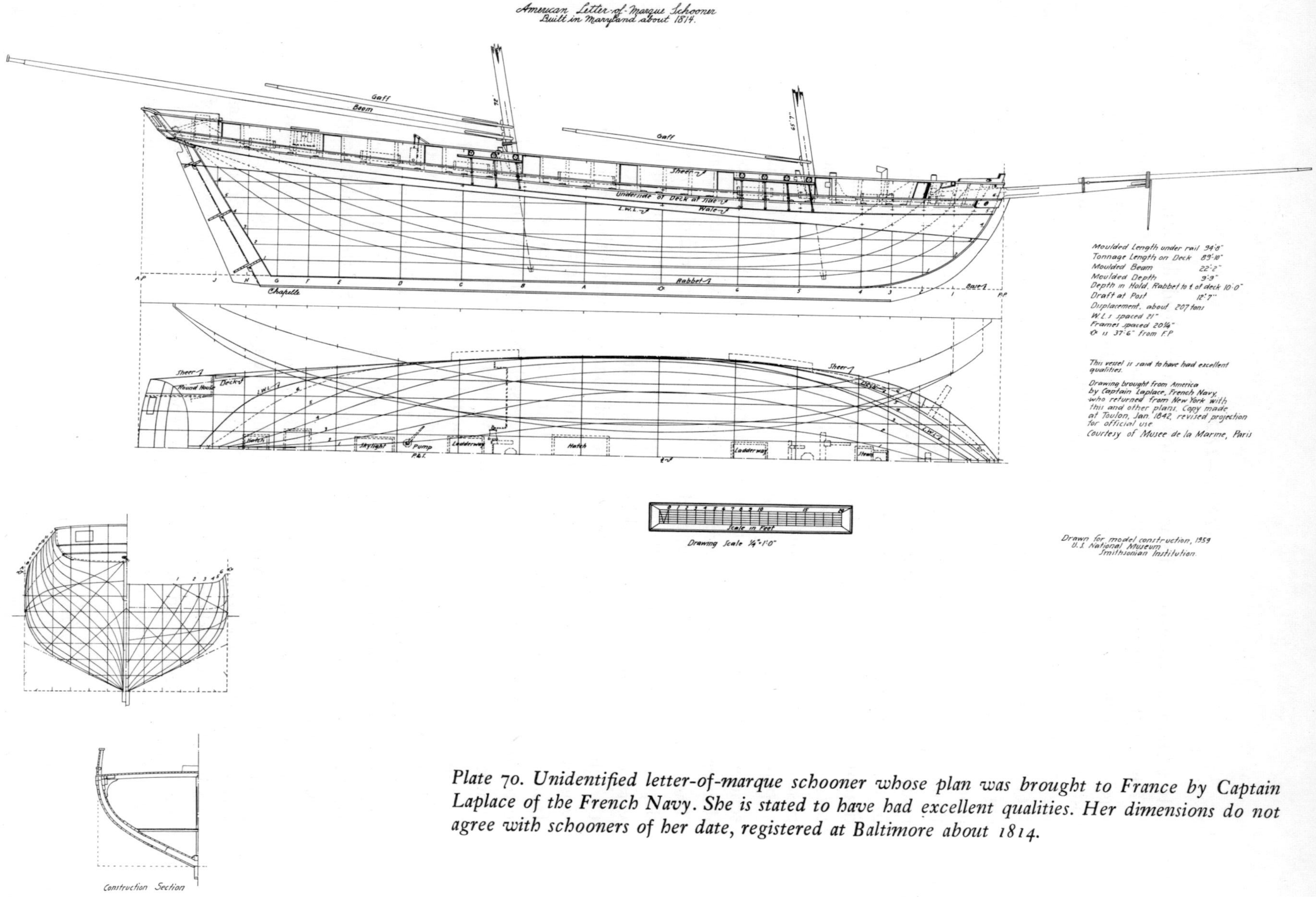

American Letter-of-Marque Schooner
Built in Maryland about 1814.
Gaff
Boom
Gaff
Sheer
Underside of Deck at Side
Wale
L.W.L.
Rabbet
Base
Chapelle
Moulded Length under rail 94'8"
Tonnage Length on Deck 89'10"
Moulded Beam 22'2"
Moulded Depth 9'9"
Depth in Hold, Rabbet to ℄ of deck 10'0"
Draft at Post 12'7"
Displacement, about 207 tons
W.L.s spaced 21"
Frames spaced 20¼"
⊗ is 37'6" from F.P.
This vessel is said to have had excellent qualities.
Drawing brought from America by Captain Laplace, French Navy, who returned from New York with this and other plans. Copy made at Toulon, Jan. 1842, revised projection for official use
Courtesy of Musee de la Marine, Paris
Round House
Deck
Hatch
Skylight
Pump
Ladderway
Hatch
Ladderway
Scale in Feet
Drawing Scale ¼"=1'0"
Drawn for model construction, 1959
U.S. National Museum
Smithsonian Institution
Construction Section

Plate 70. Unidentified letter-of-marque schooner whose plan was brought to France by Captain Laplace of the French Navy. She is stated to have had excellent qualities. Her dimensions do not agree with schooners of her date, registered at Baltimore about 1814.

vessel close to the dimensions given on the draught; the draught dimensions are not register measurements, of course. In addition, the crude methods of taking tonnage measurements preclude the interpretation of draught dimensions to give probable tonnage measurements for identification purposes. Other evidence must be available to accomplish this and in this case there is none.

The draught dimensions show the vessel to have been 105′ 6″ on the range of deck, 25 feet moulded beam and about 11′ 3″ depth in hold.

The length of the moulded load line was 99′ 2″, the moulded displacement being 267.8 long tons. The block coefficient was .38, the midship coefficient .61, and the prismatic coefficient .63. The effective length of the quarterbeam was 79′ 6″, the camber 6′ 3″; the camber-length ratio was 12.8.

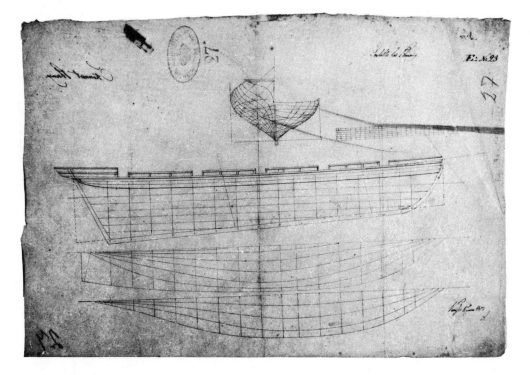

Schooner LA PHOENIX, *1810. Probably American-built but cannot be traced in French records. Royal Archives, Copenhagen.*

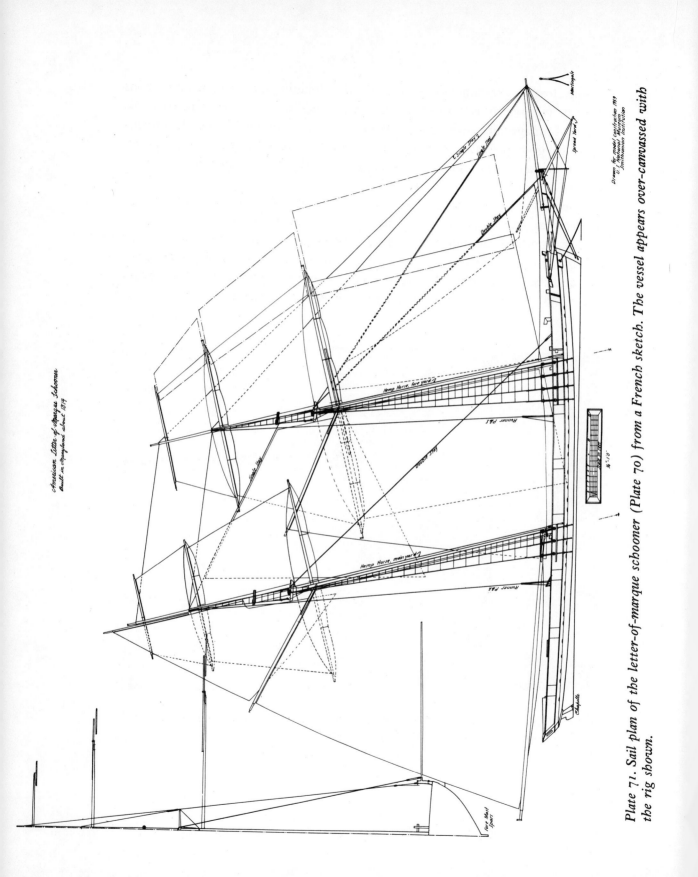

Plate 71. Sail plan of the letter-of-marque schooner (Plate 70) from a French sketch. The vessel appears over-canvassed with the rig shown.

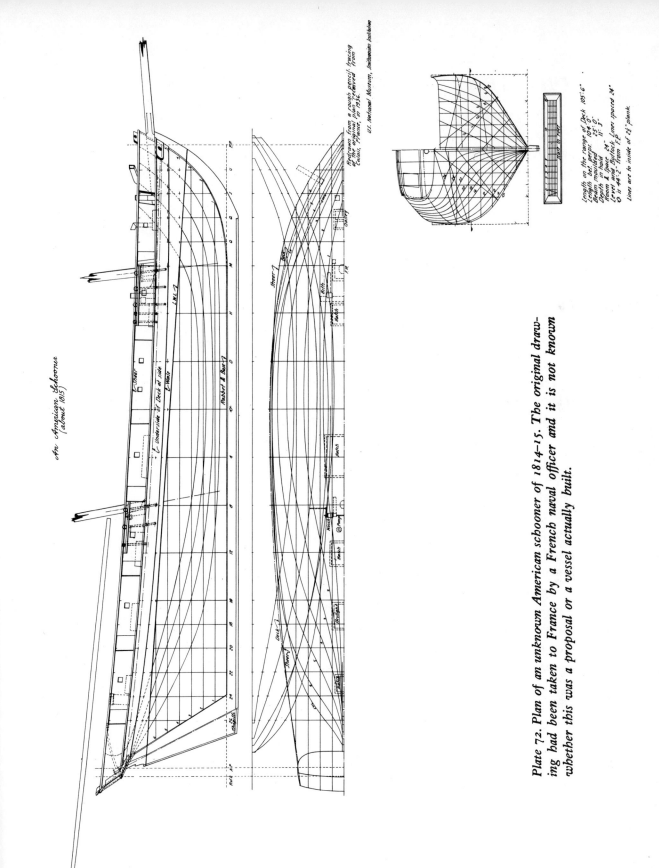

An American Schooner
(about 1815)

Redrawn from a rough pencil tracing of the original plan received from Calais, France, in 1936.

U.S. National Museum, Smithsonian Institution

Length on the range of Deck 105′ 6″
Length bet. perp. 104′ 0″
Beam moulded 25′ 0″
Depth in hold 11′ 3″
Room & space 24″
Level and Buttock Lines spaced 24″
0 to 44′-2″ from F.P.

Lines are to inside of 2½″ plank.

Plate 72. Plan of an unknown American schooner of 1814-15. The original drawing had been taken to France by a French naval officer and it is not known whether this was a proposal or a vessel actually built.

Plate 73 shows a third and last example of an unidentified draught from French sources. This plan was obtained from Baltimore in 1828, and a copy was made in 1841. The original and the copy were lost in the last war. Here again there is no assurance that the draught is of an actual vessel, though the draught dimensions are for a privateer schooner of the largest size employed during the War of 1812 by the Americans.

The draught is of dimensions that approach those of the Kemp-built *Chasseur* of 1812,* but not close enough to serve as a basis for identification. It is known that at least two other schooners built in Maryland, for owners outside the register district, approach the *Chasseur* dimensions, but again these do not comply with the draught dimensions. It seems very probable that the draught was a proposal, perhaps based upon one of the successful large privateers, but it may not represent a vessel actually built. Nevertheless, with some reservations, the draught may be used for analysis.

The plan is of a very large, sharp, and deep schooner, 116' 1" on range of deck (as scaled from the draught), 26 feet moulded beam, and 12' 4" depth in hold. The draught shows the vessel very deeply loaded, for the draft at the post scales 16 feet. This may be 1 or 1½ feet more than would have been required if the vessel were a privateer. It is possible that the deep drafts shown in these unidentified schooners' plans are because of an interest in such craft as naval cruisers, rather than as merchant or privateer vessels.

At any rate, the draught called for a moulded load line of 109' 10" and a moulded displacement of 411.5 long tons. The block coefficient was .43, the midship coefficient .67, and the prismatic .62. The effective length of the third buttock out was 89' 6" and the camber 8' 7"; the camber-length ratio was 10.2.

It would be possible to add other examples of unidentified schooners (some with names that cannot be traced) in French naval and maritime archives. However, no useful purpose is served, for such examples are no more than illustrations of the basic type already well represented by named vessels whose histories and reputations can be at least partly examined.

The end of the War of 1812 was followed by a business depression that affected the shipbuilding industry, particularly the building of sharp vessels. It would be difficult to assess the development in ship design that occurred in sharp-model craft during the war. Though the "large" schooners, brigantines, and brigs of the early years of the nineteenth century would be called medium-size by the end of the war, there was no particular increase in sharpness, or

* Register dimensions of *Chasseur*, 115' 6" by 26' 8" by 12' 9", 356 10/95 tons.

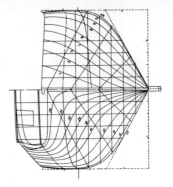

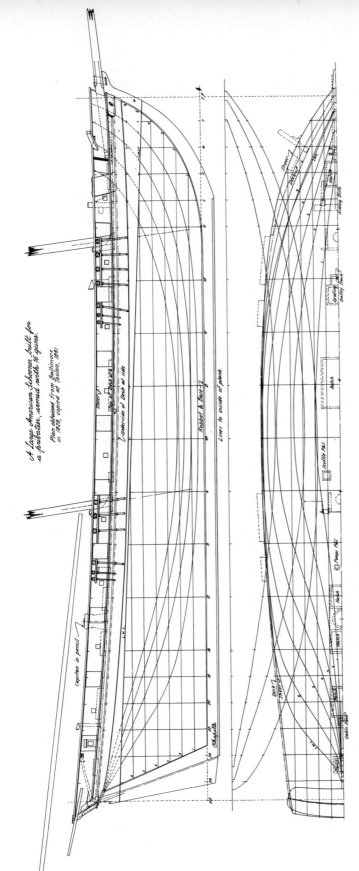

Plate 73. Plan of unidentified schooner obtained in 1828 at Baltimore by a French naval officer. It cannot be determined whether this plan is a proposal or the design of a vessel built during or after the War of 1812. The dimensions do not fit any schooner in the Baltimore register.

immediate marked change in any other basic characteristic. The square-tuck stern often used in sharp vessels between the end of the Revolution and 1810, was gradually going out of favor by 1812, and the round-tuck stern was predominant after the outbreak of the War of 1812.

While shipbuilding was generally stagnant in America after the War of 1812, some building was done. This activity was pretty well confined to small-vessel construction, of the full or burdensome model. Such a vessel is shown in Plate 74. She was designed as a schooner by William Doughty, Naval Constructor at Washington (and living in Georgetown), but before launching she was changed to a brigantine. Named *James Munroe*, she was completed late in the fall of 1815 and employed in the coastal trade. This small brigantine was about 67 feet on the range of deck, 21 feet moulded beam, 10′ 1″ depth in hold, and drew about 9′ 9″ loaded.

Munroe had a rather straight sheer, a straight keel with about 1′ 7″ drag, a curved and slightly raking stem rabbet, moderate rake in the post, short, rather full convex entrance, long, moderately fine run, round tuck, and upper-and-lower transom stern. The midsection was formed with about one foot of rise in the straight floor, four feet out from centerline, well-rounded easy bilge, slight tumble home topside above the deck. A note on the original draught stated that she was "reported to sail very fast."

There are plans and half-models of a number of small, rather full merchant brigs of 1814–25 in existence, having features similar to those of *Munroe*—the open rail, rather high freeboard, low cross seam at the top of the round tuck, and also modeled to sail quite well. Similarly built vessels were constructed in England in this period. These brigs were mostly employed in the Southern Coastal Trade, and in the West Indies, where lawlessness was then prevalent, so ability to sail fast was very desirable.

Munroe represents another example of a relatively large carrier for her dimensions, in which the designer had attempted to produce a good sailer. The slackness in trade did not encourage experimenting in large vessels at the moment, but the small carriers were available for the purpose.

The length of the moulded load waterline of *Munroe* was 63′ 7″; the moulded displacement was 172 long tons. Her block coefficient was .62, midship .72, and the prismatic coefficient was .85. The effective length of the quarterbeam buttock was 58′ 6″, camber 5′ 8″, and camber-length ratio 10.2.

The end of the Napoleonic wars, and the beginning of the commercial depression that followed in the United States, marked the end of a long period

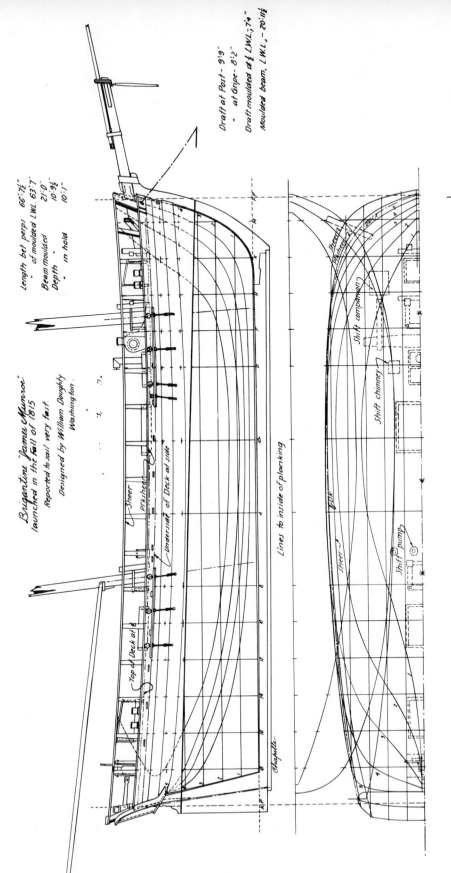
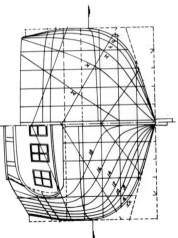
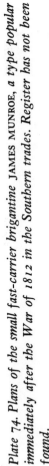

Brigantine "James Munroe"
launched in the Fall of 1815

Reported to sail very fast.

Designed by William Doughty
Washington.

Length bet. perps. 66'-7½"
   " of moulded LWL. 63'7"
Beam moulded   21'-0"
Depth   "   10'-9½"
   "   in hold   10'-1"

Draft at Post - 9'9"
   " at Gripe- 8'2"
Draft moulded at ⅝ LWL., 7'4"
Moulded beam, LWL., - 20'-11½"

Sheer

Pilothead

Underside of Deck at side

Lines to inside of planking

Top of Deck at ℄

A.P.

Chapelle

Sheer

Shift pump

Shift chimney

Shift companion

Scale in Feet

Plate 74. Plans of the small fast-carrier brigantine JAMES MUNROE, a type popular
immediately after the War of 1812 in the Southern trades. Register has not been
found.

in which great risks and great profits were the rule in merchant vessel operation. Speed had been the preeminent requirement in designing vessels, with
little need for thought about possible economic cargo capacity. Now economic operation and cargo capacity were to be the requirements most desired.
Small, fast vessels were still to be in demand in very limited areas, it is true,
but not in great number. The slaver, as a special type, did not appear immediately after the war, though this was the only important illegal trade left.
In short, the carrier was to be the dominant type in the American merchant
marine.

CHAPTER · SIX

1820 - 1845

IN THE EARY 1820'S, THE AMERICAN SHIPBUILDING INDUSTRY STARTED TO RE-
cover from the postwar depression that began in 1816. Though the United
States and Europe were now peaceful, Central and South America were in a
state of general warfare and colonial revolution against Spain. A number of
the letter-of-marque cruisers of the War of 1812 had been sold to some of
the revolutionary governments who were establishing navies with these and
other vessels as a nucleus. By 1818 they were negotiating with New York,
Philadelphia, and Baltimore shipbuilders for the construction of men-of-war,
and by 1822 a number of vessels, from schooners to corvettes, were building
or contracted for. Within the next six years, frigates, corvettes, brigs, and
schooners were built at these three cities and on the Chesapeake for South
and Central American revolutionists, for Mexico, and for the Greeks who
were rebelling against the Turks.

Henry Eckford was a particularly active shipbuilder in this construction
of vessels for foreign accounts. Born at Kilwinning, a small town near Irvine,
Scotland, he moved to Quebec when he was sixteen and was there apprenticed to an uncle, John Black, a very competent shipbuilder. In 1796, at the
age of twenty-one, he moved to New York and worked as a boatbuilder.

He married in 1799 and in the next year set up his own shipyard in Brooklyn near the present Navy Yard. He engaged largely in repair work, but in 1800 he built a ship of 324 tons. In 1805 he entered into a partnership with Lester Beebe and the firm built naval gunboats and at least six ships. The largest of these, named *Beaver*, 427 tons, was built for John Jacob Astor. In 1809, the partnership was dissolved and Eckford joined with Christian Bergh to build the naval brig *Oneida* on Lake Ontario.

This was a short employment and Eckford was back in his own yard in time to build a 554-ton ship that same year. He constructed a 522-ton ship in 1810 and continued to build until he was sent to Lake Ontario in November 1812, to build the American squadron. He remained at Sackett's Harbor until the war ended, then returned to New York where he became a naval constructor, 13 July 1817. He designed and built the 74-gun ship *Ohio*, designed a corvette, which was not built, and the schooner *Grampus*, built in the Washington Navy Yard and launched in 1821. Eckford resigned as constructor 1 June 1820. He reopened his New York shipyard, which during the next ten years turned out merchant ships, two steamers, and a number of vessels for foreign accounts. Among these latter were the large frigates *Amazon* and *South America*, as well as a number of corvettes. Eckford designed all the foreign-owned vessels, but a few were let to subcontractors for construction. He also built one large schooner, of 227 tons.

By 1828 he had become a leading shipbuilder in New York. He also had accumulated a fortune and was becoming interested financially in banking and insurance. Because of the demands of his business, Eckford arranged for his foreman and former apprentice, Isaac Webb, to operate the Eckford yard.

In the financial debacle of 1828 Eckford lost heavily and had a number of personal misfortunes, but managed to recoup. In 1831 he took one of the new corvette-type ships that he had built, the 1,000-ton *United States*, to Turkey where he sold her for $150,000. On the invitation of the Turkish government, he began building men-of-war at Constantinople. He completed a dispatch schooner and had a 74-gun ship and a frigate building before his sudden death from appendicitis or cholera on 12 November 1832.

Eckford was not only an accomplished ship designer and builder, but he was an expert manager. He had the ability to build large vessels very rapidly. He was also an excellent teacher, and had a number of apprentices who later became distinguished shipbuilders; among them were Isaac Webb and Stephen Smith. At the time of his death, Eckford was working on a book on naval architecture, but unfortunately the manuscript was lost.

In many of his men-of-war and fast merchantmen, Eckford employed much deadrise. The half-models, drawings, and offsets of his corvette-type ships often show extreme deadrise combined with rather fine ends, which undoubtedly produced fast sailing vessels. Some of his designs, however, such as those for the frigates, showed moderate deadrise and straight, rising floors with rather low, hard bilge. He cannot be said to have been completely committed to great deadrise, as was the Royal Navy Surveyor William Symonds, who was appointed in 1832.

Plate V shows a fine example of Eckford's designs for fast corvettes, ships having extreme straight deadrise. This vessel—first registered as *Hercules*, owned by Eckford and a business associate—was built in 1822 by Isaac Webb in Eckford's yard. The vessel was designed to be 118′ 6″ between perpendiculars but was set up with three feet added amidships, making the length, as built, 121′ 6″. Soon after her launch, the vessel was apparently sold abroad and renamed *Bolivar*, suggesting that she may have been sold to the Colombian Navy, or at least to Colombian citizens.

Bolivar had very little sheer, a straight keel with some drag, a curved, raking stem rabbet, and a slightly raking post. She had a round tuck with upper-and-lower transoms. Her midsection was formed with very rising, straight floor, high, round bilge, and marked tumble home. The entrance was convex and moderately sharp; the run was very long and fine; the buttock at the quarterbeam became straight a short distance forward of its intersection with the load line. The bow lines were very easy—an example of the counteraction by means of easy bow lines to full waterlines forward.

This vessel, like the French *La Vengeance* of 1800 described in Chapter 4, is an example of a "pre-clipper" clipper ship, showing much the same use of bow and buttock lines in each design. The half-model and the lines of Eckford's *United States* showed much the same buttock-bow line treatment, but the midsection was formed with extremely sharp, rising floor carried to the load line and the topside slightly curved from there to rail, becoming vertical only above the port sill. There was no appreciable bilge. *United States* was said to have been very fast and weatherly.* At any rate, she went from New York to the Azores in ten days. She outsailed the frigate *Constellation* very easily on the wind in a very fresh breeze and a heavy sea; both ships were

* Cedric Ridgely-Nevitt, "Henry Eckford's *United States* of 1831," *The American Neptune*, Salem, Massachusetts, Vol. VIII, No. 1 (January 1948), pp. 7–10.

carrying the same sails. *United States* was 126′ 2″ on deck, 36 feet moulded beam, and 17′ 3″ moulded depth. *Bolivar* was 121′ 6″ between perpendiculars, 28′ 11″ moulded beam, 15 feet moulded depth, drawing 14′ 11″ aft and 12′ 2″ forward. She had less drag than *United States*.

Such extreme ships may have resulted from Eckford's years at Sackett's Harbor, Lake Ontario, where most of the lake vessels had much deadrise. Even some of the British naval ships built there showed extreme rise of floor.

Bolivar had a moulded displacement of 363 long tons, with a moulded load waterline length of 119′ 3″. Her coefficients were block .32, midsection .55, and prismatic .63. The effective quarterbeam buttock length was 102 feet, the camber 6′ 9″, giving a camber-length proportion or ratio of 15.3.

One of Eckford's more conservative designs was that of the corvette *Kensington*, built for the Mexican Navy under subcontract at Philadelphia in 1828 by Tease. This vessel was nearly the size of the frigate *Constitution*, but was a 30-gun corvette with medium 26-pounder guns and flush-decked. Proving too large and costly for the Mexicans to operate, the vessel was sold to Russia in 1830. On her way to Russia for delivery she was dismasted, but with jury rig she was reputed to have sailed 11 knots. This information attracted much attention and Samuel Humphreys attempted to obtain her draught or offsets as he "thought he could then improve on her," according to his letter book.

Plate 75 shows *Kensington*, a vessel having a rather straight sheer, a straight keel with very little drag, moderately raking curved-stem rabbet, slightly raking post, round tuck, and upper-and-lower transom square stern. The midsection was formed with moderately rising straight floor, an easy, round bilge, and a slight tumble home in the topside. The entrance is rather full and convex, the run long and fine. It should be observed that the quarterbeam buttock is straight or nearly straight forward of its intersection with the after load line, but curves sharply just before its intersection with the load line to form the lower part of the round tuck. This was common in naval frigates in the first quarter of the nineteenth century, but it does not appear to have been a desirable feature. *Kensington*, however, relieved of the weight of much of her rig, would lighten enough to bring the entire tuck out of the water and so improve her run. As in the case of *Porto*, there would be sharp differences in performance and coefficients between load and light drafts. Though *Kensington* had the reputation of being a fast sailer, she would not have sailed so fast under jury rig had she not changed form in the

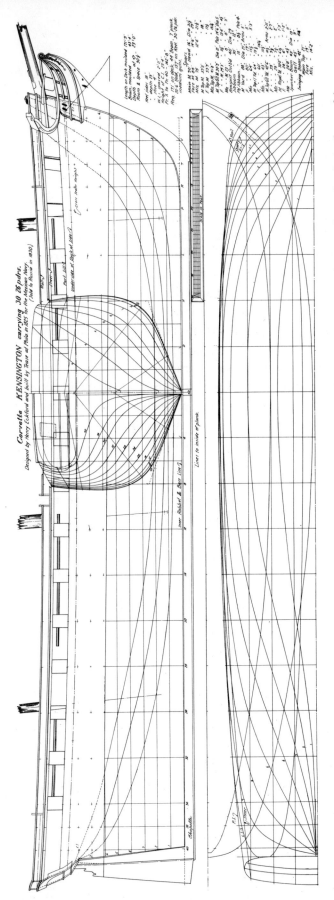

Plate 75. Ship corvette KENSINGTON *built at Philadelphia by Tease and designed by Henry Eckford, 1825. A much admired vessel in her time.*

reducing of her draft.

Kensington was 171′ 9″ on deck, moulded; 43′ 4″ moulded beam; 23 feet moulded depth at ⋈; and was registered as 171 feet on deck, 44 feet beam, and 20′ 6″ depth in hold.

Her moulded load waterline length was 165′ 2″, and her moulded displacement was 1612.7 long tons. Her coefficients were block .76, midship .70, and prismatic .67. The effective length of quarterbeam buttock was 148 feet and camber was 12′ 7″, giving a camber-length ratio of 11.5.

With the reviving trade, the building of new pilot boats became active. Here speed and seaworthiness were prime considerations. At the Virginia Capes, the pilot schooners had changed markedly. Plate 76 shows *Lafayette*, built at Norfolk in 1824 from a design by Francis Grice, later a naval constructor. This boat was considered the fastest pilot schooner working off the Capes in 1826. Her type had apparently developed sometime after 1805. *Lafayette* had "small boat" design characteristics; she was a flush-decked craft having little sheer, straight keel with much drag, slightly raking curved-stem rabbet, raking sternpost, round tuck with sharply raking flat transom above, and the midsection formed with sharply rising straight floor, very high and very slack bilge, with flaring topside, carried to top of rail. The entrance was convex, short, and moderately sharp. The run was rather long and very fine. The quarterbeam buttock, taken as the fourth outboard, became straight only a short distance forward of its intersection with the after load line. The entrance was formed with slack bow lines as in Eckford's *Bolivar*.

The position of the mainmast was far aft of the location commonly chosen in schooners. As a result she carried a very large foresail with which the vessel could be worked in all weathers, as well as a well-balanced sail area under jib and mainsail.

Since the Virginia boats did not usually search far to sea, the accommodations remained primitive; in summer the trunks over the hatches were often left ashore. In winter these were shipped and formed cabin space for the crew.

Lafayette was 61′ 3″ on deck, 60′ 7½″ between perpendiculars, 19 feet moulded beam at deck, and 7′7″ depth in hold. Her length, moulded, at load line was 57′ 10″; her displacement, moulded, was 54 long tons. Her block coefficient was .35, her midship coefficient .56, and prismatic .63. The effective length of the quarterbeam buttock was 45′ 11″ and camber was 3′ 3″, giving a camber-length ratio of 13.9. These schooners contained much cedar or juniper in their construction and were lightly built as well; apparently nothing

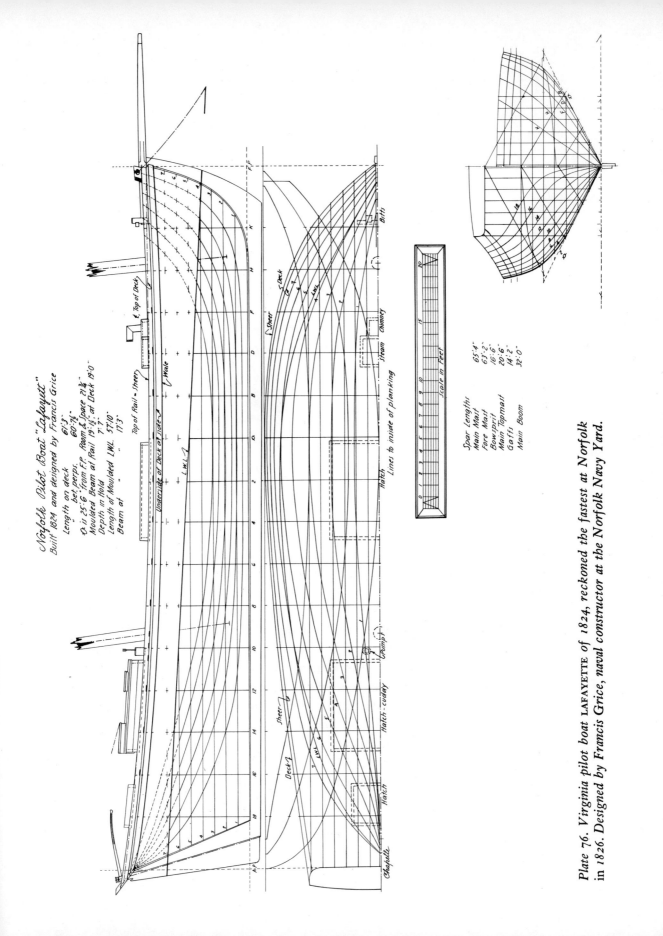

Norfolk Pilot Boat "Lafayett"
Built 1824 and designed by Francis Grice

Length on deck   61'3".
   "   bet.perps.   60'7¼".
☉ is 25'-6" from F.P. Room & Space 21¾".
Moulded Beam at Rail 19'-1½"; at Deck 19'-0".
Depth in Hold   7'-7".
Length of Moulded L.W.L. 57'-10".
   Beam at   "   17'-3".

Spar Lengths
Main Mast   65'-4".
Fore Mast   63'-2".
Bowsprit   16'-6".
Main Topmast   20'-6".
Gaffs   14'-2".
Main Boom   32'-0".

Scale in Feet

Plate 76. Virginia pilot boat LAFAYETTE of 1824, reckoned the fastest at Norfolk in 1826. Designed by Francis Grice, naval constructor at the Norfolk Navy Yard.

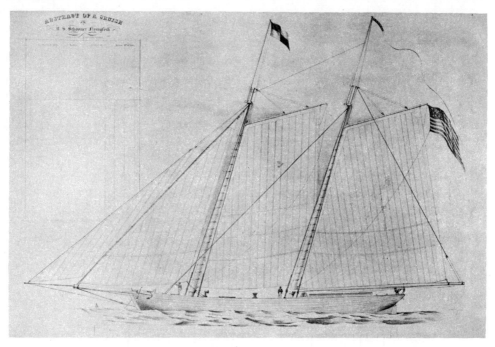

United States FLYING FISH, *pilot schooner rig, 1828–45. Peabody Marine Museum, Salem, Massachusetts.*

was spent on carvings or decoration of any kind. English naval officers who saw the Virginia pilot boats were much impressed by their speed and general sailing qualities.

New York and Boston schooners retained most of the pilot-boat characteristics that had existed at the outbreak of the War of 1812. Plate 77 shows the plan of a pilot schooner named *Brothers*, a New York boat probably built about 1826. The plan was found in France but there is no history except a remark on the plan that she was "one of the fastest pilot boats in the United States." The pilot boats were not often registered in this period, so her career cannot be traced. Plans of a Boston boat of 1832 show very similar design. The pilot boats had increased in size since 1812 and also had become more exaggerated in form, tending toward rather shallow hull proportions, and an appearance of a long, low craft with a large spread of sail.

Brothers was 71 feet on deck, 70′ 5″ length for tonnage, 18 feet moulded

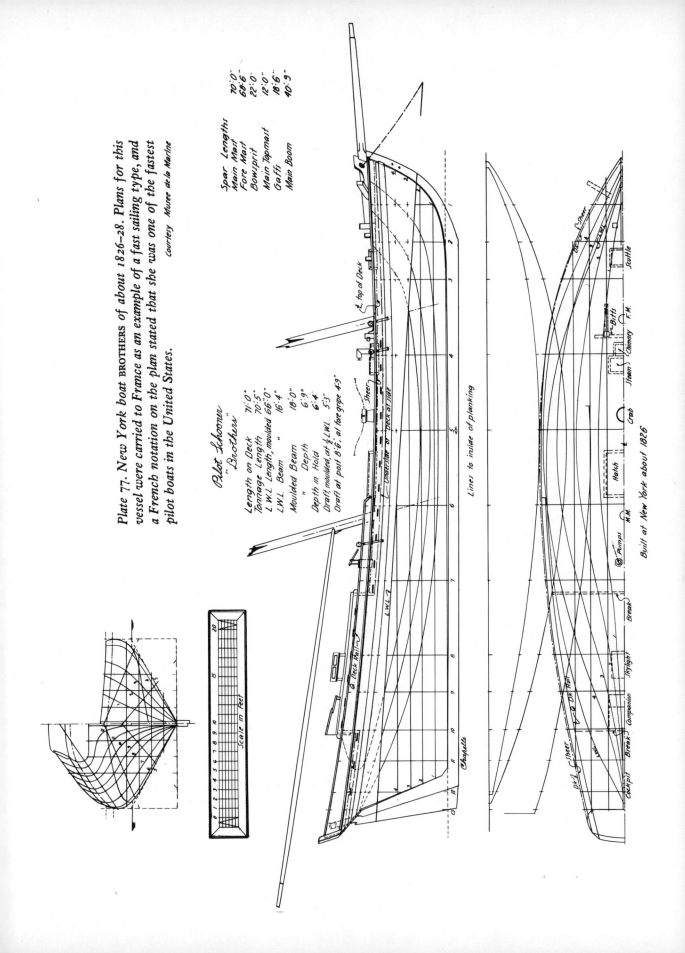

Plate 77. New York boat BROTHERS of about 1826-28. Plans for this vessel were carried to France as an example of a fast sailing type, and a French notation on the plan stated that she was one of the fastest pilot boats in the United States.

Courtesy Musee de la Marine

Spar Lengths
Main Mast   70'0"
Fore Mast   68'6"
Bowsprit   22'0"
Main Topmast   12'0"
Gaff   18'6"
Main Boom   40'9"

Pilot Schooner
"Brothers"

Length on Deck   71'0"
Tonnage Length   70'5"
L.W.L. Length, moulded   66'0"
L.W.L. Beam   "   16'4"
Moulded Beam   18'0"
    "   Depth   6'9"
Depth in Hold   6'4"
Draft, moulded, at ½ L.W.L.   5'3"
Draft at post 8'6"; at fore gripe 4'9"

Lines to inside of planking

Built at New York about 1826

Scale in Feet

beam, 6' 4" depth in hold, drawing 8' 6" aft and 4' 9" forward. The schooner had a lively sheer, with a raised quarterdeck rail aft, a pilot-boat house and sunk-cockpit, a straight keel with much drag, a well-curved raking stem rabbet, a strong rake in post, a round tuck, and a square stern with upper-and-lower transoms. The midsection was formed with strongly rising straight floor carried well out, a high easy bilge, and a short, quick tumble home. The entrance was moderately long, sharp, and convex. The run was long and very fine, with a straight quarterbeam buttock line.

The working rig consisted of a single large jib; a gaff foresail, without boom and overlapping the main and a gaff mainsail, boomed but with loose-footed sail until late in the 1830's, when the foot of this sail was often laced to the boom. Main topmast staysail was also carried and often a main gaff topsail as well. When a fore course was carried it was hoisted on a very short yard and the much wider foot was spread with a light squaresail boom—a powerful, but light, running sail.

Brothers was 66 feet moulded load waterline length and had a moulded displacement of 53.6 long tons. Her coefficients were block .30, midship .53, and prismatic .56. The effective length of the quarterbeam buttock was 50' 6" and camber was 3' 3", giving a camber-length ratio of 15.5.

Boston and New York pilot boats began to range far to sea in the 1830's and as a result their size was increased steadily. By 1840 many boats were 90 feet, or more, in length on deck.

The great development affecting sailing-ship design and construction was the establishment of the packet services, which began to influence ship-building as soon as vessels especially built for the business were desired by the merchant-owners. This occurred as early as 1821, as far as large vessels were concerned.

The packet service did not begin with the establishment of the North Atlantic lines. Soon after the War of 1812 ended, packet services, that is, departures according to a schedule, were established on the Hudson River between New York and Albany. Large sloops capable of carrying freight and passengers were employed. It is probable that the sloops before 1812 were keel hulls, but leeboards were certainly in use as early as this. By 1825, at the latest, the centerboard was well-known and in use on the Hudson, Chesapeake, and perhaps elsewhere.

Plans or half-models of the Hudson River sloop packets before 1831 have not been found, or at least have not yet been identified. Shallow, keel sloops were in use in the coastal trade; McKay showed lines* of a keel sloop 58 feet long, 20′ 9″ wide, and 8′ 5″ depth. Of this he stated that she was a good model for speed and burthen, could carry a 70 to 75-foot mast, and was suitable for either coast or river.

Plate 78 shows a packet sloop of uncertain date as to lines, which were taken from a half-model in the Mystic Seaport Marine Historical Association. This model was apparently made before 1845, judging by its appearance and construction. The deck, head, and other features were drawn from a French sketch of an American packet sloop made sometime just before 1839. The sloop was of the "sharp model" and was large, but not of the largest class. Some of the Hudson River sloops were over 80 feet long on the main rail line, whereas the sloop shown in Plate 78 was 67′ 2″ between perpendiculars, about 70 feet on the main rail. The moulded beam was 24′ 7″ and draft at post measured 9′ 6″. On 61′ 3″ length, moulded load waterline, she had a moulded displacement of 87.5 long tons. Her coefficients worked out to be block .32, midship .53, and prismatic .61. The effective length of the second buttock out was 46′ 9″, the camber 3′ 6″, giving a camber-length ratio of 13.4.

Except on the Hudson and in those services between two nearby ports that had more or less regularly scheduled runs, the sloops were out of the important areas in the packet business by about 1830, having been replaced by schooners and brigs. However, sloops remained in some coastal trades until the end of the period of sail. The New England granite trade was largely in sloops, some of which approached 90 feet in length on deck. The Hudson River sloops were the most highly developed of all commercial sloops by the mid-nineteenth century.

A number of lines were established in the coastal and transatlantic packet services in which vessels were regularly operated between two ports such as New York and Liverpool, New York and New Orleans, or Baltimore and Charleston. These services were carried out on established schedules of sailing days, with vessels leaving each port about twice a month. The lines were operated either by a number of vessel-owners in a company or partnership, or by a freight and passenger agency. Generally, packet lines operated by agents or by temporary groups of vessel-owners employed a nondescript lot of vessels. But the "regular" or company-operated lines such as the New York and Liverpool "Black Ball Line," the New York and Le Havre "Old Line," "First" and "Second" or "Union" lines, the New York and Havana "Spofford

* In *The Practical Shipbuilder* (1839), Plate 5.

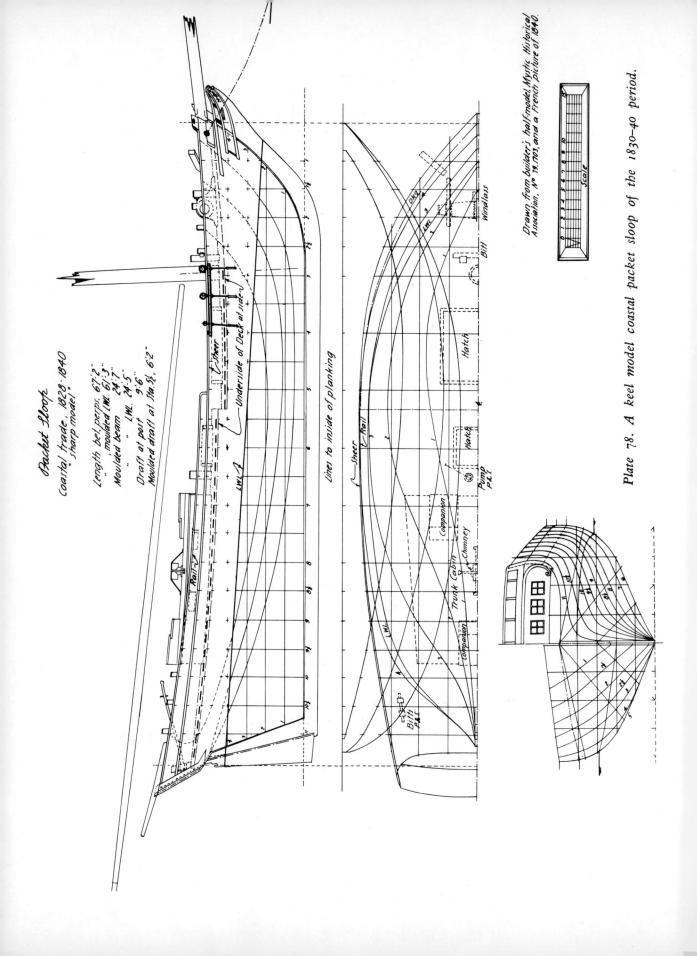

Packet Sloop

Coastal trade, 1828-1840
"sharp model"

Length bet. perp. 67.2"
" moulded LWL 61.3"
Moulded beam 24.7"
" LWL 24.5"
Draft at post 9.6"
Moulded draft at Sta. 5½ 6.2"

Liners to inside of planking

Underside of Deck at sheer

Sheer

Rail

LWL

Sheer Rail

Sheer

LWL

Windlass

Bitt

Hatch

Hatch

Pump P&L

Companion

Trunk Cabin

Chimney

Companion

Bitts P&L

Drawn from builder's half-model, Mystic Historical
Association, N° 79.1703, and a French picture of 1840.

Scale

Plate 78. A keel model coastal packet sloop of the 1830-40 period.

& Tileston Line," and the Philadelphia and Liverpool "Cope Line" had ship-rigged vessels especially built for the trade.*

Where the distance between ports was not great, a coastal line would employ schooners and brigs, some of which were undoubtedly built for packet service. The vessels especially built for the North Atlantic packet service were the result of an intensive development in design, construction, and fitting to meet rigorous requirements produced by year-round operation and the need for speed, capacity, seaworthiness, and weatherliness imposed by weather in the Atlantic Ocean, available cargoes, and the necessity of maintaining a sailing schedule against keen competition. These conflicting

YOUNG BRUTUS, *Baltimore clipper schooner of the 1820's.*

* For general history of the packet lines see Carl C. Cutler's *Queens of the Western Ocean: The Story of America's Mail and Passenger Sailing Lines* (Annapolis, Maryland, United States Naval Institute, 1961).

requirements forced the ship designers to produce fast-sailing, heavy cargo carriers, with nice compromises between speed characteristics and cargo-carrying ability.*

Though the production of ships for the packet lines began in the 1820's, plans or half-models are not available—with one exception, the Philadelphia-New Orleans packet ship *Ohio*, built at Philadelphia in 1825.† This vessel had about two feet of deadrise at the quarterbeam and was flush-decked. She was rather full-ended but was considered a good, serviceable vessel. Compared with the few surviving plans of freight ships built between 1825 and 1835, she appears to have had a somewhat longer and finer run than was usual in this class of vessel.

Aside from the published plans of *Ohio*, we are fortunate in having excellent examples of North Atlantic and coastal packet ships to examine, all built after 1832. These were from the very progressive yard of Isaac Webb and his son, William H. Webb, of New York. The Webbs, at one time operating with a partner as Webb and Allen, built vessels for the Black Ball Line, Swallowtail Line, Black Star Line, Old Line, Spofford & Tileston Line, Regular Line, and others. They thus had experience in the design of ships for the coastal trades to New Orleans and to Havana as well as in the North Atlantic packet trades.

By 1835 the size of packet ships had grown somewhat; the *Ohio* of 1825 was 103 feet between perpendiculars, and the Webb-built *Southerner* of 1834 was 134 feet between perpendiculars. This increase in size caused construction problems. Capacity was the design requirement of the packets, for the packets on the eastward run in the North Atlantic carried heavy and bulk cargoes—iron ore, lead, pig iron, lumber, vegetables, coal, and at times, flour. Cotton was carried in this trade as well as in the coastal packet trades. For these cargoes large carriers were the desired type. Westbound, the North Atlantic packets carried fabrics and manufactured goods. On both the eastward and westward runs, and in the coastal trades, passengers were accommodated. In the trade to the cotton ports, the coastal packets had to be bulk-cargo ships, of course.

---

* Robert G. Albion, *Square-Riggers on Schedule: The New York Sailing Packets to England, France and the Cotton Ports* (Princeton, N.J., Princeton University Press, 1938). Good description of packet-ship characteristics.
† Howard I. Chapelle, "The Pioneer Steamship *Savannah*: A Study for a Scale Model," *Contributions from the Museum of History and Technology*, United States National Museum Bulletin 228 (Washington, D.C., Smithsonian Institution, 1961), page 70.

HERCULES, later BOLIVAR

Built by Isaac Webb for Henry Eckford at New York
in 1822.

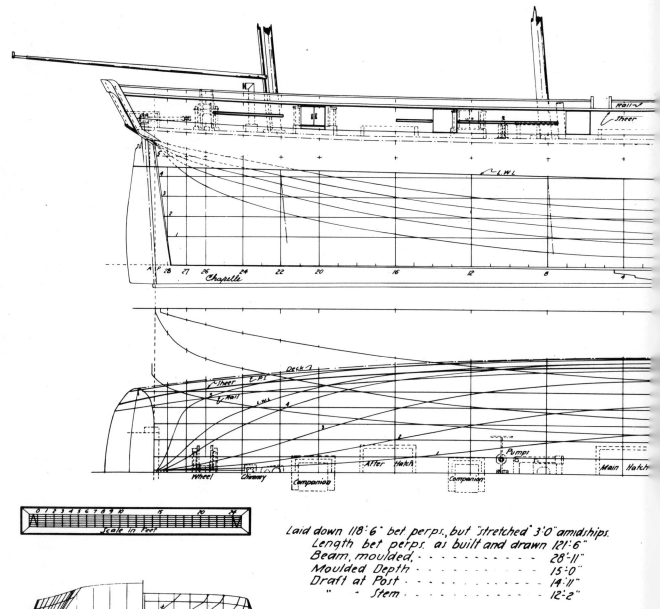

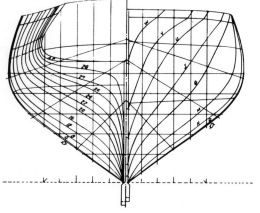

Scale in Feet

Laid down 118'·6" bet perps., but "stretched" 3'·0" amidships.
Length bet perps. as built and drawn 121'·6"
Beam, moulded, - - - - - - - - - - 28'·11"
Moulded Depth - - - - - - - - - 15'·0"
Draft at Post - - - - - - - - - 14'·11"
  "   " Stem - - - - - - - - - 12'·2"

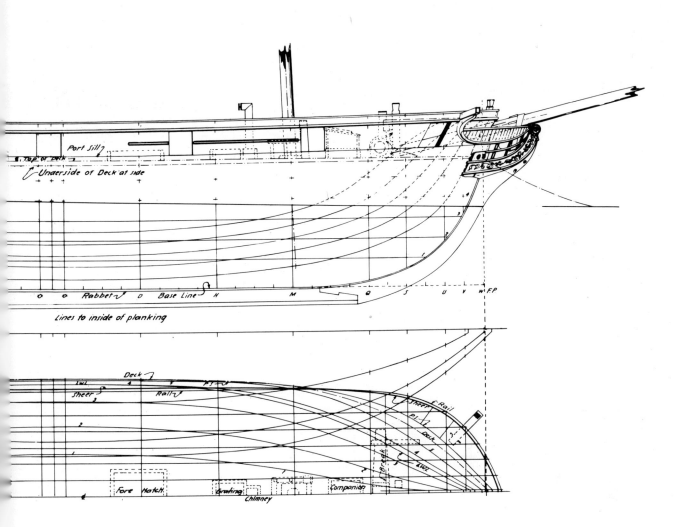

Port Sill

Top of Deck

Underside of Deck at side

o   o   Rabbet   O   Base Line   H   M   Q   S   U   V   W F.P.

Lines to inside of planking

Deck
LWL
Sheer
Rail

Sheet
Rail
Deck
LWL

Fore Hatch.   Grating   Companion
Chimney

Room & Space 2'4. 1'6" O. to O.   A.P. 1'7" abaft #28
F.P. 14'1" for'd of # Q. Buttocks 2'0" apart.
1st W.L. is 3'6" above Base. Cross Seam 15'0" above Base.
2nd W.L. is 6'0" "   " .
3rd W.L. is 8'6" "   " .
4th W.L. is 11'0" "   " :
5th W.L. is 12'6" "   " .

PLATE V. *Pre-clipper-era clipper ship* BOLIVAR *of extreme model, built in 1822
at New York.*

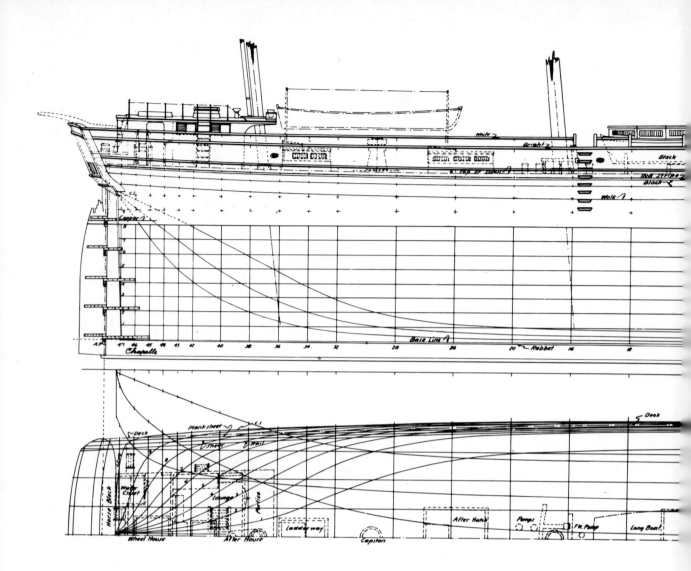

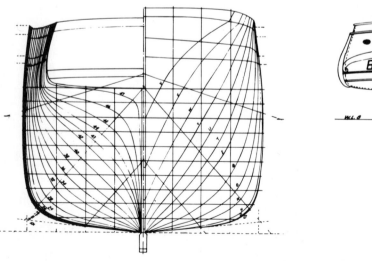

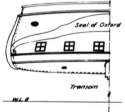

Black Ball Packet Ship
OXFORD
Built at N.Y.C. in 1836 by Isaac Webb

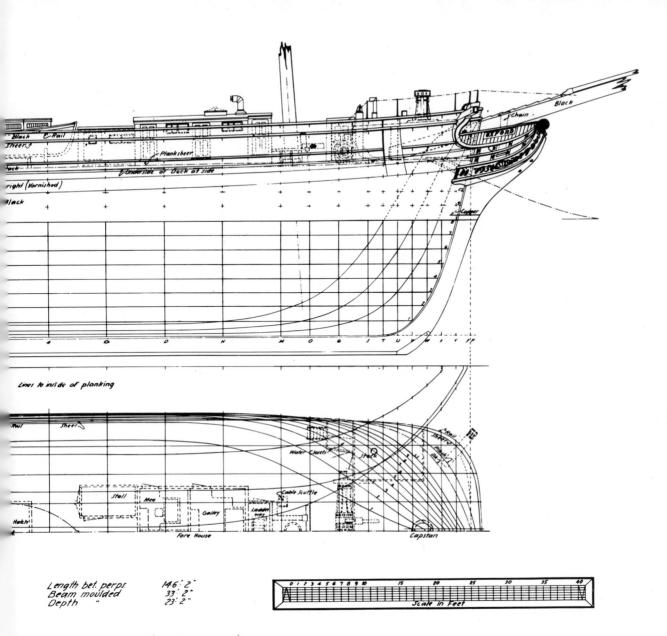

Length bet. perps.   146ˈ 2ˈˈ
Beam moulded   33ˈ 2ˈˈ
Depth   "   23ˈ 2ˈˈ

Reg. Dimensions 147ˈ6ˈˈ x 33ˈ6ˈˈ x 21ˈ6ˈˈ; 752 tons.
"Burgundy," Harve Old Line, launched 4 months
later, was her sister ship.

PLATE VI. *Black Ball packet* OXFORD, *and* BURGUNDY *on same lines, built by Isaac
Webb in 1836. The* OXFORD *was a consistently good passage-maker.*

To maintain regular sailing schedules, the coastal and Atlantic packet ships had to sail well in both light and heavy weather, particularly to windward and with the wind on the quarter. With a heavy displacement and with the large cargo capacity required, it was necessary that packets be heavily sparred, rigged, and canvassed, and that they could be driven hard in either light or strong winds. To stand such driving they had to be very strongly built and fitted. To maintain a useful span of life in such a hard service, the ships had to hold their form. This was one of the most troublesome problems in the design and construction of large wooden ships, for these had a tendency to "hog," that is, to sag at bow and stern, thus arching the keel. As mentioned with reference to the arched keel of the brig *Badger*, this occasionally helped speed, though some of the improvement may have been imaginary. Usually, however, this arching of the keel was a sign of weakness that would eventually cause the vessel to strain and leak so badly that she would become unserviceable.

The problem of longitudinal strength, mentioned in Chapter 4, became increasingly important as ships increased in length and size. The French were probably the first to try to solve the problem by means of extra longitudinal timbers, and by stanchions set on the inside keel, or "keelson," and tenoned into the underside of the deck beams. In 1746, they built a vessel having diagonally planked (see page 207) inner planking, or "ceiling." In England, the large men-of-war—ships of the line and large frigates—gave trouble, and in 1771, 1776, and again in 1791 the matter of strength in ship structure was raised in the Admiralty. Hearings were held in the House of Commons at which concrete proposals were made to increase longitudinal and transverse strength and to develop ventilation methods for the preservation of naval ships. Information was obtained on seasoning of timber. Seasoning was done by letting naval ships stand in frame, unplanked, for six months or a year, but this was not practical in merchant shipbuilding for economic reasons.

Merchant vessels in America had not commonly been large enough—that is, not long enough in proportion to depth or in some relationship to size of timber, or scantling—to show extensive weakness until after the War of 1812. Some of the lightly built privateers, however, did show weakness in at least a few instances, also the wartime-built frigates *Java* and *Guerriere* were reported as being hogged soon after commissioning.

It had been established in the English investigations that ships having nearly vertical sides—"wall-sided"—were less inclined to hog than ships having much curvature and tumble home in the topsides, because the vertically sided hulls received longitudinal strength from the planking, inside and outside the frames. This had the same effect as a deep, solid longitudinal bulkhead. It was also noted in Chapter 4 that vessels having very rising, straight floors, such as employed in the pilot boats, received this benefit. Hence the prolonged use of deadrise in the design of lightly built or long, rather shallow merchant sailing vessels, even when economic cargo capacity was of importance.

After the War of 1812, the British Navy again considered the problems of ship construction, and Surveyor Robert Seppings designed trussed frames, with diagonal members laid over the ceiling from keelson to lower deck beams—a very expensive mode of construction.

The need for greater longitudinal strength in a lightly built, shallow wooden hull was obvious in Fulton's early attempts at building steamboats; the weight of engine, boilers, and fuel caused failures in hull structure. The river steamers built after 1820 were first wooden trussed, and later many were fitted with hogging chains or trusses of timber and iron to give the necessary longitudinal strength required, even in river and bay navigation. The steamers also showed the value of long and very sharp ends for speed; the Hudson River steamers increased their speed from seven or eight statute mph in 1817 to 20 statute mph in 1838. By 1837 experiments were being made with diagonal wood strapping, placed inside the frames; no inside planking or ceiling was used in order to save weight. McKay* refers to English steamers being diagonally strapped with iron bars 3½ inches wide and ¾ inch thick, let into the inside of the frames so as to be flush and partly ceiled over with wood plank. The fastenings of the strapping passed through the outside plank. It seems probable that diagonal metal strapping originated in England where it developed so that by 1855, the modern plan came into use of placing straps between the frames and outside planking, and secured to longitudinal plates inside the garboard and sheer strakes. This mode of strapping was required by the *American Bureau of Shipping Rules for Construction of Wooden Ships* and remained in force until large wooden vessel construction ceased about 1920. In America, strapping was extended even to the built-up keelsons, which were secured by independent strapping on each side in some of the later clipper ships.

Various modes of strengthening wooden hulls were tried in the large

* In *The Practical Shipbuilder*, p. 99.

packets. Improved locked scarphs, edge-fastened planking and ceiling, iron knees, and iron strappings were all used. Caulking of the ceiling seams was found to be a very simple but effective method of markedly improving longitudinal strength in the hull. Diagonal planking was used in building the U.S. naval schooner *Experiment* in 1831; she lasted 17 years. Arched stringers in the topsides (later employed in yachts) and various schemes for fastening timbers were tried in the 1830's, particularly in steamboats.

Chiefly through improved structural details, the packets could be built in steadily increasing lengths and without hogging or opening their seams after years of hard usage. Models and proportions were chosen to obtain maximum advantage of improved timbering, which also gave power to carry sail, a fair turn of speed, and seaworthiness. It was this effort to build long, strong, and seaworthy ships that created the structural skill in the North American shipyards necessary to build the later wooden clipper ships and their successors, the "Down Easters."

Plate 79 shows the lines of the Black Ball Line packet ship *Columbus*, built by Isaac Webb in 1834. Her moulds were used to build the coastal packet ship *Southerner* for the New Orleans-Louisiana-New York Line in 1834, with two feet added to her length amidships. This packet was transferred to the Liverpool-New York New Line in 1841 for the North Atlantic trade. A short-lived coastal packet, *Star*, was built in 1835 on *Columbus'* moulds for the Taylor and Merrill Line in the New Orleans run. This ship had four feet added to her length amidships. She was lost in 1837.

The records of the Webb-built ships show that a number of packets were built on the moulds of an earlier ship, indicating that the original design was highly satisfactory. It has been widely accepted that in 1830 the New Orleans packets were especially flat-bottomed for negotiating the bars at the mouth of the Mississippi, and that therefore they were different in model from the North Atlantic packets. Also, it has been claimed, on apparently good contemporary authority, that the low-deadrise or "flat-floored" model was not introduced into the North Atlantic packet service until the Collins' Dramatic Line packets were built in 1836–37.

The drawing of *Columbus* and of her two sisterships indicates that the flat-floored packet was employed on the North Atlantic run in 1834 and that there was no difference in the models of New Orleans packets from the models employed in the Liverpool-New York service at that time.

The lines of *Columbus* show a relatively flat-floored full-model vessel with

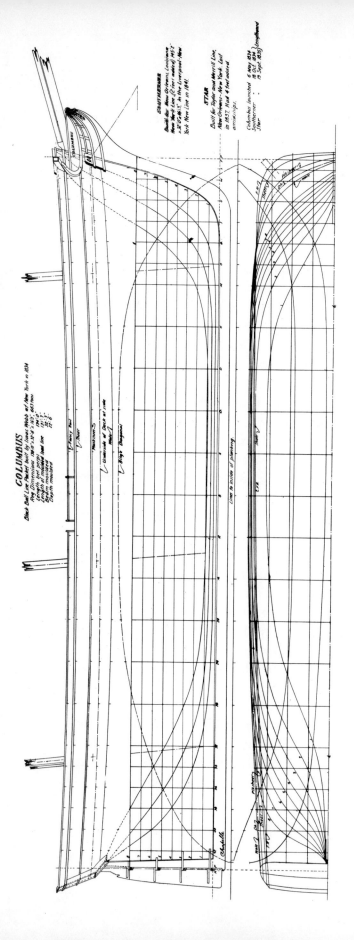

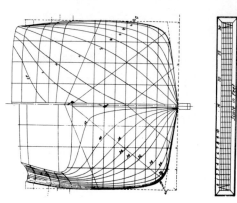

Plate 79. Lines of packet ship COLUMBUS. *Three packet ships were built on these lines, two with frames added amidships. Vessels were used for both coastal and transatlantic packet services. Built by Isaac Webb, 1834–35.*

a low and hard turn in the bilge amidships, and small tumble home high in the topsides. The vessel had rather straight sheer, straight keel with no drag, moderately raking and slightly curved stem rabbet, nearly vertical post, round tuck with upper-and-lower raking transoms, a short, convex, and full entrance with the rail nearly square-across, a short, steep run, but with a straight quarterbeam buttock from just below the load line to the cross seam of the lower transom. The run appears to have been carefully designed to retain as much speed as the length, proportions, and capacity of the hull permitted.

The design was for a vessel 134 feet between perpendiculars, 32' 3" moulded beam, 22' 6" moulded depth; her register dimensions were 138' 10" by 32' 6" by 16' 3"; 663 tons register. Those of *Southerner* were 145' 2" by 32 feet by 16' 3".

The length on the moulded load line of the *Columbus* was 131' 7", the moulded displacement was 1317.7 long tons, the coefficients were block .79, midship .89, and prismatic .76. The effective length of the quarterbeam buttock was 122 feet, the camber 14' 10", giving a camber-length ratio of 8.2.

A smaller and slightly sharper coastal packet is shown in Plate 80. This is the Havana-New York packet ship *Christoval Colon*, built by Isaac Webb in 1835 for Spofford, Tileston & Co. Line. Again, the lines show a full-model carrier having very little deadrise, with a low and very quick turn of the bilge. This vessel was 105' 3" between perpendiculars, 26' 4" moulded beam, and 16' 2" moulded depth. Her register dimensions were 106 feet by 27 feet by 13' 6". Like a number of vessels in the West Indian trade she had a few ports and could carry guns for protection against Caribbean pirates and freebooters who existed well into the 1830's. This packet was reputedly a good sailer and carrier, but fuller-ended than the 1825 *Ohio*.

The length of the moulded load line was 102' 2"; the moulded displacement was 620.8 long tons. Her coefficients were block .63, midship .88, and prismatic .72. The effective length of the quarterbeam buttock was 94' 8", camber 11' 10", giving a camber-length ratio of 8.6.

Christoval Colon had little sheer, straight keel with little drag, moderate rake in stem rabbet, nearly vertical post, round tuck, and upper-and-lower transoms above. The entrance was short, convex, but at least somewhat sharp. The run was rather short and steep, but with the quarterbeam buttock coming straight, or very nearly so, near the load line.

In the mid-1830's the North Atlantic packets were still increasing in size

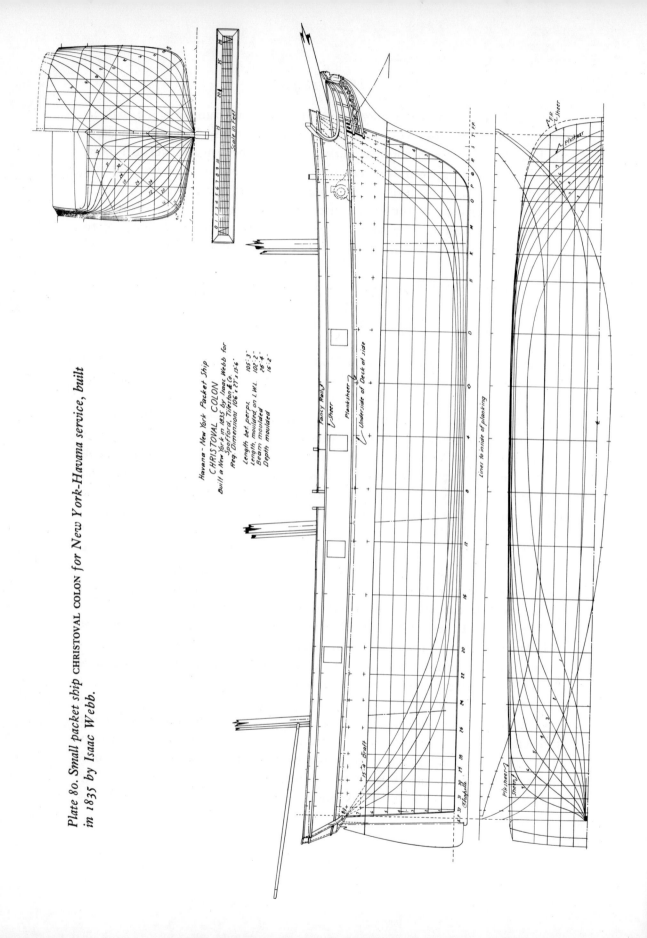

Plate 80. Small packet ship CHRISTOVAL COLON *for New York-Havana service, built in 1835 by Isaac Webb.*

Havana – New York Packet Ship
CHRISTOVAL COLON
Built a New York in 1835 by Isaac Webb for
York Spofford, Tileston & Co.
Reg. Dimensions 106 × 27½ × 13·6"

Length bet. perpls.   105'·3"
Length, moulded on L.W.L.   102'·2"
Beam moulded   25'·4"
Depth moulded   15'·2"

and were achieving a well-tested hull form for the packet service. Steamship competition was affecting the coastal packet trades and therefore experiments in sailing coastal packet designs slowly came to a halt. But the North Atlantic packets were to continue development into the 1850's, increasing steadily in size.

Plate VI shows the lines of the Black Ball Line packet ship *Oxford*, built by Isaac Webb in 1836, the year the first Dramatic Line packets were laid down. This packet was considered a very good vessel of her type and she had a record for the most short transatlantic passages. A sister ship, *Burgundy*, for the New York-Le Havre Old Line, was launched four months after *Oxford*.

Oxford had little sheer, straight keel with no drag, moderately raking and slightly curved stem rabbet, nearly upright post, round tuck, upper-and-lower transoms above, separated by an "arch board," which marked the Webb packets after 1836. The entrance was short but rather sharp for a full-model ship; the run was about ⅓ the waterline length, with a straight quarterbeam buttock near the load line crossing. The midship section was flat-floored with very little deadrise, as in the two earlier packets. There appears to have been little change in the deadrise of Webb-built packets after 1834.

Oxford was 147′ 6″ between perpendiculars, 33′ 2″ moulded beam, and 23′ 2″ moulded depth; her register dimensions were 147′ 6″ by 33′ 6″ by 21′ 6″. Her length, moulded, on the load line was 142′ 6″, she had a moulded displacement at the eight level line of 1448.6 long tons. Her coefficients were block .67, midship .90, and prismatic .75. The effective length of the quarterbeam buttock was 131′ 6″, the camber 15′ 7″, giving a camber-length ratio of 8.4.

The lines of *Oxford* show a rise in the sheer right forward; this was to avoid the optical illusion that would produce an apparent hump in the sheer here, owing to the very full rail line in half-breadth plan. New York builders developed refinements in design of this kind and viewed New England built vessels, which did not have such finish before 1850, with disdain. Plate VII shows the lines of *New York*, built by William H. Webb in 1839 for the Black Ball Line, its second packet of that name. This vessel was a handsome, well-finished ship of her class; she shows a modest increase in size over *Oxford*, but does not show any marked change in model. *New York* measured 152 feet between perpendiculars, 35 feet moulded beam, and her register dimensions were 152′ 6″ by 35′ 4″ by 22 feet. She had a quarterdeck reaching to just abaft the mainmast with solid bulwarks and her quarterdeck at fancy rail (or "top-gallant rail") height; her maindeck was flush fore and aft. The topgallant forecastle, at main rail height, was very short. This vessel had little sheer, straight keel with no drag, moderate rake in stem rabbet, nearly vertical post, round tuck, lower transom archboard and upper transom stern, short convex entrance moderately sharp at forefoot, short, steep run with straight quarterbeam buttock at intersection with load line and 20′ 6″ draft. The midsection was the standard shape used in the earlier Webb-built packet ships.

New York was 148 feet on the moulded load line, and 1828.9 long tons moulded displacement. Her coefficients were block .68, midship .91, prismatic .76, and the effective quarterbeam buttock length was 142′ 9″, camber 17′ 2″, giving a camber-length ratio of 8.2.

The packet that had the best record for passages was the William H. Webb built *Yorkshire*, Plates VIII and 81. This fine packet was launched in 1843 for Charles H. Marshall and was a Black Ball Line ship. She was 163′ 6″ between perpendiculars, 36 feet moulded beam, and 23′ 2″ moulded depth. She had a quarterdeck at fancy rail height, with solid quarterdeck bulwarks reaching to the mainmast, with a topgallant forecastle at main rail height. By 1843 the decks of the North Atlantic packets were so cluttered with deck-houses that it was troublesome to work ship in some of the worst cases. Complaints about this began in the late 1830's.

Yorkshire had nearly straight sheer, straight keel with no drag, moderate rake in stem rabbet, nearly vertical post, very short but fairly sharp entrance, particularly near the forefoot, long and easy run, quarterbeam buttock straight for a short distance at crossing of the load line, round tuck, and standard Webb transom stern. Length on the moulded load line at 20 feet draft, was 161 feet; giving a moulded displacement of 1717.3 long tons. Coefficients were block .65, midship .88, and prismatic .73. Effective length of quarterbeam buttock was 146 feet and camber was 15′ 3″, giving a camber-length ratio of 9.7.

William Webb believed this packet was a "happy combination" of cargo capacity and speed; it is doubtful if his later and larger packets were improvements in model. This ship was lost at sea after the Civil War.

The packets grew in size until, by 1854, they were over 200 feet on deck. In the meantime a "clipper packet," the *Universe*, had been built by Smith and Dimon at New York in 1850; register dimensions were 186 feet by 38′ 7″

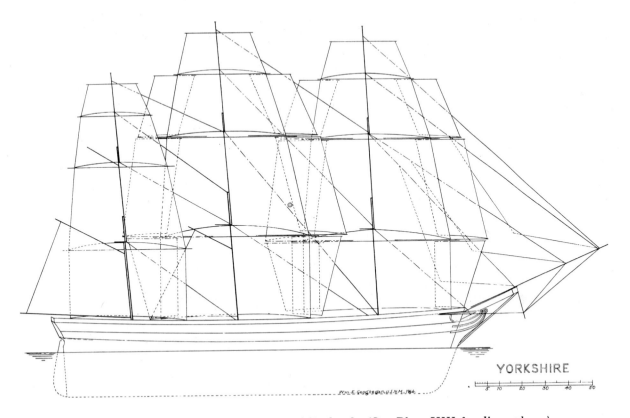

Plate 81. YORKSHIRE *sail plan from Webb's book. (See Plate VIII for lines plans.)*

by 28′ 6″. Though a fast ship, *Universe* did not equal *Yorkshire's* average in crossing time. In the middle 1850's a number of clipper ships served as packets temporarily. By this time, the development of the sailing packet had reached its zenith and she was fast losing ground in competition with steamers. The model of the packet was preserved to at least some degree in the American sailing ships of the "Down-Easter" type, though these did not look like packets.

Before turning to the other types of American vessels of this period, the technical facilities developed in this era should be examined. As already mentioned, the introduction of machine-made cotton sailcloth was a very important improvement. Another advance was in the increased production of rolled copper plate for sheathing. When postwar conditions brought down

277

New York-Le Havre packet ship LA DUCHESSE D' ORLEANS.

the cost of copper, its use increased rapidly in the merchant marine, for copper not only protected the ships' bottoms from the sea worm but also prevented or delayed marine growths, thus reducing the need for frequent cleaning of ships' bottoms and reduced maintenance expenses between voyages. Anti-fouling paints were not then in existence, but wooden sheathing over felt and tar was used in lieu of copper sheathing or anti-fouling paint in whalers and some merchant ships. While preventing damage to hull plank by sea worms, this wooden sheathing soon became foul.

Specialists in maritime history have looked upon the period 1820–45 as an unprogressive one that preceded the appearance of the clipper ship or as a kind of training period in which hard-sailing captains were produced in the American packet service. Instead, however, the period was a very progressive one, and in addition to improved construction techniques, there appeared patented rigging, deck machinery, and fittings. Such things as geared capstans and windlasses, iron-strapped blocks, geared steering, hold ventilators, geared winches, new mast and spar ironwork, and improved marine stoves and water closets came on the market. Rod rigging and turnbuckles, screw- or lever-operated, were introduced in the 1820's and 1830's. Shipyard tools improved, steam saws came into use, and a few of the more prosperous yards, such as Adam and Noah Brown's in New York, could now build vessels under cover, having constructed shiphouses, which formerly were available in only two United States Navy Yards.

Marine railways were built: New York had one in 1822, Salem in 1824, Philadelphia in 1826. Boston may have beaten all the other ports, for there is mention of a proposal to encourage building a drydock at Charlestown in 1667. In 1668 the General Court offered the right to operate a drydock without competition for 21 years, to the first who would construct such a dock. In April 1700, the Town Clerk of Charlestown entered a deed in which it is said "The Bounds of the Land sold the Owners of the dry Dock . . ."* Mr. J. Goldenberg of Chapel Hill, North Carolina, who found this reference, has not come across any other mention of the dock, leaving tantalizing questions as to whether it was ever built, and if it was, how long it operated.

The introduction of the centerboard had a great effect upon the American commercial sailing vessels. Beginning with small craft—sloops and schooners—centerboards were gradually applied to vessels of greater size, so that by 1845 they were in use in such large commercial craft as ships and barks. Centerboard barks were built in number for use on the Great Lakes. But the centerboard was most popular in the coastal trades. A centerboard coaster not only had the advantage of relatively small draft, compared to a keel vessel, but also could sail well when light, which most burdensome keel vessels could not. And centerboard vessels were often very fast sailers. Also centerboards were given to vessels that were required to handle well in confined waters, where weatherliness and good steering were most important. The centerboard would insure this at all loads and drafts. It is probable that the centerboard did much in the initial development of the large schooner-

* 1. Nathaniel Shurtleff, *Records of Massachusetts*, Att. a generall Court of Election held at Boston in New England (29 Aprill 1668), Vol. IV, Part III, pp. 367-368.
2. Nathaniel Shurtleff, ed., *Records of the Governor And Company of the Massachusetts Bay in New England* (Boston, William White, 1854), Vol. V, 1674-1686.
3. *A Report of the Record Commissioners, containing Charlestown Land Records, 1638-1802*, 2nd ed. (Boston, Rockwell and Churchill, 1883), Vol. III, pp. 168-169.

coasters of the last half of the nineteenth century, many of which had centerboards.

Leeboards have never had much appeal to American seamen, yet some local types of American vessels employed leeboards until the end of the period of sail. They were to be found on the Piscataqua River in New Hampshire, the Kennebec River in Maine, in southern New Jersey, and at the head of Chesapeake Bay, mostly in flat-bottom craft of the scow model.

The early history of the centerboard in America is obscure. As early as 1774 an English naval officer, Lieutenant Schank, had developed the drop keel. This was a centerboard that moved vertically and resembled the vertical "daggerboard" used in some small racing dinghies today. This type of centerboard was used on some primitive sailing rafts such as the *jangada* of Brazil and a bamboo raft once employed at Formosa. A number of small men-of-war, the cutter *Trial*, the ship sloop *Cynthia*, and 33-gun brigs were built for the Royal Navy between 1790 and 1797, all fitted with two or three drop keels. Four or five other experimental vessels were built for the Royal Navy, including the very radical *Dart* and *Arrow* designed by Samuel Bentham. All of these vessels gave some trouble with leaky cases. Drop keels were introduced into the United States before 1812—a draught of a 74-foot schooner, drawn by James Hutton of Philadelphia, having three drop keels has been found.* A somewhat earlier drawing has been found that indicates a drop-keel schooner was designed in Canada. The pivoted centerboard is said to have been invented by a British naval officer named Shuldham in 1809. A patent was granted 10 April 1811 at Washington to Joshua, Henry, and Jacocks Swain, of New Jersey, for a pivoted centerboard. Here the record of development becomes unsatisfactory. It is a matter of record that centerboard vessels were numerous at New York and on the Chesapeake in 1820, yet in 1825 it was proposed to build a drop-keel schooner for the American Revenue Service.†

The plan of a centerboard schooner named *Union*, having two pivoted centerboards, one afore and one abaft the mainmast, drawn in 1828, was found in the British Admiralty Collection of Draughts. This vessel, of unorthodox model, was about 80' 2" between perpendiculars, 23' 8" moulded beam, drawing 6' 6" aft and 6 feet forward. She had a pivot gun amidships with two broadside carronades on each side, firing through ports in her low

---

* Chapelle, *History of the American Sailing Navy*, p. 251.
† Chapelle, *The History of American Sailing Ships*, pp. 197–98.

bulwarks. Her centerboards had chain lanyards. She had a skeg and a very fine, hollow run.*

Though apparently an American-built vessel, the chaotic condition of the Admiralty records of the West Indian station precludes any history of the centerboard *Union* being found. The only *Union* of this period that could be traced in the Admiralty records was a much smaller schooner purchased at Kingston, Jamaica.

In 1833 Webb and Allen built a centerboard schooner for New Orleans owners (Plate 82) to be employed in the Gulf of Mexico and Cuban trade. Named *Santiago*, she was a rather full model, 67' 3" customhouse length, 20' 4" moulded beam, and 6' 1" depth in hold. Considered a good sailer, she somewhat resembled a burdensome, centerboard, Hudson River sloop in hull.

She had a strong sheer with a low raised quarterdeck having a turned-stanchion rail carried just forward of the mainmast. Her keel was straight with moderate drag, the stem rabbet curved and raking, and there was slight rake to the sternpost. Her entrance was short, convex, and full. Her run was rather short but with a straight quarterbeam buttock for a very short distance at its crossing of the after load line. Her midsection showed a slightly rising straight floor, a rather quick turn of the bilge, and a little tumble home in the topsides. Her straight floor was carried well outboard amidships.

On a moulded load waterline of 63' 6" she displaced 113.6 long tons; her coefficients were block .61, midship .80, and prismatic .73. The effective length of the quarterbeam buttock was 57 feet, the camber 4' 7", giving a camber-length proportion of 12.3. Her centerboard was just forward of the mainmast and passed through the keel, which was widened amidships to allow for it. The position of her centerboard required that her boomed foresail be rather large in proportion to her mainsail, to give proper balance of hull and rig. When she reached New Orleans she had her forecastle hatch shifted to allow side entrance, and a galley stove "camboose" was placed on deck just forward of the main hatch.

Santiago had fidded topmasts, with gaff topsails. She also had a jib boom and set a light fore yard and course, flying, when running free.

In 1843 William Webb built another centerboard schooner, the *Vigilant*,†

---

* Chapelle, *The History of American Sailing Ships*, pp. 169–72.
† *Plans of Wooden Vessels Selected as Types from One Hundred and Fifty Various Kinds . . . built by William H. Webb in the City of New York from the year 1840 to the year 1869* (New York, published by the author, n.d., 2 vols. illus.); an atlas of plans of typical vessels built by Webb, including packets, clipper ships, steamers, and small vessels.

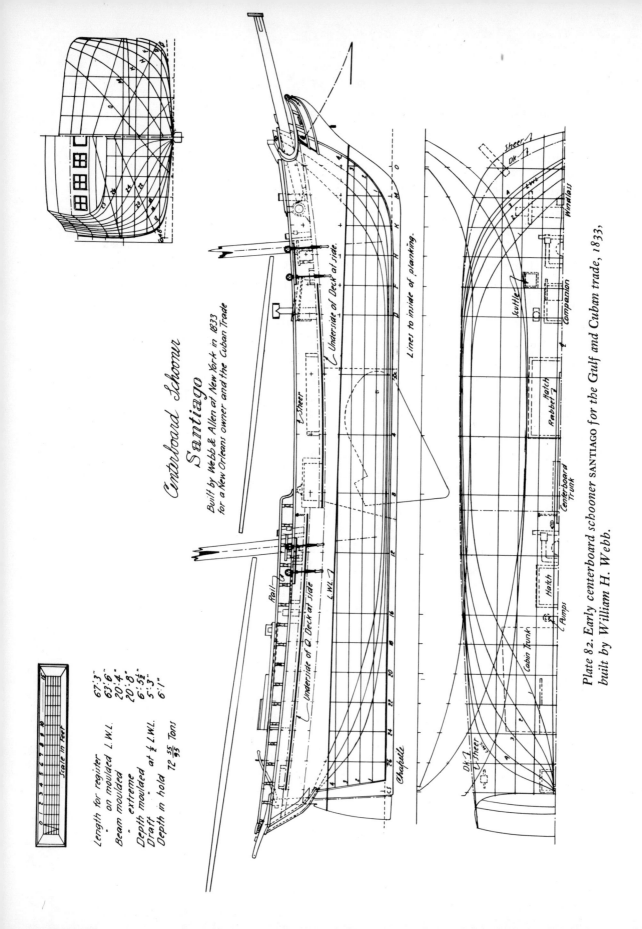

Centerboard Schooner
Santiago

Built by Webb & Allen at New York in 1833
for a New Orleans owner and the Cuban Trade

Length for register .... 67'-3"
" on moulded L.W.L. .... 63'-6"
Beam moulded .... 20'-4"
" extreme .... 20'-8"
Depth moulded .... 6'-5½"
Draft " at ½ L.W.L. .... 5'-3"
Depth in hold .... 6'-1"
72 55/95 Tons

Scale in feet

Plate 82. Early centerboard schooner SANTIAGO for the Gulf and Cuban trade, 1833,
built by William H. Webb.

for the Revenue Service. She was to serve on the Gulf station but was lost in a severe hurricane soon after her arrival on station. *Vigilant* was 56 feet between perpendiculars, 18′ 5″ beam, and 4′ 8″ depth in hold. She was sharper-ended than *Santiago* and undoubtedly a faster vessel.

Information available on centerboard vessels becomes adequate after 1845; the almost total lack of any earlier information should not be taken as evidence of nondevelopment or of nonexistence of many centerboard vessels in America at a much earlier date. By 1845, the construction and placement of the centerboard had been fully explored and some schooners and large vessels had the case alongside the keel so that the board passed through the garboard. This allowed the centerboard to be placed alongside a mast if desirable in obtaining proper balance between hull and rig. This location of the centerboard became quite common in two-masted schooners. An alternative arrangement was to have the case on the keel and to move the mainmast off center.

From the 1820's through the 1840's, the use of the builder's half-model spread along the coast. Isaac Webb is credited with the introduction of the half-model in the New York area, according to L. H. Boole.* Griffiths† credits the first model to a David Seabury at New York and also says that the 74-gun *Ohio* was built from a model made by Stephen Smith when apprenticed to Eckford. McKay‡ said "As vessels are almost universally built from models in the United States, and as it is much the most accurate and preferable method, I shall commence by showing that mode of construction." In 1845 Rogers published his two-volume work on the drawing of lines and making of half-models.¶

In some shipbuilding areas, the half-model was not popular until the late 1830's or early 1840's. The Chesapeake Bay seems to be such an area. In 1826 a British Naval officer§ visited the shipbuilding section of Baltimore and in his journal he states, "I met with a builder who had a book of draughts of all the fastest-sailing schooners built at Baltimore, which so much puzzled our

---

* L. H. Boole, *The Shipwright's Handbook and Draughtsman's Guide*, Milwaukee, 1858.
† In *Marine and Naval Architecture*, p. 47.
‡ In *The Practical Shipbuilder*, p. 13.
¶ George W. Rogers, *The Shipwright's Own Book; Being a Key to most of the Different Kinds of Lines Made Use of by Shipbuilders; Illustrated by Seventeen Copper Plate Engravings of Drafts and Model*, printed at Pittsburgh, 1845, by J. M'Millin.
§ Lt. the Hon. Fred. Fitzgerald De Roos, *Personal Narrative of Travels in the United States and Canada in 1826, Illustrated by plates, with remarks on the Present State of The American Navy* (London, William Harrison Amsworth, Old Bond Street, 1827), p. 38.

cruizers during the war." He tried to buy the book, or at least some pages, without success. This account infers that plans had been used exclusively during the war. It is also worthy of note that half-models of Chesapeake vessels, built earlier than 1840 and identified with certainty, are not to be found in any museum collection known to the author. Of course this is not conclusive evidence, but such a situation does not exist in the New England and New York areas, where half-models of earlier date than 1825 have been preserved. The lack of half-models from the Chesapeake does not prove that the builders there did not know of the half-model or that it was never used; the evidence merely suggests that the model was not common and was not extensively employed by the Bay builders. Were models extensively used, surely some half-models of vessels built earlier than 1840 would have been preserved in the Bay region.

Except that the model gave a better illustration of the shape of the hull than a lines plan, it produced some difficulties at times. The model could not be quickly and roughly made; it had to be accurate and fair to be an effective design tool. Used alone, there was some awkwardness in taking precise measurements from the model for the displacement calculations. As has been stated, the model and drawing were used by the trained builder. Sometimes the preliminary design was by model, with drawings made from it for the final design; sometimes the lines were first drawn and then checked by model. But the use of the model as the mode of preliminary design was the most approved method. Elaboration of the design process, beyond use of model only, depended upon the extent of the lofting process—some of the better yards lofted the lines completely so as to reproduce the design accurately; others laid down only the body plan and ends of the hull, final refairing being done while the hull was being planked.

A shipbuilder-designer had little time to thoroughly study hull form by means of a lines drawing alone. The supervision of the yard took up most of his time and energy, and he had personal responsibility for getting materials, payments on completed work, new business, and for hiring and firing. Hence, any shortcut in design was attractive, and the model was a superb tool for preliminary hull design. Though the final use of the half-model alone in design was undoubtedly decadent, it may have helped to produce the great American designer-shipbuilders of the mid-nineteenth century—William Webb and Donald McKay, as well as John Griffiths and others. As the model gave a three-dimensional view of a hull, exposing the optical illusions that

Packet *NEW YORK* 1839
Built by Wm. H. Webb at New York
Launched Oct 24, 1839.

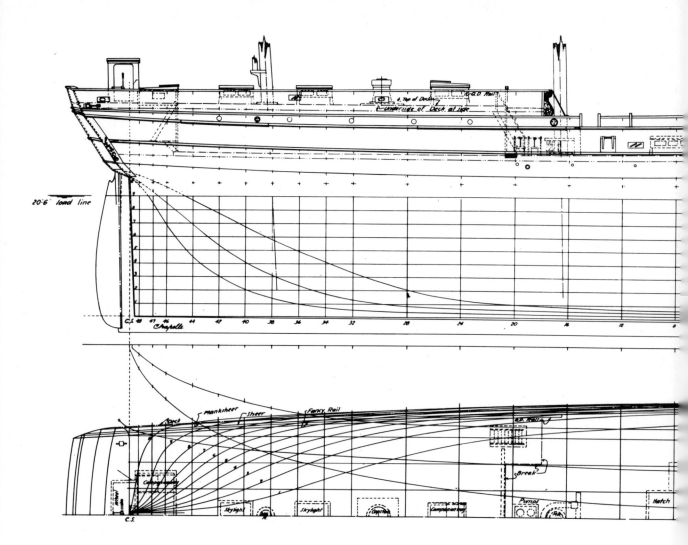

20.6′ load line

Chapelle

Norch Planksheer Sheer Fancy Rail

Skylight Skylight Capstan Companion Pump Hatch

C.S.

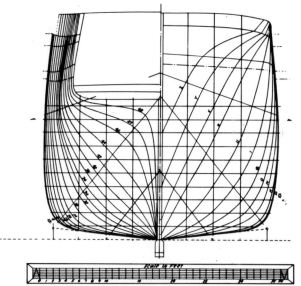

Scale in feet

Transom

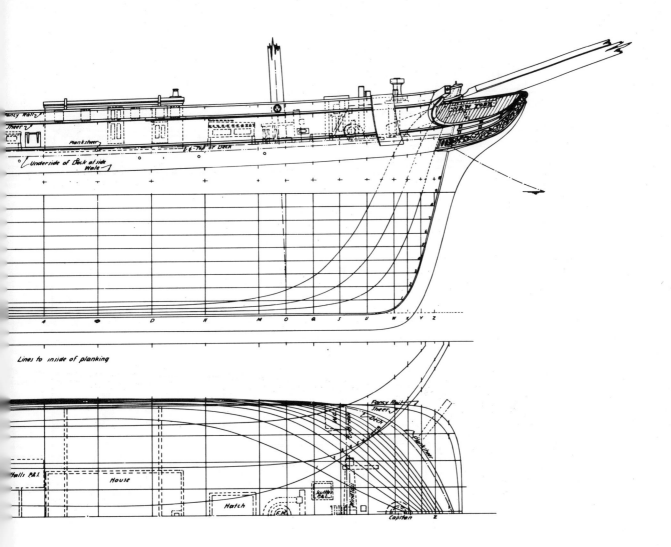

Fancy Rails
Sheer
Planksheer
E.E. Top of Deck
Underside of Deck at side
Wale

Lines to inside of planking

Fancy Rail
Sheer
Deck
Hall's P.R.S.
House
Hatch
Scuttle P.R.S.
Capstan

Length Fr. Z to C.S. - 147' 6" } Mould Loft Offsets.
Beam moulded   35' 0" }
Frames spaced 2' 0", Waterlines 2' 0", Buttocks 4' 0".
Register Dimensions - 152' 6" x 35' 4" x 22' 0"

PLATE VII. *Packet ship* NEW YORK, *second of the name in the Black Ball Line, built by William H. Webb in 1839.*

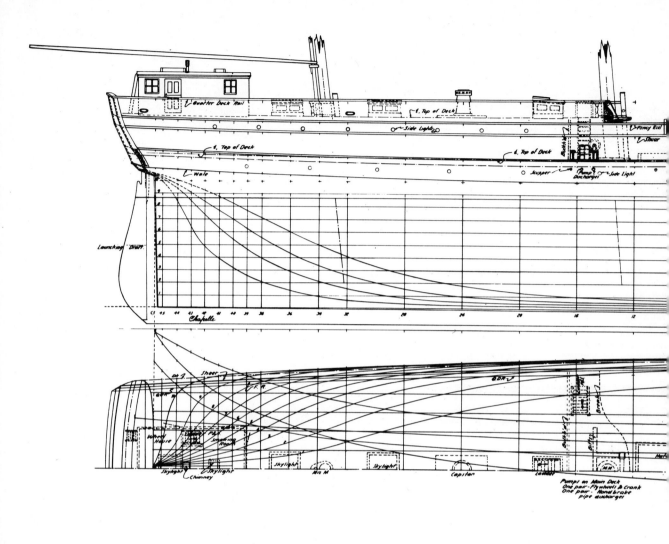

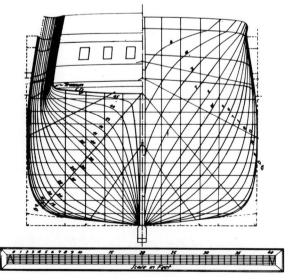

Packet Ship
YORKSHIRE
Built by Wm. H. Webb, New York,
1843
for Chas. H. Marshall

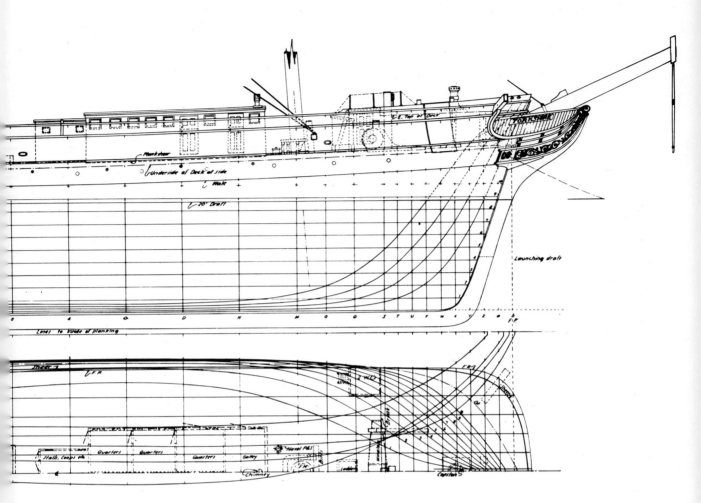

Length bet. perps.   163'·6"
Beam moulded   36'·0"
Depth   "   23'·2"
Length of moulded L.W.L. 161'·0"
Room & Space 2'·3"
Keel sides 15"

PLATE VIII. *Black Ball Line packet ship* YORKSHIRE, *built by William H. Webb in 1843; considered one of the fastest of the packet type. (See Plate 81 for sail plan.)*

normally take place, and because it could be made with common hand tools, the half-model was very useful in training apprentices to judge hull form. Hence it remains in use to this day in small-boat yards and in areas of primitive boat-building methods. Though now in some disrepute, when used with judgment, the half-model mode of design did produce some splendid vessels.

American tonnage laws required that certain measurements be taken to establish the register tonnage on which taxes and port dues were assessed. The greater the registered tonnage, the greater these charges became. To satisfy these and other costs, a vessel had to carry deadweight tons well in excess of her register tonnage. The details of the mode of measuring register tonnage need not be examined here; only suffice it to say that beam measurement was taken at weatherdeck level, or above the wales, and depth was not measured but was considered a proportion (one half) of the measured beam in two-decked vessels. Thus the true depth did not affect tonnage.

The register-tonnage cheater was a very full-ended, box-like, deep, two-decked hull, having a midsection formed with little or no deadrise in the floor, a low hard round bilge—bringing the greatest beam just above the turn of the bilge. Above this level, the topsides had marked tumble home, to narrow the beam at deck considerably. The depth was approximately equal to the maximum beam. The midship section had a resemblance to the profile of an old-fashioned iron kettle, hence vessels on this model were called "kettlebottoms." They were very slow under sail and inclined to be very tender so that they heeled much when sailing—altogether a most undesirable type of vessel from all but the economic point of view.

This class of freighter had much popularity, in New England at least, for use in the general ocean trade. One kettlebottom brig, registering a little under 300 tons, carried 700 deadweight tons of coal, and it was very common for a kettlebottom to carry twice her register tonnage in deadweight tons.

The English tonnage rule, on which the American tonnage rule was based, produced equally objectionable ships. Freight rates and other trade requirements, however, made register-tonnage cheating less attractive to American shipowners, outside of New England, than it was to British shipowners. Wherever the register-tonnage cheater was widely used, it was a check on the development of normal hull forms and proportions, and of course blocked the building of fast sailing freighters.

A very profitable trade with Chinese ports developed after the War of 1812, beginning as a revival of a trade that had developed soon after the

Revolution. Furs and American goods were exported to China; tea, fabrics (particularly silk), lacquer work, porcelain, works of art, and other exotic objects made a very profitable return cargo. Tea rose rapidly in demand and soon made up the bulk of return cargoes. The voyage to China and return was a long one, however, tying up the merchant's capital for an excessive length of time if the complete voyage could not be made quickly. The cargoes were relatively light and bulky. This led to some utilization of out-built packet ships in the trade, as these were faster than the average ocean freighter and could carry nearly equal cubic feet of cargo in the same hull dimensions and with less purchase cost, as a secondhand ship. Some fast brigs and brigantines of the Chesapeake model were employed right after the War of 1812. But vessels that had been built specifically for the trade were usually large, full-model ocean freighters. These full-model China traders were too slow and it was soon found that small sharp vessels with their limited capacity were not very profitable for so long a voyage and so bulky a cargo.

In 1832 a sharp-model ship, the *Ann McKim*, was laid down at Baltimore in the yard of Kennard & Williamson. She was an extreme design, of the old pilot-boat construction, now known as the Baltimore clipper. This term came into use sometime after the War of 1812, as the type name of the sharp-model schooners, brigs, brigantines, and ships built on the Chesapeake, or of those built elsewhere in imitation of the Bay vessels.

Ann McKim, shown in Plate 83, has been often accepted as being the original or prototype clipper ship by many early American marine-historians, but this claim was disproven by Cutler* and others in the 1930's. In view of what has been examined, concerning the clipper-model ships built before the *McKim*, no additional comment is necessary here. The plan shown is from a European drawing, possibly copied from the builder's draught. At any rate it agrees in hull form with the lines published by Hall† so far as the latter's poor engraving permits comparison.

McKim was 143 feet between perpendiculars, 31 feet moulded beam, 15′ 10″ moulded depth, drawing 17′ 6″ at post and 12′ 4″ forward at full load. She had very little sheer; straight keel with much drag; raking, curved-stem rabbet; short, heavy head; very raking post; round tuck; and lower, arch-board, upper transoms. The stern had a rather deep, heavy appearance. The

* Cutler, *Greyhounds of the Seas.*
† Henry Hall, special agent, *Report on the Shipbuilding Industry of the United States* (Washington, D.C., Government Printing Office, 10th U.S. Census, 1882), p. 84.

entrance was sharp, convex, and long; the run very long and fine. The quarterbeam buttock became straight just forward of its intersection with the after load line. The lines were drawn to a base line parallel to the load line, instead of to the keel rabbet as a base line. This departure in drafting practice apparently became common about 1828 at Philadelphia and Baltimore, and somewhat earlier in Europe. It was particularly useful in drawing vessels having much drag to the keel.

The midsection shows sharply rising straight floor, high, easy turn of bilge, and the slight tumble home in the topsides usually found in the Baltimore clipper.

The use of a pilot-boat cutwater, curved and raking, or of the simple gammon knee used in so many Chesapeake-built privateers and letter-of-marques, declined after the War of 1812. Instead, the "naval head" shown in *Ann McKim*—a short cutwater with a rather heavy appearance, such as on many men-of-war—became fashionable. The Chesapeake cutwater of this style did not extend very far forward at the figurehead or billet; the trailboards and knees were low abaft the stem rabbet; and a straight headrail, with footrail halfway up, between upper trail knee and headrail, was usual. Two or three bracket knees supported the upper rails, which braced the cutwater on each side. The hawse hole was usually in a bolster, or "naval wood," with its lower edge on the top of the upper trail knee. Sometimes the bolster was omitted and in small vessels the hawse was above the planksheer moulding, protected by a brass or copper lip or ring. The figurehead, if used, was often a bust that stood almost upright on the cutwater. Billets, or "fiddle heads," were the most common stem carvings, however.

The length of the moulded load waterline of *McKim* was 138′ 6″; her moulded displacement was 648.6 long tons. Her coefficients were block .40, midship .63, and prismatic .65. The effective length of the quarterbeam buttock was 114 feet, the camber 7′ 4″, giving a camber-length ratio of 15.6.

This vessel was first employed on voyages to South America, until about 1839, when she went into the China trade for the rest of her career as an American ship, showing that she had not been especially built for this trade. She proved to be a very fast sailer and could maintain a useful speed in most weathers. This made her successful in the trade, for a time, but her very sharp lines reduced capacity too much. Hence her model was not followed, but rather, modifications were made in the packet model by sharpening of the ends to increase the speed with only modest reductions in capacity. These

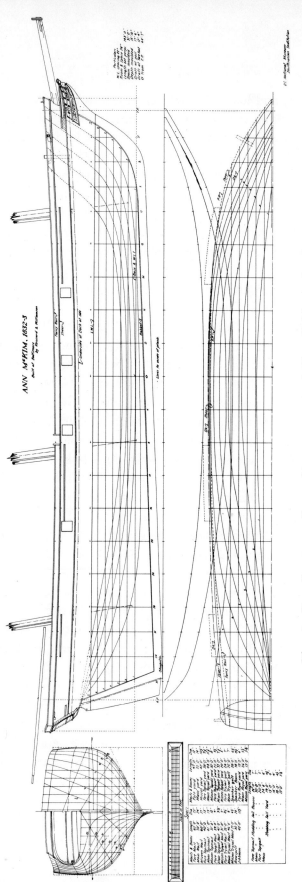

Plate 83. Pre-clipper-era clipper ship ANN MC KIM, built at Baltimore in 1832–33.

vessels could carry almost double what the very sharp Chesapeake model could, on a given register tonnage, and could maintain a good average speed, even if not as fast in some conditions of weather as the sharp model. For a while these moderate changes in the packet model sufficed. One of the first of the modified "China Packets" was *Helena*, built by William Webb and launched in 1841. Her register dimensions were 134' 6" by 31' 4" by 20 feet, 598 tons. *Helena** was slightly sharper in entrance, and longer and finer in the run, with more deadrise than the crack packet *Yorkshire*, which was built somewhat later. *Helena* had a good average speed and made some excellent passages on the China run.

In 1844 Webb built two successful packet modifications especially for the China trade, *Panama* and *Montauk*. *Montauk*, the smaller of the two, had register dimensions of 128 feet by 29' 6" by 17 feet; *Panama's* dimensions were 135 feet by 31' 8" by 20 feet.

Montauk, shown in Plate 84, was considered a good passage-maker; she was credited with a 77-day run from New York to Anjier (the record was 73 days). Her plan shows she was 128' 9" on deck, 29' ½" moulded beam, and 19 feet moulded depth. In hull form she showed the influence of the packet model, particularly in her profile. She had very moderate sheer, straight keel with no drag, raking and generally straight stem rabbet, nearly upright post, round tuck, upper-and-lower transoms, long well-formed run with straight quarterbeam buttock at its intersection with the after load line, short entrance, but rather sharp, particularly below the load line. The midsection was formed with about 20 inches deadrise at the third buttock-bow line out, the rise being straight. The bilge was well-rounded and the topsides showed a moderate tumble home. The hull was marked by a heavy flare in the foremost sections, just abaft the stem, giving a full, round Fancy Rail at the bow, as well as a full main rail or sheer line, in the half-breadth plan. This ship was a slaver in 1859, then disguised as a whaler, and later burned off Matanzas, Cuba, as bark *Adela* in 1860.

In view of the supposed advantages of flat-floored midsections of some of the packet ships in producing fast sailing, it is interesting to note that these early vessels built by Webb for the China trade had somewhat more deadrise than the packets, though by no means were they sharp models. Some ship-

---

* *Plans of Wooden Vessels Selected as Types from One Hundred and Fifty Various Kinds . . . built by William H. Webb in the City of New York from the year 1840 to the year 1869*, 2 vols., illus. with plans (New York, published by the author, n.d.).

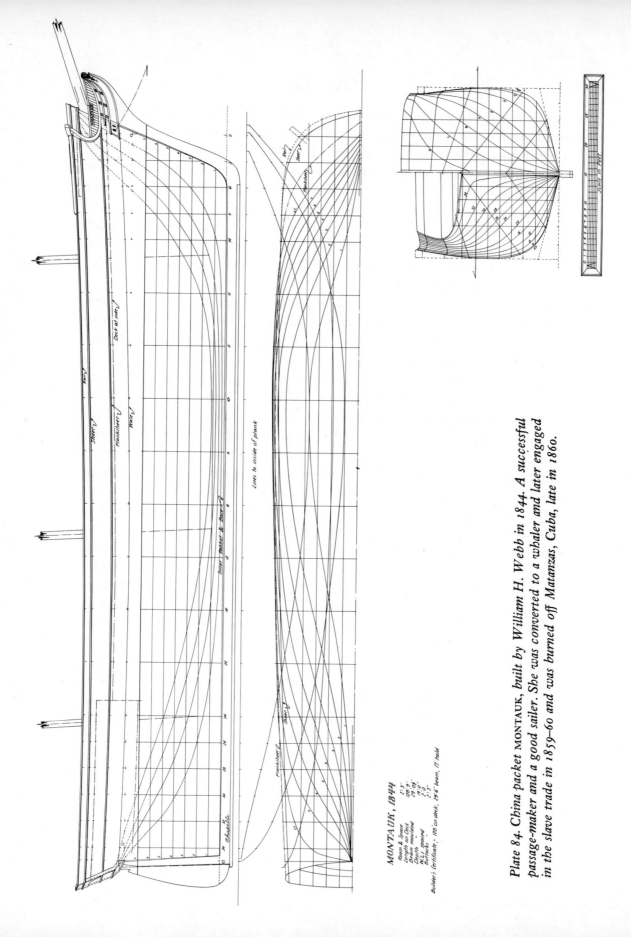

MONTAUK, 1844

Room & Space	2'·3"
Length on Deck	109'·3"
Beam moulded	29·0¾
Depth	19·0·
W.L.'s spaced	3'·0·
Buttocks	2'·3·

Builder's Certificate, 120 on deck, 29·6' beam, 17' hold

Plate 84. China packet MONTAUK, *built by William H. Webb in 1844. A successful passage-maker and a good sailer. She was converted to a whaler and later engaged in the slave trade in 1859–60 and was burned off Matanzas, Cuba, late in 1860.*

masters believed that for working to windward in light and moderate weather, the deadrise ship had an advantage. These conditions were considered to be dominant in the China voyage. In the North Atlantic packet trade, however, strong winds were considered the prevailing condition and some designers considered that North Atlantic weather was best met in flat, or nearly flat, bottom models. The need for weatherly qualities in strong winds exercised marked control over the design of the North Atlantic packets.

Montauk measured 122′ 6″ on her moulded load waterline, drawing 16′ 6″; her moulded displacement was 763.2 long tons; her block coefficient was .53, her midsection coefficient .85, and her prismatic coefficient .63. The effective length of her quarterbeam buttock was 106′ 10″, camber 12′ 6″, giving a camber-length ratio of 8.5.

Panama, shown in Plate 85, was a larger *Montauk*, but with a shorter run and slightly fuller entrance. She was 132′ 6″ between perpendiculars, 32′ 2″ moulded beam, and 21′ 2″ moulded depth. Otherwise she resembled *Montauk* in sheer elevation and in form of midsection. By shortening her run and giving her a slightly fuller entrance, her cargo capacity was made proportionately greater than in *Montauk*, but at some sacrifice in high potential speed.

The length of the moulded load waterline of *Panama* was 130′ 1½″ and her moulded displacement was 1127.5 long tons, on 18′ 2″ draft. Her block coefficient was .59, midships .85, and prismatic .69. The effective length of the quarterbeam buttock was 124′ 4″, camber 14′ 6″, giving a camber-length proportion of 8.6. This vessel should not be confused with the clipper ship of the same name, built at New York by Thomas Collyer in 1853, which was also in the China trade.

Small commercial vessels, built to sail well, were still being turned out extensively on the Chesapeake. These were predominately schooners, brigs, and brigantines, though some fast small ships and barks were also constructed there. These vessels were built for various trades—to Florida and the Bahamas for fruit, to Brazil for coffee, and to Africa for slaves. A few were built for the coastal packet trades as well, where good sailing qualities were necessary.

Schooners were the most numerous—those intended for long voyages crossed yards on the foremast at least, and some carried a square topsail and occasionally a topgallant on the main as well. Soon after the War of 1812, the Chesapeake builders began constructing vessels having somewhat less

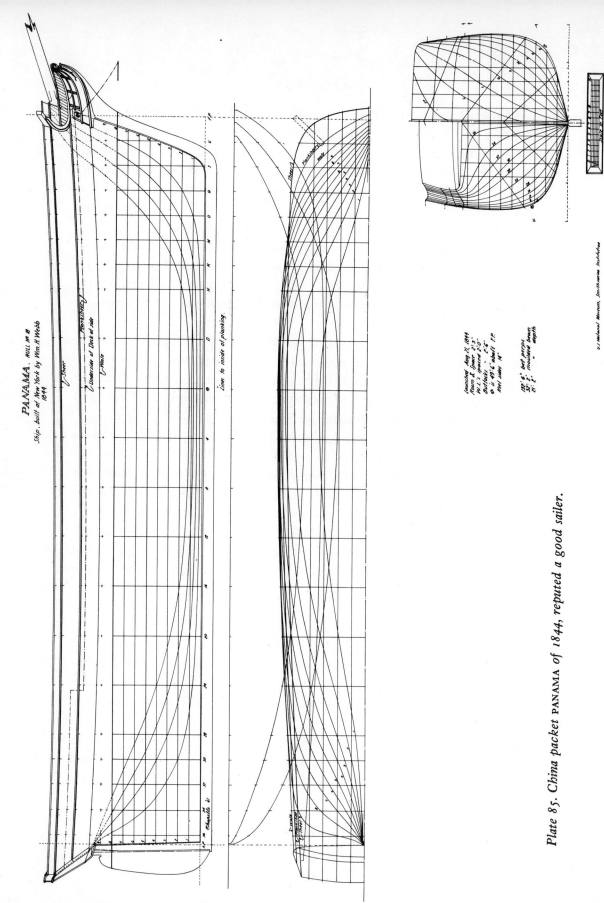

PANAMA. HULL No. 8

Ship, built at New York by Wm. H. Webb
1844

Plate 85. China packet PANAMA of 1844, reputed a good sailer.

French hermaphrodite LA GAZELLE, *designed by Marestier; on the American hull form of the Baltimore clipper.*

deadrise and depth than had been usual in the privateers built during the war. These were quite popular, for they had less draft than the older vessels, carried as much cargo, and sailed about as well. The lighter draft made them more useful traders, for obvious reasons.

A good example of the new variant in the Chesapeake model is shown in Plate 86. This plan was found in the Lenthall Collection, Franklin Institute, Philadelphia, and was annotated "A fast-sailing merchant vessel built at Baltimore." No date is on the plan, but she was probably built around 1830. The name of the vessel was *Isabella*, but no schooner of this name having similar dimensions has been found in the Baltimore ship registers. The plan had been given to Lenthall by J. Foster, a master shipwright. There were a number of slaver schooners of this name and rig, but information about them that would help identification of the drawing is lacking.

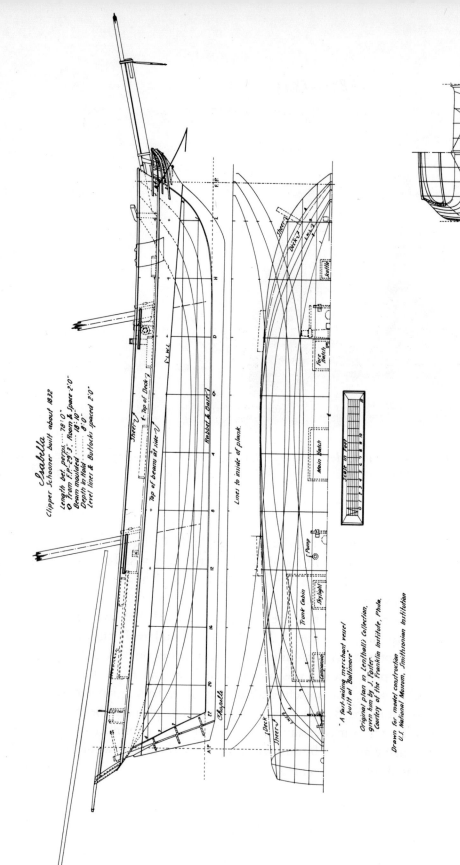

Plate 86. Baltimore clipper schooner ISABELLA of about 1832, of a type used in the West Indies trade and in slaving.

At any rate, the plan shows rather light displacement for a merchant schooner. *Isabella* had moderate deadrise in the midsection, with straight rise of floor, slack bilge, and slight tumble home in the topside. The sheer was slight and the keel straight with much drag. The rake of the stem rabbet was great and markedly curved where it left the keel; the sternpost also had strong rake. The schooner had a round tuck and upper-and-lower transoms above. The entrance was rather short, convex, and sharp; the bow lines were also very easy. The run was not very long but was rather fine; the quarter-beam buttock became straight for only a very short distance below its crossing of the load line. Her weatherliness was increased by use of a deep keel outside the rabbet. Her cutwater and head work represented the new stem design favored on the Bay after the War of 1812.

Isabella was 78 feet between perpendiculars, 18' 10" moulded beam, and 8 feet depth of hold. Her moulded load waterline measured 75' 4" and her moulded displacement was 109 long tons. Her coefficients were block .47, midsection .70, and prismatic .67. The effective length of the quarterbeam buttock was 65' 6", and the camber 4' 9". The camber-length ratio was 13.9. This was an attractive schooner; unfortunately spar dimensions were not recorded.

A similar schooner is shown in Plate 87. The plans of this unnamed clipper schooner were published in France in 1855 and said to be "of about 1835"—a merchant schooner 79' 3" on deck, 77' 3" between perpendiculars, 19 feet moulded beam, and 8' 3½" moulded depth. She drew 10' 6" at the post when loaded. She belonged to the same type as *Isabella* but was a little sharper in the ends.

She had slight sheer, straight keel with much drag, curved and strongly raking stem rabbet, raking post, rather short convex entrance, and was rather sharp at the load line. She had a short run with straight quarterbeam buttock at crossing of after load line. Her midsection was similar to that of *Isabella*—straight, moderately rising floor, rather easy turn of bilge but a little firmer than in *Isabella*. A very slight tumble home was worked into the topside. Her keel was very deep, below the rabbet, as in *Isabella*. Again, the displacement was rather light for a merchant schooner. The heavy flare in the topsides near the bow is noticeable in these schooners.

The moulded load line measured 74' 5" and moulded displacement was 112.8 long tons. The vessel's coefficients were block .45, midship .64, and

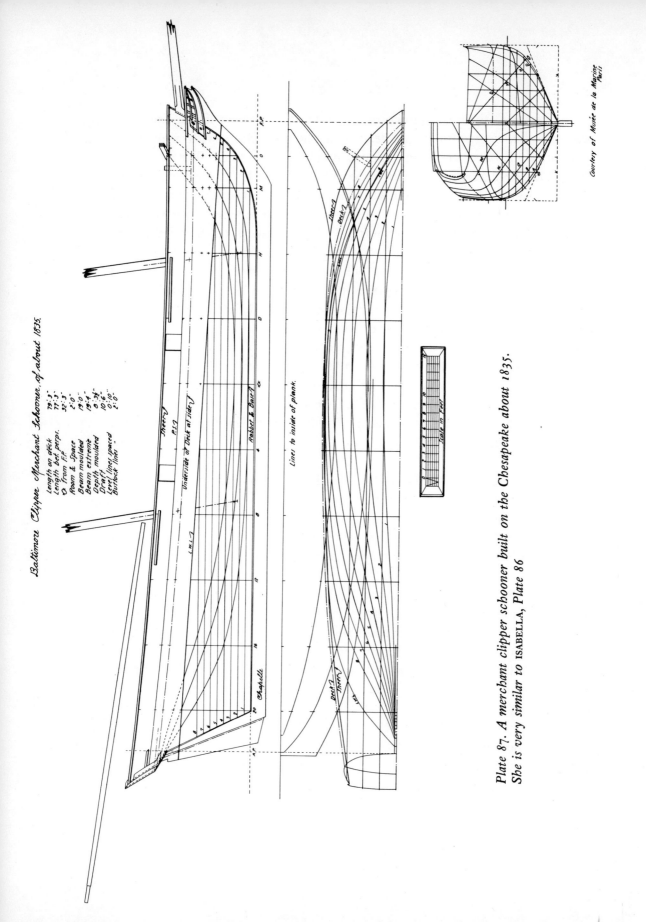

Baltimore Clipper Merchant Schooner, of about 1835.

Length on deck	79.3"
Length bet. perp.	77.3"
⊗ from F.P.	32.3"
Room & Space	2.0"
Beam moulded	19.0"
Beam extreme	19.4"
Depth moulded	8.3½"
Draft	10.6"
Level lines spaced	0.10"
Buttock lines "	2.0"

Theory
P.1
Underside of Deck at side

Rabbet & Base

L.W.L.

Chapelle

Lines to inside of plank.

Scale in Feet

Theory
Deck 1

Deck 2
Theory

Plate 87. A merchant clipper schooner built on the Chesapeake about 1835.
She is very similar to ISABELLA, Plate 86

prismatic .65. The effective length of the quarterbeam buttock was 63′ 8″, the camber 4′ 9″, giving a camber-length ratio of 11.2.

A small brigantine, built sometime after the War of 1812, probably about 1828–35, is shown in Plate 88. This vessel was constructed by Andrew Flannigan at Baltimore. It is believed that this builder was the son of William Flannigan, the very active and competent shipbuilder who built the three-masted schooners at Baltimore in 1805. The brigantine in Plate 88 cannot be identified; the plan was one belonging to a Danish naval architect, Hillmann, left to the Webb Institute of Naval Architecture and now in the Mariners' Museum, Newport News, Virginia. This well-modeled vessel was 88′ 10″ between perpendiculars, 22′ 7½″ moulded beam, 7′ 1″ depth in hold, and 9′ 10″ draft at post, loaded. Her sheer was slight, her keel straight with moderate drag, her rake of stem strongly curved and moderate, and there was marked rake in the post. The entrance was rather short but sharp; the run was long and somewhat full, but the quarterbeam buttock was straight for a very short distance below its intersection with the after load line. The midsection was formed with very little rise to the straight floor, a slack, round bilge, and curved tumble home above the load line. Her round tuck was formed on a low cross seam, above which were upper-and-lower transoms, giving the stern a rather heavy appearance. Her cutwater was short and deep in the throat, finished with a bust figurehead of a man wearing a helmet.

The length of her moulded load waterline was 84′ 10½″; her moulded displacement was 211 long tons. Her block coefficient was .53, her midsection .79, and her prismatic .68. The effective length of the quarterbeam buttock was 75′ 4″, the camber 6′ 3″, giving a camber-length ratio of 12.0.

This design is proof that the use of a full midsection with rather sharp ends, to combine speed and cargo capacity, was practiced at Baltimore long before the China packets or the later clipper ships appeared. Again, a deep keel was employed to assure weatherliness.

The slave trade gave a profitable market for fast schooners and brigs, as well as for a few clipper barks and ships, and eventually produced vessels of unusually sharp lines, built primarily for speed. While American citizens were never very numerous as owners, captains, or officers of slavers, they did play an active, if often devious, part in the trade.*

* United States House Documents, Vol. 5, Nos. 112–124, except 123, 26th Congress, 1st Session, 1839–40, *Doc. 115,* Havana, Slave Trade. Also Admiralty and Parliamentary papers on the slave trade and its suppression. The sources used here for descriptions of slavers and slaving practices are *United States House Documents,* Vol. 4, No. 140–165, 28th Congress, 2nd Session, *Doc. 148,* 1844–45, U.S. Minister Wise, Brazil Slave Trade.

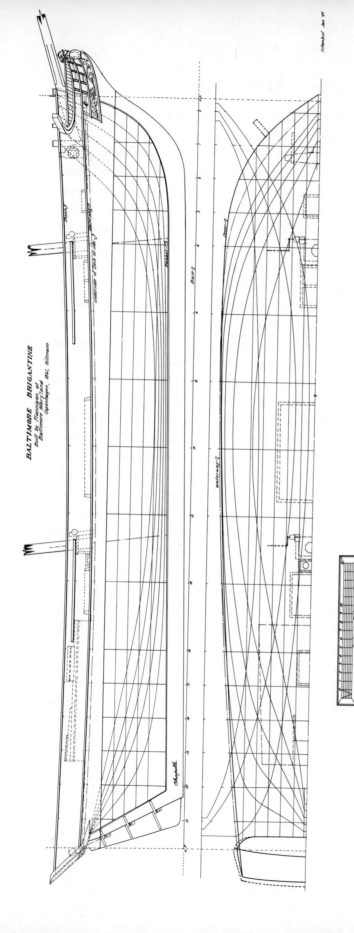
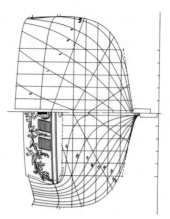

Plate 88. Baltimore-built brigantine trader of about 1828–35. A fast carrier designed by Flannigan.

By an Act of Congress dated 22 March 1794, no person could build or fit a vessel for the slave trade and any such vessel was subject to forfeiture. An Act of 2 March 1807 prohibited the importation of slaves. The Treaty of Ghent, 10th article, was an agreement between Great Britain and the United States to suppress the slave trade with their "utmost endeavors." An act was passed by Congress on 20 April 1818, increasing the fines and the length of imprisonment of crews, officers, and owners; and the Act of 14 May 1820 made slave-trading an act of piracy, a capital crime punishable by death. These laws were sweeping, making it a criminal act to build, own, fit out, supply, charter, man, or officer a slaving vessel, and it was clearly intended that this applied to the shipbuilder, owner, agent, investor, customs officer, and to the suppliers of stores and goods, as well as to the crew, officers, and master. The effect of these laws, ill-enforced though they were, was to drive most Americans out of direct participation in the trade—though there were always some adventurers and criminally-inclined active in the trade to its very end, and merchants as far north as Machias, Maine, were named in one presidential message to Congress as taking part in the "Black Ivory" trade.

By the end of 1835 England had treaties with Spain, France, Portugal, and Brazil for suppression of the slave trade, allowing British cruisers to stop, search, and seize vessels of these nations, suspected and known to be slaving. Furthermore, a "manifestly equipped" vessel could be seized; this meant a cargo of trade muskets, ammunition, spirits, tobacco, printed fabrics, gold, and trade goods; particularly if handcuffs, leg irons, oversize cook range and "coppers" (kettles), and many water barrels were also on board. In other words, if the vessel's cargo and equipment, fittings and stores showed that she was intended for the trade she could be seized. The record shows that the majority of slave vessels seized by the Royal Navy were "manifestly equipped" for slaving but had no slaves on board.

Though the British used diplomatic persuasion, they could not get the United States to sign any treaty allowing search of American ships at sea by the British Navy. This was too similar to the search and seizure the Americans had suffered in recent wars.

The effect of this situation was to make the American flag an effective cover for at least half of a slaving voyage and the Cuban and Brazilian slavers were quick to develop a suitable mode of obtaining this advantage. By 1830, slave traders had Cuba (Havana chiefly) and Brazil (Bahia and Rio) as centers of operation in the Americas.

The method evolved was a simple one. It would be "arranged" to have a fast sailing vessel, usually between 60 and 90 feet on deck, come to, say, Havana with a cargo. Here the cargo would be sold and the vessel offered for sale or charter. The slave dealer or his agent would "charter" the vessel for three voyages—back to some port, preferably in southern United States, where she would load a token cargo and clear for Liverpool, England. On arrival there she would dispose of her cargo as best she could and load a cargo euphemistically referred to by charter and by the government reports as "particularly suited to the African Coast Trade" or "Coast Goods," making her "manifestly equipped" as stated in the British treaties. The vessel then cleared for the African Coast, with a stop at Havana. This dogleg in her voyage was to allow her to pick up some passengers to be carried to Africa. It should be noted that when she cleared from Liverpool (Bristol in some instances) she would be liable to seizure if she had been under French, Spanish, Portuguese, Brazilian, or British flag according to the "manifestly equipped" clause. Since she was under the American flag, however, and so had an American register, she could not be searched and seized (as "manifestly equipped") by the British, nor by any United States naval or revenue vessel for that matter, even if it were an obvious and well-established fact that the vessel had been and was in the slave trade but without slaves on board.* The United States did not recognize "manifestly equipped" as an illegal cargo.

The vessel, having reached Havana, would pick up the passengers and sail to the slave compounds on the African Coast. Upon arrival, or as soon as the vessel was ready to load slaves, the American crew was turned ashore, to be carried back to Havana, or to United States, by a tender. At this stage of the operation the registry and flag of the vessel was changed from United States to Spanish, Portuguese, or Brazilian, and her name changed also. The run with slaves aboard was made under one of these flags, the "passengers" becoming the slaver's crew and officers. It should be noted that, at the time of the "charter" at Havana, the American owner, through his captain, received "earnest money" usually amounting to $9000, plus a nominal monthly charter payment, running the "duration of the charter." These payments actually exceeded the original cost of the vessel, and in fact, were the purchase payments in full. Therefore, ownership actually changed at the time of the

---

* Vessel characteristics of a slaver, other than model and rig, were: large, grating hatches, bulkheads at ends of the hold, oversize cooking hearth and "coppers," and an unusually large number of water casks, considering size of crew. These features would allow seizure under the treaties as "manifestly equipped" if cargo alone did not serve.

charter at Havana, or in a Brazilian port, rather than at the completion of the charter on the African coast.

By 1835, this system of obtaining slave vessels was standard in the trade. The early slave ships used a "slave deck," made of rough lumber brought by the vessel as was part of her "manifest" equipment. It took time to build the slave deck and more time to get rid of it after the run was completed. By 1835 the slaves were stowed without a slave deck. The water casks were stowed level, in one or more tiers according to the size of the vessel, and rush mats were spread on them, just before the slaves were loaded. The mats thus served as a substitue for the timber slave deck, and could be prepared in a very short time. By this means a slaver named *Montevideo*, beginning with an empty or "swept" hold, loaded and stowed stores and 800 slaves in seven hours. The value of this cargo would be about $180,000.

Preparations to load slaves at the African slave compounds began with the necessary stores. Watercasks were filled with farinha, jerked beef, and other stores and buried in the sand on the beach, ready to move at an instant's notice. Slaves were inspected and branded and brought in chained gangs to the immediate vicinity of the loading beach. Loading was done with dugout canoes and the ship's boats, often at night. One of the requirements for a loading beach was that the depth of water be sufficient to float the vessel within five minutes rowing or paddling time from the shore. Every effort was made to expedite the loading of slaves so that the slaver might not be caught in the act. The British cruisers often appeared suddenly off known loading beaches and sent armed boats into river mouths and creeks, in the hope of catching a slaver in the process of loading.

Such abuse of the American flag was very prevalent, from 1835 or 1836 to about 1855, and created a very profitable market for fast sailing vessels. Baltimore and the Chesapeake Bay counties seem to have been the most active building localities for slaving vessels. These craft were lightly built and in most instances especially designed for the trade. Consular and British government reports repeatedly claim that the Chesapeake builders turned out most of the slave vessels, after about 1835–36. However, such reports should be received with caution, since they deal with an illegal trade for which no complete list of the vessels involved could possibly be made.

A few of the slavers known to have operated between 1836 and 1841, some of which were captured by British cruisers, will serve to show the usual range of size in slaving vessels. These were all built at Baltimore or in the district, and the following data are taken from customhouse records. Builder's Certificates, and Register dimensions where available, are given in parentheses.

Catherine, brig, built 1839, 86′ 3″ on keel, 24′ 2″ beam, 11′ ¾″ depth, 242 60/95 tons, builders Butler and Robert Lambden.

Clara, schooner, built 1838, 58′ 10″ keel, 18′ 7″ beam, 7′ 10″ depth, 88 88/95 tons, builders J. A. and E. L. Robb, billet head, (reg. 74′ 9″ by 18′ 6″ by 7′ 10″, 95 11/95 tons).

Hazard, schooner, built 1838, 72′ 6″ keel, 19′ 6″ beam, 8′ 3″ depth, 114 tons, builder William K. Smith, billet head, (reg. 83 feet by 19′ 9″ by 8′ 3″, 122 5/95 tons).

Anaconda, schooner, built 1836, 60′ 6″ keel, 19′ 3″ beam, 7′ 6″ depth, 91 89/95 tons, builders Smith and Henry, had 30 sweeps, (reg. 76′ 10″ by 19′ 3″ by 7′ 7″, 100 37/95 tons), pilot-boat rig.

Delorez, schooner, built 1836, 62′ 8″ keel, 21′ 1½″ beam, 8′ 7″ depth, 119 57/95 tons, builder Walter Price, figurehead, (reg. 81 feet by 21′ 3″ by 8′ 3″, 131 4/95 tons), 30 sweeps, pilot-boat rig, small fore-topsail, large course.

Emanuel, schooner, built 1836, 61′ 1″ keel, 21′ 2″ beam, 8′ 6″ depth, 115 64/95 tons, builder L. H. Dunkin, billet head, had 28 sweeps, (reg. 80′ 6″ by 21′ 3″ by 8′ 6″, 128 78/95 tons).

Only the register descriptions were found for the following vessels:

Viper, schooner, built 1836, 60′ 6″ keel, 19′ 3″ beam, 7′ 6″ depth, 91 89/95 tons, builder John A. Robb, snake figurehead, pilot-boat rig, 77′ 2″ by 19′ 3″ by 7′ 7″, 100 86/95 tons, 26 sweeps.

Ontario, schooner, built 1833, Dorchester County, 72 feet by 21′ 2″ by 7′ 2″, 95 37/95 tons, billet head.

Eagle, brig, 92′ 7″ by 22′ 8″ by 10′ 11″, 205 73/95 tons, billet head.

Euphrates, schooner, built Dorchester County 1833, 69′ 6″ by 21′ 6″ by 6′ 8″, 85 78/95 tons, figurehead, very sharp.

Florida, schooner, 74′ 6″ by 19′ 1″ by 6′ 7″, 83 40/95 tons, billet head, built at Baltimore in 1838.

Laura, schooner, 83′ 6″ by 20′ 8″ by 6′ 5″, 99 21/95 tons, woman's bust figurehead, built 1838.

Perry Hall, schooner, also called *Perry Spencer*, built in Talbot County in 1837, 60 feet by 18′ 6″ by 5′ 9″, 57 28/95 tons.

Venus, ship, built at Baltimore in 1838, by M. and George Gardner, 125′ 4″ by

28′ 9″ by 14′ 3″, 466 9/95 tons, woman's bust figurehead, pierced for 18 guns, very sharp.

Wyoming, brig, built 1838, 88′ 5″ by 22′ 2″ by 8′ 10″, 154 71/95 tons, billet head.

Asp, schooner, built 1839, 87 feet by 21′ 10″ by 8′ 3″, 140 14/95 tons, billet head.

Asp, schooner, built 1839, 81′ 2″ by 21′ 4″ by 9′ 2″, 140 63/95 tons.

Lark, schooner, built 1839, 72′ 4″ by 19′ 3″ by 7′ 8″, 94 35/100 tons, billet head.

The registers of some of these vessels are endorsed "sold to foreigners" or "sold at Havana." All had square sterns, round tuck, and no galleries. Some of the vessels were so shallow as to suggest they might have had centerboards. Shallow draft was desirable when the vessels were to be loaded off a slave-compound beach.

Plans of only three named slavers of this period have yet been found. These are the schooner *Theresa Secunda* of 1832, the schooner *Dos Amigos* of 1832, and the brig *Diligente* of 1836–39. In addition, three American-built clipper ships—*Sunny South*, *Nightingale*, and *Haidee*—were in the trade in the 1850's. One yacht, the *Wanderer*, was also in the trade in the 1850's and her builder's model is in the New York Yacht Club.

In addition, at least three plans of supposed but unnamed slavers exist—one pilot schooner and two brigs. In addition, there are incomplete body plans of two slaver schooners captured by the British Navy and sold to enter the Mediterranean fruit trade about 1830, recently found by Mr. William Salisbury in England. These were drawn by William Parsons, one-time student at the School of Naval Architecture, showing only three cross sections for each. One is a 153-ton schooner measuring 82 feet between perpendiculars, 61′ 7″ on the keel for tonnage, 21′ 8″ extreme beam, and 21′ 4″ moulded beam. The midsection has a straight, strongly rising floor, and a slack round bilge with very slight tumble home above the deck. The other is a 102-ton schooner, 72′ 2″ between perpendiculars, 57 feet on the keel, 18′ 4″ extreme beam, and 18 feet moulded beam. This schooner has very hollow floors, a high and rather hard bilge, and slight tumble home above the load line.

The available information shows that slavers were built on at least three basic models, all of light displacement for their dimensions: a shoal keel-model such as *Isabella;* a deep-keel model having straight, sharply rising floor, high and rather slack bilge; and a deep, hollow-floor model with a high, rather hard bilge. It is probable that some of the very shoal slavers had midsections formed with only slight deadrise and were fitted with centerboards, as the registered depth in the hold was so small.

Since the profits in the slave trade were often enormous, a slave dealer could afford to buy and lose a number of vessels. Two or three were often bought at a time, one as a tender and the others as slavers. The ship *Venus* is a case in point as to what profits were possible. When building in the Gardner yard at Baltimore in 1838, she was much admired for her good looks and sharpness of lines; she was described by the press as a "noble corvette" and "must out-sail anything that floats." It was also said, with the usual lack of supporting evidence that marks maritime pronouncements in newspapers, that she was "the sharpest clipper-built vessel ever constructed here." *Venus* probably was somewhat similar to *Bolivar* in model.

Though rumored that she was intended for the Mexican Navy or for some South American government, she turned up in Havana in August 1838, 24 days out of Baltimore, with a cargo of bricks consigned to Don José Mazorra, who happened to be one of the leading slave dealers in Havana. She went through the usual process of charter, and in due time turned up on the African coast. Here she changed crews and register, becoming Brazilian and renamed *Duquesa de Braganza*. She loaded 860 slaves. Though seen loading and chased by a British cruiser, she escaped easily, throwing overboard a few spare spars. It was estimated that she cost between $30,000 and $50,000 to build and equip, and if all her operational costs for the voyage to Africa amounted to $50,000, an excessive sum, her profit on this one voyage was very close to $200,000! Her slave cargo brought $340 per head, or a gross of $292,400.

Plate 89 shows the lines of the slave schooner *Theresa Secunda*. This vessel was built at Philadelphia in 1831, according to Basil Lubbock,* and was captured with 460 slaves on board, by H.M. brig *Pelorus*, when under the Spanish flag, on 19 March 1832. Condemned at Sierra Leone 13 April 1832, she was sold to Lieutenant Colonel, the Honorable R. F. Greville, and renamed *Xarifa*. Under this name she was on the Royal Yacht Squadron rolls until 1839, when she was sold. Her lines, as a yacht, were taken off, and from these a sister ship named *Empress* was built at Rotterdam, Holland.

If built for a slaver, the vessel might be handsome but she would be very lightly built. This seems to have been the case with *Theresa Secunda*, for after a short career Colonel Greville sold her as a yacht. She had been caught in a severe gale off the Isle of Wight and in clawing offshore she became badly

* Basil Lubbock, *Opium Clippers* (Glasgow, Brown, Son & Ferguson Ltd., 1933), p. 267.

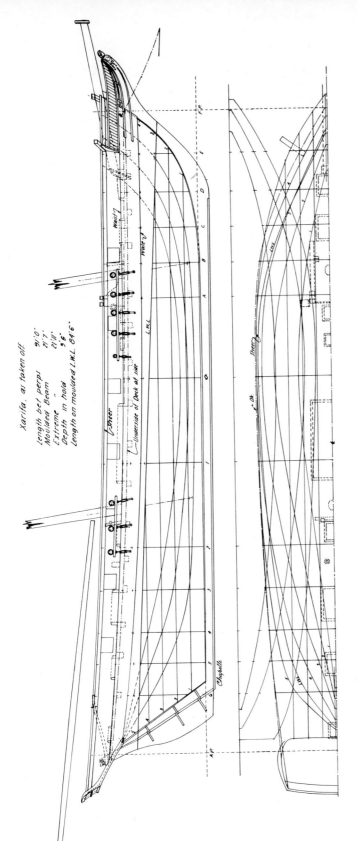
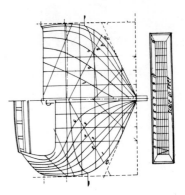
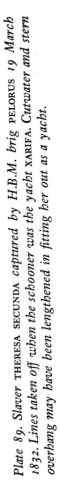

Xarifa, as taken off.

Length bet perps	91'·0"
Moulded Beam	21'·7"
Extreme "	21'·11"
Depth in hold	9'·6"
Length on moulded L.W.L.	84'·6"

Spar Dimensions

	whole	moulded	Dia.
Main Mast	75'·0"	67'·8"	18"
Main Mast	73'·0"	65'·8"	19"
Fore Mast	23'·0"	11'·0"	17"
Bowsprit			
Main Top Mast	24'·0"		7½"
Fore Top Mast	31'·7" – Pole 3'·7"		
" Gall Mast	0'·6"	18'·6"	
" Royal Pole	4'·0"		
Jibboom	39'·0"	9'" arms	9"
Fore Yard	55'·0"	2'·3"	7"
Tops'l Yard	29'·2"	4'·0"	6"
" Top Gall Yard	23'·6"		4"
Main Boom	50'·5"		8"
Fore Gaff	23'·6"		6"

Plate 89. *Slaver* THERESA SECUNDA *captured by H.B.M. brig* PELORUS *19 March 1832. Lines taken off when the schooner was the yacht* XARIFA. *Cutwater and stern overhang may have been lengthened in fitting her out as a yacht.*

strained. In her place Colonel Greville then had *Anonyma*, a 115' 4" by 29' 10" by 13' 9" clipper brig, built by William Camper at Gosport, England. *Anonyma* somewhat resembled an American clipper brig but had less rake to the stem. She eventually became an opium clipper on the China coast.

The sale of slaver prizes, usually by auction at Lloyds in London, led to condemned vessels appearing again in the trade. As a result Parliament passed an act, effective early in 1837, forbidding further sales. The brigs *Cazador* and *Diligente* were the last sold at auction. When the act became effective there were 24 prizes at Sierra Leone. The schooner *Gazita*, which was one of the 24, was cut in two and sold; the remaining 23 were hauled out and burned. Only two slavers were ever taken into the Royal Navy as cruisers—the *Dos Amigos* as *Fair Rosamond*, R.N., and the brig *Black Joke*, R.N., ex-*Henriquetta*, both Baltimore-built. The *Sunny South*, named *Manuela* when taken, was used as a store ship, under the name *Enchantress*, for a while at the Cape of Good Hope; eventually she was wrecked.

Theresa Secunda had an almost straight sheer, a straight keel with moderate drag, curved and strongly raking stem rabbet, strongly raking post, round tuck, upper-and-lower transoms, rather short, convex, and sharp entrance, and a moderate length of run with straight quarterbeam buttock at the intersection with the load line. The midsection had straight, strongly rising floor, slack, round bilge, and slight tumble home above the deck. She measured 91 feet between perpendiculars, 21' 7" moulded beam, and drew 10' 8" at the post, and 7' 8" at the fore gripe. She was 9' 6" depth in the hold.

On a moulded load waterline of 84' 6" she had a moulded displacement of 144.1 long tons. Her coefficients were block .38, midsection .61, and prismatic .62. The effective length of the quarterbeam buttock was 68' 3", camber 6 feet, giving a camber-length ratio of 11.4. Her rig was that of a fore-topsail schooner, crossing a fore royal. Her lines were taken off when she was a yacht, and it is possible that her stern and cutwater had been lengthened. She had the reputation of being very fast and a good sea boat.

The schooner *Dos Amigos*, built at Baltimore, was 83 feet on the range of deck, or between perpendiculars, 22' 8¼" moulded beam, and 10' 4½" depth in hold. She had square topsails and topgallants on both masts, royal on the fore only.*

Plates 90 and 91 show the plans of the slaver brig *Diligente*, taken off at Bermuda and dated 12 November 1839. The building place and date of launch

---

* Plans were published in Chapelle's *The History of American Sailing Ships*.

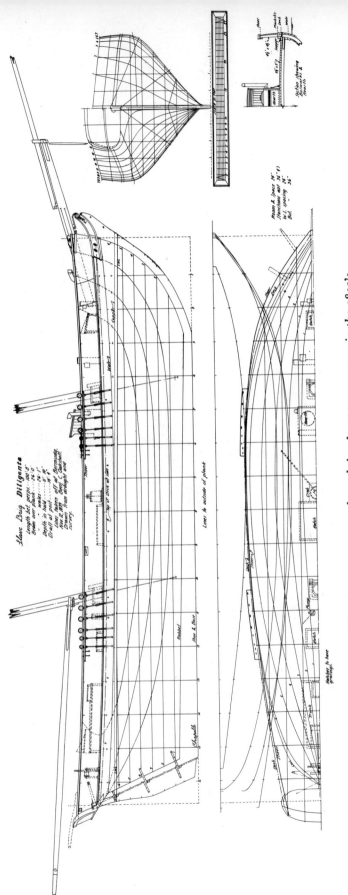

Plate 90. DILIGENTE, *a slaver brig of a type common in the 1830's.*

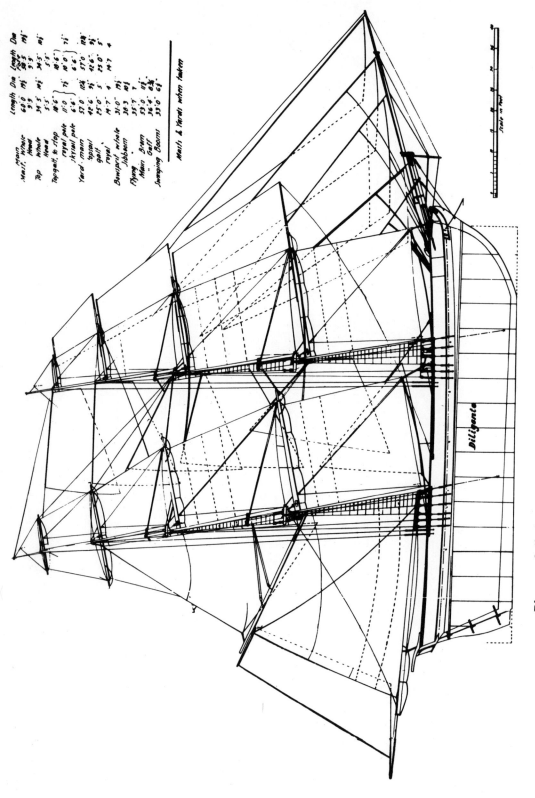

	Length	Dia	Length	Dia
Mast; Whole	61·0	11¼	58·5	11¼
Head	3·5		3·5	
Top Whole	34·5	10¼	34·5	10¼
Head	5·5		5·5	
Topgallt, to stop	18·6 }	7½	18·6 }	7½
royal pole	11·0		11·0	
Skysail pole	6·6		6·6	
Yard - main	57·0	10½	57·0	10½
topsail	42·6	9½	42·6	9½
gallt	15·0	5	15·0	5
royal	14·7	4	14·7	4
Bowsprit whole	31·0"	10½		
Jibboom	30·3	7		
Flying Boom	35·7			
Main Gaff	23·0	11½		
Boom	36·4	8½		
Swinging Booms	33·0	6½		

_____

Masts & Yards when taken

Diligente

Scale in Feet

Plate 91. Sail plan of DILIGENTE, *showing the large rig of this type vessel.*

Slaver brig DILIGENTE, *as taken off in 1839. This vessel was twice captured and condemned for slaving. United States National Museum.*

of this vessel cannot be satisfactorily established by her available records. She was a twice-condemned slaver taken 12 January 1837 as *Paquete de Cabo Verde* by the boats of H.M.S. *Scout* in the Bonny River on the African coast while under Portuguese flag. She had on board 436 slaves, a crew of 22, and 13 passengers. The brig had two 18-pounder carronades and small arms aboard. Condemned at Sierra Leone, she was sold to an American named Lake; soon after, she was resold to Miguel Bentinotte, a slave dealer at the Gallinas for £1000. She cleared from Havana in April 1837, arriving at Cadiz 30 September 1837. Here she was sold as *Ferroz Africano* to Gabriel Lopez, an attorney to Francisco Cordova de Mello, of Cape Verde, who was

309

the nominal owner of all Spanish slaving vessels transferred to the Portuguese flag right after Spain's treaty with England in 1835 for the suppression of the slave trade. She received a license from the Portuguese Consul-General at Cadiz and was renamed *Diligente*. She was taken by H.M.S. *Pearl* 24 April 1838 after a long chase, with 478 slaves on board, and was condemned in August 1838 at Sierra Leone, though the brig was at Bermuda. She was probably broken up there, as required by the Parliamentary act, in 1839. This account is based upon documents in the Admiralty and other government reports, but the devious and rapid changes in ownership may have led to some errors in this history of the brig.

Diligente was an extreme clipper in model, having slight sheer, straight keel with little or no drag, very raking curved-stem rabbet, raking post, short, convex, and moderately sharp entrance, and a long, easy run with the quarter-

Spanish slaving barque CONCHITA, *taken by the Royal Navy steamer* FIREFLY 27 *August 1857. Museo Maritimo, Barcelona, Spain.*

Woodcut of American slaver captured by H.M.S. ANTELOPE.

beam buttock becoming straight just before its intersection with the after load line. She had the usual round tuck and upper-and-lower transom square stern. Her midsection was formed with sharply rising and slightly hollow floors, high and hard turn of the bilge, with some tumble home above the deck. The lines were taken off with the bottom of the keel as the base line. This gives her the appearance of being deeper forward from keel rabbet to load waterline than aft. Actually the keel rabbet was very nearly parallel to the load line. Lines are to the outside of planking, as taken off.

Diligente measured 100′ 8″ between perpendiculars, 26 feet extreme beam, 11′ 10″ depth in hold, and 14′ 4″ draft at post. On her load waterline she measured 96′ 4″, and her displacement to outside of plank was 305.6 long tons. Her coefficients were block .45, midship .66, and prismatic .68. Effective length of quarterbeam buttock was about 80′ 4″, camber 6′ 10″, giving a camber-length ratio of about 13.1.

There is a possibility that should be mentioned. Schooners and brigs somewhat similar to the model of this brig were also built in Spain, near Barcelona, in the 1830's and 1840's as shown by plans and models preserved in Spain. *Diligente* was a very fast vessel, which explains the efforts to get her back into the trade by numerous changes in ownership and name.

A draught of a supposed slave brig is shown in Plate 92. This drawing of an unidentified vessel appears to be of English origin and was found in Norway, without any documentation, other than that it was marked in pencil "probably a slaver" and titled "An American-built Brig, reputedly a fast sailer." This draught has the same objections as other unidentified plans used in this study. Nevertheless, the vessel shown is of some interest. She is about the size of the slaver brig *Black Joke*, which was taken into the Royal Navy, but is definitely not that vessel, for *Black Joke* never had her lines taken off, nor was she in any dockyard in England.

The brig shown measured 91 feet between perpendiculars, 26′ 3″ moulded beam, and 12′ 1″ depth in hold. She drew 13′ 6″ at post loaded. Tonnage was given on the original draught but is illegible due to water stains. She was of clipper model, having a moderate sheer, straight keel with moderate drag, raking and slightly curved stem rabbet, and moderate rake in sternpost. The entrance was rather long and sharp, with some hollow below the load line. The run was unusually long and fine; her quarterbeam buttock became straight some distance forward of its intersection with the after load line. The vessel had a round tuck and upper-and-lower transom square stern. The midsection was formed with rising, slightly hollow floor; moderately firm, high bilge; and slight tumble home above deck. This brig had a woman's bust figurehead.

On a moulded load waterline length of 85′ 6″ she had a moulded displacement of 261.8 long tons. Her coefficients were block .39, midship .62, and prismatic .65. The effective length of the quarterbeam buttock was 70′ 3″, the camber 7′ 3″, giving a camber-length ratio of 9.8. The drawing shows a small brig, probably built somewhere between 1825 and 1830, whose characteristics and dimensions were similar to those of known slaver brigs. Her beam, however, appears to be greater in proportion to length than in any of the slaving brigs listed.

Plate 93 shows the lines of a Baltimore clipper brig of 1845. This plan was

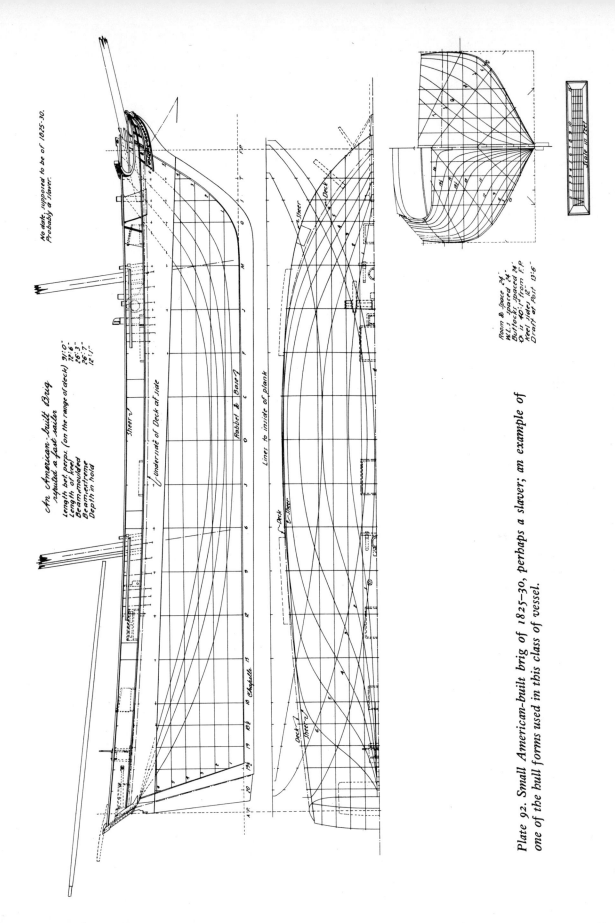

No date, supposed to be of 1825–30.
Probably a slaver.

An American-built Brig
reputed a fast sailer

Length bet. perps. (on the range of deck) 91'-0"
Length of keel 72'-6"
Beam-moulded 26'-3"
Beam-extreme 26'-7"
Depth in hold 12'-1"

Sheer
Underside of Deck at side
Rabbet & Base
Lines to inside of plank

Sheer
Deck
Deck
Sheer
Deck
Sheer

Room & Space 24".
W.L.s spaced 24".
Buttocks spaced 24".
⊕ is 40¼" from F.P.
Keel sided 12".
Draft at Perf. 13'-6".

Scale in Feet

Plate 92. Small American-built brig of 1825–30, perhaps a slaver; an example of
one of the hull forms used in this class of vessel.

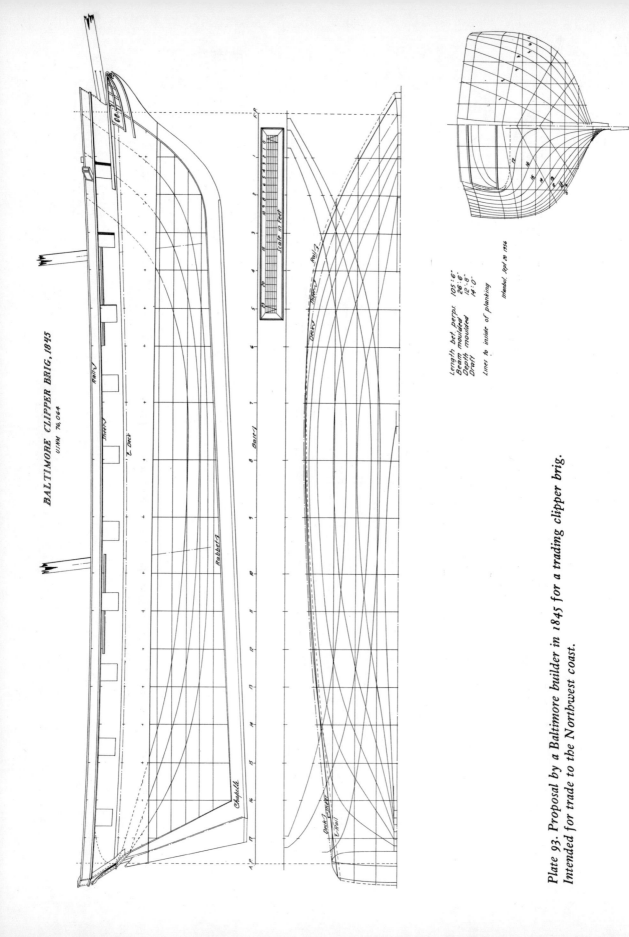

BALTIMORE CLIPPER BRIG, 1845

U/MM 76,064

Scale in feet

Rail

Sheer

Z Deck

Rabbet

Chap.lib

Deck

Rail

Draft

Deck

V-Rail

Length bet. perps.   105′-6″
Beam moulded   26′-6″
Depth moulded   12′-8″
Draft   14′-0″

Lines to inside of planking

Istanbul, April 20, 1956

Plate 93. Proposal by a Baltimore builder in 1845 for a trading clipper brig.
Intended for trade to the Northwest coast.

drawn from the half-model, now in the United States National Museum, which was sent by a Baltimore builder to John N. Cushing, Sr., of Newburyport, Massachusetts, in January 1845. The model was a proposal by the builder for a brig for the northwest Pacific Coast trade, to cost $10,765. Cushing owned only kettlebottom vessels, except for the brig *Dove*, which was built in 1817 at Newbury for the West Indies trade and was relatively sharp compared to the kettlebottoms. Because of his preference for full-model vessels, he rejected the Baltimore proposal. The name of the Baltimore builder is not given in the museum records.

The brig proposed was to be 105' 6" length between perpendiculars, 26' 6" moulded beam, 12' 8" moulded depth (rabbet to deck), and the draft loaded was to be 14 feet. The vessel was to have slight sheer, straight keel with strong drag, strongly raked, curving stem rabbet, raking sternpost, round tuck, upper-and-lower transom square stern. The entrance was to be quite long, convex, and sharp. The run was to be of moderate length and fine, the quarterbeam becoming straight just before it crossed the load line. The midsection was to have strongly rising straight floor; slack, round bilge; and slight tumble home above deck. On a moulded load waterline of 98' 9" she would have had a moulded displacement of 285.1 long tons and her coefficients would then be block .41, midship .77, and prismatic .64. The effective length of the quarterbeam buttock would be 82 feet, camber 6' 7", giving a camber-length ratio of 12.4.

Had this vessel been built she would undoubtedly have been a fast sailer, but not a carrier. The model may be older than the recorded date, but in any case it is one of the two Chesapeake Bay half-models made before 1850 that are documented and available.

A brig built at Baltimore two years earlier than the Cushing model is shown in Plate 94. This vessel was designed and built under contract for the United States Navy by Langley B. Culley and launched 1 August 1843. The reason for building a naval vessel in a privately-owned shipyard at this time is not clear, but may have been political. The second naval vessel to bear the name *Lawrence*, she was in that service only three years.

The Navy appears to have received only her half-model and perhaps a deck layout, indicating she may have been designed by model. She was very deep draft, 16' 6" at the post, and it was this and one other objection that led to her disposal. The board of officers that condemned the brig at New York in 1846 reported also that with her armament of ten guns—eight 32-pounder car-

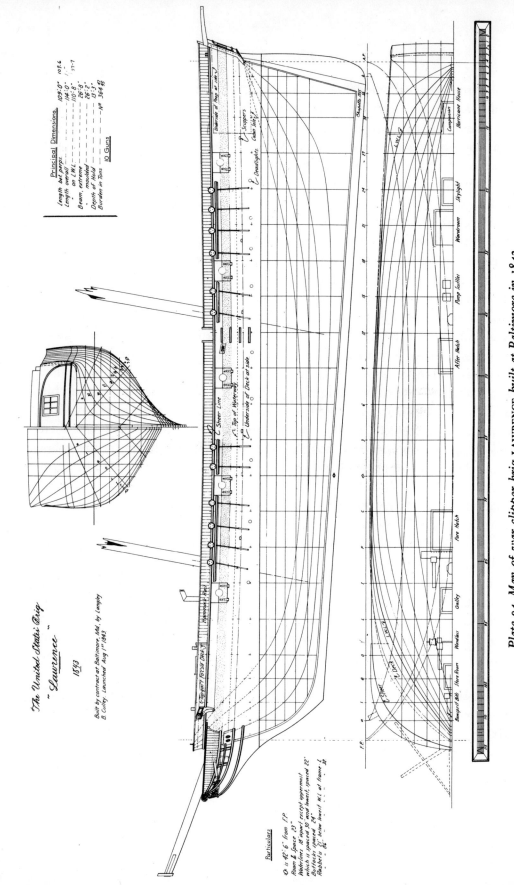

The United States Brig
"Lawrence"
1843

Built by contract at Baltimore, Md. by Langley
B. Culley, Launched Aug 1st 1843

Principal Dimensions.

Length bet. perp. ---- 109'0" 105.6
Length overall ------- 114'0'   1
 "   on LWL ------- 110'8"   33·7
Beam, extreme ------- 26'8"
  "   moulded -------- 26'2"
Depth of Hold -------- 13'3"
Burden in Tons ------- N° 364.95
      10 Guns

Particulars

Φ is 42'·6" from F.P.
Room & Space 23"
Waterlines 18 apart except uppermost
   which is spaced 30 and lowest, spaced 22"
Buttocks spaced 24"
Rabbet is 21" below lowest W.L. at Frame Φ
  "   86"   "   "   at Frame 32

Plate 94. Man-of-war clipper brig LAWRENCE built at Baltimore in 1843.

ronades and two medium 32-pounder guns—she could not carry sufficient stores. At the time of her sale, various false rumors about the vessel circulated, one of which was that the condemnation was based upon her being rotten and that after being sold she passed a survey, in the highest class, as a merchantman. The truth was that she did obtain a high classification in survey as a merchant vessel but it was also true that she was never condemned by the Navy as rotten or because of poor construction.

Lawrence was 114 feet long over the rail cap, 109′ 6″ between perpendiculars, 26′ 8″ extreme beam, 26′ 2″ moulded beam, 13′ 3″ depth in hold, and 364 47/95 tons. She had very little sheer, straight keel with much drag, curved, moderately raking stem rabbet, raking post, round tuck, upper-and-lower transom square stern, short, convex, and moderately full entrance, and a long run, with quarterbeam buttock becoming straight very close to the load line. Her midsection showed sharply rising straight floor, high round easy bilge, and some tumble home above the deck. She had very great flare just abaft the stem.

On a moulded load line of 107′ 7″ she had a moulded displacement of 404.1 long tons. Her coefficients were block .44, midship .62, and prismatic .72. The effective length of quarterbeam buttock was 74′ 0″, camber 8′ 0″, giving a camber-length ratio of 9.2.

Lawrence apparently required much ballast due to her form, which reduced her stowage capacity. Her half-model, once in possession of the Department of the Navy, cannot now be located.

Out of about one hundred vessels known to have engaged in running opium into China between 1823 and 1860, only 17 or 18 were American-built. Six were former slavers; at least five were probably built on the Chesapeake. One schooner, *Dhaulle*, was built at Baltimore. Lieutenant Fitzgerald De Roos, R.N., who saw her building there in 1826, reported, "There we saw a schooner building for the purpose of smuggling on the coasts of China. Everything was sacrificed to swiftness and I think she was the most lovely vessel I ever saw." Four vessels were built at New York, one at Medford, Massachusetts, three at Boston, two at Portsmouth, New Hampshire, and one "built in America." The trade was not illegal so far as the United States was concerned; a number of American merchants had a financial interest in it, and a few engaged actively in this immoral trade. Though a few vessels were built expressly for the opium trade, the number was too small and the specifications and requirements were too general, to have had any influence on American sailing-vessel design. At most, a few shipyards obtained profitable contracts.

Late in the 1830's or early in the 1840's the counter stern began to develop in American sailing vessels. This development cannot be precisely followed at present because there is a lack of sufficient material on the subject.

The earliest appearance of a vestigial counter yet found was in the United States Naval brig *Perry*, built at Norfolk Navy Yard in 1843. She was a clipper brig designed by Naval Constructor Francis Grice. In her stern the round tuck was carried to the knuckle, the lower transom being moulded in a curve athwartship. The planking was apparently carried over the lower transom in a fair curve from the round tuck below it. The rudder stock passed through the counter or lower transom, as was usual with an overhang stern of the period.*

The round stern, first employed in the Royal Navy, had been introduced into American naval vessels in the frigates of the *Potomac-Raritan* class, laid down in 1819–20 and altered to round stern during the early stages of construction. The round stern was formed with three knuckles in large vessels, two in small. The lowest knuckle was in reverse and at the top of the round tuck, in lieu of the old "cross seam." Gradually the reverse knuckle disappeared and the planking was carried fair from the round tuck to the knuckle, at main deck level or a little below at the extreme stern. The round stern was used in a number of steamships built in the 1840's but was not employed very often in American sailing vessels prior to 1851, so far as can now be proven.

In naval vessels, the spaces between the headrails that supported the outer cutwater were planked in over the knees of the head, from the upper trail knee to the headrail at hammock-rail, or fancy-rail, height. This began in frigates, but by 1838 the heads of small men-of-war—brigs, brigantines, and sloops-of-war—were closed in. This made destruction of the headrails and cutwater by heavy seas less common, and gave both protection and more privacy to the seats of ease—or toilets—usually located in the head. This was adopted in merchant vessels in the 1840's, as will be seen later.

American-built schooners appeared in one other illegal occupation—piracy. After the downfall of Napoleon, and the end of the War of 1812, the West Indies and areas in the South Atlantic became scenes of piratical activity. At first the revival of piracy could be charged to the privateers fitted out of rebellious Spanish colonies in South and Central America. Criminal activities

* Chapelle, *The History of the American Sailing Navy*, pp. 450–453; lines, deck arrangement, and sail plan.

by these privateers were sporadic, as a rule.

During the long wars, however, settlements of freebooters, privateersmen, and criminals had become established on the coasts of Cuba, Haiti, San Domingo, and Puerto Rico. These habitual rascals continued wartime looting in the form of outright piracy, from 1815 through the 1830's, accompanied by cruelty and frightful crimes. Their vessels were either captured or purchased small schooners. Some slaving vessels, manned by such rascals and engaged in piracy, operated in the South Atlantic, off the coast of Africa.

In the early 1820's the United States and Great Britain carried on an intensive campaign to suppress these criminals. The American Navy, though quite successful in capturing or killing pirates, had the usual difficulties of obtaining convictions in American courts.

The British Navy, operating with the aid of realistic courts, must receive credit for the eventual suppression of piracy as well as of the slave trade. In the process they captured many piratical vessels and took some of the small schooners into naval service in the West Indies.

Of the piratical schooners captured, the following were taken into the Royal Navy. Their descriptions are from pre-purchase dockyard surveys, afloat.

H.M. schooner *Kangaroo*, ex-*Las Damas Argentinas*, 1828, Baltimore-built, topsail schooner, coppered and copper-fastened, three years old, 85 tons, "very superior sailing qualities," long 18-pounder gun on a pivot amidships, low bulwarks.

H.M. schooner *Lion*, ex-"piratical vessel," 1823, American-built, partially copper-fastened and sheathed as high as the light load line, 61' 8" on deck, 19' 1" moulded beam, 5' 9" depth in hold, about 87 tons, R.N., about two years old. Had square course topsail and topgallant on foremast. Drew seven feet aft, four feet forward. Course, topsail, topgallant on foremast. Fast.

H.M. schooner *Renegade*, ex-pirate *Zaragosana*, 1823, fitted with two 32-pounder carronades on pivots, one 12-pounder on a truck carriage, 76' 3" on deck, 18' 10" moulded breadth, 7' 4" (?) depth in hold, 114 81/94 tons, R.N., drew 11' 6" at post, 5' 1" at gripe. Sold 1826 (rotten), low bulwarks, "good model."

H.M. schooner *Assidious*, ex-*Jackall*, pirate, 1823, one 32-pounder carronade on a pivot, one 12-pounder on a truck carriage. Sold in 1825 (rotten). 51' 6" on deck, 16' 1½" moulded beam, 6' 6" depth in hold, 53 56/94 tons, R.N., American-built, three to four years old. Coppered to light load line. Very fast sailer, low bulwarks.

Lion, Renegade, and *Assidious* were flush-decked, with low bulwarks, cabin trunk aft, gammon knee or curved stem, round tuck, square stern, with rising straight floor amidships. Surveys showed them to be well-built, though lightly constructed; but of course these vessels were especially selected for survey.

The period between 1820 and 1845 is important not only for the changes in ship design and construction, but also for a national economic change that ships may fairly be said to have brought about. A merchant at Albany, New York, for example, dealing in imported goods in 1812—most luxury and many necessary products were then imported—had to stock his store for about 12 to 18 months. Orders for new goods might be mailed to Liverpool, England, but the mail would not reach its destination quickly. It would go to New York within a week if the weather were good. Here it would await a ship bound to Liverpool. Since there was then no regular service between New York and Liverpool, it might be a month or more before a ship was cleared for that port, and that ship might go to Mobile, or New Orleans, on her way to Liverpool. Hence, the voyage might take three months or more. The goods ordered would have the same delays in movement, even after steamboats cut the time between Albany and New York to the daylight hours.

The establishment of the packets changed all this, shortening the time required for mail or the return freight to move to only about two months each way. This reduced the period for which a merchant had to stock to three or fourth months, reducing risk and also freeing some of the merchant's capital for other investments. Speed in the packets, as far as the owners and merchants were concerned, was now a desirable commercial requirement, as never before, for by this means fairly regular schedules of sailing could be maintained. What was usually sought in the sailing-packet period was not maximum potential speed, however; but rather, a reasonably high, maintained, or average speed under the commonly prevailing weather conditions of the North Atlantic and eastern coast of North America. As a result, packets were capable of somewhat higher potential speed than the usual ocean freighter of the time, in order to have a satisfactory maintained speed but not the maximum potential speed that might be attained. This requirement produced the clipper ships of the following decade (1845–1855) beginning with the "China packets," as we shall see.

CHAPTER · SEVEN

1845 - 1855

THE PACKET PERIOD HAD PRODUCED MANY SKILLED SHIPBUILDERS, BUT ONE WAS to have especially great influence on the development of the clipper ship. This was Isaac Webb, a former apprentice of Henry Eckford, later his fore-man, and finally his successor in the New York yard. Webb purchased the yard after Eckford's death in Turkey, and then took on as a partner John Allen, Eckford's half brother and a shipwright. Webb and Allen built numerous vessels, including several of the fine packets described in Chapter 6.

Isaac Webb, like Eckford, had the knack of teaching, and three of his apprentices became very prominent—William H. Webb, his eldest son; John W. Griffiths; and Donald McKay. A younger son, Eckford Webb, was also an apprentice to him, as was Donald McKay's older brother, Laughlin. Isaac Webb's knowledge, therefore, did not die with him (he died in 1840) but was projected through his pupils, the most influential of the many clipper ship builders.

It is difficult to follow the history of clipper ship design and construction in America, for as we have seen, the type appeared in the guise of a fast sailing ship long before the period usually considered to have been the "clipper ship era." The construction of ships accepted as "clippers" in this period (large, very fast sailing ships built without much regard to cargo capacity and operating costs) was limited to the period 1845 to 1855. It was only during this decade that any large extreme clipper ships were built, though a few small sharp-model clippers were built later than 1855 for the South American coffee trade and the Florida and West Indian fruit trade. Most of these latter were barks, brigantines, and schooners—that is, small craft, under 700 tons register, with only a few of extreme model.

In order to follow the involved history of the development in the design of the clippers, it is necessary to understand that in the extreme clippers, no single type of hull form was used. Instead, there were really three basic models: the sharp deadrise, fine-ended Baltimore clipper; the full-midsection, very small deadrise sharp-ended clipper ship; and a compromise between these two, in which the deadrise was very marked but not extreme. The Baltimore clipper, represented by *Ann McKim*, was only a variation of the old American model. The full-midsection clipper was a refinement of the packet model. The third, or compromise model, was the experimental type in which the speed characteristics of much deadrise and fine ends were delicately balanced against the economic factor of cargo capacity. None of these models became wholly dominant in the clipper class of vessel, for each had inherent advantages only in certain areas of employment. The development of the full-midsection "extreme clipper" from the packet model was a gradual retreat from economic cargo capacity that in many instances eventually produced as unprofitable a carrier as the old Baltimore clipper model.

We have seen in the China Packets *Panama* and *Montauk* the early development of the full-midsection clipper ship. In 1845 John W. Griffiths, then employed by Smith & Dimon, designed the China packet *Rainbow*. She was a logical development of the sharp-ended packet model, having a little more deadrise, slacker bilges, a rather sharper but short convex entrance, combined with a longer and finer run than vessels like *Panama* and *Montauk*.

In 1843 Griffiths had proposed a ship having the important features of *Rainbow* when he exhibited a half-model at a fair held in the American Institute in New York. According to Griffiths the model attracted both the attention and criticism of many New York shipbuilders, some of whom were violent in their objections to the principal features of the model. As a result of the arguments over his model, Griffiths gave a series of lectures in the American Institute on the science of ship design and construction. One of the features of these lectures was his urging the use of half-models. These lectures were the first held in the United States dealing with naval architecture and they apparently prompted the publishing of Griffiths' *Treatise on the Theory and Practice of Shipbuilding* at New York in 1851.

Griffiths' proposals for improvement, as illustrated in his half-model and explained and defended in his lectures, were to flare the upper part of the stem rabbet strongly forward (in profile) above the load waterline. This would sharpen the forebody at the deck and rail, thus reducing the shock and turbulence caused when a full-model ship, having the upper part of her bow almost square across at rail, as seen in some of the packets, plunged into a heavy head sea. Griffiths pointed out that such battering not only hindered a ship's forward motion but often caused much damage. He also pointed out that the forward flare in the stem rabbet would make a ship easier to plank, since the proposed stem rabbet profile would fair easily into the heavily flaring forebody cross sections in the body plan. He also suggested that his proposal would improve a ship's appearance, doing away with the box-like appearance of the packets.

Another of his suggestions was to sharpen the entrance and run by the use of hollow waterlines or level lines—lift lines in a half-model—near the stempost and sternpost and below the load waterline. It was this proposal that drew particularly violent objections from many shipbuilders, for as has been seen, some designers, such as Josiah Fox and Laughlin McKay, had been strongly prejudiced, at least in theory, against hollow in the lower part of the entrance and run. On the other hand numerous draughts have shown that not all American ship designers either accepted or knew of this theory, for hollow was often used to some degree in the entrance or run, or in both. Webb had used hollow in the entrance and run of both *Panama* and *Montauk*, for example. This matter of hollow in the lower portion of the ends remained controversial among ship designers throughout the clipper ship era, as can be seen in the lines of some of the noted clippers.

Griffiths' third proposal was to lighten, or raise, the quarters at the stern to reduce the resistance when heeled and to prevent pounding under the stern in heavy seas. This would be possible by rounding athwartship the cross seam or the lower edge of the lower transom. It would also reduce or eliminate most of the reverse curves in the outer buttock lines that were common with the wide upper-and-lower transom then in use. Griffiths also suggested that the cross seam be raised to main-deck level and he seems to have implied the use of a short counter or overhang stern, which appeared in a few American vessels at least as early as 1843 when Francis Grice, a naval constructor, used it in the design of the U.S. brig *Perry*.

In these proposals of Griffiths' nothing was said about a full midsection or about the amount of deadrise to be employed, though later he had very strong opinions in favor of the full midsection. Perhaps he assumed that a full midsection would be used as a matter of course.

In 1847 a "marine architectural institute" was established in New York where Griffiths presided and taught drafting and model-making. The institute lasted for about two years.

Rainbow, shown in Plates 95 and 96, illustrates the practical application of Griffiths' proposals. Stephen Smith, of Smith & Dimon, usually designed the firm's ships but Griffiths certainly designed *Rainbow*, as is confirmed by nearly all contemporary references.

According to one statement, *Rainbow* caused such adverse criticism while on the stocks that her owners delayed completion of the ship for a year. However this claim is not mentioned in Griffiths' papers, nor in his publications. Such an incident would have given Griffiths great satisfaction later when the ship proved so successful, and he surely would have mentioned it if it were true. It might be added that *Rainbow* was certainly not such an extreme design that she should have caused violent criticism, even by the most conservative shipbuilder of the period. There have been assumptions that *Rainbow* was extraordinarily hollow in her waterlines and this has led to a false impression that she was an extreme clipper. As shown in Plate 95, she was an improved China packet, hardly medium sharp at best, with very slight hollows in the ends below the load line.

Rainbow was 160′ 9″ between perpendiculars, 31′ 8″ moulded beam, and 19′ 5″ moulded depth. Her register dimensions were 159 feet by 31′ 10″ by 18′ 4″. She had slight sheer, straight keel with no drag, raking and flaring stem rabbet, slightly raking post, and counter-and-transom square stern. Her entrance was moderately sharp and convex. There was no dead flat, or parallel body, amidships; her run was long, fine, and with the quarterbeam buttock straight some distance forward of its intersection with the after load line. The midship section was formed with a slightly rising straight floor, and a slack, round bilge with slight tumble home in the bulwarks. She had an unusually deep keel below the rabbet.

Rainbow, on a moulded load line of 154′ 3″, had a moulded displacement of 1043.1 long tons. Her coefficients were block .47, midship .70, and pris-

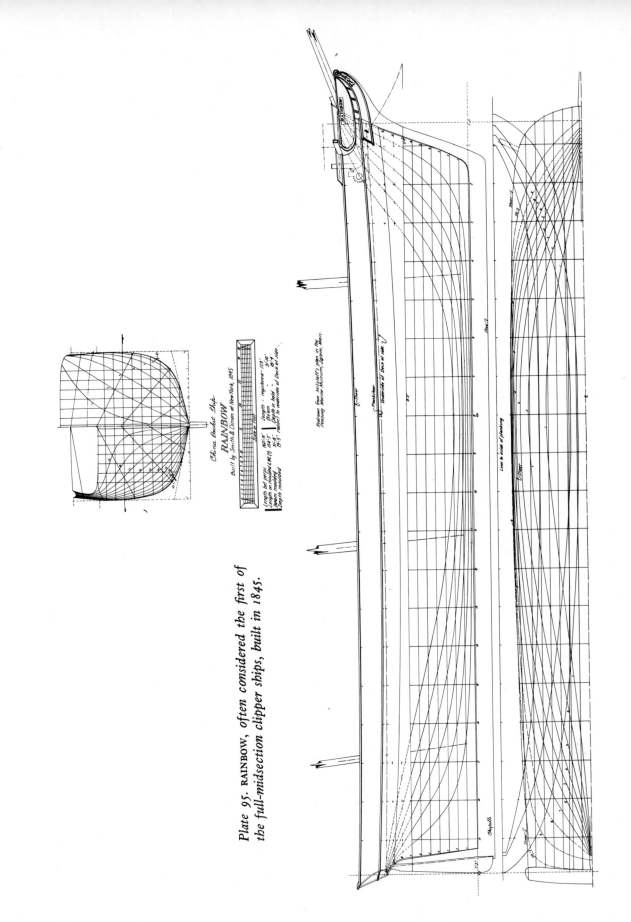

Plate 95. RAINBOW, often considered the first of
the full-midsection clipper ships, built in 1845.

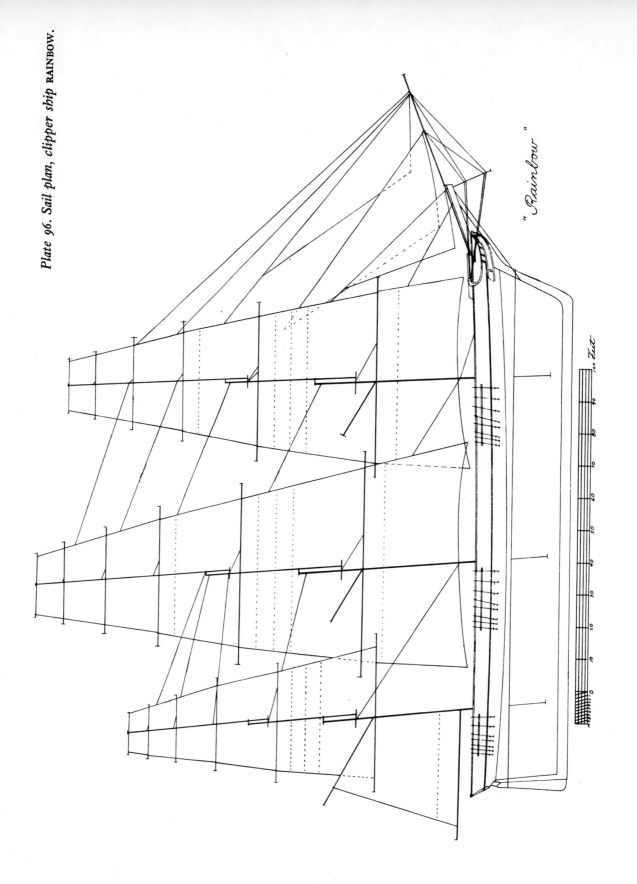

Plate 96. Sail plan, clipper ship RAINBOW.

"Rainbow"

Fut

matic .67. The effective length of the quarterbeam buttock was 129′ 6″, camber 12′ 4″, giving a camber-length ratio of 15.3 .

Rainbow went "missing with all hands" in 1848, after having made a great reputation for fast passages.

A year before *Rainbow* was launched, Brown & Bell launched the China packet *Houqua*. This vessel, whose register dimensions were 142′ 4″ by 29′ 10″ by 16′ 8″, was described as sharp-ended for her type and time, and a fast sailer. Unfortunately her half-model is not available. Allegedly she was modeled by Captain Nathaniel Palmer, but his claim should be accepted only with reservations. She was probably in the class of Webb's *Helena* rather than in that of *Rainbow;* certainly she was not an extreme model.

The performance of *Rainbow* led her owners to have another and larger ship built in 1846, to be commanded by their very successful master in the China trade, Robert H. Waterman. He had made an outstanding record of fast passages in the New York-China run. Smith and Dimon were again chosen as builders and Griffiths as the designer, apparently with complete freedom to carry out his theories in her model.

The result was the famous *Sea Witch,* shown in Plates 97 and 98. This ship held more records for fast passages than any other China packet, yet it was said that her maximum speed was not over 15½ or 16 knots. Probably Waterman was largely responsible for her record-making performance, but there can be no doubt that she was capable of maintaining a high average speed, for her size, in a wide variety of weather conditions.

Sea Witch was Griffiths' masterpiece; the expression of his design ideas as set forth in 1843–45. She also represented in some degree many of the theories of hull design that he was to express later in his publications. Nevertheless, *Sea Witch* did not show the extremes that Griffiths finally advocated. *Sea Witch* is the only named clipper ship whose offsets he published, and her lines and sail plan are one of the three designs of his clippers that he retained. These are now in the Museum of History and Technology, Smithsonian Institution, Washington, D. C.

Sea Witch had little sheer, a straight keel except close to the forefoot where there was a slight rocker, and there was no drag. The stem rabbet flared forward strongly; the post raked a good deal. The square stern was formed by a very short overhang counter with a raking transom curved athwartship. Griffiths claimed that this was the first ship built at New York to have a "nondescript" head (no projecting cutwater or supporting mouldings). Her en-

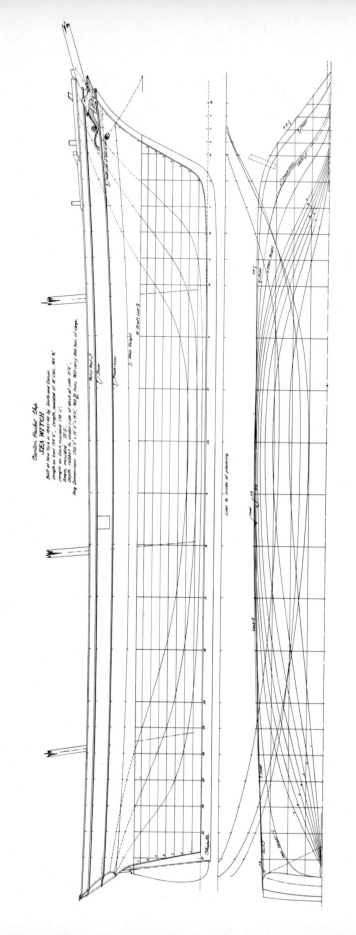
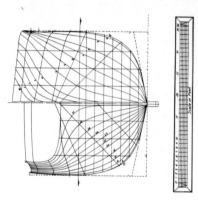

Plate 97. SEA WITCH, built in New York, 1846; the first of the very sharp-ended full-midsection clipper ships.

trance was long, concave, and sharp; the run moderate in length and without any very marked hollow below the load line. The quarterbeam buttock was straight a little before it intersected with the after load line. The midsection showed straight, slightly rising floor, and a slack round bilge with very slight tumble home above the main deck. The flare in the fore sections of the body plan was unusually great.

Sea Witch measured 178′ 2″ on deck, 33 feet moulded beam, and 21′ 6″ moulded depth. Her register dimensions were 170′ 3″ by 33′ 11″ by 19 feet, 907 35/95 tons register. She could carry about 1000 tons of cargo, drawing 19′ 6″.

On a moulded load line of 166 feet and drawing 18 feet, she had a moulded displacement of 1249.5 long tons. Her coefficients were block .51; midship, .80, and prismatic .64. The effective length of the quarterbeam buttock was 135′ 10″, camber 13′ 8″, giving a camber-length ratio of 9.8. Her figurehead represented a Chinese dragon. No deck plan exists.

Her run from China to New York in 1847 will serve to show how *Sea Witch* made fast passages. For the ten days between 25 May and 3 June she averaged 263.4 nautical miles for each sea day; her hourly average was slightly over 10½ knots. This ship holds the sailing record for a passage between Hong Kong and New York, 77 days, among other record and near-record passages.

Smith & Dimon did not follow *Sea Witch* with any more clipper ship designs of equal caliber. A conservative firm, the next ship they built was *Memnon*, launched in 1847. Her lines, shown in Plate 99, were taken from her half-model. On the back of this the following note was found, written in pencil: "Disected [sic] and lines taken from this model by D. J. Lawlor, Boatbuilder, Chelsea, Mass., for Mr. Samuel Hall, Jan. 24, 1856." Hall was a prominent Boston shipbuilder.

In design *Memnon* was a retreat from the model of *Sea Witch*, in fact, she bore some resemblance to *Rainbow*. She was fuller than *Witch* and more of a carrier. She proved to be a good passage-maker. Her career was short, for she was lost a few days out of Whampoa, in Gaspar Straits, in 1851, while employed in the tea trade to England. She made a voyage from New York to Liverpool during which she arrived off Point Lynas in 14 days, 7 hours, havnig passed the steamer *Europe* on the way.

Memnon measured 171′ 6″ from the stem rabbet at main deck to the centerline of the rudder post, 37′ 2″ moulded beam, and 23′ 10″ moulded depth.

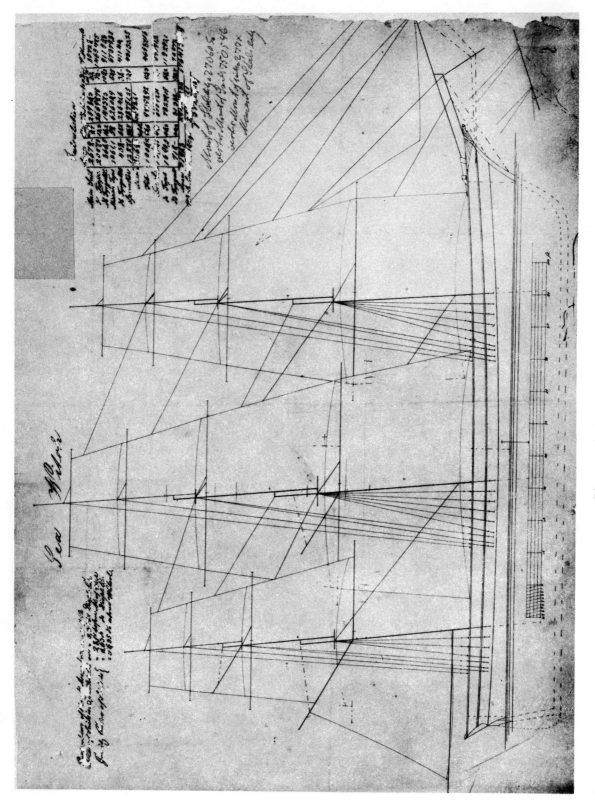

Plate 98. Sail plan of SEA WITCH.

Her registered dimensions of 170 feet by 36 feet by 21 feet make her slightly smaller in registered tonnage than she actually was.

On a moulded load line of 167′ 5″, *Memnon* had a moulded displacement of 1837.5 long tons. Her coefficients were block .57, midsection .87, and prismatic .67. The effective length of the quarterbeam buttock was 158′ 3″, camber 16′ 7″, giving a camber-length ratio of 9.5.

This ship had slight sheer; straight keel without drag; moderately raking and flaring stem rabbet; slight rake to post; convex, moderately full entrance with some hollow below the load line; and a rather long, moderately fine run. The quarterbeam buttock was straight for a short distance forward of its inter-section with the after load line. Her square stern was formed with a curved cross seam, upper-and-lower transoms curved athwartships and very raking. The lower transom was quite small and its rake was so great that the quarter-beam buttock almost faired into its rake. *Memnon* had a sharper entrance and a finer run than *Yorkshire*. The midsection was formed with small rise of straight floor, moderately hard turn of bilge with a slight tumble home above. She was painted with a wide white stripe and false gunports, the top of which came to the planksheer moulding.

Although not a clipper in model, she was admired as a combination of a fast sailer with a profitable cargo capacity, which may well explain Hall's interest in her lines. Her design was the culmination of a trend in the development of the full-model China packets, soon to be replaced by the out-and-out, full-midsection clipper ship.

It is mere speculation to attempt explanations of the return to the packet model in *Memnon*. The counter, used in *Rainbow* and *Sea Witch*, was dropped, and the simple cutwater of the latter ship was replaced by the old cutwater and head rails.

In 1850 Smith & Dimon built *Mandarin;* register dimensions 151′ 6″ by 33′ 6″ by 19′ 3″. Her lines, on a very small scale, were published by Griffiths in *The U. S. Nautical Magazine and Naval Journal.* Based on this, *Mandarin* was slightly sharper in entrance and a little fuller in run, than was Isaac Webb's *Columbus* of 1834, for example. This retrogression in design produced a vessel that made the run from New York to Melbourne, Australia, in 69 days, 14 hours in 1855–56, an all-time record. This shows the value of a single fast passage criterion in attempting to judge a sailing vessel's model or lines. It cannot be now determined whether Griffiths had anything to do with *Man-darin's* design, but it seems unlikely in view of the complete rejection of his

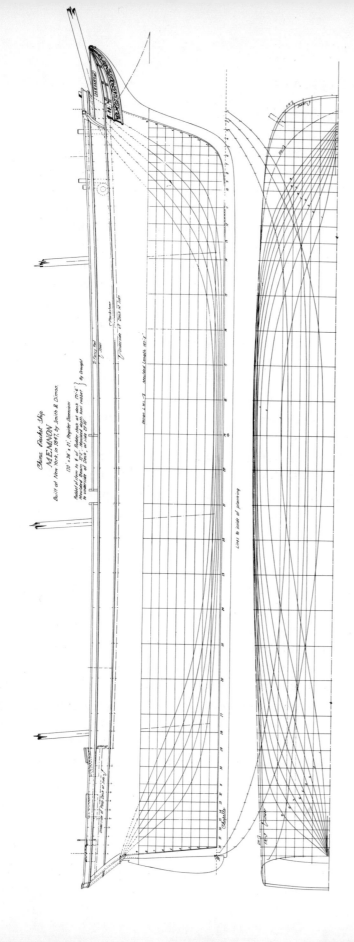

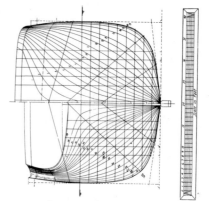

*Plate 99. MEMNON, built at New York in 1847,
a fast-carrier China packet model.*

STAGHOUND
Built at East Boston, Massachusetts
1850
by Donald McKay

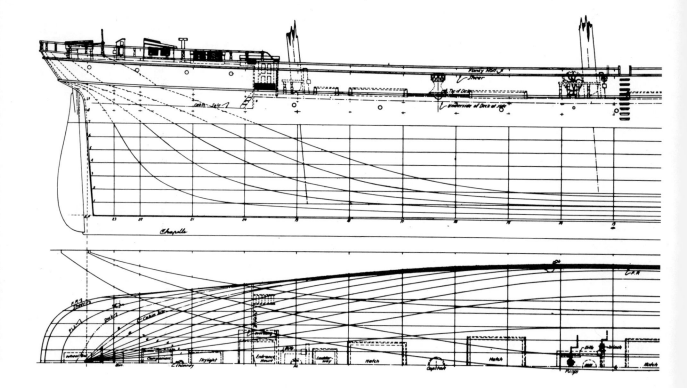

Chapelle

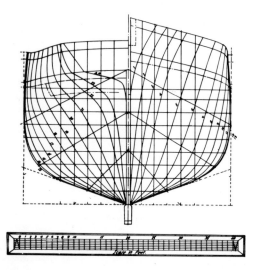

Scale 14 Feet

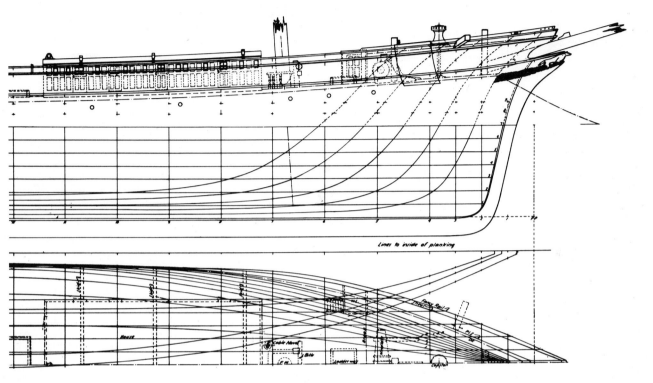

Length bet perps ..... 210:0'
" ,moulded LWL-203:9'-21'draft
Beam moulded ...... 39:0'
Depth moulded ...... 21:3'
Keel sides 15"
Reg. Dimensions 215'x 39'8"x 21', 1534 Tons.

Lines to inside of planking

PLATE IX. STAGHOUND, *first clipper ship built by Donald McKay, launched in 1850.*

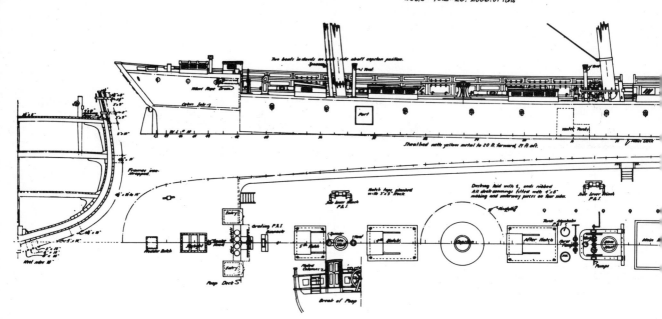

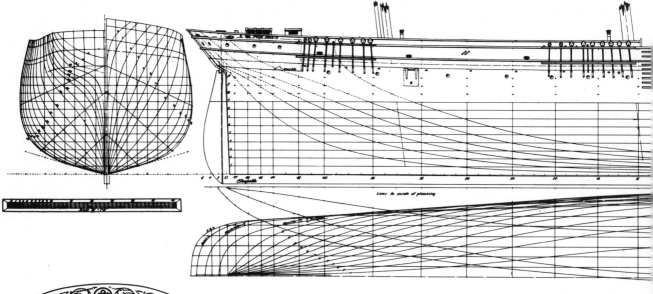

CHALLENGE
NEW YORK

230.6 × 43.2 × 26. 2006.51 Tons.

Particulars

Frame Spacing		
0 to 11	36"
Y to Y	34"
11 to Y	32"
11 to 16	30"
16 to 24	32"
24 to 32	34"
32 to 40	36"
40 to 47	38"
Sta 47 to Cross-seam	24"
Z to 6	24"

Waterlines spaced 2" to WL 12, 1'3 WL 12
to 13, 1'7½ WL 13 to 14
Keel sides 14"
Bottom Plank 4"
Face of Cutwater 3" below WL 12
Length, Frame k to C.S. 225' 2"
Moulded Beam 42' 5"

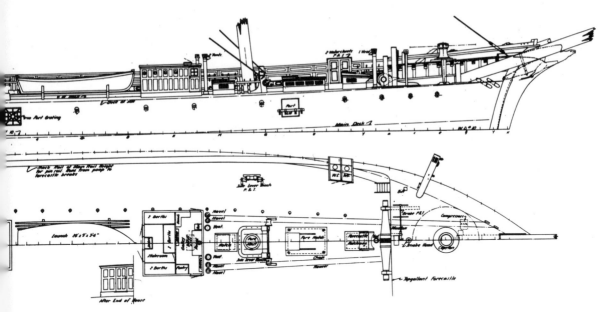

Inboard profile and deck layout of CHALLENGE.

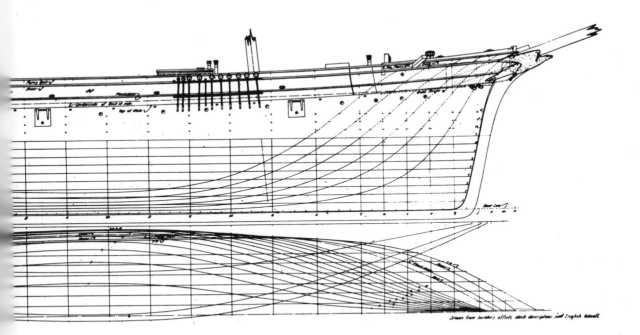

PLATE X.   CHALLENGE, *extreme clipper built by William H. Webb in 1851.*
Sketch of stern ornament as placed on scale model of CHALLENGE *(sail plan, Plate 104).*

theories that were exhibited in this ship's model.

Mandarin had marked sheer, straight keel with no drag, moderately raking and flaring stem rabbet, slight rake to post, round tuck, upper-and-lower transom, and square stern. Transoms were strongly curved athwartship. The entrance was full and the lower waterlines had no hollow. The run was short and full, and the quarterbeam buttock was much curved near its intersection with the load line. The small scale drawing, however, is not accurate enough to allow positive judgment about this, particularly in so full a model. There were only slight hollows in the lower waterlines aft. The midsection had very slight rise of straight floor, low and rather hard turn of the bilge, and was rather wall-sided above.

The next important ship launched by Smith & Dimon was the so-called clipper packet *Universe* registered in 1850; she is mentioned in Chapter Six. This vessel was built for Williams and Guion's "Black Star" Liverpool line and was a two-decked ship of 1297 tons register.

There can be no doubt that Griffiths was the designer of this ship; her half-breadth plan, sheer elevation, sail plan, and transom were shown in his *Treatise on the Theory and Practice of Shipbuilding.** Her entrance showed marked hollow just abaft the stem rabbet and then filled out into a moderately full fore body. Her run was quite short, with some hollow in the waterlines giving very steep buttocks, with the quarterbeam straight just before its crossing of the load line. Her midsection showed slight rise of floor, a full, round bilge, and slight tumble home. She had about 20 feet of deadflat amidships and was considered a good and fast packet, but without an outstanding passage record. She was by no means a clipper but rather a somewhat sharp-bowed packet. Her stern was much like that of *Memnon*, again rejecting the counter used in *Rainbow*.

After launching this ship, Smith & Dimon built some large steamships, apparently designed by Griffiths, and one clipper ship for Russian owners. Griffiths' career after 1850 will be dealt with when his later design theories are examined.

Houqua having been a successful vessel, her owners ordered an improved ship from Brown & Bell in 1846. Her design has also been commonly credited to Captain Nathaniel Palmer. While it is likely that he had her built according to his ideas, she was not the work of an amateur designer. The new ship, designed for the China trade, was launched on 14 August 1847 and named

* Plate 19, Sec. 1 and 2; Plate 20; and Plate 26.

Samuel Russell. Her register dimensions were 173′ 6″ by 34′ 6″ by 19′ 11″. Her lines, taken from her half-model, are shown in Plate 100. Like *Sea Witch*, she was a clipper rather than a packet model and her bow was a variation of that used in *Witch*. Originally she was to have a conventional, straight, raking stem rabbet above the heel of the stem and the usual cutwater and head rails. But before work had proceeded very far, the bow of the model was altered. Instead of the conventional head, the bow was padded out to give an imitation of the closed naval head mentioned in Chapter Six. She apparently had two stem pieces; the planking rabbet was carried out on the foremost stem piece. This, as can be seen in Plate 100, allowed her rail to be carried forward as in the *Witch*, with all the attendant advantages. The knightheads and the main supporting timbers were at the after stem piece, and were carried up through a topgallant forecastle deck. *Samuel Russell* proved to be a handsome and very fast ship, apparently well suited to her trade in all respects. She is said to have sailed 15 to 16 knots.

According to her model, she measured 177′ 6″ moulded length on deck, 33′ 3″ moulded beam, and 22′ 1½″ moulded depth. She had a rather straight sheer, straight keel, slightly raking and curved, flaring, stem rabbet, slight rake to post, round tuck, and upper-and-lower transom square stern. Her entrance was long and convex until near the stem rabbet where the lower waterlines were concave. The run was long and fine; the quarterbeam buttock became straight well forward of its intersection with the after load line.

The midsection was formed with rising, straight floor, well-rounded bilge, and slight tumble home above the main deck.

On a moulded load waterline of 171′ 9″, she had a moulded displacement of 1291.4 long tons. Her coefficients were block .52, midship .75, and prismatic .70. Effective length of quarterbeam buttock 140′ 10″, camber 12 feet, giving a camber-length ratio of 11.7.

In 1848 the owners of *Russell* had a larger but similar vessel built—by this time Brown & Bell had dissolved partnership and Jacob Bell alone was the builder. On 1 August 1849 the new ship *Oriental* was launched, having register dimensions of 185 feet by 36 feet by 21 feet, 1003 tons. Intended for the China run, she engaged in the English tea trade with China until she was wrecked on the River Min, China, 25 February 1854. Her lines were taken off at Blackwall on the Thames in January 1851, in Green's Yard.

She had a profile very much like that of *Russell*, except for an angular forefoot at the rabbet. She also had the double stem pieces, to form her upper

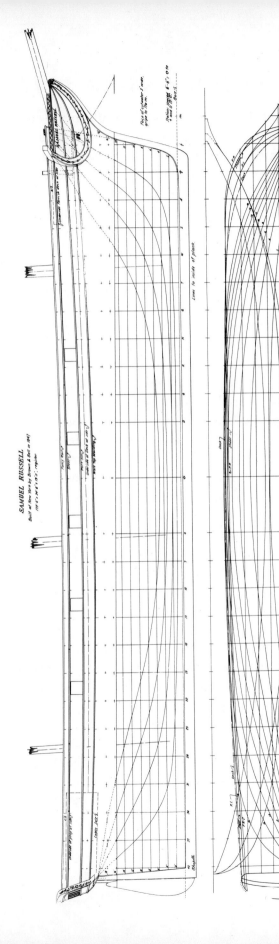

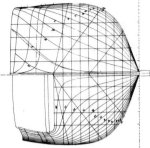

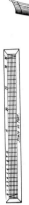

Plate 100. SAMUEL RUSSELL, *early New York clipper for the China trade, built in 1847.*

bow, as in *Russell*. Her lines, shown in Plate 101, are as taken off, to the outside of plank. Her take-off dimensions show length between perpendiculars 181′ 6″; length inside of stem to after side of post, upper deck 174′ 9″; length on lower deck from stem rabbet to after side of post, 173′ 6″; beam (extreme) 35′ 3″; depth in hold 20′ 5″; moulded depth at midsection (𝕏)22′ 6″.

On a load waterline 171′ 6″ long, she had a displacement of 1642.8 long tons. Her coefficients were, block .58, midship .93, and prismatic .71. Effective length of quarterbeam buttock was 148′ 4″, camber 14′ 2″, giving a camber-length ratio of 10.5.

Both *Samuel Russell* and *Oriental* sailed best when trimmed slightly by the stern, thus giving a little drag to the keel not shown in the model or lines. Reports of *Oriental's* performance showed her to have reached nearly 16 knots for short periods, and she could maintain a speed of 12½ knots without strain or fuss. An extremely well-built and finished ship, she was admired wherever she went. According to various reports and references, neither *Russell* nor *Oriental* was very heavily sparred and canvassed.

Oriental had a slight sheer, straight keel, and a rather upright lower stem rabbet with flaring reverse curve above and slight rake to the post. Her square stern was formed with a round tuck, lower transom, arch piece, and upper transom, all curved athwartships. Her entrance was rather long, sharp, and convex with only slight hollow in the forefoot. The run was rather short; the quarterbeam buttock was straight as it approached the intersection with the after load line, with reverse under the quarters; and there was very slight hollow in the after, lower water, or level, lines. The midsection had less dead-rise in the straight floor than did *Russell;* the bilge was about as slack, but the tumble home was a little more pronounced and more round.

Oriental proved to be an excellent passage-maker. She made a record passage, New York to Hong Kong, of 80 days, 10 hours, in 1850, while *Samuel Russell* held a record for a run from New York to Canton of 93 days.

A fourth ship, *N. B. Palmer*, was built by Westervelt & Mackay in 1851. This vessel measured 202′ 6″ by 38′ 6″ by 21 feet register. Though her design has also been assigned to Palmer, contemporary evidence credits her to Westervelt, a very competent ship designer and clipper-ship builder.

The appearance of relatively sharp-ended, full-bodied ships such as *Sea Witch*, *Samuel Russell*, and *Oriental* aroused much interest among shipowners, since their quick round voyages proved to be very profitable. Such voyages reduced the period of time that investment was tied up in cargoes, just as the

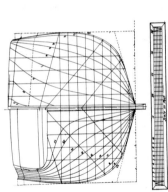

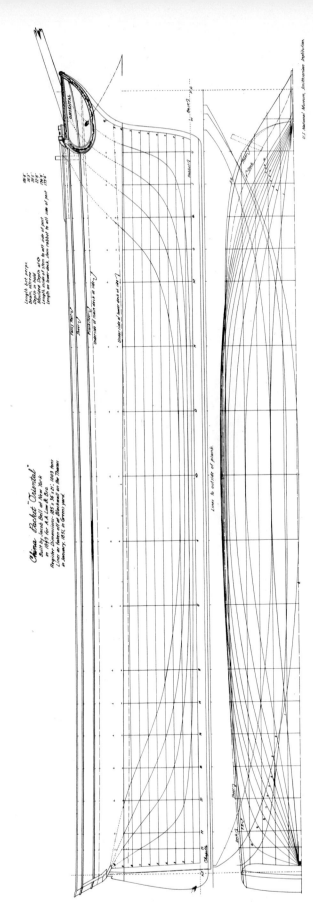

China Packet "Oriental"

Built by Jacob Bell at New York
in 1849 for A. Low & Bros
Register Dimensions: 185 x 36 x 21: 1003 tons
Lines as taken off at Blackwall on the Thames
in January, 1851, in Green's yard.

Length betw. perps. 185'4"
Beam, extreme 35'3"
Depth in hold 19'1"
Moulded Depth 20'6"
Length inside at stem to aft. side of post
Length on lower deck, stem rabbet to aft. side of post 173'6"

Plate 101. ORIENTAL, *a noted China packet, built in 1849.*

U.S. National Museum, Smithsonian Institution.

packet service earlier had reduced the length of time that investments in inventory of goods had to be maintained by merchants. Shippers in the China trade were so influenced by the performance of these ships that a demand developed for faster, more regular, and more evenly scheduled voyages.

The advantages of a full-bodied, sharp-ended, fast carrier in the China trade were thus becoming apparent to both shipowners and merchants, for the cargoes in this trade were generally bulky, though light in weight. But it was also apparent that sharp ends, if carried to extremes, would reduce cargo capacity as effectively as sharp deadrise and would produce an equally uneconomic ship. The question that plagued designers and owners alike was: how much cargo capacity could be given up to obtain speed in the China trade and still have a profitable vessel? Trial and error alone would establish the answer and owners would proceed in the experiment with utmost caution.

Had no other important trade appeared, the China trade would probably not have created the large, extreme clipper ships of the 1850's in America. But the discovery of gold in California in 1849 created boom conditions in American sea trade, which were further intensified by the late-1850 Australian gold discoveries that led to the great five-year immigration, which began in early 1851.

During 1850, orders for large, very fast, sailing ships began to be placed with builders of proven skill, but time was required to build a ship, and few of the large clippers were launched that year. In the meantime the gold rushes continued to expand trade, and with fast-rising freight and passenger rates, the demand for ships skyrocketed. Available China and old North Atlantic packets were diverted to the New York- or Boston-to-San-Francisco run and all manner of craft were impressed to carry freight and gold seekers to the gold fields.

As passenger and freight rates continued to rise steadily toward unheard of levels, difficulties arose for many ship owners who had been reluctant and slow to gamble the large sum necessary to build a large, fast clipper that could only be profitable in a high freight and passenger rate trade where dispatch was an absolute requirement. The desire of shippers and passengers alike was to reach the gold strikes as soon as possible, so the old slow-sailing ocean freighters began to find they could not demand high rates, soon after the first few months of the gold rush.

As a result, orders for a steadily increasing number of new, large, fast ships began to be placed in shipyards; the emphasis was now on speed and the clipper was in increasing demand.

On 9 June 1850, William Webb launched *Celestial*, his first clipper ship, intended for the *China* trade. She was registered as 158 feet by 34 feet by 19 feet and only 860 tons. Her offset tables show that she actually measured 158′ 9″ on deck, from stem rabbet to centerline of rudderpost; 35′ 8″ moulded beam; and 20′ 6″ moulded depth from underside of main deck at side to inner rabbet of the keel at ⚓. Her lines are shown in Plate 102.

Celestial was praised as a very handsome ship, but more importantly she proved fast and profitable. She engaged mostly in the tea trade, being too small to be employed very long on the California run in competition with much larger ships.

Celestial had a moderate sheer, rising somewhat sharply over her bow rake; her keel was deep amidships but less at the ends, giving a marked rocker in the shoe. The stem rabbet was curved where it met the straight keel rabbet, raking forward in nearly a straight line until above the load line and then flaring forward from just below deck-level to the rails. The post had little rake. The square stern was formed in the round-tuck style, with the cross seam showing marked deadrise, and upper-and-lower transoms, strongly raked—the lower transom was very small. The entrance was quite short and rather full and convex except near the stem, where from load line down there was slight hollow. The run was rather short; the quarterbeam buttock became straight a little forward of its intersection with the after load line. The main rail, in the half-breadth plan, showed some hollow at the stem, somewhat as in *Witch*.

The midsection was formed with a moderate rise of straight floor, a full, round bilge, with marked tumble home in topsides. The flare in the forward sections in the body plan was great, but less extreme than in *Witch*.

On a moulded load line of 152′ 6″ the *Celestial* had a moulded displacement of 1388.1 long tons. Her coefficients were body .56, midship .84, and prismatic .67. The effective length of the quarterbeam buttock was 130′ 6″, camber 14′ 2″, giving a camber-length ratio of 9.2.

An examination of Plate 102 and of Plate 97 (*Sea Witch*) might lead to interesting speculations as to the influence of Griffiths' theories on Webb, or on *Celestial's* owners, for there are similarities in the designs of these two ships. Unfortunately there is no other documentary evidence to guide speculation on this matter. Webb's design had a longer and perhaps a better-formed run, but Griffiths' clipper had the sharper entrance. Comparisons of these two ships show that Webb's was a little more conservative in design than Griffiths'.

Contrary to much that has been written on the subject, the designs of

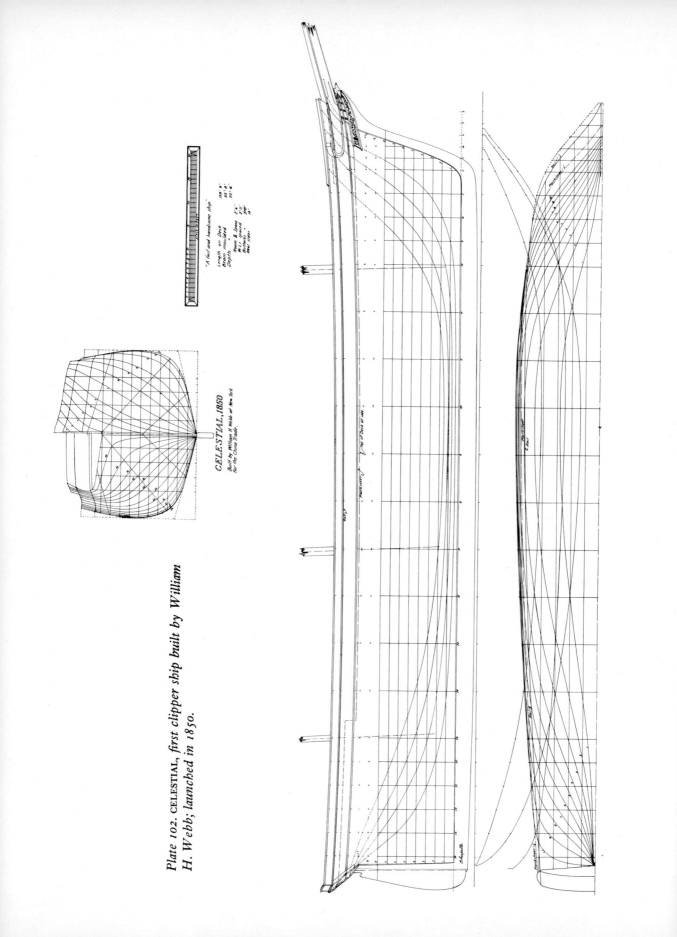

Plate 102. CELESTIAL, *first clipper ship built by William H. Webb; launched in 1850.*

CELESTIAL, 1850

Built by William H. Webb at New York
for the China Trade.

Griffiths, Webb, and McKay had a lot in common and there was no important difference in opinion among these designers as to basic characteristics of hull form—a matter that will be discussed later in more detail.

Of the other New York and Boston built clippers launched in 1850, we have scant basis for judgment. It is perhaps true that a few were clippers, but there is no reliable evidence available to establish which were clippers in the accepted sense.

During the 1840's New England merchants, with few exceptions, had not shown interest in fast freighters. The exceptions were those merchants who owned packet vessels and some others who had small vessels built for the opium and coffee trades. On this basis, it has been an historical assumption that New Englanders were backward in building clipper ships in the early 1850's. The launching dates of clippers in 1850, however, show this assumption to be unsound.

Lines of two large New England built clippers of 1850 survive. One was *Staghound*, designed and built by Donald McKay—his first clipper. McKay had begun building at Newburyport in a partnership, as Currier & McKay, in 1841. In 1842 the yard built the noted coffee carrier *Courier*, of 380 tons, perhaps a sharp model. In 1843 McKay changed partners and built as McKay & Pickett. Late in 1844 he dissolved that partnership and removed to East Boston where he began building as the sole owner of the yard; his first ship under this arrangement was the packet *Washington Irving*. By 1850 McKay had built 13 packets and four ocean freighters, and had achieved a local reputation for sound design and construction.

Before building *Staghound*, McKay gave an interview to a reporter of the Boston *Atlas*, published on 26 August 1850, in which he declared that he was familiar with all clipper models and showed the half-model of the *Staghound*, but misstated the proposed design's dimensions. Her register dimensions were 215′ by 39′ 8″ by 21 feet. Her lines, Plate IX, were drawn from McKay's half-model take-off in the Clark collection, which was on a quarter-inch to one foot scale. It was also checked against a complete set of lines on an eighth-inch to one foot scale in the same collection and against the contemporary lines published by Griffiths in his magazine. These show her to have measured 210 feet between perpendiculars, 39 feet moulded beam, and 21′ 3″ moulded depth. On a 21-foot draft her moulded load waterline length was 203′ 9″, her moulded displacement then being 1964.1 long tons. Her coefficients were block .46, midship .71, and prismatic .64. The effective length of her quarterbeam buttock was 153′ 8″, camber 14 feet, giving a camber-length ratio of 10.9.

Staghound had a graceful sheer, straight keel, no drag, a rather upright but flaring stem rabbet, slight rake to the post, with a round, counter stern. Her entrance was long, convex, and sharp with only a vestige of hollow near the forefoot. The run was long and very fine with the quarterbeam buttock straight for some distance forward of its intersection with the after load line. In the run there seems to have been only a trace of hollow at the heel of the sternpost. She had a staghound for a figurehead with a scroll from its feet to around the hawse holes, with no trailboards or head rails—only the planksheer moulding being carried out to the back of the figurehead, by means of knees and moulding filler pieces.

Her midsection was formed with a rising, straight floor, and her deadrise was great compared with that of *Celestial, Sea Witch, Oriental,* or *Rainbow.* The turn of the bilge was easy and the tumble home slight. The flare forward was moderate.

The *Staghound* proved to be a fast ship but in spite of her greater size, her form made her a poor carrier compared to *Oriental* and other of the earlier fast ships.

She was not the first New England built clipper to be launched in 1850, for she was not launched until 7 December, having been laid down in August. Because there are so few half-models or plans of ships built in this year, it is impossible to determine how many could be classed as clippers. Certainly there were a few sharp-model ships launched in New England during the year. One of these was *Surprise,* launched in October, whose lines exist.

Surprise, Plate 103, was built by Samuel Hall, then one of the leading New England shipbuilders. Samuel Hartt Pook, the son of Naval Constructor Samuel Pook, was employed by Hall and has commonly been credited with her design. Hall took exception to this in a letter to a Boston newspaper and claimed Pook had designed the ship under his detailed supervision and that he had determined what characteristics the ship should have. It is a well-known fact, however, that the man who drew the lines, or made the half-model, was the hull designer and his work determined her level of performance. It may be added that Pook had the lines of *Surprise* in his possession when he became a naval constructor. This plan is now in the Records of the Bureau of Construction & Repair, U.S. Navy, in the National Archives, in Washington, D.C.

The lines, shown in Plate 103, were drawn from this plan. The register

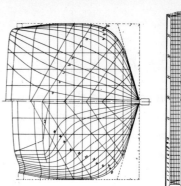

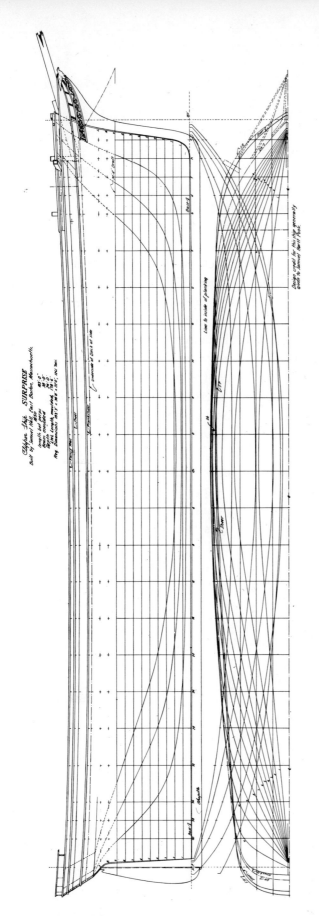

Plate 103. SURPRISE, *designed by Samuel Hartt Pook, built in 1850. A successful combination of carrier and clipper.*

dimensions of this clipper were 183' 3" by 38' 8" by 22 feet. The lines show that she actually measured 183 feet between perpendiculars, 38 feet moulded beam, and 24 feet moulded depth. Her designed load draft was 20' 6": The moulded load line was then 178' 6" long, her moulded displacement was 2549.9 long tons, and her coefficients were: block .73, midship .81, prismatic .82. The effective length of her quarterbeam buttock was 154' 10", camber 15' 8", making the camber-length ratio 9.8. She had a large displacement for her length.

Surprise had a moderate sheer, straight keel, no drag, rather upright stem rabbet flaring forward a little above the load line. The sternpost raked slightly and the stern was a round short counter that had become common in American sailing ships in the late 1840's, probably adapted from steamships. The entrance of *Surprise* was of moderate length, convex, with only slight hollow in the waterlines near the forefoot. The run was long and fine with but slight hollow near the post below the load line. The quarterbeam buttock was straight for a short distance forward of its crossing of the after load line. The flare of the forward sections in the body plan was moderate. The midship section was formed with a rising, straight floor and a full, rounded bilge with small tumble home in the topside.

This ship, shorter than *Staghound*, was considered to have been a good carrier and a fast sailer, with a number of rapid passages to her credit. She was a handsome ship with an eagle in flight as her figurehead and the seal of the State of New York on her stern. This ship was really a medium or half-clipper, of great depth in proportion to length.

Other ships launched in New England during 1850 that may have been clippers were *Gamecock*, a possible; *Sea Serpent*, highly probable; and *Witchcraft*, probable. The latter was modeled by Pook, but *Gamecock* was claimed by Samuel Hall.

At New York *Eclipse* and *White Squall* were apparently clippers and some of the Baltimore-built ships and barks may have had claims to the clipper classification. Without half-models, however, there is uncertainty, for contemporary writers applied the term "clipper" very loosely, as the evidence of some half-models and lines drawings have shown.

In the next year, however, it is possible to class a large number of ships as clippers with certainty. On 5 May 1851 Webb launched *Challenge*, an extreme clipper and apparently then the largest merchant ship afloat; which she was for a very short time, at least, and by a very narrow margin. Her registered dimensions were 230′ 6″ by 43′ 2″ by 26 feet, 2006.51 register tons. She is shown on Plates X and 104. A rigged model is in the Museum of History and Technology, Smithsonian Institution, and lines and spar plan were published by Webb. *Challenge* had a huge eagle in flight as a figurehead and a vine and scroll on her round stern. At the time of her launch, Webb had the extreme clippers *Comet* and *Gazelle* on the stocks, also the medium clippers *Invincible* and *Swordfish* under construction. *Comet* was a few inches longer than *Challenge* but with less beam and depth.

Webb's offset tables for *Challenge* show the ship was 227′ 4″ on deck, 42′ 4″ moulded beam, and 26′ 5″ moulded depth, base line to underside of deck at side. Since the offsets show the ship as laid down, and are the most reliable guide in judging size, it is again evident that the tonnage measurements cannot be relied upon.

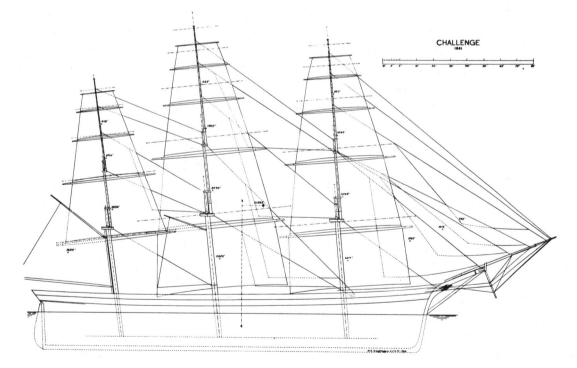

Plate 104. Webb's spar plan of CHALLENGE, *1851, showing enlarged rig in broken lines (lines and inboard profile and deck layout, Plate X).*

Challenge was practically flush-decked, having only a very short poop about 25 feet long. A very handsome ship, as can be seen by the plans, she had slight but graceful sheer, straight keel with no drag, rather upright but flaring stem rabbet, nearly upright post, round counter stern, with a long, sharp, concave entrance, and a long and very fine run. The quarterbeam buttock was straight for a short distance forward of its intersection with the after load line. The midsection was formed with straight, rising floor; the deadrise was about 33 inches at the fourth buttock out. The bilge was well-rounded, with marked tumble home in the topside. There was no dead-flat amidships, though there was some shoulder in the upper waterlines just forward of the midsection.

The rig plan, shown in Plate 104, illustrates the designed rig as Webb intended and the much larger rig the master and owners required him to use. As a result she came out a very lofty-rigged ship and very much "overhatted" or oversparred. Her first voyage was disappointing, probably due to this as well as to the voyage having been made at the poor time of year for fast passages. *Challenge* could sail very fast, and held at least one record passage, but she had few opportunities to show her paces and had a number of misfortunes. After having had her rig twice reduced and having once been totally dismasted, she was sold to English owners.

The rig of *Challenge* illustrates the ship designers' occasional difficulties with owners and their favorite captains. It was a long-standing practice for some owners to relieve a master of a command and place him as an inspector or agent in the shipyard where the owner was having a ship built. It was said that one such captain initialed every timber that went into the ship! It was not uncommon for the master to usurp the designing of the rig, as Waterman did in *Challenge*, and this usually resulted in oversparring. In a few instances the owner or master attempted to model the ship, usually with disastrous results.

In the case of the building of *Rainbow*, the controlling owner, feeling that the improvements in her model should be accompanied by the best possible rig, wrote to authorities in England to obtain their recommendations. In the meantime, as the building of the ship progressed, it became necessary to place the mast partners and steps, and this was done by Smith and Griffiths. When the "expert" recommendations arrived it was too late to change, so the ship's rig remained as designed. Smith & Dimon did not inform the owner of this, however, so he firmly believed that much of the success of *Rainbow* was due to his having obtained the advice of foreign experts.*

There are stories such as the one told about shipmaster Nathaniel Palmer "whittling out a half-model" during a voyage and carrying it ashore "in his pocket." These are mere fables. The half-model required to design a clipper would have to be at least four or five feet long. Anything pocket-size would be too small in scale to be accurate enough for taking off offsets. Also the investment required to build a clipper ship generally discouraged the use of amateur talent in design.

The *Challenge*, on a moulded load line 221′ 6″, had a moulded displacement of 2204.4 long tons. Her coefficients were block .46, midship .77, and prismatic .60. The effective length of the quarterbeam buttock was 166 feet, camber 15′ 2″, giving a camber-length ratio of 10.9.

Challenge was Webb's most extreme clipper design, with *Gazelle* a close second. But the latter, a sharp-deadrise model, was disclaimed by Webb because her design was dictated by the owners. Each ship—whose lines and sail plan he later published with printed comments—had terse annotations on her offset table as well. *Gazelle* was an inferior example of sharp-deadrise hull form because she was too full in the run to permit a very high potential speed. She was far from a complete failure, however, for she made a number of good passages.

Swordfish, a very successful ship launched in 1851, was called a "medium clipper" in Webb's book; he annotated her offset table "not a clipper." Yet her published plan shows her to have been a rather sharp-ended ship having some hollow in her entrance at the load line and below, with fine, long run and with quarterbeam buttock straight for a short distance forward of its intersection with the after load line. She had little rise of straight floor and was a full-midsection ship. She was small for her class, being only 170 feet on deck. She proved to be very fast, and hence had a better right to be called "clipper" than some of the more well-known designs.

Comet, shown in Plates XI and 105, was launched in 1851 and became one of Webb's most successful clippers. With *Young America*, launched in 1853, *Comet* was an exceptional passage-maker and regularly outsailed ships in company. Both vessels were capable of maintaining relatively high speed in any sailing weather.

Comet had moderate sheer, a straight keel with no drag, a rather upright,

* "Story of the Masting of Clipper Ship Rainbow," *Nautical Magazine and Naval Gazette*, Vol. VI (April 1857–September 1857), pp. 52–53.

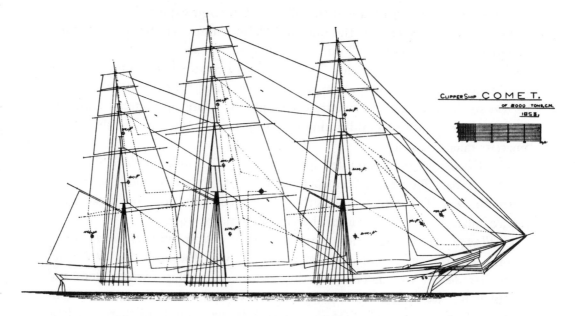

Plate 105. Webb's spar plan for the clipper ship COMET.

somewhat flaring stem rabbet, nearly upright post, a long, sharp, concave entrance, with no apparent shoulder in the upper waterlines forward of the midsection. The run was long, and very fine in the lower waterlines; the quarterbeam buttock became straight well forward of its intersection with the load line. The midsection, placed 90 feet abaft the stem rabbet on the load line (at 21′ 6″ draft) was formed with very moderate rise of short, straight floor extended by a long gentle sweep into a well-rounded bilge with a curved tumble home in the topside.

The rig, as shown in Webb's book and reproduced here in Plate 105, was well proportioned. *Comet* had many fast passages to her credit and held the record of 76 days, 7 hours, from San Francisco to New York and 35 days, 6 hours, from San Francisco to Cape Horn. As the decorative model of this vessel shows, she was a ship of great beauty, with very restrained decoration. This model, which was donated by William H. Webb to the Smithsonian Institution's Museum of History and Technology, shows the general deck arrangement. Originally it was mounted on a mirror. A similar model of the *Young America*, given by the builder, is also in the same Museum.

COMET
Clippership built by William H. Webb at New York in 1851.

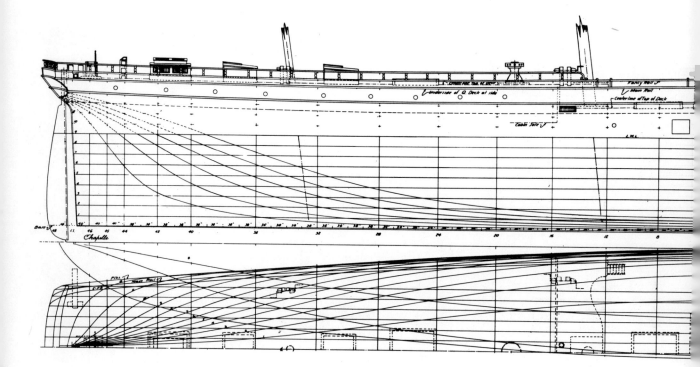
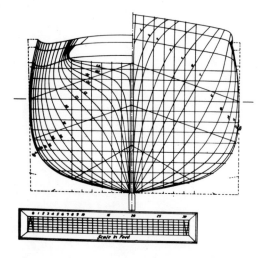

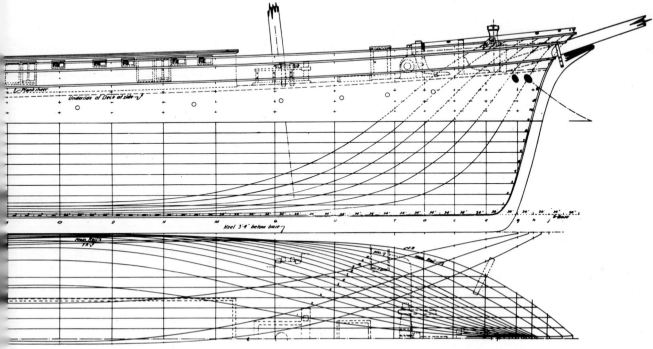

Length on the Main Deck   228´·3˝
Beam, moulded,   41´·0˝
Depth at side, moulded,   22´·10½˝

PLATE XI. *Lines of the clipper ship* COMET, *a noted passage-maker and a good all-around sailer. Her deep keel, outside the rabbet, undoubtedly helped her in going to windward. The variation in frame spacing, from 30 to 40 inches, was a feature in Webb's design of clippers* (COMET's *spar plan, Plate 105*).

WILD PIGEON

Built by George Raynes at Portsmouth N.H. 1851

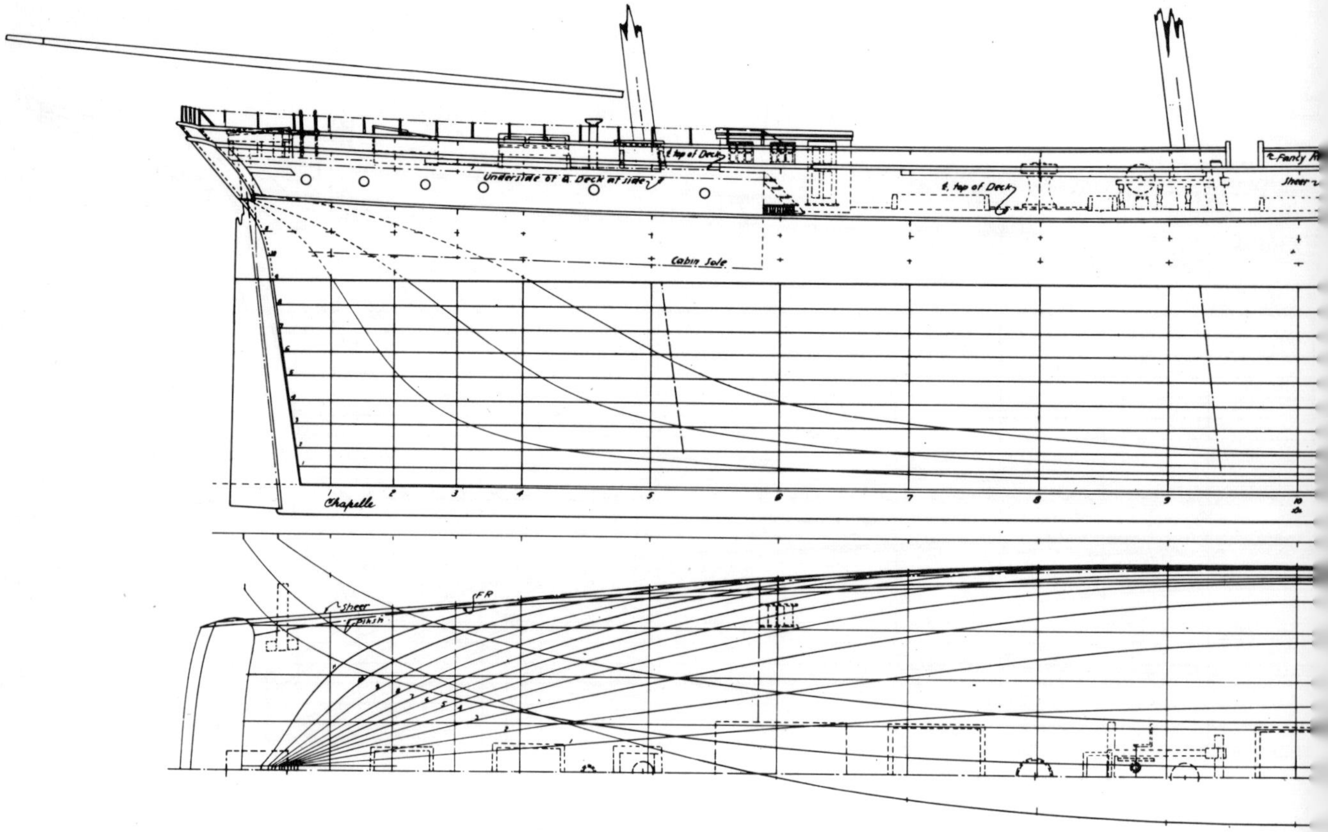

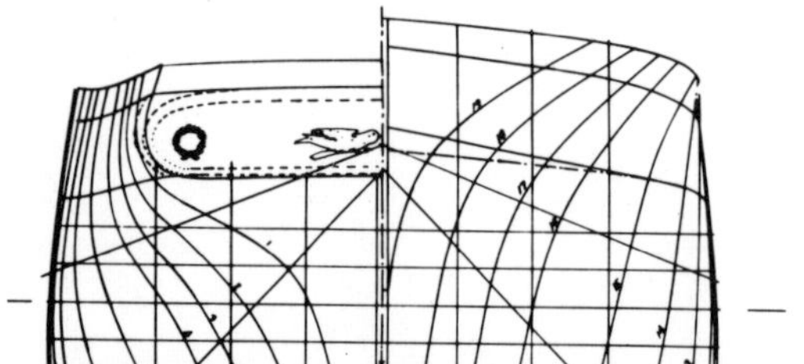

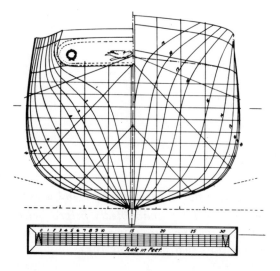

Spars

Masts	Dia.	Whole length	Head	Yards	Dia.	Whole length	Arms
Fore	29"	79'	13'	Fore	18"	67'	$4\frac{1}{2}$'
Top	$15\frac{1}{2}$"	45'	8'	Top	$14\frac{1}{2}$"	55'	5'
Topgal't	11"	24'	0'	Topgalt	10"	38'	14'
Royal	9"	15'	0'	Royal	7"	$25\frac{1}{4}$'	$2\frac{1}{4}$'
Skysail	7"	11'	pole $2\frac{1}{2}$'	Skysail	$4\frac{1}{2}$"	21'	$1\frac{1}{2}$'
Main	30"	85'	$13\frac{1}{2}$'	Main	$19\frac{3}{4}$"	76'	$4\frac{1}{4}$'
Top	16"	47'	$8\frac{1}{2}$'	Top	16"	61'	5'
Topgal't	11"	26'	0'	Topgal't	$10\frac{1}{2}$"	41'	$3\frac{1}{2}$'
Royal	$9\frac{1}{2}$"	$16\frac{1}{2}$'	0'	Royal	$7\frac{1}{2}$"	$27\frac{1}{4}$'	$2\frac{1}{4}$'
Skysail	$7\frac{1}{2}$"	12'	pole 3	Skysail	5"	23'	$1\frac{1}{2}$'
Mizzen	24"	73'	$11\frac{1}{2}$'	Crossjack	15"	56'	$3\frac{1}{2}$
Top	$13\frac{1}{2}$"	36'	7'	Top	11"	44'	4'
Topgal't	9"	20'	0'	Topgal't	8"	$27\frac{3}{4}$'	$2\frac{1}{2}$'
Royal	7"	12'	0'	Royal	$5\frac{1}{2}$"	$21\frac{3}{4}$'	$1\frac{1}{2}$'
Skysail	5"	9'	pole $2\frac{1}{4}$	Skysail	$3\frac{1}{4}$"	18'	1

Bowsprit 28" dia. 28' outside bitts-
Jibboom and flying jibboom in one, divided at 18' and 15' outside of cap; 6' pole
Spanker boom 51', 3' pole, gaff 40', 7' pole.
Main Spencer 24', Fore Spencer 26'.

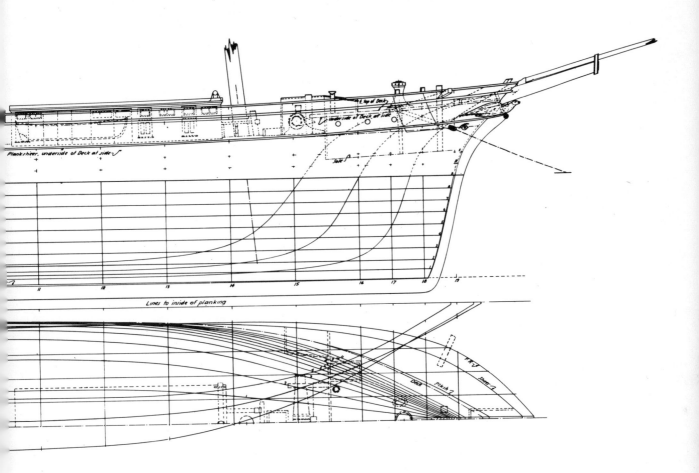

Length at main deck level, 170′6″
Beam, moulded. 35′4″
Depth, moulded, at side 22′4″

PLATE XII. *Medium clipper* WILD PIGEON, *reputed a good sailer in light winds and a profitable carrier; built at Portsmouth, New Hampshire, in 1851.*

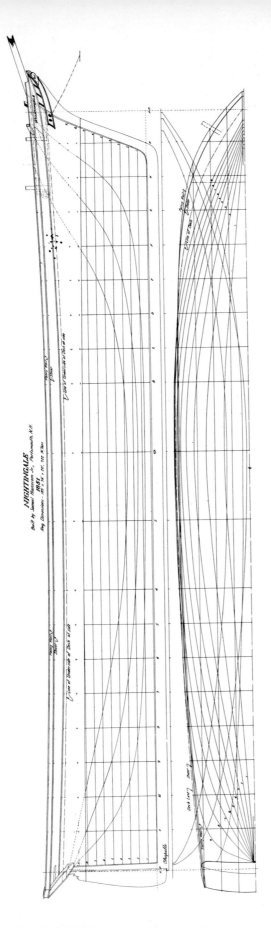

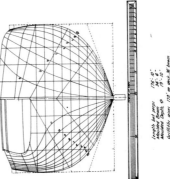

Plate 106. Lines of extreme clipper NIGHTINGALE, considered a very fast ship. She was a slaver in 1860.

Comet's registered dimensions were 228 feet by 40′ 4″ by 22 feet, but her offset table shows her to have been 228′ 3″ on the main deck, 41 feet moulded beam, and 22′ 10½″ moulded depth, rabbet to underside of deck at side, at midsection.

On a moulded load waterline of 223′ 6″ her moulded displacement at 21′ 4″ draft was 2476.8 long tons. Her coefficients were block .53, midsection .84, and prismatic .63. The effective length of the quarterbeam buttock was 179′ 4″, camber 16′ 3″, giving a camber-length ratio of 11.0.

A clipper having very sharp deadrise was launched 16 June 1851 at Portsmouth, New Hampshire. This was the *Nightingale*, designed and built by Samuel Hanscom, Jr., and intended to transport Americans to London's great industrial exhibition and to take very little freight. The builder was unable to complete the vessel for her intended use, and she was sold as a trader. After a rather disappointing maiden voyage she was tuned-up and became a very fast sailer employed in the English tea trade. She was much admired for her beauty, and was considered by some contemporary authorities to have been the fastest American vessel in the tea trade and one of the fastest in the American merchant marine. She eventually went in the slave trade but after her capture she returned to freighting.

Her lines are shown in Plate 106. She measured 176′ 10″ between perpendiculars, 34′ 6″ moulded beam, and 19′ 10″ moulded depth at midsection. These lines seem to agree with the 1/10-inch to one foot scale lines plan published by Griffiths. Plate 106 may have been based on that plan. The customhouse dimensions of this ship were 185 feet by 36 feet by 20 feet and Griffiths stated that she measured 178 feet on deck, 36 feet extreme beam, and 20 feet in hold. Griffiths' dimensions were probably taken from the register and the difference in length may have been an error in transcription.

Nightingale had a rather straight sheer, straight keel (the vessel was trimmed to sail with a slight drag), rather straight raking stem rabbet with moderate flare above the load line, upright post, round tuck, and upper-and-lower transoms. The entrance was long, convex, and sharp, with no hollow in the forefoot. The run was long and fine, with no hollow in the lower level lines. The quarterbeam buttock became straight well forward of its intersection with the after load line.

The midsection was formed with sharply rising, very short straight floor; the bilge formed with a very long sweep to the load line, hardening slightly as the sweep rose. A curved tumble home formed the topside.

On a moulded load waterline of 171′ 6″, the moulded displacement was about 1316.8 long tons. The coefficients were block .54, midship .74, and prismatic .67. The effective length of the quarterbeam buttock was 147′ 6″ and camber 12′ 8″, giving a camber-length ratio of 11.6.

This ship was a better example of the sharp deadrise model than Webb's *Gazelle*, because of her well-formed ends. As a carrier, *Nightingale* was less economic for her size, however, than *Gazelle*. Many maritime historians have stated that the sharp-deadrise model was replaced by the full-body, fine-ends model as a matter of improvement in speed and in the progress of hull design. It will become apparent, however, that the choice was not made upon any such grounds, but rather by trade conditions. As a result, the sharp-deadrise model was never fully replaced in the clipper type of ship.

George Raynes launched a clipper ship named *Wild Pigeon* at Portsmouth, New Hampshire, during the late summer of 1851. Her registered dimensions were 178 feet by 35 feet by 20 feet, 996 register tons. Plate XII shows this vessel; the lines were taken by the late Carl C. Cutler from the builder's half-model. *Wild Pigeon* was a very handsome ship, as can be readily seen, but she was not an extreme clipper. Rather, she was a good carrier with sharp but short ends that would not allow a high potential speed for her length. Yet she was reputed to be a fast sailer in light and moderate winds and could stay alongside some very fast ships in such weather. She appears in the sailing records for only two passages—a 59-day run in 1858 from Pisagua, Bolivia, to anchor in New York, and a 50-day run from Talcahuano, Chile, to New York in 1860.*

Wild Pigeon had a moderate amount of sheer, straight keel, slightly raking but flaring stem rabbet, angular forefoot, raking post, short counter stern, sharp, convex, rather long entrance with full buttock-bow lines, and no hollow in lower waterlines. The run was formed also with no hollow in the lower waterlines and was not long, but the buttock lines, though steep, were straight, or very nearly so, at their intersections with the after load lines and much reverse curve above these. The midsection was formed with moderately rising, straight floor, well-rounded bilge, and slightly curved tumble home above.

The actual measurements of the ship were 170′ 6″ length on the main deck level, 35′ 4″ moulded beam, and 22′ 4″ moulded depth to deck. On a moulded

---

* Carl C. Cutler, *Five Hundred Sailing Records of American Built Ships* (Mystic, Connecticut, The Marine Historical Society, 1952).

Lithograph of clipper ship NIGHTINGALE.

load waterline of 164′ 9″ she had a moulded displacement of 1594.2 long tons (19′ 6″ draft), and her coefficients were block .56, midsection .82, and prismatic .69. The effective length of the quarterbeam buttock was 137′ 10″ and the camber 14′ 10″, giving a camber-length ratio of 9.3. This was another attempt to design a fast vessel of the clipper type with fair capacity for her dimensions.

Oculi were used as decoration on this and at least one other of the Raynes-built clippers. Since the vessels had been intended for the China trade these were appropriate decorations.

The Raynes masterpiece, however, was the beautiful and very fast *Witch of the Wave*, also launched in the spring of 1851. This was an extreme clipper 204′ 6″ between perpendiculars (about 220 feet on the main rail), 39′ 8″ moulded beam, and 21 feet depth of hold. She had inner and outer stems as in *Oriental.* Her ornate figurehead was carved with a sea shell as a canopy over it; the figure was a young woman in "flowing vestments of white, fringed with gold, bearing aloft a scarph, half unfurled in the breeze." Branches of gold descended from her feet to encircle the hawse holes. She had eyes "glowering" from each bow. At the stern Venus was shown in a shell drawn by dolphins, with an imp riding a dolphin on the port side and with "members of the finny family" on the starboard side. Name and hail in gold were above this with a star on each side and a wreath of roses below, all enclosed in a gilded frame. She was painted black, with a red line or "boot top" above her copper, which was up to 18′ 9″ forward and 19′ 3″ aft. She was splendidly fitted below deck for passengers and highly finished throughout.

Plate XIII shows this fine ship; she had moderate sheer, straight keel (she was apparently expected to have a little drag as can be seen by the way she was coppered), strongly raking and flaring stem rabbet, nearly vertical post, short counter, transom stern, long, sharp straight entrance, with no hollow in the lower level lines (all her forward level lines become straight in the approach to the stem), long, easy run with the quarterbeam buttock coming straight forward of its intersection with the load line and with reverse curve above. The midsection had much rise in the straight floor, a well-rounded, rather easy turn of the bilge and a rounded tumble-home topside. This vessel can be classed as a compromise between the sharply rising-floor model of the Baltimore-clipper type and the rather flat full-body-fine-ends model. This compromise class would include *Staghound,* for example.

Witch of the Wave was 195′ 3″ long on her moulded load waterline (20-foot draft); her moulded displacement was 1911.9 long tons. Her coefficients were block .51, midship .71, and prismatic .66. The effective length of her quarterbeam buttock was 157 feet, camber 13′ 8″, giving a camber-length ratio of 11.4. She was 204′ 6″ between perpendiculars, 39′ 8″ moulded beam, and 24 feet moulded depth to planksheer.

This ship was a very good passage-maker, appearing five times in Cutler's list of Sailing Records, which might indicate consistence in performance and an ability to sail well in most weather conditions and in most company.

By the end of 1851 a number of large clipper ships were on order or under construction in the yards of builders who would become prominent in clipper ship design or building. Hence, this is an appropriate place to discuss the state of ship design in these yards. It is true, unfortunately, that today some of these designers and builders are not represented by enough half-models

Woodcut of American clipper ship WITCH OF THE WAVE.

or plans—some by none—to allow a comprehensive examination of the subject. Nevertheless enough evidence survives to permit conclusions concerning the design practices of some of the most prominent shipbuilders and designers.

Griffiths is the most informative, for his books on shipbuilding and design express his opinions very fully, with later ideas expounded in his *Nautical Magazine*.* In spite of this, his principles have been misstated by most American maritime historians. In Griffiths' *Treatise on the Theory and Practice of Shipbuilding* (1851–57) he made it abundantly clear that he considered a long, sharp, and hollow entrance necessary for speed, and recommended that the section of greatest area,$\bowtie$, be placed abaft the midlength of the load line. He also recommended that the midsection have floors that were flat, or nearly so, and a full body, but that the ends of the ship were

* *The U.S. Nautical Magazine and Naval Journal* (1853–55) and *The Monthly Nautical Magazine and Quarterly Review* (1855–57).

to be fine. The position of the midsection tended to make the run short, with rather steep buttocks, often rounded all the way up to, and above, the load line. As his theories developed he came to the conclusion that with a fine, very hollow entrance, a short full run was proper; on the other hand a full, convex entrance required a long, fine run. He was unalterably opposed to the latter combination, however. He also opposed wall-sided, very hard-bilged, flat-floor hulls, as well as the Baltimore clipper model.

It may appear odd that Griffiths was so committed to a short, full run with steep, rounded buttocks, when his great successes—*Rainbow* and *Sea Witch* —had fine runs and straight buttocks. Griffiths thus seems to have rationalized his theories to a degree that they completely overrode his powers of observation. He arrived at other conclusions—correct or incorrect—that length was important in a ship designed for speed; that deckhouses produced undesirable effects in windage and on stability; that a rough bottom greatly hindered speed; the totally erroneous one that stability was obtained only in the midbody, "not in any degree by the ends"; that Beaufoy's experiments in resistance (in which ship forms were not tested) were useless; that catamarans were of very little value; that an increase in sharpness in steamer hulls did not necessarily insure lower power requirements; that a boat was usually closer winded with one sail than with two; and that in designing the sail plan, balance of rig and hull was possible by mathematics, and that the position of the center of buoyancy was directly involved. Following this line of reasoning, he recommended that the center of effort (or "center of propulsion") should be forward of the center of buoyancy, and the center of buoyancy should be abaft the middle of the load waterline; the center of lateral plane (center of gravity of the underwater hull profile) should be abaft the center of buoyancy. It was to his credit that so many of these conclusions were proved correct by modern standards.

As a writer he left much to be desired, being prone to such metaphorical excesses as "The silent foot fall of time has thrust us across the threshold of an era in which the car of lightning mounts its frictionless wheels and is spurred onward by commercial enterprise."*

After Griffiths left Smith & Dimon he designed few sailing vessels and turned his interest to steamships. He designed some large sidewheelers, including a number of large coastal vessels such as *Keystone State, Georgia,*

* John W. Griffiths, *Treatise on the Theory and Practice of Shipbuilding,* p. 97.

John L. Stevens, Kamschatka (a large man-of-war steamer for Russia), as well as the sloop-of-war *Pawnee* for the United States Navy.

In 1853 Griffiths published his second book, *The Shipbuilder's Manual and Nautical Referee*, a less pretentious work than his *Treatise on the Theory and Practice of Shipbuilding*.

About 1853 Griffiths went into partnership with W. W. Bates, son of S. Bates of Manitowoc, Wisconsin, a prominent Great Lakes shipbuilder. As Griffiths, Bates & Co., or Griffiths & Bates, they published *The U.S. Nautical Magazine and Naval Journal*, beginning in 1853. In 1855 this also appeared as *The Monthly Nautical Magazine and Quarterly Review*, with the numbering of the volumes changed. This magazine was published monthly until September 1857, and has been a very useful technical reference for the whole clipper ship era. Griffiths remained active in ship design until into the 1870's, publishing a two-volume work, *The Progressive Shipbuilder*, in 1875. Strongly opinionated, and contentious, he was nevertheless an important contributor to the development of American naval architecture. He held patents on a wood-bending machine and constructed two ships with bent frames.

In order to show his theories in practice, the lines of an 1851 clipper ship designed for German owners are shown in Plate 107. Her name has not yet been established. The original drawing is now in the Griffiths collection in the Smithsonian's Museum of History and Technology.

The design is for a full-midsection clipper ship, 180' 6" on the L.W.L., 34' 9" moulded beam, and 21 feet moulded depth, rabbet to deck at side. The vessel had a graceful sheer, straight keel, but with slight rocker near the forefoot, and no drag. The stem rabbet raked and flared moderately, the post was upright, the stern was formed with a short overhang—the knuckle line of which was not carried forward very far.

The entrance was long, sharp, and convex; the midship section was abaft midlength of the load line. The run was short and full. The quarterbeam buttock was carried in a curve to and above the after load line and then reversed. The midship section was formed with very slight deadrise, a well-rounded bilge, and slight tumble home. The flare in the forward sections in the body plan was marked but much less extreme than in *Sea Witch*. The lines have not been refaired but are traced from the original.

On a moulded load line of 180' 6", drawing 16' 10", her moulded displacement was 1424.8 long tons. Her coefficients were block .58, midship .89, and prismatic .65. Effective length of quarterbeam buttock was 138' 6", camber

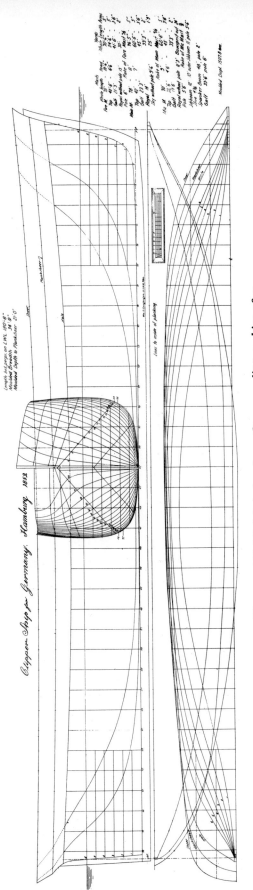

Plate 107. Griffiths' design for a German clipper ship; 1851.

13 feet, giving a camber-length ratio of 10.7.

William Webb can be judged only by his designs, for his publishing was confined to the two-volume book of plans that he produced privately after his retirement. Some of the plans included were drawn from offset tables by Griffiths and by Charles P. Kunhardt.* In addition, the Webb mould-loft offset book has survived and this allows drawing lines of many ships that Webb did not publish. However, offsets or plans do not exist for vessels he designed that were subcontracted to other builders for construction.

His clipper ships were *Celestial, Comet, Challenge, Invincible, Gazelle, Swordfish, Flying Dutchman, Young America,* and *Flyaway;* all of these

Mexican revenue cutter built by William Webb in 1851.

---

* Charles P. Kunhardt, Naval Academy graduate in 1870, later yachting editor of *Field & Stream* magazine. Lost at sea in 1889.

were fast, well-built ships. Lines and sail plans for all except *Celestial* were published by Webb.

Webb believed in a full midsection and fine ends, but after 1851 his designs were not extremely sharp-ended and they had only moderate hollow in the entrance. Unlike Griffiths, however, Webb retained a long, clean run, with some straightness in the quarterbeam buttocks, in all of his clippers and medium clippers. He placed the section of largest area, ⚌, slightly forward of the middle of the load line, and after *Challenge* he used moderate deadrise— except in *Gazelle* for which, as has been said, he did not take full responsibility.

He attempted to retain sufficient cargo capacity to make his clippers reasonably profitable. His record as a shipbuilder shows him to have been extremely versatile in design; turning out fine steamers and small vessels, as well as packets, clippers, and freighters in great number. Apparently his interest in ship designs was not confined to one type. His vessels were all very well built. He employed much metal strapping and showed an example of this in the plan of *Ocean Monarch* among his published designs. Webb endowed the school now known as the Webb Institute of Naval Architecture, one of the leading professional schools of its kind.

Donald McKay has suffered at the hands of over-enthusiastic New England maritime historians who have claimed that all of the ships he built between 1850 and 1858 were clippers, extreme clippers, or medium clippers, and that all were very fast. Their designer has been hailed as a genius who dominated his profession during the clipper ship era. Dissenting from this idea, one New England maritime historian* accused McKay of being a publicity-seeker whose ships were uneconomic, over-rated, and ugly.

Donald McKay was a capable designer of ships that were generally successful. He was probably not as versatile as Webb, and certainly he was not as good a business manager. In his most successful ships McKay used size— particularly length—to obtain sustained speed in strong winds. McKay seems to have been uncertain as to what hull form to use for a given trade. In his four Australian packets, he ranged from the very sharp *Lightning* to the very full-ended *Donald McKay*—all for the same weather conditions and courses. *Sovereign of the Seas* and *Flying Cloud*, his earlier clippers—both successful in the Cape Horn run—were sharp; therefore it would seem logical for all the Australian packets to have also been sharp-ended.

* William Armstrong Fairburn, *Merchant Sail* (Center Lovell, Maine, Fairburn Marine Educational Foundation, Inc., 1945–1955, six vols.).

The evidence dealing with McKay's designs is peculiar in that so many of the surviving plans of his ships are on ⅛-inch to one-foot scale. Most of these are in the United States but two have been found in Norway. In addition there are four known plans on ¼-inch scale, two in the United States and two in Norway. It is uncertain how many half-models exist, and the identification of one that is claimed to have been his is in question.

Some published lines of McKay's ships also exist but most, if not all, of these can be traced to lines in the Clark collection, now in the Francis Russell Hart Nautical Museum at Pratt Institute of Naval Architecture, Massachusetts Institute of Technology, Cambridge, Massachusetts. This collection contains Captain Arthur Clark's plan material, lines of some English clipper ships and the ⅛-inch scale lines of McKay's *Flying Cloud*, *Staghound*, *James Baines*, *Lightning*, *Sovereign of the Seas*, and *Great Republic*. The ⅛-inch scale plan of *Champion of the Seas*' lines has not been found; however Basil Lubbock, in the *Colonial Clippers*,* published her lines. Also the ⅛-inch scale lines of *Donald McKay* and *Flying Fish* are in the Bergens Sjøfarts Museum. Captain Arthur H. Clark gathered his collection with the intention of publishing it, but the publishers of his book† did not use them.

The ¼-inch scale plans in the Clark collection are of the take-offs of the half-models of *Staghound* and *Flying Fish*. At Bergen are *Star of Empire* and *Henry Hill*, showing ends of each ship and body plans on ¼ inch to one foot.

Half-models consist of a questionable one, *Sovereign of the Seas*, in the Mariners' House, Boston, and of *Staghound*, in the Old State House museum of the Marine Society, Boston. A half-model of one of McKay's packet ships, *Daniel Webster*, a small scale half-model of *Great Republic*, and a ¼-inch scale model of *Romance of the Seas* are in the Boston Museum of Fine Arts, in the Coolidge collection. A ¼-inch scale half-model of the *Great Republic* is in the Museum of History and Technology, Smithsonian Institution, Washington, D.C.; this model is also questionable.

Staghound and *Lightning* lines, on 1/10-inch to one-foot scale, were published by Griffiths in *U.S. Nautical Magazine*, and *Great Republic*, *Sovereign of the Seas*, *Flying Cloud*, *Staghound*, *James Baines*, and *Lightning* were

---

* Lubbock, *The Colonial Clippers* (Glasgow, Brown, Son & Ferguson, Ltd., last edition 1948, reprinted 1955), facing p. 49.
† *The Clipper Ship Era* (New York-London, G. P. Putnam's Sons, 1910).

published in the *Report on the Shipbuilding Industry of the United States.** Hall's lines appear to have been based on the drawings in Clark's collection.

Plans drawn on ⅛-inch scale, unless made with extreme care, lack precision. In the drawings used here, redrawing gave an opportunity to check on the degree of precision obtained in each. The ⅛-inch scale plans in Clark's collection and all those at Bergen were drawn by an expert draftsman, apparently from McKay's ¼-inch scale lines and half-models that were burned while in storage on McKay's farm at Hamilton, Massachusetts. The best mode of testing the plans was to enlarge them to ¼-inch scale by dividers and then to refair. If this could be done with only very little adjustment of either body or half-breadth plans, the lines were accepted as accurate. If much change had been required to fair, the ⅛-inch scale lines should be viewed with suspicion, of course.

McKay has usually been described as an adherent of hull forms having flat floor, full midsection, and fine ends. Though he did not repeat the very rising straight floors used in *Staghound*, some of his clippers had moderate rise of floor, while some had very little.

A number of his clippers, such as *Romance of the Seas* and *Lightning*, had very fine, hollow ends. In *Staghound* he had used practically no hollow but she had a sharp entrance and a long run. In some ships built for the England-Australia packet service he used short entrances and runs. *Champion of the Seas*, for example, had a short, sharp entrance and a short, but fine, run. *Donald McKay*, on the other hand, was an out-and-out reversion to the packet model, with short, full ends, and very steep buttocks in the run—the inconsistency in design is apparent. *Star of Empire* was similar in model to *Donald McKay*, but slightly sharper in the ends.

Sovereign of the Seas, *Romance of the Seas*, *Lightning*, and *Staghound* had long runs, but *Flying Fish*, *Flying Cloud*, and *Great Republic* had short runs. In all observed cases where the run was long, the quarterbeam buttock shows some distance of straight line just before it intersects with the after load line, but this became very short or almost nonexistent in short-run vessels. In the Clark collection plan of *Flying Cloud* this was very apparent, but there are errors in projections in this drawing.

It must be again observed that contrary to general belief, the basic design principles of Griffiths, Webb, and McKay were very much alike. All three

* By Henry Hall (10th U.S. Census, 1880), Vol. 8.

men used the sharp entrance, full midsection, with very moderate deadrise, some hollow in the ends, straight buttocks, and the midship section placed close to mid length of the load line in some of their ships. In basic design they differed only in the emphasis placed on the run, and the exact placement of the midsection, afore or abaft mid load-line length. Each of these designers had respect for economic requirements, but their ships differed in final execution according to the desires of the owners and trade requirements, of course. Therefore, some of the ships designed by these three men were not formed for maximum speed potentials. Webb and McKay occasionally built vessels on speculation, but McKay gambled on two large clippers, one of which, *Great Republic*, nearly caused his ruin when she was partially burned; he had insufficient insurance. McKay also appears a less than able manager in that he failed to obtain a range of building contracts each year. Whereas Webb, in a year, might built two or three clippers, a steamer, a freighter, and a bark, and might even build a couple of fishing sloops, McKay built only clippers and packets until the economics of the period forced him to look for general freighter and steamer construction in order to continue in business.

McKay's vessels were undoubtedly handsome, although some modern scale models, drawings, and lithographs belie this statement. However, contemporary descriptions and a few contemporary paintings show handsome ships. The figurehead on a McKay ship usually raked forward strongly, with its eyes on the horizon, in which might be termed "flight position." At its feet there was generally a carved scroll swept aft to, or over, the hawse holes, trailboard fashion. In *Flying Cloud* the scroll was replaced by a single moulding or trail knee, running from the foot of the figure to abaft of, and under, the hawse holes. The figureheads in many modern models of these ships are too much like the "cigar-store Indian" used in some later Down Easters, which had a "plastered on" effect.

Samuel Hartt Pook was the son of a United States naval constructor and first came to attention as the designer of some of the early New England built clippers while in the employ of Samuel Hall of Boston. It is now impossible to list all the clippers Pook designed, but the most notable ones were *Ocean Telegraph* (1851), *Golden West* and *Defiance* both launched in 1852, *Red Jacket* (1853), *Herald of the Morning* (1853), *Belle of the West* (1853), and *Fearless* (1853).

The surviving half-models show that Pook's designs were not radical. They had sharp, convex entrances, with very moderate hollow near the forefoot.

The runs were moderately long and fine, with some distance of straight in the quarterbeam buttock at and below the load line. Some of his designs show much flare in the stem rabbet. The midsections had very slight rise of straight floor, well-rounded, somewhat hard turn of bilge with but slight tumble home. Pook's vessels seem to have been capable of a rather high sustained speed and some, such as *Red Jacket*, had records of high hourly speed. Also, his designs did not sacrifice cargo capacity unduly; he apparently never produced a very extreme clipper. Pook seems to have worked as a naval architect, not as a builder, though occasionally he was an employee of a yard. It is said that he found private professional practice so poorly paid that he finally followed his father's footsteps and became a United States naval constructor.

It is apparent that the chief differences among clipper ship designers were in the use of, or in the amount of, hollow to be used at the ends, the degree of sharpness of entrance, the form and length of run, and the amount of deadrise to be employed to obtain both a high potential speed and a high sustained or average speed. By 1852 designers seem to have become aware that extreme clippers, with very sharp lines and with or without much deadrise, produced the highest potential hourly rate of speed, but that extreme models were not necessary to produce the high average or sustained speed that gave record and near-record passages. Since the extreme clippers were obviously poor carriers as well, there was a rapid drift away from the extreme clipper ship model. Webb, for example, began to produce clippers whose ends were not very hollow and whose runs, though fine, were not very long.

There were shipbuilders in New York—such as Jacob Bell, J. A. Westervelt, Roosevelt & Joyce, Perine, Patterson & Stack, and J. and E. Lupton—who had reputations for their designs of clipper ships but whose work has not been preserved in a sufficient number of plans or half-models to permit conclusions regarding their designing practices.

There were also clipper ship designers in New England who are similarly represented with too few half-models or plans to permit discussion of their theories or practices in design. One exception to this in New England was George Raynes of Portsmouth, New Hampshire. A number of half-models of his ships have been found, including *Wild Pigeon* and *Witch of the Wave* already described, as well as *Tinqua* and others. Based on these, Raynes' clippers used little or no hollow in the ends, and the waterlines were convex at load line, and straight below near the forefoot. The runs showed at least some distance of straight quarterbeam buttock forward of its intersection with the after load line—though in *Wild Pigeon*, for example, the buttock was very steep. The designer did not surrender cargo-capacity unduly, despite his use of rather marked deadrise.

So far, only individual designers' practices have been discussed, without regard to the state of the art of naval architecture in the 1850's. Though the builder's half-model was still accepted as the prime tool in hull design, a trend began that eventually led to its replacement by mathematical analysis and plans. This trend first appeared in the large, progressive yards, supported by Griffiths' activities in publishing the results of calculations of individual ships. The builder's model reached its height in popularity about 1851 and then began a slow decline until its use was finally relegated to the more primitive "country yards" and boat shops.

Griffiths' books and magazines were the only effective transmitters of technical information available to American shipbuilders in the 1850's. Griffiths published in his magazine the lines of a number of noted ships, often with basic calculations. Controversial discussions also took place in the magazine and Griffiths and Bates, the editors of *Nautical Magazine*, entered into these discussions with much enthusiasm. Some notice was taken of foreign developments and there were articles on at least one British clipper and on the *Great Eastern*, with the lines of these ships shown. The editors took delight in criticizing naval vessels, naval constructors, and the Navy. Articles on the New York shipbuilders and lists of vessels lost or damaged also appeared occasionally. But the many articles, comments, and plans of American sailing ships and steamships gave the magazine its importance as a technical reference for American shipbuilding practices of this period.

The use of mathematics in ship design had increased; displacement, centers of effort, buoyancy, gravity, and lateral plane were now calculated in the more progressive yards. Stability calculations of a primitive nature were being made. By 1852 Griffiths had begun to recognize the importance of plans (even though he still recommended the use of half-models) in making necessary calculations. A great deal of thought was being given to construction. New York and Boston shipbuilders were employing diagonal strapping of wrought iron more commonly, as well as improved wooden structural methods. The deck-machinery inventions of the 1830's and 1840's were now in common use. These included geared windlasses, crabs and capstans, steering gear, improved pumps, cargo and rigging winches, ventilators, patented rigs, improved blocks,

WITCH OF THE WAVE
Built at Portsmouth, N.H. by George Raynes in 1851, sold foreign in 1857.

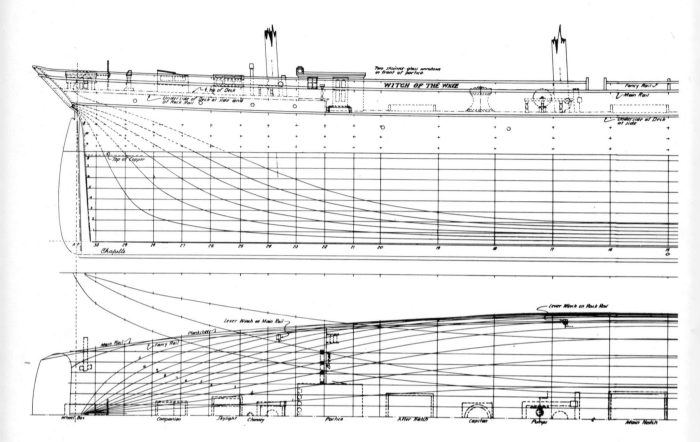

WITCH OF THE WAVE

Chapelle

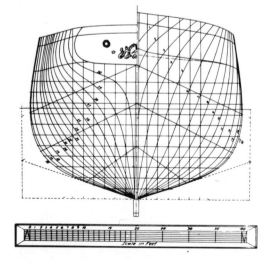

Masts	Dia	Whole Length	Heads		Yards	Dia	Whole Length	Arms
Fore	31"	81'	14'		Fore	19½"	71'	4½'
top	16"	47'	8½'		top	16½"	57'	4½'
topgal't	11½"	20½'	0"		topgal't	10½"	43½'	3½'
Royal	10"	16½'	0"		Royal	8"	34'	2½'
Skysail	8"	11'	pole 2½'		Skysail	5"	29'	1½'
Main	33"	90'	14½'		Main	21"	81'	5'
top	17"	50½'	9'		top	17½"	63'	5'
topgal't	12"	28'	0"		topgal't	11½"	48'	3½'
Royal	10½"	18'	0"		Royal	8½"	38½'	2½'
Skysail	6½"	12'	pole 3'		Skysail	5"	30'	1½'
Mizzen	26"	79'	12'		Crossjack	15½"	61'	3½'
top	14½"	41'	7½'		top	12"	49'	3½'
topgal't	10"	22'	0"		topgal't	9"	37'	2'
Royal	8"	14'	0"		Royal	6"	30'	1½'
Skysail	6"	9½'	pole 2'		Skysail	3½"	24'	1'

Bowsprit 30" dia, 28' outside innerstem.
Jibboom 17" dia 35' outside cap, divided at 10' and 20', 7' pole.
Spanker Boom 50', gaff 38', Main Spencer gaff 25', Fore Spencer gaff 27'.
Rake of Foremast 1¼", Main 1½" and Mizzen 1¾" to each foot of length.

Scale in Feet

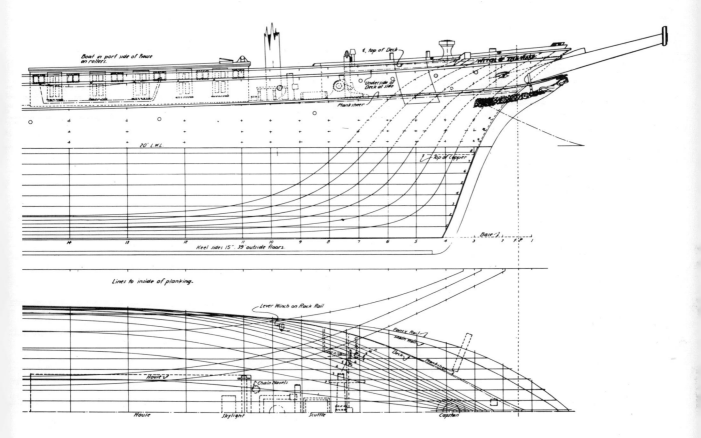

Boat in port side of house
on rollers.

‡, top of Deck

WITCH OF THE WAVE

Underside of
Deck at side

Planksheer

20' LWL

Top of Clipper

Keel sides 15". 39 outside floors.

Base 7.

F.P.

Lines to inside of planking.

Lever Winch on Rack Rail

Fancy Rail

Main Rail

Deck

Planksheer

House

Chain Navels

House

Skylight

Scuttle

Capstan

Length bet. perps.   204'-0"
Beam, moulded.   39'-8"
Depth to planksheer 24'-0"

PLATE XIII.   WITCH OF THE WAVE, *built at Portsmouth, New Hampshire, in
1851, was a fast sailer, and like* WILD PIGEON, *had occuli. Though not an extreme
clipper, she had many fast passages to her credit.   She was designed primarily
for the Far East trade.*

Clippership
SWEEPSTAKES
Built by Daniel & Aaron Westervelt at New York, 1853

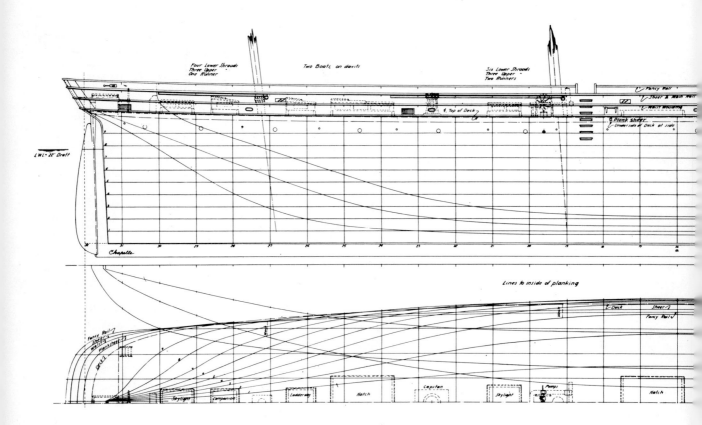

Four Lower Shrouds
Three Upper
One Runner

Two Boats, on davits

Six Lower Shrouds
Three Upper
Two Runners

℄. Top of Deck

L.W.L = 22" Draft

Chapelle

Lines to inside of planking

Skylight Companion Ladderway Hatch Capstan Skylight Pumps Hatch

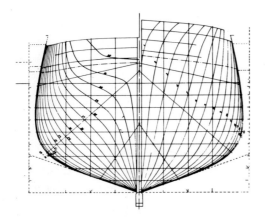

Half-Model, Mystic Marine Museum.

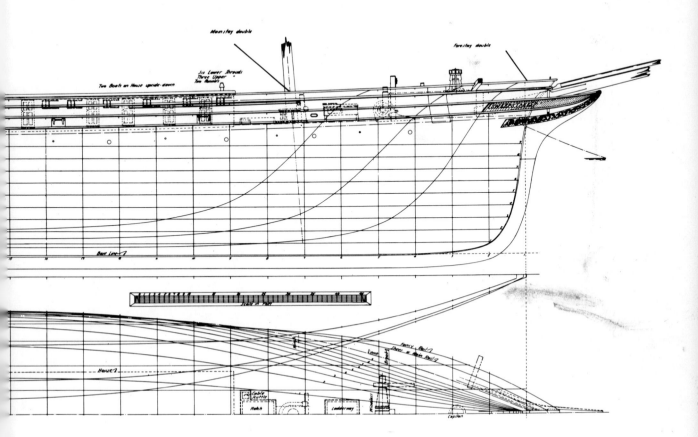

Mainstay double

Forestay double

Two Boats on House upside-down

Six Lower Shrouds
Three Upper "
Two Runners

Base Line 7

Scale of Feet

House 7

Cable
Scuttle

Hatch

Ladderway

Windlass

Capstan

Fancy Rail 7

Level

Brace & Main Rail 7

Length on Range of Deck - 232' 4"
    " Sta 1 to Sta 32 - 232' 6"
Stations spaced - 7' 6"
Beam moulded - 42' 4"
Depth " - 24' 10"
Level Lines spaced 2' 6"
Tonnage Length, lofted - 231' 6"
Buttocks spaced - 5' 0"
Reg. 216' 4" x 41' 6" x 22' 0", 1735 tons.
Currier & Ives lithograph- 220' on deck, 245' overall,
                41' 6" Beam, 21' 9" in hold, 1680 Tons.

PLATE XIV. SWEEPSTAKES, *an extreme clipper built in 1853 for trade to India.*

cranes, jeers, and other mast and spar ironwork, such as turnbuckles, or "rigging screws."

Even among the clippers there were some poorly-built ships launched in the 1850's. Hastily and inadequately-built vessels were launched with green timber in their structure and other of the common faults, such as small scuppers, and badly fitted cargo ports, sidelights, deck lights, companionways, scuttles, and hatches, causing leakage and cargo damage. Because of weak bitts, bowsprits were not well secured, and spars and ironwork were of insufficient strength.*

As a result of such structural and fitting deficiencies, as well as some instances of poor fastenings, damage claims became increasingly numerous and insurance rates began to rise. A number of New England built ships of the clipper period are recorded as working and straining so badly in heavy weather that they soon required extensive structural repairs, including refastening. Two such ships were *Benares* and *Ganges*, built by Hugh McKay in 1855–56.† Weak construction in hard-driven ships of the clipper type was soon exposed and their economic life was short.

In 1852 the English naval architect Scott Russell, designer of *Great Eastern* and proponent of the "wave-line theory" of resistance, claimed that the American use of hollow waterlines in their vessels was the result of the publication of his theory. Griffiths denied this, stating that the American use was the product of progressive experiments and observation, in which no mathematical formulae were used. Since steamers had been built in America during the 1830's and 1840's, with long, sharp, and often hollow ends and as some had been converted to sail, it is a moot question whether these features influenced American clipper ship design. However, Griffiths specifically denied this on the same grounds that British ship designers had been advancing—that steamer hulls were generally not suited for sail propulsion and therefore proved nothing. This was a weak argument, since some American and British steamers had been converted to sail and had proved very fast. It was therefore logical that the very long, sharp bow and the round counter stern of American steamers be copied in the clippers.

Drawing of lines had now reached the modern degree of precision. The base line, when drag of the keel was great, was now more commonly parallel

---

* *Scientific American*, Vol. IX (October 23, 1853), page 45.
† *George Blunt Wendell, Clipper Ship Master 1831–1881* (Mystic, Connecticut, The Marine Historical Association, Inc., 1949).

to the designed load line, with body-plan sections perpendicular to both base and load line. Buttocks, diagonals, and waterlines were projected as they are today. Lines of clippers and packets, and their half-models, were commonly on ⅜-inch to one foot or ⅓-inch to one foot scale, though some secretive designers used graphic, nonstandard scales. Models and lines were usually "moulded," or to inside of the planking. Therefore a correction had to be made in displacement calculations to obtain actual displacement, but moulded displacement was all that was usually calculated. The draftsmanship in ship plans in the 1850's was often of poorer quality than it had been early in the century.

The practice of laying the keel with a slight sag in the middle, say an inch in 100 feet of length, became standard practice and Griffiths recommended that offsets should show this and insure that the keel be properly put together. This was one of the many modes of preventing change in form by hogging. The amount of space allotted to superior wooden ship construction in Griffiths' books showed the concern for strong construction methods by American ship design authorities.

It has been the fashion for American maritime historians to look patronizingly on British shipbuilders, assuming that they knew little or nothing about the design of fast sailers until they began copying American clippers. It is time to examine this concept.

It is a matter of record that British shipbuilders were producing fast sailers whenever they received an order for such a vessel. White at Cowes, and Camper at Gosport, to name but two, built many fast cutters, schooners, brigs, and brigantines, as well as a few ships for the opium and other trades where speed was of prime interest. White also built some fast brigs for the Royal Navy. During Sir William Symonds' term of office as Surveyor of the Royal Navy, a large number of fast brigantines, brigs, and ships were designed under his supervision and there was also competition between various merchant ship designers in an effort to improve on Symond's vessels during the 1830's and 1840's. As evidence of their speed, these Royal Navy vessels were able to capture many fast American-built slavers.

The existence of these craft did not influence the design of English ocean freighters, however, until a change was made in the British tonnage measurements in 1836. This change was found to be unkind to the existing tonnage-cheaters, so British shipyards began a search for a hull form or proportions that would be favored by the new mode of tonnage measurement.

In 1839 William Hall, of the Aberdeen shipbuilding firm of Alexander Hall & Sons, made a study of the problem, and with some primitive model tests convinced a client to allow him to alter the forebody of his vessel *Scottish Maid* on the stocks. This schooner's long, fine run made her well-suited to the experiment, which consisted of replacing the original curved and moderately raking stem with one of great rake and of very strong flare forward at the rail. By altering the forebody frame, the new stem could be faired with straighter, sharper waterlines than before. This alteration reduced the original registered tonnage of the schooner, and as the model tests had indicated, improved the schooner's speed as well. For a time the new forebody design was employed only in local schooners, but by 1844 it had been used on a steamer and on a few full-rigged ships. These vessels were not very sharp but were perhaps comparable to the contemporary American China packets previous to *Sea Witch* and *Russell*.

When the British China trade was thrown open after the East India Company lost control of it, there was need for faster ships to meet the open competition. In 1850, Alexander Hall built the extreme clipper *Stornoway*, whose register dimensions were 157 feet by 28' 8" by 17' 8". This ship had a long hollow entrance and a long easy run with pronounced straight quarter-beam buttocks. She had the raking, flaring bow of the Hall design; her midsection had a rising straight floor and well-rounded bilge. The half-model of this ship, now in the Glasgow Art Gallery, in no way suggests the use of any contemporary American model as the basis for her design.

There is no need here to trace the details of the history of British clipper ship construction; it may be said, however, that the British followed the same trend in constructing sharp-ended ships after 1845 that the Americans followed, until the clipper appeared in 1850. Much has been made of the influence of American ships in the English tea trade on British ship design.

It should be recognized that prior to 1851, only *Samuel Russell* and *Oriental*, representing the American sharp-model ships, were in the tea trade. It is most unlikely that these vessels had any technical influence on British ship design, whatever the press may have stated. *Oriental* was not the first American sharp-model ship to appear in English ports, for *Samuel Russell* as well as *Venus* and other Baltimore clippers had been at Liverpool much earlier for cargoes "suited to the African Coast." Certainly *Venus* and other fast American vessels made no apparent impression abroad. Though lines of *Oriental* were taken off in Green's Blackwall Yard on the Thames, the British

367

clipper *Challenger*,* built by Green, showed no evidence, in the author's opinion, of the adaption of *Oriental's* lines in the English ship's design. Later, the American ship *Challenge* was taken off, but comparison with the offsets shows that the take-off was sketchily done and not correct in many details. No claim has ever been made that *Challenge* influenced British design.

The one attempt by the British to design and build a large clipper packet for the Australian run, to compete with such big American-built vessels as *Lightning*, was a failure. The loss of *Schomberg* on her disappointing maiden voyage, through the neglect of her master, prevented any tuning up that might have made her successful. This ship was built by Hall at Aberdeen in 1854. The earlier British clippers, built in 1850–53 included some that were as sharp-ended as many of the American clipper ships—*Stornoway* 1850, *Chrysolite* 1851, *Challenger* 1852, *Lord of the Isles* 1853, and *Cairngorm* 1853. The British iron clippers built in 1853 and later in the clipper ship era were often not only very sharp-ended but handsome and fast as well. The English development was independent of American evolution of the clipper. Both were the product of trade requirements, but the requirements were not the same for each, and thus the design characteristics of English and American clippers were quite different. English clipper development reached its height in the 1860's and 1870's when the most noted ships were built.

A few American clipper ship plans were sent abroad—one to Germany and one to France by Griffiths. At least two clippers, built in the United States, were for European owners—aside from the four English Black Ball Line clippers built at Boston. A number of clipper ships were built in France, Spain, Holland, and in Scandinavia in the early 1850's. There can be no doubt that the lines of American clipper ships were carefully studied abroad, but surviving plans of European origin that have been examined seem to show no evidence of extensive copying of American hull lines by European designers.

Returning to the examination of individual American clippers: In 1852 a highly finished, very handsome clipper was launched by Aaron C. Bell at New York. She was named *Jacob Bell*, in honor of his father, who it will be recalled, had been a prominent New York shipbuilder. At the time of Jacob Bell's death his yard had been building the clipper on speculation. This fine ship was burned by the Confederate raider *Florida*, 13 February 1863.

* David R. MacGregor, *The Tea Clippers* (London, Percival Marshall & Co., Ltd., 1952); shows lines of *Challenger* and of other early British clippers.

Plate 108 shows the lines of *Jacob Bell;* there is a small half-model of her in the Clark collection. She was 200' 3" between perpendiculars, 37' 4" moulded beam, and 25 feet moulded depth. Her register dimensions were 200' 11" by 38' 5" by 22 feet. She was a medium-sharp model, capable of a satisfactory sustained speed, and made a run of 78 days, New York to Bombay, in 1856.

Jacob Bell had a moderate, graceful sheer, straight keel, a slightly raking and flaring stem rabbet, upright post, round stern, and a sharp, convex entrance with only slight hollow near the forefoot. The run was long but not very fine. The quarterbeam buttock became straight only a little before its intersection with the after load line. There was moderate hollow in the lower run near the sternpost. The midsection had marked rise of straight floor, well-rounded bilge, and slight tumble home in the topside. The head was built in naval fashion—bust figurehead, carved trail boards, closed headrails, and a large cutwater, greatly resembling the bows of some United States first-class sloops-of-war.

On 18' 6" draft, the moulded length was 196' 9" on the load line; moulded displacement 1785.7 long tons; the coefficients were block .53, midsection .80, and prismatic .67. The effective length of the quarterbeam buttock was 167' 6", camber 13' 9", giving a camber-length ratio of 10.8.

During 1852 a number of other ships were launched that were probably on clipper models, but unfortunately only a few are represented by half-models whose identity cannot be questioned and a much smaller number by plans or offset tables. And some of these turned out to be rather full-model craft upon close inspection. Offsets exist for Webb's *Australia,* and there is a lines plan, ⅛-inch to one foot scale, for McKay's *Sovereign of the Seas.* Half-models exist for *Carrier Pigeon,* built by Trufant & Drummond at Bath, Maine; *Golden Fleece* built by Paul Curtis, Boston; and *Tinqua* built by Raynes at Portsmouth, New Hampshire. These models are all well identified, but *Golden Fleece* was found to have been a relatively full model and *Carrier Pigeon's* model is some feet shorter than the register dimensions indicate. Other half-models of ships launched in 1852 include one identified as *Sovereign of the Seas* and one identified as *Golden West.* The first, published by Cutler,* is a fuller ship, with a different stern, than the ship shown in the well-drawn ⅛-inch scale plan of *Sovereign* in the Clark collection. The model identified as *Golden West* strongly resembles a painting of that ship

---

* *Greyhounds of the Seas,* page 548.

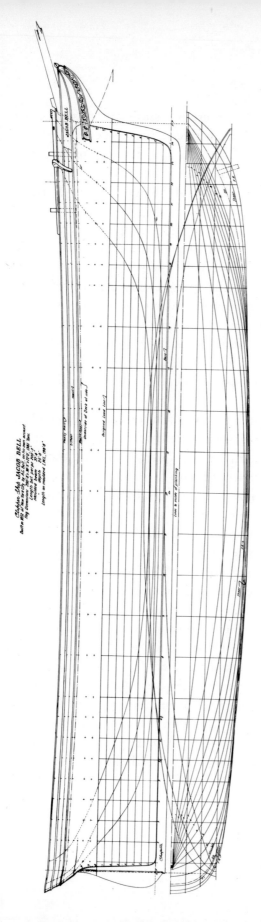

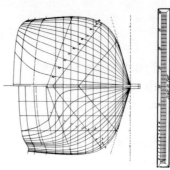

Plate 108. JACOB BELL, clipper ship built in 1852 at New York by A. C. Bell.

but does not comply even approximately with her register according to any standard scale, nor with any graphic scale, in fact, due to the model's proportions. Hence this ship could not be included for any calculations relating to this study.

Australia was called a packet by Webb, and her offsets, when laid down, produced a packet model of her date, in spite of her inclusion in most lists of American clippers.

It may be that one or more frames were added amidships in the case of *Carrier Pigeon* and other half-models. The general inaccuracy, however, of the registered dimensions, as well as doubt as to the ship's frame spacing, leave an unanswerable question as to the exact amount of added length amidships that would be required to reproduce the lines of the actual ships. Hence, *Sovereign of the Seas,* as shown in the ⅛ inch to one foot scale lines plan in the Clark collection, has been chosen for inclusion here. This plan agrees in most respects with the partial lines drawing in Hall's report. The lines, shown in Plate 109, have been tested by enlargement and refairing. Furthermore the lines were accompanied by results of calculations for a 20-foot draft, showing beyond any doubt that the drawing was the work of a naval architect or master shipwright who would not knowingly have preserved a lines plan and calculation results that were inaccurate. This ship had established a reputation for unusual speed. Claims were made of hourly runs at 19 and even 22 knots. A day's run of 411 nautical miles, as well as a number of very fast passages, make *Sovereign of the Seas* of particular interest here.

The register dimensions of this vessel were 258′ 2″ by 44′ 7″ by 23′ 6″. Duncan MacLean gives length of keel 245 feet, length on deck between perpendiculars 258 feet, from knightheads to taffrail 265 feet, extreme breadth of beam 44 feet, at gunwale 42 feet, depth 23½ feet, and 8 feet between decks. Hall states she was 231′ 4″ on the load line, 43′ 2″ moulded beam, and 26′ 3″ moulded depth, displacement 2,403 long tons. The Clark drawing gives her dimensions as 239 feet on deck, 230.15 feet load line, rabbet to rabbet, 41 feet moulded beam, 42 feet extreme beam, 25.9 feet depth, base to planksheer, 20-foot draft, with a moulded displacement of 2408.33 long tons. But by scale, the Clark plan measured 230′ 4″ on the load line, as shown in Plate 109. In refairing, it was noticed that the body-plan sections were spaced 10 feet, as were those of *Lightning* and others in the Clark collection, and also of *Flying Fish, Star of Empire,* and *Donald McKay* in the Bergen collection. This indicates that the surviving lines plans may be all from a common

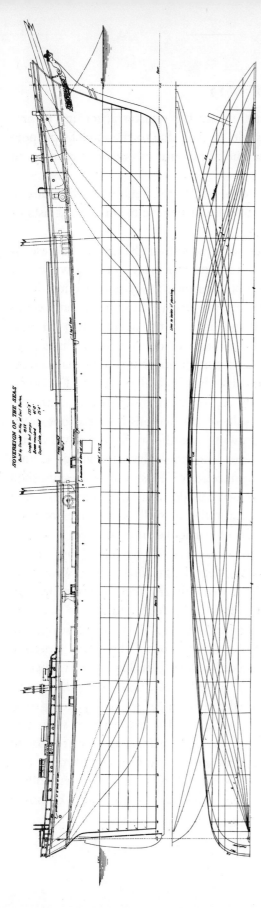

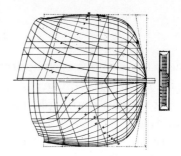

Plate 109. The noted McKay-built clipper SOVEREIGN OF THE SEAS, *for which a speed of 22 knots was claimed. Considered by many contemporary writers to have been McKay's finest clipper ship.*

source. The Bergen plans, however, do not have calculations, nor are dimensions given, except in part for *Henry Hill*. The draftsmanship does not seem to be the same in the Clark plans as in the Bergen drawings. In both sources, all the plans have two buttock-bow lines projected, again suggesting a common source.

It should also be noted that plans of *Sovereign of the Seas* and of *Lightning*, on ⅛-inch to one foot scale, are in the Peabody Museum of Salem, Massachusetts,* but these seem to be rather crude copies of the Clark drawings—perhaps by some later and certainly less skilled draftsman.

These notes on the plans of McKay clippers show the uncertainties that exist as to the exact dimensions and the form of some of the better-known vessels. The notes also indicate troublesome inaccuracies in the registered dimensions, particularly the length, which the register frequently seems to overstate. The Webb plans and offsets give more confidence in reproducing ship's lines and in the calculation of results than do either the half-models or the plans of McKay clippers.

Sovereign of the Seas was a very handsome vessel having a marked sheer, straight keel, moderately raking and flaring stem rabbet, nearly upright post, round stern, a long, very sharp concave entrance, and a long and hollow run; the quarterbeam buttock, showing much reverse at the stern, was straight for a short distance forward of its intersection with the after load waterline. The midsection was at mid length of the load line and was formed with a short, moderately rising straight floor, combined with a long sweep out to a well-rounded bilge, with a slight, curved tumble-home. The cutwater carried a figure of Neptune, half man and half fish blowing a conch shell. As often in McKay's ships, a gilded scroll or vine extended aft from the bottom of the figurehead to around the hawse holes, in trailboard fashion.

As shown in Plate 109, she measured 230′ 4″ moulded length on the load line, at 20′ 6″ draft, and had a moulded displacement of 2492.6 long tons. Her coefficients were block .51, midship .82, and prismatic .62. The effective length of the quarterbeam buttock was 166′ 3″, camber 16 feet, giving a camber-length ratio of 10.4. *Sovereign of the Seas* was built on speculation and was sold to German owners in 1856 through an American house.

Some of the many noted clippers launched in 1853 were *Belle of the West, Fearless, Herald of the Morning,* and *Red Jacket,* all designed by Pook; *Spit-*

* There is also a ¼-inch scale drawing of *Flying Fish* in the Peabody Marine Museum collection.

fire, *Competitor, Dreadnought, Eagle Wing,* and *Reporter.* Webb built *Fly-away,* the bark *Snap Dragon,* and the notable *Young America.* McKay had a busy year, turning out the four-masted clipper *Great Republic, Romance of the Seas, Chariot of Fame, Empress of the Seas,* and *Star of Empire. Great Republic* and *Romance of the Seas* were extreme clippers; *Empress of the Seas* may have been. Richard C. McKay* lists *Staghound, Flying Cloud, Staffordshire, North America, Flying Fish, Sovereign of the Seas, Westward Ho, Bald Eagle, Empress of the Seas, Star of Empire, Chariot of Fame, Great Republic,* and *Romance of the Seas,* as extreme clippers and *Lightning, Champion of the Seas, James Baines,* and *Donald McKay* as clippers—a largely incorrect classification. The *Star of Empire* and *Chariot of Fame* were certainly packet models. As will be seen, *Lightning* was an extreme clipper, but *Donald McKay* was a packet model according to the existing ⅛ inch to one foot lines plan of that ship.

Plate 110 shows the lines of *Romance of the Seas,* as taken from the half-model. A long, narrow vessel with sharp ends, she seems to have been one of McKay's experiments in hull proportions and an extreme clipper. In 1856 she ran from San Francisco to Shanghai in 34 days 4 hours, next to the record of 32 days 9 hours set by *Swordfish* in 1853. She does not appear to have had the kind of hard driving that might have established her character for speed.

Romance of the Seas was 231′ 6″ between perpendiculars, 37′ 6″ moulded beam, 20′ 4″ moulded depth to deck. Her register dimensions were 240′ 9″ by 39′ 6″ by 20 feet. She had a graceful sheer, straight keel, moderately raking and flaring stem rabbet, nearly upright post, round stern, long, sharp, convex entrance with hollow near forefoot; long, fine run with the quarter-beam buttock straight for an unusual length forward of its crossing of the after load line, hollow in the lower run. "Female figurehead, in a flowing gown, ribbon with Scott on one side and Cooper on the other, with a vine carried around the hawse holes, trail-board fashion." Her midsection was formed with a moderately rising straight floor, well-rounded bilge, and slight, curved tumble home.

On a moulded load waterline of 229′ 2″, at 18′ 3″ draft, her moulded displacement was 2012.5 long tons. Her coefficients were block .51, midship .80, and prismatic .64. The effective length of the quarterbeam buttock was 179 feet, camber 13′ 9″, giving a camber-length ratio of 13.1.

* In *Some Famous Sailing Ships and Their Builder Donald McKay* (New York, G. P. Putnam's Sons, 1928).

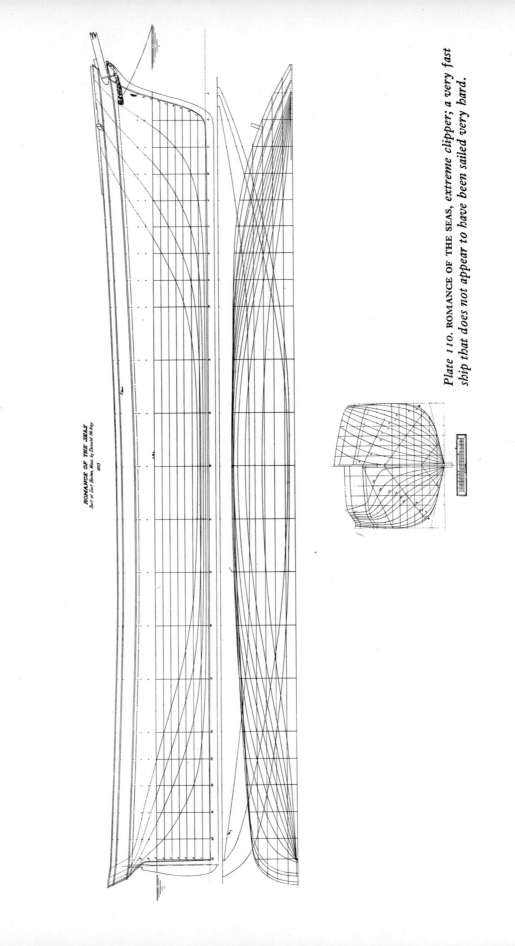

ROMANCE OF THE SEAS
Built at East Boston, Mass. by Donald McKay
1853

Plate 110. ROMANCE OF THE SEAS, extreme clipper; a very fast ship that does not appear to have been sailed very hard.

A very fast clipper named *Sweepstakes* was launched at New York in 1853, built by Daniel and Aaron Westervelt. This vessel was designed for the Far East trade and was an extreme clipper in model. Her register dimensions were 216′ 4″ by 41′ 6″ by 22 feet, 1735 tons. She measured, as shown in Plate XIV, 232′ 4″ on the whole range of deck, 42′ 4″ beam moulded, and 24′ 10″ moulded depth. The Currier & Ives lithograph of this ship gives 245 feet overall, 41′ 6″ beam, 21′ 9″ depth in hold, 1680 tons.

This ship had a rather straight sheer, straight keel, with rockered forefoot, well-rounded stem rabbet, flaring strongly as it approached the rail, nearly upright post, round stern, long, sharp, and concave entrance, fine run with quarterbeam buttock straight for some distance forward of its intersection with the after load lines, and much hollow in the lower portion of the run, near the post. The midsection was abaft the mid length of the load line and was formed with marked rise of straight floor, a rather hard turn of the bilge, with a strong, curved tumble home in the topside. This handsome ship was credited with speeds up to 18 knots and held the record for the run from New York to Bombay—74 days (1857).

On a moulded load waterline of 227′ 10″, at 22 feet draft, her moulded displacement was 2661.3 long tons; her block coefficient was .50, midship .79, and prismatic .64. The effective length of her quarterbeam buttock was 146′ 9″, camber 13′ 10″, giving a camber-length ratio of 15.6.

The peak of extreme-clipper construction was probably reached in 1852–53; by this period freight rates had begun to fall steadily and the uneconomic character of the type began to be recognized. Nevertheless, a few extreme ships were built in 1854. McKay obtained orders in England for four large vessels; these were *Lightning, James Baines, Donald McKay*, and *Champion of the Seas*. They were for the Liverpool-Melbourne run and were intended for what was really a packet service. Though all were intended for this run, no two were alike in model. The run, around Cape Horn, or around the Cape of Good Hope, required a powerful vessel, able to carry sail in strong winds. In rounding either cape, the approved course was well to the southward. The average passages, according to Maury's *Sailing Directions*, were 110 days by way of the Horn, 124 days by Good Hope, from Europe or the United States, if these courses were followed. On these courses a ship would be expected to have strong winds, but they might be storm winds, with head winds as well, near the capes. Ships on this run to Australia in the 1850's often carried only a moderate weight of cargo and depended upon express goods and passengers for the bulk of their income. Hence the vessels were usually on their light-load draft, well-ballasted, with rather high sides, which brought them to their best sailing trim. With strong fair winds abaft the beam, a heavy following sea, and some favorable current created by strong winds, they often traveled very fast. It was on this run that nearly all of the great hourly speed records were made and also the better part of the record 24-hour runs.

Plates XV and 111 show *Lightning*, first of the four ships for the English Black Ball Line to be launched, 3 January 1854, for the Liverpool-Melbourne packet service. This vessel's design complied to a very great extent with the stated theories of Griffiths. The position of the midsection abaft the middle of the load line, the very sharp hollow entrance, the short run, and the full midsection were characteristics of Griffiths' theories of design. In fact, the only departure from Griffiths' theories in *Lightning* was a very fine though short run, with a straight buttock at quarterbeam.

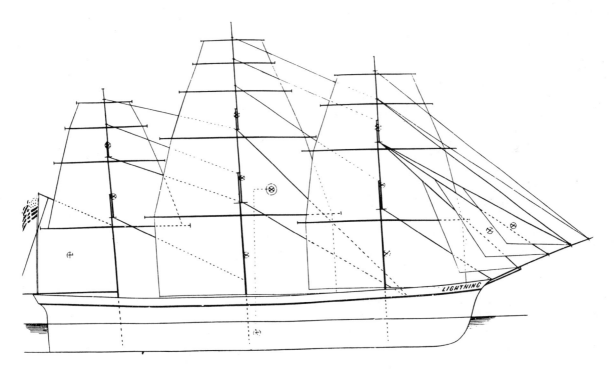

Plate 111. Sketch of spar plan, clipper ship LIGHTNING.

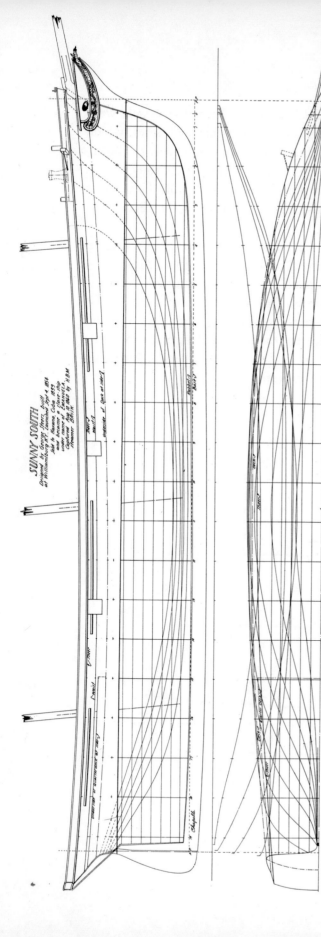

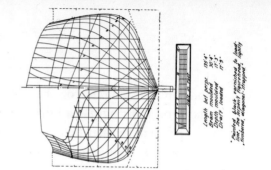

Plate 112. *Extreme clipper* SUNNY SOUTH, *designed by George Steers, 1854. Later she was a slaver under the name* MANUELA, *then became store ship* ENCHANTRESS *for the British Navy African Station where she was wrecked.*

The registered dimensions of *Lightning* were 243 feet by 42' 8" by 23 feet. Her plan, published by Griffiths, and the Clark plan are in agreement in showing her to have been 228 feet, moulded, by scale, on the 20-foot draft load line, 43 feet moulded beam, 44 feet extreme beam, 233' 8" length on range of deck, and 22' 8" moulded depth at side. She was about 247' 6" from knightheads to taffrail. Hall gives slightly different dimensions: 228 feet on the load line, register length 243, moulded beam 42' 8", moulded depth 25 feet.

Lightning had a graceful, moderate sheer, straight keel, well-rounded forefoot, strongly flaring stem rabbet, and nearly upright post. Her entrance was very long, fine, and quite hollow from the 20-foot draft line down. Her run was shorter than the entrance, but very fine, and hollow below the 20-foot draft line near the post. Her quarterbeam buttock was straight for some distance forward of its intersection with the 20-foot draft line, with reverse curve above. The midsection was nearly eight feet abaft the middle of the 20-foot draft load line. It was formed with slight rise of straight floor, a low, full, round bilge, and moderate and curved tumble home above. She had a female figurehead in flowing robes with a bolt of lightning in an outstretched hand, and a gilded scroll from her feet to over and abaft the hawse holes, trail-board fashion.

At a draft of 20 feet, her moulded load waterline measured 228 feet, her moulded displacement was 2661 long tons, and her coefficients were block .54, midship .75, and prismatic .61. The effective length of her quarterbeam buttock was 170' 10", camber 16' 4", giving a camber-length ratio of 10.5. This vessel was destroyed by fire at Melbourne in 1869.

Of the other two ships built in 1854 by McKay for the Liverpool-Melbourne packet service, *Champion of the Seas* was sharp-ended with much less hollow than *Lightning* and with a much steeper buttock at quarterbeam. She was launched 19 April 1854. The third ship was *James Baines*, launched 25 July 1854. This was a clipper whose sharpness and hollowness in the ends was between *Lightning* and *Champion of the Seas*, but whose fore-rake was greater than any of the others. The fourth ship built for this run was the *Donald McKay*, launched in January 1855. This was a packet ship of the same type as Webb's *Australia*, having no claim to being of the clipper mould; she was a very large ship with a large rig, which enabled her to make some very good passages. McKay sold the medium clippers, or packet-model ships, *Commodore Perry* and *Japan* to the James Baines' interests (British Black Ball Line) in 1854. No plans have yet been found of these ships nor of some of the other vessels McKay built in 1854, 1855, and 1856, but their suitability for packet service indicates that they may have been full-model, or packet-model, ships. McKay's last really sharp-model vessel was probably the bark *Henry Hill,* launched in 1856. By this time the construction of large extreme clippers and clippers had ceased and the full model had replaced them. Some of the full-model ships were packet models, often erroneously called medium clippers, for the demarcation between packet and medium or half-clipper had become poorly defined—as in the cases of *Donald McKay* and some of Webb's ships.

Another extreme clipper built in 1854 was *Sunny South.* This vessel's registered dimensions were 144′ 8″ by 31′ 4″ by 16′ 6″ and she was designed and built by George Steers at Williamsburg, New York. Her owners were Napier, Johnson & Co., New York, and she was intended for the China trade. She was diagonally strapped, well-built, and handsomely finished. Apparently, she was too small to be profitable in the China trade. She was sold to Havana, and as *Manuela* was considered to be the fastest slaver out of that port. Her history was traced in Chapter 6.

This vessel measured 135′ 4″ between perpendiculars, 30′ 4″ beam, 17′ 3″ moulded depth, and 17′ 9″ loaded draft. She had black topsides, varnished bottom, and a gilded sea-serpent figurehead. Griffiths reported that she was over-sparred due to her captain's interference with the rigging of the ship.

Plate 112 shows the lines of this yacht-like vessel. She had a marked and handsome sheer; rockered keel; strongly rounded forefoot; moderately flaring stem rabbet; nearly vertical post; raking, deep-V transom with rudder stock passing through it; long, sharp, and concave entrance; long, fine, and concave run with the buttocks straight forward of their intersections with the after load line. The midsection had strong rise to the straight floor, a rather hard turn of bilge, and much tumble home above.

On a draft of 17′ 9″ her moulded length of load line was 149 feet and her moulded displacement was 901.1 long tons. Her coefficients were block .43, midship .78, and prismatic .62. Effective length of the quarterbeam buttock was 118 feet, camber 12′ 6″, giving a camber-length ratio of 9.4.

Griffiths and others said that this ship resembled the Steers-designed schooner-yacht *America,* particularly at the bow. Steers also made a model for a larger clipper ship that was never built, intended to be an improvement over *Sunny South.* The half-model of this project is in The Mariner's Museum, Newport News, Virginia.

LIGHTNING

Clippership built at East Boston, Mass. by Donald McKay

1854

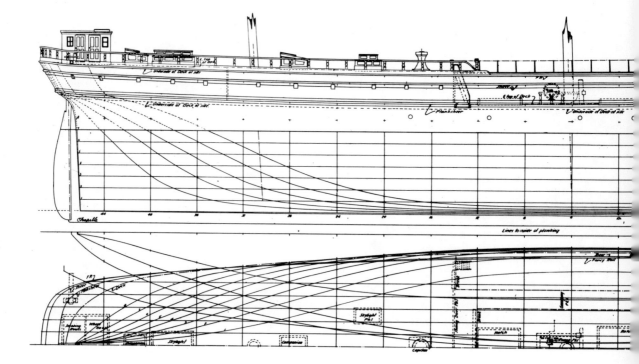

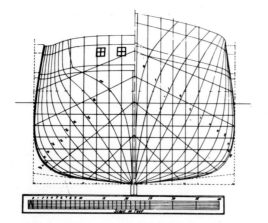

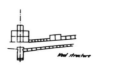

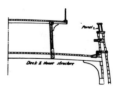

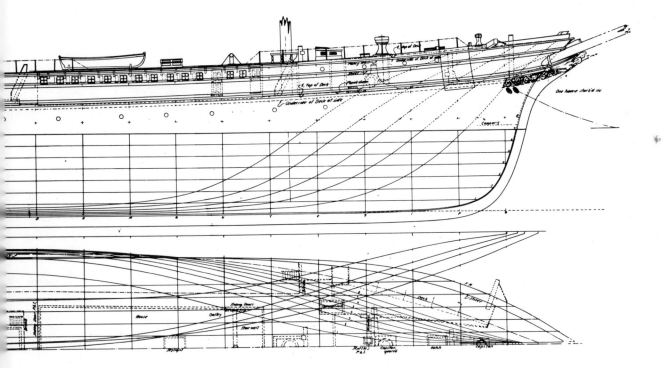

PLATE XV. *Extreme clipper* LIGHTNING, *Donald McKay's radical design. Be-sides being one of the sharpest of the large clippers, she had an unusual deck arrangement. Her long poop was connected to the deckhouse roof by two gang-ways. The deckhouse roof was carried forward and joined to the topgallant fore-castle deck,* making the vessel flush-deck as far as working the ship *was con-cerned.*

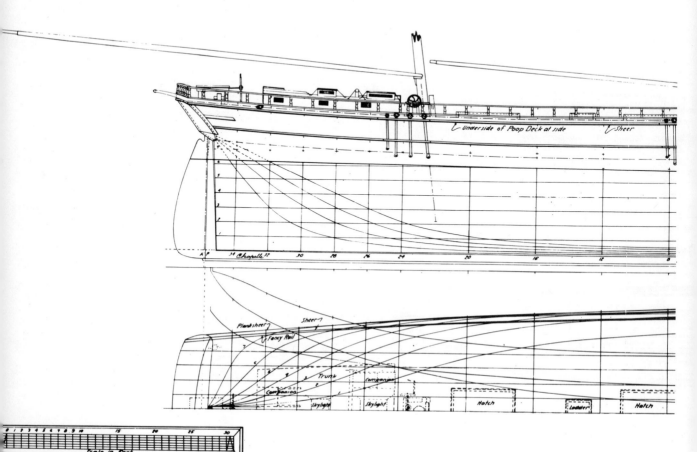

Underside of Poop Deck at side   Sheer

J. Chapelle J?
    32   30   28   26   24   20   16   12   8

Planksheer   Sheer
Fancy Rail

Trunk   Companion

Companion

Skylight   Skylight   Hatch   Ladder   Hatch

Scale in Feet

Drawn from plan by H.W. Schokker, Amsterdam
1860, and by reference to The Monthly Nautical
Magazine

U.S.N.M. Smithsonian Institution

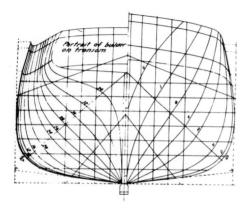

Portrait of builder
on transom

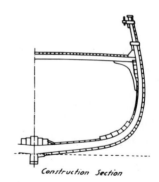

Construction Section

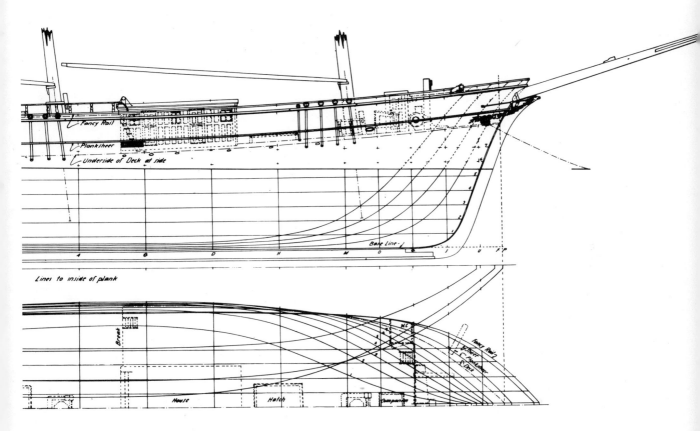

Length bet. perps.   130'0"
Beam moulded   29'8"
Depth in Hold   12'6"

Lower Masts 89' total length, 26" dia.
Fore & Mizzen topmasts 52' } 12" dia
Main Topmasts 54'
Fore & Main Booms 39'   Spanker 58'
Gaffs 38', Bowsprit outboard 27'
Jibboom 20, Flying Jibboom 14, pole 4'
Mastheads 14'

Vessel painted white

PLATE XVI. *Tern schooner* ECKFORD WEBB, *claimed to have sailed 16 knots.*
Built at New York, 1855.

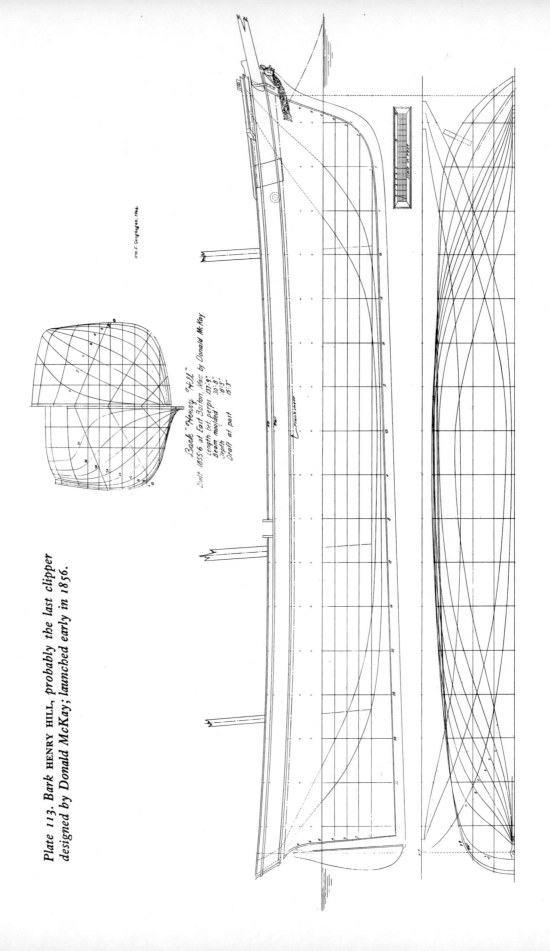

Plate 113. Bark HENRY HILL, *probably the last clipper designed by Donald McKay; launched early in 1856.*

The last year in which large sharp-model sailing merchant ships were built in the United States is supposed to have been 1855, but with the scant evidence now available, it is impossible to name a single extreme clipper launched in that year. The *Andrew Jackson* (1855), shown in Cutler's *Greyhounds of the Seas*, can be considered a clipper, or perhaps as a sharp medium clipper, but none of the other 1855 half-models now available were of the very sharp-model clipper type. There apparently were relatively few large vessels of the extreme clipper type built in the United States during the whole clipper ship period, and their construction ceased very suddenly in 1854.

During the period 1850–55, however, a number of small barks of about 500 tons register were launched. Some were sharp models, particularly those in the coffee trade. In addition, there were some fast centerboard schooners, barkentines, and barks built on the Great Lakes. Small fry such as fruit schooners—some with centerboards—packet brigs, brigantines, river sloops, pilot schooners, and probably a few slavers, were built on the Atlantic Coast with speed as one of the prime requirements. Three-masted schooners, usually referred to as "tern schooners," had become popular and were being built as vessels of 300 register tons and upward. After the small Baltimore terns of 1805–06, a few larger three-masted merchant schooners had been launched. These ranged in size from about 150 register tons to a little over 300, but the total number of terns had been small and the rig did not become popular until the 1850's. With the demand for larger schooners in the boom days of the early 1850's, it was discovered that the huge spars and sails of the big two-masters made them heavy-working. Sails and spars could be reduced in a tern, so a trend was established that led to the four-, five-, and six-masted schooners of the end of the eighteenth century.

The 1850's were marked by a rapid increase in the number of centerboard vessels built on the Atlantic Coast and the Great Lakes; some were of large size. At this time, centerboard sloops and schooners were still very numerous in the rivers and bays on the Atlantic Coast but they were fighting a losing battle with steamers.

The bark rig was somewhat more economical than the ship rig and it began to appear extensively in the 1830's. It was some time, however, before the bark rig was used in sharp clipper vessels, and it was not used in the large, extreme clippers until economics forced a reduction in sail area and the size of the crews.

Webb built a number of small barks, one of which was *Snap Dragon*, a medium clipper launched in 1853 for general freighting. She had a rather steep short run and a somewhat short but sharp entrance. She was a 618-ton register vessel. Webb showed two other barks in his published plans; these were full models.

McKay built three barks. Only one was of the clipper type—the 569-ton *Henry Hill,* which was laid down in 1855 and launched in 1856.

This small vessel's lines (Plate 113), found in the Bergen collection, were on a ¼ to one inch scale. The registered dimensions were 140′ 6″ by 30′ 6″ by 14′ 6″, 568 68/95 tons register. She was somewhat different from the other McKay ships whose lines are available, for she had much drag to her keel. As a result, her base line was not her keel rabbet, but was in the new mode—the base line being a lower level line, parallel to her designed load waterline. The moulded load waterline was recorded as 132.56 feet, her moulded breadth was 30′ 8″, and her length on deck was 138′ 3″. Her moulded depth at ⓧ was 16′5″. The midsection was 8.7 feet forward of the middle of the load waterline.

Henry Hill had marked sheer, straight keel with about 4′ 6″ drag, strongly rounded forefoot, moderately flaring stem rabbet, slightly raking post, and counter round stern. Her entrance was sharp and hollow at the forefoot; her run was fine with the quarterbeam buttock becoming straight a little forward of its intersection with the after load line. Her midsection was formed with very short straight floor having little rise, a long sweep out to the bilge, which was full and round, and a rather strong tumble home above.

On a moulded load waterline of 132′ 6½″, she had a moulded displacement of 663 long tons. Her coefficients were block .41, midship .68, and prismatic .61. Effective length of the quarterbeam buttock was 113′ 8″, camber 10 feet, giving a camber-length ratio of 11.4. There is no indication of the trade for which this vessel was intended. She had a small bust figurehead of her namesake.

Another design for a clipper bark is shown in Plates 114 and 115. A drawing of this bark, showing profile, spar plan, and half-breadth, was found in a Swedish shipyard by the late Captain Sam Svensson and presented to the author. It is now on exhibit in the Hall of American Merchant Shipping, Museum of History and Technology, Smithsonian Institution, Washington, D. C.

The drawing was made in 1855 by Edward Lupton at New York. Lupton was a shipbuilder, who with his brothers, built the small clipper *Black Sea* at Greenpoint, New York, in 1855. Edward Lupton designed a number of fast

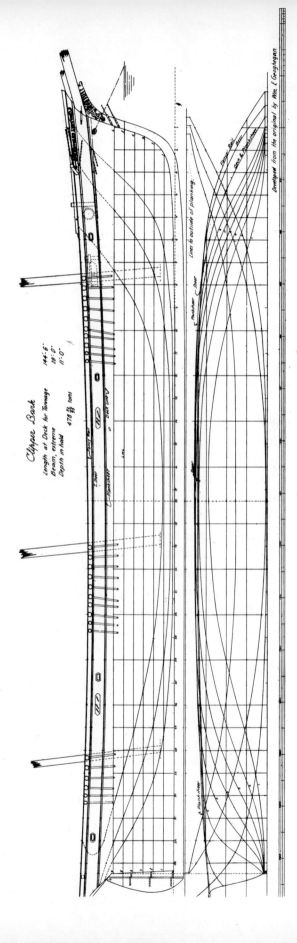

Clipper Bark

Length at Deck for Tonnage   144'-6"
Beam, extreme   28'-0"
Depth in hold   11'-0"

470 73/95 tons

Developed from the original by Wm. L Geoghegan

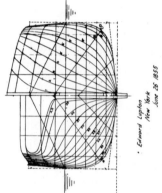

Edward Lupton
New York
June 28 1855

Plate 114. Clipper bark designed in 1855 by Edward
Lupton, a well-known shipbuilder at New York.

schooners, brigs, and brigantines and with various partners built a number of steamers, including a revenue cutter. Though the designer put his name on the sheer profile, no vessel of this name has been found in the customhouse records, so the design may have been merely a project and never built. Nonetheless, the design has value in that it shows a competent designer's ideas for a fast sailing bark of this date.

This vessel was flush-decked, having a slight but graceful sheer, straight keel with a rockered forefoot, and a strongly rounded, raking, and flaring stem rabbet; the post was slightly raked. The stern was formed with a raking, deep-V transom; the rudderstock passed through it. The entrance was long, sharp, and concave near the stem; a slight shoulder appears in the upper level lines near the foremast. The run was shorter than the entrance, the quarter-beam buttock becoming straight for a short distance forward of its intersection with the after load line, giving a fine and hollow run. The midsection is raked and slightly abaft mid length, formed with slightly rising straight floor, a rather firm, round bilge, with slight tumble home above. The vessel measured* 141′ 6″ on the load line at 12-foot draft, 144′ 9″ on deck for tonnage, 28-foot beam to outside of plank, 11 feet depth in hold as scaled from the lines, 478 22/95 tons, and she could carry 550 tons of cargo. The original plan is dated 26 June 1855 and is unusual in that the lines are drawn to outside of all planking. Plates 114 and 115, which show the lines and spar plan, indicate that the vessel was greatly over-sparred and over-canvassed.

At 12-foot draft and a waterline length of 141′ 6″ rabbet to rabbet, she displaced 645.3 long tons; her coefficients were block .57, midship .86, and prismatic .66. The effective length of the quarterbeam buttock was 120′ 10″, camber 7′ 8″, giving a camber-length ratio of 15.9.

In April 1855 a large tern was launched from Eckford Webb's yard in the New York district, Plate XVI. Named for her builder, the *Eckford Webb* was 130 feet between perpendiculars, 29′ 8″ moulded beam, and 12′ 6″ depth of hold. The vessel was employed for a time in 1855–56 as a North Atlantic packet, though originally built for Dunham's New York-Savannah service. In 1858 she was back on the New York-Savannah run. She was reported to have gone 16 knots during a 21-day passage across the Atlantic and was pictured in *Illustrated London News*. Her sail plan was found in the files of Alexander Stephen & Sons' Shipyard at Glasgow (Plate 116) showing that

---

* The original plan gives her waterline length as 144 feet, apparently from face of stem to L. of rudder stock and 145 feet on deck for tonnage.

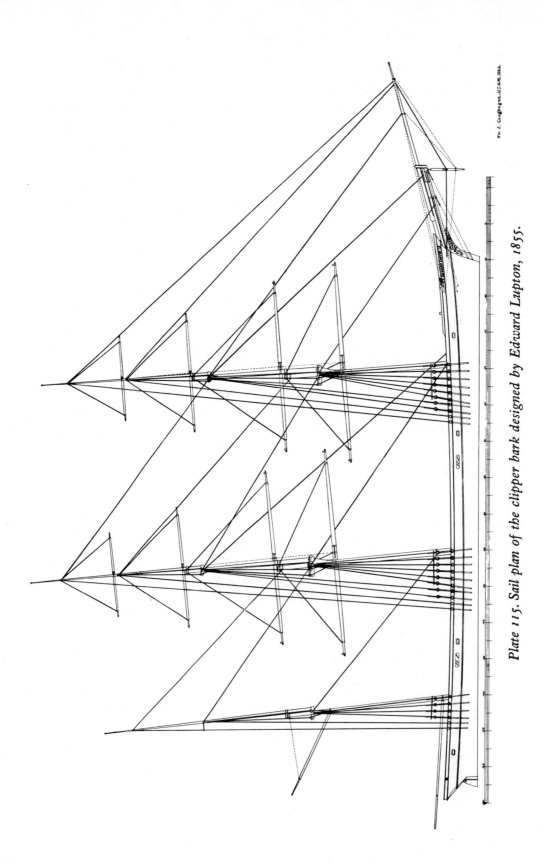

Plate 115. Sail plan of the clipper bark designed by Edward Lupton, 1855.

her quarterdeck rail had been closed in for the Atlantic crossings, though shown too high.

The schooner had marked sheer, straight keel with slight drag, raking and slightly flaring stem rabbet, slight rake to the post, short, sharp entrance with marked hollow near forefoot, short run, hollow near post below the load line, and the quarterbeam buttock rather steep, but straight for a little distance forward of its intersection with the load line. Midsection forward of the middle of the load line, formed with slightly rising, straight floor and firm, round bilge with marked tumble home above. Her rig was in the modern form with a large mizzen. Griffiths published her lines in his magazine* with spar dimensions. He stated that she was white, had an eagle head as a figurehead, and a bust of Eckford Webb on the stern. Her register dimensions were 137 feet by 30 feet by 13′ 2″. A medium clipper in model, she might be classed as a sharp packet. She was 130 feet between perpendiculars, 29′ 8″ moulded beam, and 12′ 6″ depth. On a moulded load waterline length of 124′ 3″ her moulded displacement was 773.6 long tons; the coefficients were block .64, midsection .88, and prismatic .72. The effective length of the quarterbeam buttock was 110′ 6″, camber 10′ 9″, giving a camber-length ratio of 10.3.

One of the very fast commercial centerboard schooners of this era was *Clipper City*, designed and built by S. Bates & Son at Manitowoc, Wisconsin, in 1854. The vessel was modeled by W. W. Bates, partner to Griffiths in publication of *The U. S. Nautical Magazine*. She was intended for a fast, light-draft lumber schooner, to be employed on Lake Michigan. Her lines and sail plan were published in Griffiths' magazine† with a short article describing her. She was claimed to have sailed at 18¾ mph with a fair, strong wind. In one voyage she averaged 15⅓ mph during a run of 115 miles, and in another, 18 mph for 90 miles—it was estimated that for short periods she reached 20 mph during this run. The above is in statute miles, not in nautical miles, due to Lake practice of employing land miles.

Plates 117 and 118 show the lines and sail plan of this schooner; the deck layout was reconstructed by use of a rather inadequate description. Bates wrote that she was 100.92 feet on deck for tonnage, 97.33 feet on the designed waterline, 27.12 feet moulded beam, 27.72 feet extreme beam, 8.08 feet depth in hold, 185 tons register, and could carry 100 to 110 thousand feet of lumber,

* *The Monthly Nautical Magazine and Quarterly Review*, Vol. 2 (April-September, 1855), No. 4, pp. 308–311.
† *The U. S. Nautical Magazine and Naval Journal*, Vol. 3 (October 1855 to March 1856), No. 4 (January 1856), pp. 331–35.

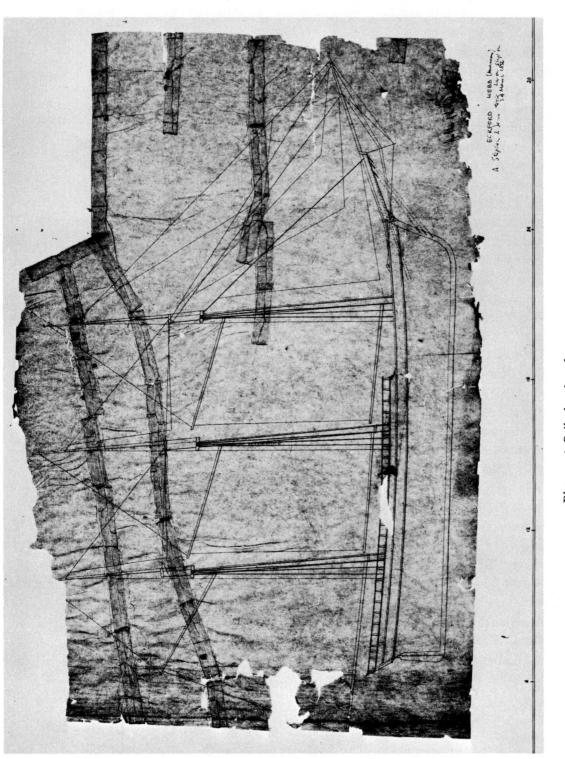
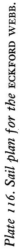

Plate 116. Sail plan for the ECKFORD WEBB.

drawing 7 to 7½ feet—about 145 tons. Her working sails totaled 5,732 square feet, and she displaced 121½ tons ready for cargo. Much larch (hackmatack) was used in her construction (top timbers, hold stanchions, bilge strakes, centerboard trunk, clamps, deck framing, and knees) to save structural weight. Her moulded displacement was 246 long tons; block coefficient was .54, midship .86, and prismatic .63. The camber-length ratio of the quarterbeam buttock was 14.6 (length 79 feet, camber 5′ 5″).

Clipper City had a strong sheer, and a keel rockered for about one third of its length at the fore end, but straight aft, little or no drag. The stem rabbet was well-rounded at forefoot, raking and flaring a good deal above. The post was nearly vertical; the sharply raking transom was of a deep U-form, with rudderstock passing through it. The entrance was very long and fine, and concave near the stem. The run was short; the quarterbeam buttock was straight for a short distance forward of its intersection with the after load line. The bow line at quarterbeam was very easy and the designer intended this to "lift the vessel" forward when sailing hard. The midship section has a flat straight floor, full round bilge, and a slight tumble home above. The rig was that of a fore-topsail two-masted schooner without a fore course, but with a square topsail and topgallant.

She was raised six inches over her depth as modeled, her original depth having been 7.58 feet. Bates consulted with Griffiths in 1853, while designing *Clipper City;* as a result she was given a centerboard that was lengthened by four feet, making it 24 feet long and nine feet deep. Griffiths designed the sail plan. A somewhat similar vessel was designed by Bates and built at Manitowoc, Wisconsin, by S. Bates & Son in 1853–54, named *Mary Stockton,* and employed in the grain trade on the Lakes. Under the name *Manitowoc* she was represented by an incomplete offset table and body plan in Griffiths' *Shipbuilder's Manual.* In rig she was a three-masted barkentine, square-rigged from course to skysail on the foremast, with fore-and-aft on main and mizzen —the mizzen gaff sail being smaller than the main. Yet Bates and Griffiths called her a schooner. She was 132 feet long, rabbet to rabbet on the load line, 29.2 feet moulded beam, 9.42 feet from base to gunwale at ⚹, drawing 8.50 feet and displacing 457 tons, and would carry 297 tons. She had two centerboards, one just forward of the mainmast and the other about three feet forward of the mizzen. Having very sharp entrance and a shallow hull, she must have been very fast, but no information on her speed has been found in Griffiths' books and papers. She was designed on the same lift theory as was

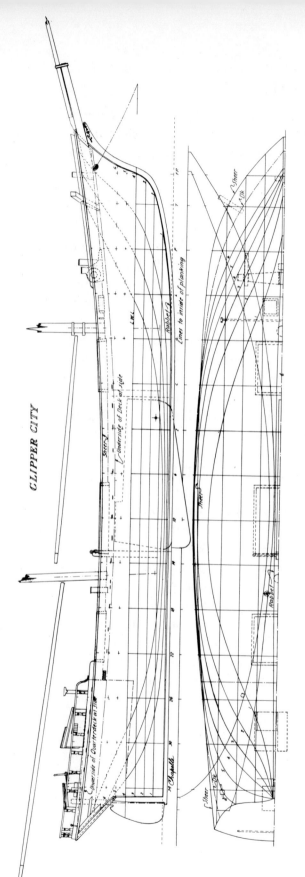

CLIPPER CITY

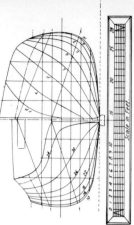

Scale in feet

Built at Manitowoc Wis by J Butts
& Son in 1854. Modelled by
W W Bates

Length on moulded L.W.L.   97'-4"
Beam moulded   27'-1⅝"
Depth in hold   7'-7"
Length on deck for tonnage, 100.36 feet.

Spars

Fore Mast whole 73'-4"   Main Mast whole 81'-6"
  - head 10'-6"   - head 11'-6"
Fore Topmast, hounded 24'-6'; Main Topmast 40'-9"
          - 13'-8", 6'-0"   - + Pole 8'-0"
Fore Top-'l Yard 36'-7"; (arms 3'-0 each), Fore Yard
48'-6" (arms 2'-0 each), Fore Topgal'l Yard 27'-4"
(arms 2'-0 each). Fore Gaff 28'-0, pole 2'-9"; Fore Boom
36'-0; Main Gaff 32'-0, pole 5'-4", Main Boom 48'-6";
   pole 4'-0"; Bowsprit 12-0 out-bd, Jibboom outside cap
   12'-0 + 8'-0 + 4'-0".

Plate 117. CLIPPER CITY, a very fast centerboard
schooner. The slack bow lines were intended to produce "lift," to prevent diving and broaching when running or reaching at high speed—a theory of W. W.
Bates and John Griffiths in 1854. The relatively short
run and long entrance were in accordance with Griffiths' ideas.

used in *Clipper City*, but to a more extreme degree.

The pilot schooners had represented the maximum development of the fast sailing models of their period. In the clipper ship era the pilot boats reached such excellence in design that there was little change in hull characteristics thereafter, until sailing pilot boats became obsolete. George Steers had established a great reputation as a designer of pilot boats by 1851, having modeled the *Wm. G. Haggstaff* and the better known *Mary Taylor*. He designed the schooner yacht *America* in 1851 and went to England on her. On his return he designed *Anthony B. Neilson* and *George Steers*. He had also designed many yachts and a number of steamers, including the big *Adriatic* of the

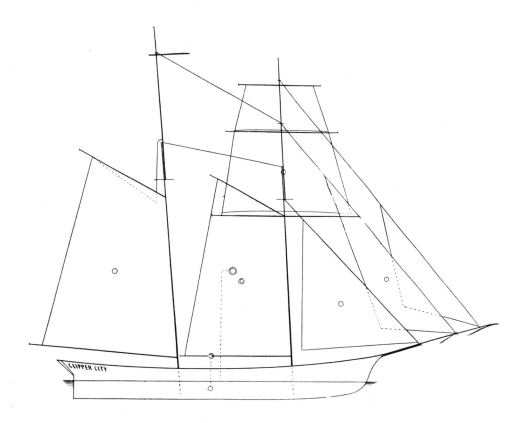

Plate 118. Sail plan for CLIPPER CITY.

Collins Line. His sole clipper, *Sunny South*, has been described earlier in this chapter. On 25 September 1856, Steers met an untimely death at the age of thirty-six as the result of being thrown from a carriage.

Moses H. Grinnell, Plate 119, shows one of his outstanding pilot schooners, built for the Jersey pilots in 1850. She was very sharp-ended, with high dead rise, and was reputedly very fast. The lives of pilot boats were often short; *Moses H. Grinnell* was lost in 1859 or 60, the *Anthony B. Neilson* in 1856, and *George Steers* in 1865. Their business kept them at sea when weather conditions had driven small vessels of their size to shelter. Many were overwhelmed by violent gales and hurricanes, or driven ashore, or run down by steamers.

Moses H. Grinnell had a rather marked sheer and a keel rockered forward for over a third of its length, becoming straight with moderate drag aft. The forefoot was much cut away, the stem rabbet was formed with a long sweep up from the rockered keel, flaring and raking above. The post was vertical with a round stern above, which formed a small counter. The entrance was long, sharp, and concave; the run was fine with the quarterbeam buttock straight for a short distance forward of its intersection with the after load line. The midsection was abaft the midlength of the load line, formed with sharply rising straight floor, a high, firm bilge, with slight tumble home above, to deck level. Most pilot boats of this period had low, log rails, as in *Grinnell*, instead of bulwarks.

The design of this pilot schooner seems to have been the basis for that of the schooner-yacht *America*. Only a few pilot schooners had clipper bows, a plain upright or somewhat curved stem being usually preferred. Round sterns had a period of popularity in the 1850's but the very raking deep-V transom was most common. These schooners had large working rigs, usually a main gaff topsail and a main-topmast staysail were the only light sails carried. They followed the pilot-boat practice of working under their large lug foresails.

Steers' half-model of *Grinnell* is in the Mariners' Museum at Newport News, Virginia, and her profile and half-breadth plan* are shown in Griffiths' *Treatise on the Theory and Practice of Shipbuilding*. Her customhouse dimensions were 73' 6" by 18' 9" by 7' 2", 88 6/94 tons. The schooner was owned by George W. Blunt of New York.

On a designed moulded load waterline 67' 4" long, she had a moulded dis-

---

* Plate 4, Sections 1 and 2.

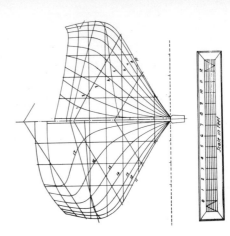

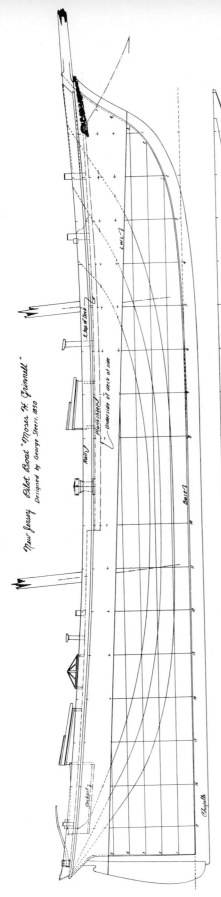

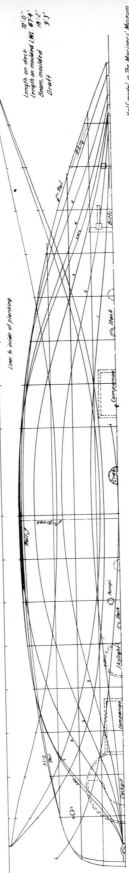

New Jersey Pilot Boat "Moses H. Grinnell"
Designed by George Steers. 1850

Length on deck 72'0"
Length on moulded LWL 67'4"
Beam, moulded 18'2"
Draft 9'3"

Half-model in The Mariners' Museum
Newport News, Va.

Lines to inside of planking

Plate 119. The MOSES H. GRINNELL, designed by George Steers in 1850, was the
prototype of his famous schooner yacht AMERICA, in which be improved the run
and suppressed the shoulders in the entrance shown here.

placement of 73.9 long tons and her coefficients were block .33, midship .59, and prismatic .57. The effective length of the quarterbeam buttock was 47′ 10″, camber 4′ 1½″, giving a camber-length ratio of 11.7. Her draught moulded dimensions were 72′ 8″ on deck, 18 feet beam, and 8′ 8″ depth (rabbet to planksheer at ⚏). She had the usual dimensions for a New York or Boston pilot boat of her period, though some much larger schooners were employed in the pilot services. In the 1850's the pilot boats appear to have ranged from about 58 feet registered length to 84 feet, with an occasional boat as large as 90 feet.

The naming of pilot boats for prominent merchants or businessmen was due to the desire of the pilots to obtain funds for construction of a vessel and the honored business man could be relied upon to contribute. Builders' names were also used, as the honored yard would often take shares in the boats they built. Some names were used more than once; three successive pilot boats at New York were named *James Gordon Bennett*, after the New York newspaper publisher. Some vessels carried more attractive names, such as *Pet*, *Dancing Feather*, and *Hope*.

These vessels were usually without decoration or other frills, but they were all well built and well finished. They were coppered and copper-fastened; and some of them had long lives, 15 to 20 years in the pilot service. But generally the mortality was high; between 1838 and 1860 fifteen New York boats were lost; and in 1888 alone, eight New York pilot boats were sunk. A single hurricane gale might account for two or three boats, despite their seaworthiness.

Griffiths and others have stated that *Grinnell* was the first commercial sailing vessel to have the very long, sharp, and concave entrance, but this claim is false since, as we have seen, such entrances had appeared in Hudson River steamers much earlier and some concavity had also been used in at least a few earlier sailing vessels. The entrance of *Grinnell*, however, was more extreme than any earlier recorded merchant sailing vessels.

Mention has already been made of the Hudson River sloops, those large centerboard carriers, especially designed for the service, that had reached their peak in development by the 1830's. The model of these sloops had become nearly standardized in design, varying only in degree of the individual design characteristics and in dimensions. They ranged in size from about 50 feet over the rail to nearly 80 feet. Except for a few sloops engaged as packets between small river towns, which carried a few passengers, the Hudson River sloops and schooners had become freighters by 1850. The sloop *Victorine*, a very fast sailer, shown by Griffiths on Plate 25 in his *Treatise on the Theory and Practice of Shipbuilding*, was one of a fleet of four such sloops belonging to the West Point Foundry and used to carry goods and supplies to and from the foundry as far as New York City.

Plate 120 shows the design characteristics of a typical Hudson River sloop, the *First Effort*, built at Mount Pleasant, New York, in 1830 by William and Thomas Collyer. Her customhouse measurements were 65 feet by 23′ 6″ by 5′ 9″, 72 37/95 tons register.

This sloop had much sheer, a straight keel, but with some rocker in the keel rabbet, a strongly raking curved stem rabbet, and a slightly raking post. The square stern was formed with a sharply raking deep transom, with rudder-post passed through its lower portion. The entrance was short, full, and convex, but with easy bow lines. The run was of moderate length with the quarterbeam buttock becoming straight a short distance forward of its intersection with the after load line. The midship section was forward of the middle of the load line and was formed with slightly rising straight floor, a firm round bilge, and very little tumble home in the topsides.

These sloops had a large centerboard and were heavily rigged with a large jib and a gaff mainsail. They sometimes set a gaff topsail. They could turn very quickly; when jibing they turned in the direction that the jibe moved the main boom, thus reducing the shock of the boom on the mainsheet and preventing the sharp heel sometimes produced by a jibe. The term "North River Jibe" has ever since been applied to this maneuver by American seamen—North River was the old name for the Hudson.

On a moulded load waterline of 61′ 4″, the sloop in Plate 120 had a moulded displacement of 93.4 long tons. Her coefficients were block .44, midsection .74, and prismatic .60. The effective length of the quarterbeam buttock was 48′ 6″, camber 4 feet, giving a camber-length ratio of 12.1. This fine sloop was modeled by Thomas Collyer; his brother, William, fourteen years old, was his partner in the building. They remained in partnership until 1847. Both later operated shipyards in New York. The Collyers became prominent in the design of river steamers. Their Hudson sloop *First Effort* measured 71′ 9″ at moulded rail, 24′ 4″ moulded beam, and 6′ 6″ moulded depth. She was rammed and sunk at her wharf at Marlboro, on the Hudson, in 1864 or 1865. This sloop had a pilot-boat stem; most Hudson sloops had long heads and billet. The *First Effort* had a slight rocker in her keel, apparently an unusual feature in this type of sloop.

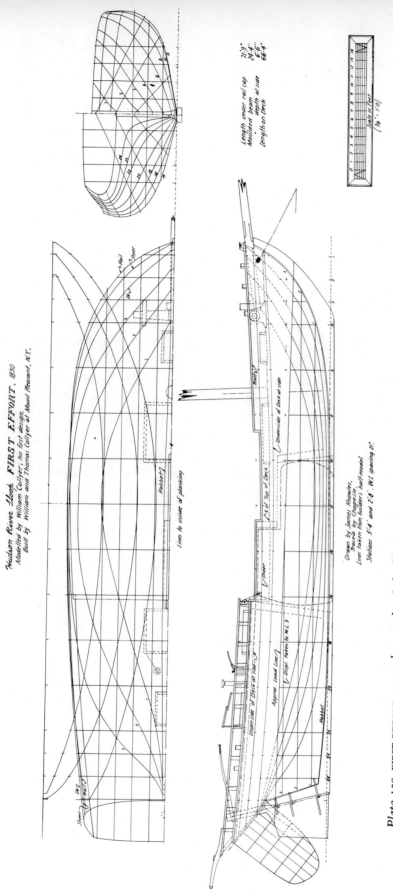

Hudson River Sloop FIRST EFFORT, 1850
Modelled by William Collyer; his first design.
Built by William and Thomas Collyer at Mount Pleasant, N.Y.

Lines to inside of planking

Drawn by James Knowles.
Traced by Chapelle.
Lines taken from builder's half-model.
Stations 5'-4" and 2'-8" W.L. spacing 2':

Length under rail cap   71'-9"
Moulded beam   24'-4"
depth at side   6'-6"
Length on Deck   66'-4"

Scale in Feet
(3/16" = 1'-0")

Plate 120. FIRST EFFORT, a good example of the Hudson River sloop model in which fast sailing was a prime requirement. Further refinement occurred in 1845–50, though the commercial importance of the sloops was rapidly declining.

Hudson River schooners were similar in model to the sloops, but with less beam in proportion to their length. The schooner was less popular on the Hudson than the sloop; however, the schooners were employed in the River and Sound coastal trade more extensively than the sloops.

Plans have now been shown that give a cross section of the American merchant vessels designed for speed under sail. A number of elementary calculations have been made for each vessel. These serve to show the trends in design in America, between 1700 and 1855, and the design techniques used.

Some conclusions may now be reached on the progress in a technical art and science of the design of sailing vessels, during one hundred and fifty-five years, in the United States.

Woodcut of tern schooner ECKFORD WEBB.

CHAPTER · EIGHT

Conclusions and Comment

THE MATERIAL THAT HAS BEEN PRESENTED IN THIS STUDY IS DIVIDED INTO TWO groups: the plans for visual examination and analysis, and the mathematical factors of hull design for analysis and classification. The information obtainable through examination of the sheer draughts of 103 vessels has been outlined in the text, leaving only certain comments to be required in a summarization.

The plans, or draughts, have produced some precise information. Perhaps the most important is the fact that the advantages of sharp-ended hulls were known long before the American shipbuilders had produced any distinctively American type of fast sailing vessel. The draughts also show that there was no progressive development in the degree of sharpness—ships did not become increasingly sharp in the ends during the period studied here. It may be injected here that the very recent discovery made by Professor G. S. Baker of a manuscript by Samuel Fortree (Fortrey) in the Pepysian Library, Magdalene College, Cambridge, entitled *Of Navarchi,* adds to the evidence on these matters. The manuscript is reported to establish that model tests, made in 1670, led to the conclusion that a sharp entrance was advantageous for speed

Conclusions and Comment

as was length of hull, and also that hollow in the vicinity of the forefoot (even though the load waterline be full), could be expected to produce a fast sailing vessel. It was recognized that much of the speed advantage of hollow at the forefoot would be lost if the vessel heeled at a great angle, bringing the full upper works of the bow into the water; this would also produce weather helm. However, the author of the manuscript also considered that hollow near the lower sternpost as well as near the forefoot would be very useful in producing a fast sailer. This condition existed in some degree, incidentally, in vessels designed by the old tangent arc system.

The draughts also show that the foregoing propositions were employed time and again by both European and American designers of fast sailing vessels. It would be difficult, in fact, to find many theories regarding hull form for sailing craft that were not tried or at least suggested for trial during the years between 1700 and 1855.

Though hollow at the load line, just abaft the stem rabbet, appeared in some vessels before the clipper ship era, as well as during that period, it often produced more or less of a shoulder where the entrance met the midbody of the hull. This tended to reduce the potential for high speed by producing wave-making resistance. The same was also true if there were any marked hump or shoulder at the fore end of the run. However, the effects of shoulder were somewhat lessened if the shoulders in each level line (or waterline), from load line down, were shifted aft in the forebody and forward in the afterbody. Generally, shoulders produced waves whose magnitude, in size and consumption of driving force, varied with the speed of the vessel and "hardness" of the shoulders. It is also true that bow waves were considered undesirable, and many designers attempted to eliminate such waves by using very sharp or hollow entrances. Too often such attempts led naturally to the formation of these shoulders abaft the hollow, thus moving the adverse effects of a bow wave aft to the vicinity of the shoulder. It may have been the practical experience with, and observations of, this characteristic that prejudiced many designers of fast sailing vessels against hollow at forefoot and at heel of sternpost.

The use of a straight quarterbeam buttock at the intersection of this buttock with the after load line appears quite often in the draughts shown here, but there were marginal ships in which the straight of the buttock was very short. If this is the case in a lines drawing or half-model, it must be accepted that the straight of the buttock may have been lost in the mould loft and so might not have existed in the completed hull. The value of straight quarter-beam buttocks is recognized by designers now more than formerly, as a result of hydrodynamic discoveries of the behavior of flow in the run. The relationship of the length of straight in the average or quarterbeam buttock to a given speed-length ratio is still to be explored. The angle such a buttock takes to the after load line is an important and related factor. As the speed-length ratio increases, the angle decreases. This can be seen in the draughts and the angles can be measured for comparison. The speed components to be sought in the run are straight flow at a small angle to the load line.

The entrance follows much the same rule, but the buttock-bow angle is often controlled to some extent by the softness or hardness of the bow lines. Generally high speed-length ratios require softness in the sweeps in the entrance at the load line of sailing craft. Generally the conditions that produce speed are found when the quarterbeam buttock-bow line camber is relatively shallow, producing small angles at the forward and after intersections with the load line.

The supposed "introduction" in the 1830's of the flat-floored full midsection in the packets has been shown to have been false, for this midsection (combined with more or less sharpness in the ends) was used in the eighteenth century, and probably earlier. The shape of the full midsection, however, was never a standard one.

A fast sailing ship design seems to have been the creation of individual, skilled judgment, which was created by intensive study of fast sailing vessels encountered in a designer's career. It is doubtful that the American designer, before the clipper ship era, used much of the contemporary theoretical processes of design, but rather, he had a picture in his mind of the desired hull to be designed, formed before he began work on the draught or half-model. The ideal or picture might be subject to modification or compromise, but never compromised out of existence. Instead, the design might be refined as it progressed in draught or model. There has long been a shipyard saying, "if it looks right it is right," and there is much truth in this. It is not enough to have a suitable underbody; the topside hull design must match the underbody, for the water passing around the hull, particularly when the hull is heeled, is a source of wave-making resistance.

Because successful design of fast sailing vessels was so nearly an art, ship designers were loath to impart their knowledge, theories, and opinions to any persons but their apprentices—indeed this was the foundation of the shipbuilders' apprentice system. Hence there were no books by practical ship-builders and designers in America, prior to Griffiths' works, that gave specific rules or instructions on the designing of fast sailing vessels.

The shape of the midsection has been repeatedly discussed in this study, particularly as to the amount of deadrise employed; and its advantages and disadvantages have been stated. Recent hydrodynamic judgments of the effects of deadrise should be mentioned. In comparing the speed potentials of two vessels of equal displacement—one with flat floors, hard bilges, and nearly vertical sides, the other of the V-Baltimore-clipper form; the flat-floored full midsection vessel would have the apparent advantage because of a lower prismatic. The flow lines around the V-section hull, however, will commonly be easier, but increased beam, depth, or length will be required with the V-section to obtain an equal displacement, with the attendant disadvantage of increased building costs.

It must be recognized that in any type of sailing vessel, speed is affected by the relation of its displacement to the size of its rig—the weight-power factor. Our inability to extract a specific numerical factor of horsepower for a rig makes the displacement-rig ratio too vague to be of any use here. Nevertheless, manipulation of displacement is, in the final analysis, a practical step in the improvement of a design in order to obtain a greater speed. In step design—that is, the repeated redesign of a given sailing vessel to obtain a faster sailer—it is always possible to reduce displacement by reducing structural weights and ballast weight.

It was this method that produced the fast pilot boats, privateers, slavers, and early American yachts. The comparison of vessels, requiring equal displacement to obtain results, is contrary to the practical processes of vessel design, though it is of interest theoretically in order to try to find out the effects of single hull-elements on vessel performance.

Before proceeding with the mathematical comparisons of 100 of the vessels whose draughts are used in this study, there are some explanations necessary regarding the selection or rejection of design factors in this final discussion.

One of these factors is "wetted surface." This is the emmersed underbody, which includes all of the surface of the hull and its appendages below the load waterline. Its importance is related to skin friction, which actually constitutes all resistance in a vessel moving at low speed, before wave-making begins. On this fact, the theory of wetted surface as a resistance factor is based.

The task of measuring the actual wetted surface area is tedious and time-consuming. The usual method is to measure the outline of the sections in the body plan, from keel to the load line, and compute mean girth, which is then multiplied by the length of the load line. No correction is usually made for wave formations, nor for expanded length. Expansion of wetted surface from two half-models, using panels and longitudinal expansion (as in a plating model), showed that the various approximations by formulae and the vertical expansion method were up to nearly 5 percent in error, depending upon the hull shape.

Wetted surface has become a bugaboo in yacht design and much is made of the need of reduction of its area since, in the opinion of many, wetted surface controls skin friction, or is even synonymous with it. The value of wetted surface in representing skin friction was established by towing a flat plate on edge. Whether or not this gave a true value for calculating skin friction in a wooden vessel or on curved surfaces is problematical.

It is worthy of comment, however, that the amount of wetted surface is closely related to the amount of displacement in given hull dimensions, hence the variation in wetted surface that is possible, through manipulation of hull form alone, is slight if these limitations are maintained.* In merchant sailing vessels the chief areas to be considered in a reduction of wetted surface would be the forefoot, fore gripe, keel, post—part of which affects weatherliness—and also the rudder-blade area, if reduction in displacement is not permissable.

Skin friction in large wooden vessels was largely a matter of skin roughness, since their bottoms were never as smooth as a racing yacht's. It is clearly impractical to try to assess the comparative degree of roughness or foulness of vessels no longer in existence. Even copper-sheathed hulls did not have a really smooth bottom, for the plates were laid over tarred felt and the fastening nails dented the whole surface in a manner best described as "quilting." In addition, plate laps would add to the skin friction, even though the plates were thin. Foulness in even small quantity produced far more skin friction or drag than the mere area of wetted surface indicates. With these facts in view, no attempt was made to establish comparative wetted surface areas, nor to attempt comparative roughness-coefficient calculations. It may

---

* Historically the reduction of wetted surface in sailing yachts was accomplished largely by a decrease in displacement that allowed marked changes in hull form. This could be done in only a few commercial sailing vessels—pilot boats and fishing schooners, for example—in which no cargo, or a relatively small cargo, needed to be considered.

be stated only that vessels before 1800 were generally handicapped by foul bottoms,* which coppering eventually reduced.

The curves of areas for the vessels shown in this study have not been prepared, as it was decided that comparison of these curves would not be informative. Saunders stated that curves of area were more of an effect than a cause.† The desirable form of the curve of areas is best determined by comparisons with the curves of successful vessels of the same size and type, rather than comparisons with some theoretical or ideal form of the curve.

Another feature employed by some American designers was the use of "constant deadrise" in the afterbody. In this, the straight rise of floor in the sections (from amidships aft) was parallel, or very nearly so, to the straight rise of floor of the midsection in the body plan. This appeared, to some degree, in sharp American schooners before 1840, as can be seen in schooners such as *Revenge, Nonpareil, Experiment,* and *Snapdragon.* By 1850, the use of constant deadrise in the run became rather common in pilot schooners and fast small craft. Warp in the straight rise of floor in the run, seen most often in the lines of sailing vessels, may have had adverse effects on the flow lines in direct proportion to the amount of warp employed. Constant deadrise in the run is now often apparent in the lines of fast motorboats and of shallow sailing craft. The area of constant deadrise of the sections in the run is often in a rather narrow band outboard of any hollow garboard that may exist and well inboard of the turn of the bilge in each section, running from amidships aft to the transom or counter.

The values of the block, midship section, and prismatic coefficients were explained in Chapter 2. In tabulating these, for comparison, the displacement-length ratio has been added. The formula for the displacement-length ratio, in which D = displacement in long tons and L = length on the L.W.L in feet, is:

$$D \div (0.010L)^3$$

The numerical value of this ratio increases with the degree, or ratio of fullness (or "fatness"), of the hull. An increase in displacement-length ratio is presumed to show a decrease in resistance in the speed-length ratios below wave-

---

* The American frigate *Hancock*, "though foul," was reported by her captors to have sailed thirteen knots while not carrying all possible sail. Her speed-length ratio was then 1.11, and it seems possible that she could have reached 1.25, or better, had her bottom been clean and smooth, and the ship under all possible sail.

† *Hydrodynamics in Ship Design*, Vol. 1, p. 355.

Coefficients etc. of 100 Vessels, 1700-1855

Chapter	Name	Rig	L.W.L.	Displ. Long Tons	Block Coef.	Midship Coef.	Prismatic Coef.	Camber Length R.	Displ. Length R.	Date
Chap.	Galley	Brigt.			Not	Calculated.				
	Danish Sloop	Ship	65'-10"	117.5	.50	.75	.67	10.4	408	1665 to 1720
Chapter 2	Peregrine Galley	Ship	83'-4"	218.2	.51	.81	.65	9.4	382	1700 1720
	Ferrett	Slp.	62'-3"	132.7	.48	.75	.63	8.5	557	1710-11
	St. Ann	Sch.	54'-0"	27.6	.40	.64	.61	17.0	175	1736
	Lyme	Ship	115'-3"	528.2	.49	.74	.66	10.9	347	1739
	Bermuda Sloop	Slp.	58'-10	129.3	.44	.64	.63	7.9	629	1750
	Mediator	Slp.	59'-6"	124.4	.44	.71	.62	7.7	590	1741
	Neptunus	Ship	76'-3"	188.5	.42	.79	.55	8.4	429	1720
Chapter 3	Sir Edw. Hawke	Sch.	56'-0"	91.2	.39	.69	.70	9.0	314	1767
	Badger	Brig.	64'-9"	122.3	.73	.74	.64	8.7	445	1776
	Swift	Brigt.	70'-11"	87.8	.37	.64	.60	14.2	246	1778
	Harlequin	Ship	76'-7" 76'-4"	197.9 154.5	.46 .45	.68 .67	.68 .63	9.5 10.1	443 338	1780
	Codrington	Ship	74'-0"	313.7	.60	.87	.71	7.2	774	1774
	Rhodes	Ship	96'-5"	292.7	.42	.64	.65	11.9	326	1778
	Mohawk	Ship	93'-10"	274.7	.40	.65	.61	10.8	331	1779
	Rattlesnake	Ship	87'-7½"	221.3	.50	.71	.60	12.2	325	1779
	London	Ship	89'-4"	362.8	.49	.81	.62	8.1	514	1770
	Berbice	Sch.	66'-9"	73.6	.35	.62	.57	12.1	204	1780
	Steel's Va. Privateer	Sch.	74'-7"	155.7	.41	.66	.61	10.2	373	1790?
	Steel's Fast Sch.	Sch.	72'-1"	110.5	.47	.67	.62	11.5	296	1790?
	A Bien Acquis	Ship			Not	Calculated				
Chapter 4	Coureuse	Sch.	50'-8"	32.2	.38	.69	.56	13.3	265	1785
	Swift	Sch.	44'-5"	33.8	.41	.79	.61	12.7	391	1794
	Enlarged Swift	Sch.			Not	Calculated				
	Steel's Va. Pilot Boat	Sch.	49'-10"	31.0	.38	.65	.62	12.7	247	1790?
	Revenge	3 m. Sch.	74'-0"	109.2	.39	.60	.65	13.2	269	1805
	La Superieure	Sch.	80'-0"	160.6	.39	.62	.63	12.9	308	1801

Chapter	Name	Rig	L.W.L.	Displ Long Tons	Block Coef.	Midship Coef.	Prismatic Coef.	Camber Length R.	Displ Length R.	Date
Chapter 4	La Vengeance	Ship	105'-0"	330.4	.34	.61	.56	10.8	259	1800
	Numa	Brig	89'-6"	189	.42	.64	.64	14.2	290	1801
	Nimble	Sch.	53'-0"	34.6	.37	.59	.63	17.3	232	1806
	Canton Yacht	Sch.	46'-2"	22.8	.32	.62	.68	15.0	234	1805-8
	Bermuda Water Tanks	3-M Sch.	68'-4"	136.4	.48	.72	.67	10.8	434	1804
	Bergh's ship	Ship	75'-10½"	330.2	.59	.86	.64	6.8	752	1804
	Steer's design	Sch.	82'-3"	176.3	.36	.60	.59	10.7	319	1805
	Nonpareil	Sch.	82'-6"	177.7	.32	.59	.59	10.7	311	1807
	Fly	Sch.	76'-8"	142.4	.31	.60	.65	12.6	312	1811
	Dominica	Sch.	84'-6"	141.8	.38	.59	.64	14.7	231	1809
	Experiment	Sch.	71'-4"	96.2	.31	.51	.62	14.7	213	1810
	Hannibal	Ship	129'-10"	934.6	.48	.68	.70	11.1	425	1811
Chapter 5	Lynx	Sch.	88'-0"	191.3	.37	.63	.59	11.7	288	1812
	William Bayard	Sch.	91'-8"	205.9	.39	.61	.64	14.1	265	1812
	Grecian	Sch.	89'-0"	216.4	.35	.54	.65	13.2	307	1812
	Zebra	Sch.	98'-5"	247.5	.40	.59	.67	15.6	261	1812
	Transfer	Sch.	90'-0"	176.0	.36	.60	.61	14.9	241	1812
	Neufchatel	Herm. Sch.	107'-5"	253	.39	.64	.62	17.0	204	1812
	Dash	Sch.-Bright.	99'-7"	220.5	.38	.60	.63	15.1	224	1813
	Reindeer	Herm. Sch.	116'-5"	580.0	.48	.72	.68	10.9	366	1814
	Spark	USN Brig	96'-11"	293.6	.42	.63	.66	13.0	321	1813
	Achilles	Sch.	62'-0"	64.4	.38	.63	.64	14.5	273	1812
	Snap Dragon	Sch.	84'-10"	157.7	.34	.56	.62	15.9	257	1812
	Letter-of-Marque	Sch.	85'-0"	193.6	.48	.76	.63	12.0	315	1815
	105' Schooner	Sch.	99'-2"	267.8	.38	.61	.63	12.8	276	1814
	116' Schooner	Sch.	109'-10"	411.5	.43	.67	.62	10.2	309	1812-14
	James Munroe	Bright.	63'-7"	172.0	.62	.72	.85	10.2	672	1815

Chapter	Name	Rig	L.W.L.	Displ. Long Tons	Block Coef.	Midship Coef.	Prismatic Coef.	Camber Length R	Displ Length R	Date
Chapter 6	Bolivar	Ship	119'-3"	363.0	.32	.55	.63	15.3	210	1822
	Kensington	Ship	165'-2"	1612.7	.76	.70	.67	11.5	357	1828
	Lafayette	Sch.	57'-10"	54.0	.35	.56	.63	13.9	529	1824
	Brothers	Sch.	66'-0"	53.6	.30	.53	.56	15.5	186	1826
	Keel Packet Sloop	Slp.	61'-3"	87.5	.32	.53	.61	13.4	379	1830~40
	Columbus	Ship	131'-7"	1317.7	.79	.89	.76	8.2	574	1834
	Christoval Colon	Ship	102'-2"	620.8	.63	.88	.72	8.6	581	1835
	Oxford	Ship	142'-6"	1448.6	.67	.90	.75	8.4	506	1836
	New York	Ship	148'-0"	1828.9	.68	.91	.76	8.2	561	1839
	Yorkshire	Ship	161'-0"	1717.3	.65	.88	.73	9.7	412	1843
	Santiago	Sch cb	63'-6"	113.6	.61	.80	.73	12.3	446	1833
	Ann Mckim	Ship	138'-6"	648.6	.40	.63	.65	15.6	438	1832
	Montauk	Ship	122'-6"	763.2	.53	.85	.63	8.5	485	1844
	Panama	Ship	130'-1½"	1127.5	.59	.85	.69	8.6	511	1844
	Isabella	Sch.	75'-4"	109.0	.47	.70	.67	13.9	254	1830
	Merchant Schooner	Sch.	74'-5"	112.8	.45	.64	.65	11.2	273	1830
	Flannigan's Design	Brignt.	84'-10½"	211.0	.53	.79	.68	12.0	345	1825-30
	Theresa Secunda	Sch.	84'-6"	144.1	.38	.61	.62	11.4	238	1831
	Diligente	Brig	96'-4"	305.6	.45	.66	.68	13.1	341	1839
	Slaver	Brig	85'-6"	261.8	.39	.62	.65	9.8	417	1820-30
	Clipper Brig	Brig	98'-9"	285.1	.41	.77	.64	12.4	284	1845
	Lawrence	USN Brig	107'-7"	404.1	.44	.62	.72	9.2	324	1843
Chapter 7	Rainbow	Ship	154'-3"	1043.1	.47	.70	.67	15.3	284	1845
	Sea Witch	Ship	166'-0"	1249.5	.51	.80	.64	9.8	273	1846
	Memnon	Ship	167'-5"	1837.5	.57	.87	.67	9.5	396	1847
	Samuel Russell	Ship	171'-9"	1291.4	.52	.75	.70	11.7	254	1846
	Oriental	Ship	171'-6"	1642.8	.58	.93	.71	10.5	325	1848
	Celestial	Ship	152'-6"	1388.1	.56	.84	.67	9.2	334	1850

Chapter	Name	Rig	L.W.L.	Displ. Long Tons	Block Coef.	Midship Coef.	Prismatic Coef.	Camber Length R.	Displ. Length R.	Date
Chapter 7	Staghound	Ship	203'-9"	1964.1	.46	.71	.64	10.9	232	1850
	Surprise	Ship	178'-6"	2549.9	.73	.81	.82	9.8	448	1850
	Challenge	Ship	221'-6"	2204.4	.46	.77	.60	10.9	204	1851
	Comet	Ship	223'-6"	2476.8	.53	.84	.63	11.0	221	1851
	Nightingale	Ship	171'-6"	1316.8	.54	.74	.67	11.6	410	1851
	Wild Pigeon	Ship	164'-9"	1594.2	.56	.82	.69	9.3	357	1851
	Witch of the Wave	Ship	195'-3"	1911.9	.51	.71	.66	11.4	527	1851
	Griffiths' Hamburg Ship	Ship	180'-6"	1424.8	.58	.89	.65	10.7	242	1851
	Jacob Bell	Ship	196'-9"	1785.7	.53	.80	.67	10.8	233	1852
	Sovereign of the Seas	Ship	230'-4"	2492.6	.51	.82	.62	10.4	204	1852
	Romance of the Seas	Ship	229'-2"	2012.5	.51	.80	.64	13.1	168	1853
	Sweepstakes	Ship	227'-10"	2661.3	.50	.79	.64	15.6	224	1853
	Lightning	Ship	228'-0"	2661.0	.54	.75	.61	10.5	222	1854
	Sunny South	Ship	149'-0"	901.1	.43	.78	.62	9.4	272	1854
	Henry Hill	Bark	132'-6½"	663.0	.41	.68	.61	11.4	454	1855-6
	Lupton's Design	Bark	141'-6"	645.6	.57	.86	.66	15.9	227	1855
	Eckford Webb	3 M Sch.	124'-3"	773.6	.64	.88	.72	10.3	406	1855
	Clipper City	C.B. Sch.	97'-4"	246.0	.54	.86	.63	14.6	267	1854
	Moses H. Grinnell	Sch.	67'-4"	73.9	.33	.59	.57	11.7	243	1850
	First Effort	C.B. Slp.	61'-4"	93.4	.44	.74	.60	12.1	405	1830

making. In sailing craft this range of speed is very common, particularly in light winds. In a modern keel sloop-yacht the ratio would usually be between 350 and 385. The only modern power hulls having much resemblance to clipper ship hulls are the harbor and coastal tugs in which the range of displacement-length ratios is 200 to 450. It should be emphasized again that the displacement-length ratio can be utilized only in low speed-length ratios.

Length on the designed load line is given—length being an important factor when related to displacement. These elements in the tabular list are often helpful in visualizing the proportions in making comparisons of the hull forms.

The quarterbeam buttock camber-length ratio has been discussed; it should amend the value of the prismatic somewhat, for it shows the depth-length proportions of the hulls under comparison. If two vessels have the same or nearly the same prismatic, the one with the larger quarterbeam buttock camber-length ratio can usually be presumed to be the faster, for reasons made clear earlier. The camber-length ratios are generally high in very fast sailing vessels; the exceptions are extremely sharp-ended.

When coefficients and ratios are concerned, we are faced with the same basic problems that are found in hull-lines analysis. A hull having favorable elements, in both areas of investigation, is presumed to be a relatively fast vessel, theoretically. But the experienced designer knows this presumption is not necessarily true. The balance of rig and hull, proper steering characteristics, sufficient power to carry enough sail, efficient sails and rigging, smooth planking or skin, proper proportions of appendages and other less apparent factors can offset many of the advantages of form, of coefficients, and of proportions. Hence, the comparisons to be made deal with possibilities, not certainties, in the vessel's performance.

In examining the tabular assembly of characteristics, it is apparent that it is quite impossible to establish the ranges of prismatics and displacement-length ratios, suitable for a given speed-length ratio or ratios, within precise limitations. This is due to the fact that the performances of these vessels cannot be accurately estimated on the two factors mentioned. Nevertheless, some fairly sound conclusions are possible.

The upper ranges of speed-length ratios, based upon known or fairly well supported claims for maximum sailing speed in merchant ships, can be established. Cutler's book on sailing records* is used for speed references. This source shows that the ships, whose lines and elements are included here, that

* *Five Hundred Sailing Records of American-Built Ships.*

reached very high hourly speeds were *Sweepstakes* 18 knots, *Lightning* 19 knots, *Sovereign of the Seas* 19–22 knots. Other clippers mentioned are *James Baines* 21 knots, *Champion of the Seas* 20 knots, *Great Republic* 19 knots, *Flying Cloud* 18½ knots, and *Donald McKay* 18 knots. It will be recalled that the speed-length ratio is calculated by the following formula—Speed in nautical miles divided by the square root of the load line length. Applied, the results are:

Ship	W. L.	Speed	Speed-Length Ratio
Sovereign of the Seas	230′	22	1.45
		19	1.25
Lightning	228′	19	1.26
Sweepstakes	228′	18	1.13

And for *James Baines*, whose dimensions are available here but whose lines are not, we have W. L. 210 feet, speed 21 knots, speed-length ratio 1.45.

Referring to the table, it will be seen that the displacement-length ratios of the ships were *Sovereign* 204, *Lightning* 222, and *Sweepstakes* 224. It will also be seen that their prismatics were *Sovereign* .62, *Lightning* .61, and *Sweepstakes* .64. *Challenge* would fit into these ranges of factors—her prismatic was .60, her displacement-length ratio was 204. The buttock camber-length ratios of these ships were: *Sovereign* 10.4, *Lightning* 10.5, *Sweepstakes* 15.6, and *Challenge* 10.9.

Earlier and smaller vessels that might have been capable of reaching speed-length ratios in this range, because of their coefficients and ratios, would be:

	Prismatic	Camber-Length ratio	Displacement-Length ratio
Berbice, 1780, schooner	.57	12.1	204
Neufchâtel, 1812, schooner	.62	17.0	204
Bolivar, 1822, ship	.63	15.3	210

To do this, *Berbice* would have to reach a speed of 9.25 knots for a speed-length ratio of 1.13, and 11.87 knots for a speed-length ratio of 1.45. At a speed-length ratio of 1.25 she would have to reach 10.23 knots. It is doubtful, in the opinion of the author, however, that she could exceed 10 knots, because of her lack of power to carry sail in strong wings, as indicated in her lines. *Neufchâtel*, claimed to have exceeded 12½ knots while being chased by a British squadron, would have reached 1.25 speed-length ratio at 12.9 knots. *Bolivar* would have to sail 13.64 knots to obtain a speed-length ratio of 1.25. Her lines indicate that this may have been possible, but she could reach the speed-length of 1.13 without much doubt. Any extensive study of the speeds reported for clipper ships will show that 1.25 is a realistic potential speed ratio for the best of the clipper ships, and that ships rarely met weather conditions allowing higher speeds—also that this was true of some earlier, smaller vessels.

It is a simple calculation to obtain the rate of speed, on any selected length of load waterline, that produces the desired speed-length ratio—multiply the $\sqrt{\text{load line length}}$ by the selected speed-length ratio; the answer is the speed in knots of the vessel for a given ratio.

It is interesting to note that many vessels in the table, having low prismatics also, have rather low displacement-length ratios. This may indicate that these very fast vessels could reach a high potential speed when enough windpower was applied, but were not so responsive in light winds and low power. However, a more extensive study is required before this would be fully established as a characteristic of the clipper ships having very high maximum speed.

The clipper ships that were particularly noted for short passages, with more than one entry in Cutler's records, include such vessels as:

	Prismatic	Camber-Length ratio	Displacement-Length ratio
Sea Witch	.64	9.8	273
Comet	.63	11.0	221
Nightingale	.67	11.6	410
Witch of the Wave	.66	11.4	257

Some small vessels showed unusual speed. *Clipper City*, a centerboard Great Lakes schooner, 97′ 4″ on the load line, was reported to have attained a speed of 16.7 knots, with a strong wind on the quarter. Her speed-length ratio was then 1.65! Her prismatic was .63, her camber-length ratio was 14.6 and her displacement-length ratio was 267. It is obvious, from the tabular information, that no conclusions based upon coefficients and hull ratios alone, could determine, in advance of trials, what exact maximum speed-length ratio will be obtained. It seems apparent from a study of sailing speeds, that some merchant vessels under 115 feet load-line length may have reached speed-length ratios in excess of the 22 knot-1.45 speed-length ratio of the great clipper ships.

Occasionally a vessel will be found whose performance was better than her coefficients indicated. The tern schooner *Eckford Webb,* having a prismatic of .72, camber-length ratio of 10.3, and a displacement-length ratio of 406, is recorded as having made 16 knots. This is a speed-length ratio of 1.43. It seems probable, however, that the *Webb* was flying light and so had, in her light trim, a much smaller prismatic than .72. *Porto (Harlequin)* in the tables shows the results of a change in displacement on the prismatic—.68 to .63— enough change to produce a marked alteration in performance.

One interesting case is the *Surprise,* rated as a clipper ship but with very high prismatic. The reason for this was her unusual proportions: 178' 6" on the load line, combined with great depth and a displacement of 2549 long tons; greater than in *Challenge,* 221' 6" L.W.L., or *Sovereign of the Seas,* 230' 2" L.W.L. As a result her prismatic was .82, in spite of her rather sharp ends; in fact she was a well-developed "fast carrier" rather than a clipper ship.

Vessels of the extreme clipper type were in the .60 to .67 prismatic, the prismatic increasing with the amount of deadrise in the midsection. Fast sailing vessels not extreme clippers ranged from .66 to .71. Small schooners such as pilot boats often had prismatics as low as .56 but some were as high as .64; many had comparatively high displacement-length ratios. Pilot boats, however, can be said to have followed a distinct pattern in coefficients in each area of use—Norfolk, Philadelphia, New York, and Boston—each having a special range in coefficients.

It should be noted, also, that privateers and letters-of-marque were usually within the prismatic range of .59 to .67; the Chesapeake-built vessels often in the .59 to .63 range. These prismatics were reduced in effect by increased camber-length ratios in many instances; the displacement-length ratios are generally above those of the large extreme clippers of the .60 to .64 prismatic range. Their buttock camber-length ratios were commonly above 10.0.

Some general conclusions concerning possible speed qualities of vessels shown by plans in this study can be reached by listing vessels of closely related ratios and coefficients. Such groupings will show that the sharpest clippers in the 1850's did not have greater fineness in the ends or lower prismatic coefficients than was reached in some much earlier vessels.

This leads to one possibility—that there had been no important basic gain in the hydrodynamic design of ships. It therefore would be possible that the gain in speed, in knots, of fast sailing ships of the 1850's over earlier vessels was due to the increase in size, particularly in length, that had developed between 1830 and 1850. The important area of development would then be in construction—allowing wooden ships to be built of great length, with sufficient longitudinal strength to prevent change of form.

Perhaps the most important observation that can be made is that many small vessels—sloops, schooners, brigs, and brigantines—came into existence that seem to have been capable of reaching higher speed-length ratios than the larger ships. But it is plain that this was accomplished by excessive reduction in cargo capacity.

Though evidence to establish the fact is lacking, there appears to be some logic in a suggestion that extremely high speed-length ratios became possible only after the centerboard was introduced. *Clipper City* was not an isolated case of a very fast centerboard merchant vessel in the 1850's. The assumption that the handsome clippers of the 1850's were supreme as designs of seagoing vessels for fast sailing is certainly now untenable.

The speed-length ratios of modern sailing ocean-racers have not yet exceeded 1.4 on their fastest point of sailing, so speed per foot of length has not improved since 1855. To windward it would be another story, however, for on this point of sailing modern sails and rigging are the results of nearly a century of intensive effort for this purpose alone, in fact at the expense of speed in running and reaching. Another factor in the failure of modern sailing ocean-racers to attain very high speed-length ratios is the hull form (here the product of measurement rules to a great extent), in which the buttock-bow camber ratio is necessarily small, even with a very low prismatic, and this prevents very high potential speed after wave-making takes place. The buttock-bow line camber indicates the concentration of displacement amidships. In these sailing yachts, the wave formation created at their maximum speed is commonly marked by a deep trough formed amidships and this is the result of a relatively short load line and concentrated displacement. Hence, the modern sailing ocean-racer, like the clipper ship, is not the best form for high sailing speed.

In order to understand the problems of the sailing ship designer it is necessary to explain his difficulties. It seems obvious, in this examination of fast sailing vessels, that there was little scientific information of sufficiently precise nature to guide design. In spite of the amount of American and European literature on naval architecture, there was not much information of a practical nature to be extracted from textbooks. Hence the sailing vessel designer was forced to apply visual methods—basically a mode of comparing new designs with existing successful vessels of about the same size and type. But here there was also a lack of exactness in design data.

The mathematical attempts at solution of problems in sailing vessel design have been the most popular, on the assumption that only by this method could "scientific naval architecture" be created. This attitude is still maintained today so that in academic naval architecture, attempts to apply the mathematical method to such complex problems as sail carrying power, dynamic stability, total resistance, and even seaworthiness, continue, even though it is admitted that such calculations are very inadequate, and even unreliable.

What has been termed in the past "scientific naval architecture" has been misleading or totally incorrect in so many instances—for example, the long, fruitless search for a universal low-resistance hull form that produced the Chapman thesis of controlled distribution of displacement, and culminated in the long-lived but erroneous Wave Line Theory of Scott-Russell. Balance of hull and sails, by means of comparative positions of the centers of gravity of sail plan, drawn on a plane, and of the hull profile of the submerged underbody upright—all obviously having no relation to the true centers of effort and lateral plane—has been the only mathematical solution of the balance problem since the 1840's, though it is obviously a theoretical fiction. The use of various mathematical solutions of static stability to solve problems in dynamic stability is another example. The emphasis on wetted surface, the area of which is usually recommended to be established by formula, or at best, by an incomplete calculation of the true area, has led to confusion between mere area of wetted surface and skin friction caused by rough surfaces in the submerged underbody. This also has been a theoretical factor since the 1840's.

Complaints against such formalized mathematic treatment of complex problems have been made, but a satisfactory alternate has not been found. The designer, "by eye and judgment," using visual judgment of lines or half-model, was almost as confused as the academic textbook naval architect. As we have seen, there was no method of deciding how much emphasis was to be given the various selected characteristics, such as deadrise, hollow floors, straight buttock length in the run, hollow or sharp entrance, hardness or softness of the bilge, and amount of sail to be carried. Again, comparison with existing successful vessels was the only practical method of obtaining that "happy combination" of hull and rig features that produced the outstanding fast sailer. This certainly hindered changes and unusual design ideas.

It must not be assumed that the failures of both the academic and practical ship designers to produce the required precision in design guides were the results of a lack of effort or intelligence. Certainly all logical approaches had been employed. The cause of failure in every case was the complexity of the problem and inability to measure the combined effects of the numerous elements of design, when in a "happy combination."

Today, resort to the model-testing tank, wind tunnel, or flow study would be mandatory in a new important design. Model testing of sailing craft, as we have seen, is not a new idea. However, model testing, though effective in predetermining performance to some degree, has given very few general design principles useful in predetermining design characteristics. The same is true of flow-line studies. What both model testing and flow studies have shown has been verification, in some degree at least, of the more basic ideas produced by hull-form elements and proportions, which have been used by practical designers in past generations.

Often, what appears to be a logical step in improvement of a design—on the basis that a little medicine helped the patient, so more medicine should hasten improvement still more—turns out to be very harmful. It is not surprising, then, to find it difficult to show a chronological development in the design of sailing vessels, by means of an increase in technological knowledge, particularly in hydrodynamics.

As a result, sailing vessel design has remained a "mystery and art," as it was described in the old apprentice-shipwrights' indentures, and this has made it so fascinating a profession throughout the ages.

Appendix

Spar Dimensions of Clipper Ship *Sweepstakes*

Designed by Daniel Westervelt, built by his father, Jacob Westervelt, of New York, in 1737. Length of keel, 216'; length on deck, 228'; beam, 41' 6"; depth of hold, 21' 6" 23/95 tons.

| | Masts | | | Yards | | |
	Whole Length	Dia.	Head	Whole Length	Dia.	Arms
Foremast	86'	3'	15'	78'	1' 9"	5'
Fore topmast	49'	1' 6"	8' 7"	62' 6"	1' 5"	5' 6"
Fore-topgallant	32' 6"	1' ½"	5' 3"	43' 6"	11½"	2' 9"
Fore-royal	20'			33'	9½"	2'
Fore-skysail	12'		7' 6"	27'	6"	1' 6"
Mainmast	90'	3'	15'	83'	1' 10"	5'
Main-topmast	51'	1' 6½"	9'	67'	1' 5"	5' 6"
Main-topgallant	34'	1' 1"	5' 6"	48'	1'	2' 9"
Main-royal	21'			38'	9½"	2'
Main-skysail	13'	10½"	9'	31'	7½"	1' 6"
Mizzenmast	82'	2' 5"	13'	65'	1' 5½"	3' 10"
Mizzentopmast	42'	1' 3"	8'	50' 3"	1'	4'
Mizzen-topgallant	29'	11"	4' 6"	35' 3"	9"	2' 3"
Mizzen-royal	16'			26' 6"	6"	1'
Mizzen-skysail	10'			21'	5"	1'
Bowsprit outboard	26' square	2' 9"	pole 6'			
Inner jib boom	16'					
Outer jib boom	15' 3"					
Flying jib boom	50'	10"	outboard 10'	pole 5'		

415

Appendix

	Masts			Yards		
	Whole Length	Dia.	Head	Whole Length	Dia.	Arms
Spanker boom	56′					
Spanker gaff	47′	10″				
Swinging booms	49′	10″				
Topmast studding-sail boom	50′ 11″					
Topgallant studding-sail boom	42′					
Royal studding-sail boom	34′					

Foremast 47′ abaft the knightheads on main deck
Mainmast 67′ abaft foremast
Mizzenmast 60′ abaft mainmast and 50′ to stern
Width abreast the foremast on the main rail outside of bulwarks   38′
Width abreast the mainmast on the main rail outside of bulwarks   41′
Width abreast the mizzenmast on the main rail outside of bulwarks   33′
Width across the stern   27′

Note: The mast positions in the draught do not agree with the measurements given here.

Spar Dimensions of Clipper Ship *Sovereign of the Seas*

Mast rake 6/8, 7/8 and 1¼ inch per foot, commencing with foremast.
Bowsprit 20′ outboard, 34′ dia., stive 4″ per foot.
Jib boom and flying jib boom in one spar, 15′ and 12′, 7′ end.
Spanker boom 61′, 2′ end, gaff 45′ with 5′ end.
Main Spender gaff 24′, 2′ end.

	Masts			Yards		
	Whole Length	Dia.	Head	Whole Length	Dia.	Arms
Fore	89¾′	41″	16′	80′	22″	5′
Top	50′	19″	10′	63′	17½″	5½′
Topgalt	27½′	14″	0	47′	14″	3¼′
Royal	18′	11½″	pole 10′	37′	8″	3¼′
Main	92½′	42″	17′	90′	24″	5′
Top	51′	19½″	11′	70′	19½″	5½′
Topgalt	30′	14¾″	0	53½′	15″	4′
Royal	20′	12″	0	42′	11″	3′
Skysail	14′	10″	pole 8′	35′	9″	2′
Mizzen	82¾′	34″	14′	70′	Crossjack 20″	4′
Top	43′	16″	9′	56′	15″	4½′
Topgalt	24′	11″	0	43′	11″	3′
Royal	17′	9½″	pole 8′	32′	7″	2′

Appendix

CONTEMPORARY ACCOUNTS OF CLIPPER SHIPS

Showing Griffith's theories by his comments on four clippers and partial specifications for the vessels.

Clipper Ship STAG-HOUND, of Boston from *The Monthly Nautical Magazine*

THE construction of this ship may be said to mark the introduction of the late clipper era at Boston. The building of fast vessels for foreign trade had for several years been adopted in New-York, having been first undertaken by Wm. H. Aspinwall, for whom Smith & Dimon, constructed the clipper-ship *Rainbow*, in 1843, which was followed by the *Howqua* and *Samuel Russell*, by Brown & Bell; and the famous *Sea-Witch*, also built by Smith & Dimon. It will be entirely proper to add, that the model of the *Sea-Witch* had more influence upon the subsequent configuration of fast vessels, than any other ship ever built in the United States. Her tables will be found in Griffith's MARINE and NAVAL ARCHITECTURE, published in 1850. In 1848 and 1849, New-York entered upon the era of steamship building, and by her late experience in modeling sailing vessels for high speed, found herself competent to contend successfully with the marine architects of Great Britain, and set afloat steamer after steamer, which found no match under any foreign flag upon the ocean.

Such was the condition of enterprise in New-York, for several years, before Boston awoke to distinguish herself in *clipper* building, and give to the world many of the fastest fleets, and largest ships in commercial service. The bold mind of Donald McKay grew restless under the idea, that a sister city was monopolizing the construction of fast vessels, and for many years he urged Boston merchants to enter the lists with Messrs. Aspinwall, Capt. N. B. Palmer, and others, and dispute for the palm of speed.

For a long time it was held by mercantile opinion that fast vessels were not so profitable as duller sailers, carrying larger cargoes; but the rise of freights, consequent upon the discovery of gold, and the emigration to California, determined the argument in the favor of all ambitious ship-builders and merchants, and *clippers* became the watchword of commercial men all over New-England, and in New-York. It only remained for the enterprise and genius of Boston to find exponents of her will among merchants and mechanics, to lay the foundation of an era in ship-building and navigation which should astonish the world. The leading minds at length stood forth.

Messrs. Geo. B. Upton, and Sampson, and Tappan, ordered the construction of the *Stag-Hound*, at the hands of Donald McKay, to exceed the tonnage, and excel the speed, of any ship of her class afloat. She was designed longer and sharper than any other vessel in the merchant service in the world. Her model was not undertaken without a thorough exploration of all discovered mysteries in modeling for speed, and the most celebrated models were sought out, and examined with care. The result was the production of the *Stag-Hound*, a vessel designed with special reference to her builder's beau ideal of perfection in every sea quality. His intelligent owners gave him the entire responsibility of design, model, construction, rig, and finish, while they stood by, having no other duties to perform than the financial task of footing the bills. To the wise and generous course of the owners, Mr. McKay was indebted for his opportunities for success. Nothing more clearly indicates the taste of a mercantile community than its ships; and nothing bears stronger testimony to the greatness and liberality of the mercantile mind, than the spirit manifested in carrying forward its enterprises. The noble, the generous, and the strong, are ever found wise and successful. The common manner of ordering a new ship, is for the merchant to select, or dictate, dimensions and model, and sketch a few specifications in a contract, which, when fulfilled, terminates the builder's responsibility. The success or failure of a ship, under such circumstances, ought to be, but seldom is, attributed to the merchant alone. This system is so common in all seaports, that builders rarely have an opportunity to show their skill as *designers*. As a general rule, the merchants, not the mechanics, ought to be held responsible for the qualities of their ships. Yet, in almost every instance, without exception, where ship-builders have had an opportunity of displaying their skill in the finer duties of their vocation, the result, as in the case of the *Stag-Hound*, has been most satisfactory.

The dimensions of the *Stag-Hound* are as follows:—Keel, 207 feet; between perpendiculars

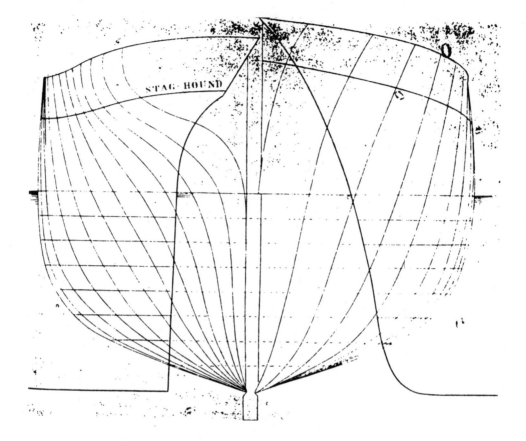

on deck, 215 feet; beam, 40 feet extreme; hold, 21 feet; and registered tonnage, 1,600 tons. Her depth of keel is 46 inches; dead rise at half floor, 40 inches. Perhaps the gravest mistake in her model, consisted in the great amount of dead rise, detracting from her stability and capacity, without a commensurate return in diminishing the absolute *resistance*, as it has been thought to do. Her keel is of rock maple and oak in two depths, sided 16 inches, and bolted with copper. The floors are sided from 10 to 12 inches, and moulded from 14 to 16 inches, bolted with 1¼ inch copper bolts. Her top timbers are of hackmatack, but the rest of her frame, and the stanchions, are of white oak. She has three depths of mid-ship keelsons, which, combined, mould 42 inches, and side 15 inches. The sister keelsons are 14 inches square, bolted diagonally through the navel timbers, or first futtocks, into the keel, and horizontally into the lower piece of keelson, and each other. Her hold stanchions are 10 inches square, kneed to the beams, and to the keelson.

The ceiling on the floor is 4½ in., square bolted; that from the bilge to the deck, in the hold, is 7 in. thick, scarphed and square bolted. A stringer 12 by 15 in. receives the ends of the hanging-knees, which are of hackmatack in both decks. The hanging-knees in the hold are sided from 10 to 11 in., moulded from 2 ft. to 26 in. in the throat, and have 16 bolts and 4 spikes in each. In the between-decks, the knees are sided about 10 in., and moulded in the throats about 20 in., fastened with 18 bolts and 4 spikes. The lower deck beams average about 16 by 17 in.; and those of the upper deck are 10 by 16 in., of hard pine. There is a pair of pointers 30 ft. long in each end; and three breast-hooks, and after-hooks, all of oak, closely bolted. The hold is calked and payed, from the limber boards to the deck. The height between-decks is 7 ft. The water-ways of lower deck are 15 in. square; the strake inside of them, 9 by 12 in.; and the two over them, combined, 10 by 18 inches. The ceiling above is 5 in. thick, square bolted. The between-deck stanchions are of oak, turned, secured with iron rods through their centres, which set up below. The upper deck water-ways are 12 in. square; and the two strakes inside of them, each 4½ by 6 in., let over the beams below. The planking of both decks is 3½ in. thick, of white pine. Her garboards are 7 in. thick, bolted through the keel and each other, and through the floors, and riveted. The strakes outside of them are graduated to 4½ in. on the bottom; and the wales, of 16 strakes, are each 5½ by 6 in., planked up flush to the plank-sheer. Her stanchions are 8 by 10 in., and the plank-sheer and rail, each, 6 by 16 inches. The bulwarks, including the monkey rail, are 6½ ft. high; and between the main and rack rails, there is a stout clamp, bolted through the stanchions, and through both rails. The bulwarks are very narrow, tongued and grooved, and fastened with composition spikes. Great pains were taken in driving her tree-nails and butt-bolts. She was salted, and has ventilators in her decks and plank-sheer, fore and aft. Her bowsprit and windlass-bitts, also the foretopsail sheet-bitts, are of white oak, strongly kneed above and below. Her main topmast stays lead on deck, and set up to bitts before the foremast. She has a top-gallant forecastle, at the height of main rail, in the after-wings of which, there are water-closets for the use of crew. Abaft the foremast, she has a house 42 ft. long by 24 ft. wide, and 6 ft. high, for the crew, with apartments for galley, store-room, &c. The upper part of house is ornamented with panel work.

Her cabins are under a half poop-deck, the height of the main rail, and have a descent of three feet below the upper deck. Along the sides, and around the stern, the poop is protected by a rail worked on turned stanchions. The poop is 44 ft. long, and in its front is a portico to the entrance of the cabins. The after cabin is 32 ft. long by 13 ft. wide, and 6 ft. 8 in. high. Its after-division is fitted into a spacious state-room, with two berths. Before this there is a water-closet on each side, then a state-room; before that a recess of eight feet on each side, and then two state-rooms. The sides of the cabins are splendidly finished with mahogany Gothic panels, enameled pilasters and cornices, and gilded mouldings. It has a large skylight amid-ships, and every state-room has its deck and side-light also. The cabin furniture is first class. The forward-cabin contains the captain's state-room, which overlooks the upper deck on the starboard side; it also contains the pantry and staterooms for the three mates and the steward. It is 12 by 18 ft., neatly painted and grained, and lighted as abaft. Inside the ship is painted pearl color, relieved with white; and outside, black, from the water-line to the rail. She has patent copper pumps, which work with fly-wheel and winches,—a patent windlass, with ends which ungear, and two beautiful capstans, made of mahogany and locust, inlaid with brass. She has a cylindrical, iron water tank of 4,500 gallons capacity, the depth of the ship secured below the upper deck, abaft the mainmast, and resting upon a bed of timbers over the keelson.

MASTS AND SPARS.

The masts of the *Stag-Hound* rake alike, viz.:—1¼ in. in the foot. The distance from the stem to the centre of foremast, on deck, is 50 ft.; thence to the main, 67 ft.; thence to the mizzen, 56 ft.; and thence to the stern post, 42 feet. The following are the dimensions of her masts and yards:—

	Diameter. in.	Length. ft.	Mastheads. ft.
Fore	32½	82	13
Top	16	46	9
Topgallant	10	25	0
Royal	9	17	0
Skysail	8	13	pole 7
Main	33	88	14
Top	17½	51	9½
Topgallant	12	28	0

	Diameter. in.	Length. ft.	Mastheads. ft.
Royal	11	19	0
Skysail	10	15	pole 9
Mizzen	26	78	12
Top	12½	40	8
Topgallant	9	22	0
Royal	8	16	0
Skysail	7	11	pole 6

YARDS

Fore	20	72	yard-arms 4½
Top	15	57	5
Topgallant	10	42	3
Royal	7	32	2
Skysail	6½	24½	1½
Main	22	86	4½
Top	17	68	5
Topgallant	15	53	3½
Royal	10½	42	2½
Skysail	7	32	1½
Crossjack	16	60	4
Mizzen topsail	11½	48	4½
Topgallant	10	36	2½
Royal	7	27	1½
Skysail	6	22	1
Bowsprit	28½	24—4½ in. steve.	
Jib boom	16½	outside of cap, divided at	
Flying jib boom		38 { 18 and 15 ft. for inner and outer jibs, with 5 ft. end.	
		18 ft. outside of wythe, with pole	4
Spanker-boom	13	60	pole 2½
Gaff		44	5
Fore and main spencer gaffs, each		25	2

Her fore and main are made masts; the former being 29½ in., and the latter 30 in. in diameter at the truss bands. Her topmasts and jibboom are of hard pine.

The fore and main rigging is 10 in., four stranded, patent rope, wormed and served over the ends up to the leading trucks; the mizzen rigging is 8 in., the fore and main stays, 9½ in., the fore and main topmast backstays, 9¾ in., the topmast rigging, 4¼ in., set up on the ends; the mizzen topmast rigging, 4¾ in., mizzen topmast backstays 7¾ in., fore and main topgallant backstays and jibboom guys, 6½ in.; and the other standing rigging in like proportions. She has chain bobstays and bowsprit shrouds, martingale stays and guys, and topsail sheets and ties, patent trusses, &c. Her fore and main chain plates are 1⅞ in. iron.

With respect to her model, it will be seen that the floor has a large angle of dead-rise, and is long in a fore and aft direction. When launched she drew 10½ ft. forward, and 11½ ft. aft, including 39 in. keel, clear of garboards. In January, 1851, the *Stag-Hound* sailed from New-York for San Francisco, under the command of Capt. Richardson. She performed the voyage in 115 days, or 107 days sailing time, having lost her topmasts, and touched at Valparaiso.

She has made three other passages from New-York to San-Francisco in 124, 121 and 110 days respectively. The sailing distance, on the last voyage, was 16,408 miles, and the daily average 158 miles.

From Whampoa to New-York, the *Stag-Hound* has made three passages in 85, 91 and 92 days. All these, and her many other passages, are considerably shorter than the average of clipper voyages in the corresponding months of the year, between the same ports; yet the *Stag-Hound* has failed for want of opportunity to reach a degree of speed quite equal to the best performances of ships, either of her own, or of less displacement.

Appendix

Clipper Ship LIGHTNING, of Boston
from *The U.S. Nautical Magazine and Naval Journal*

It always affords us pleasure to furnish a tangible exponent to the progress of Marine Architecture in every part of our continent, from the smallest coasting schooner to the noblest clipper which circumnavigates the globe. In a former number of the Magazine we published the lines of the *"Stag-Hound,"* the first of the numerous fleet of celebrated clippers which has been built by Mr. Donald McKay, at Boston, within a period of four years. Through his politeness we now publish the draught and calculations of the famous Australian racer, "LIGHTNING," one of the latest and sharpest ships which her builder has constructed. This vessel was built in 1854, and fairly reflected the skill of Mr. McKay at that period. She is owned in England, and sailed from Boston to Liverpool in 13 days and 20 hours, and, on her first trip to Melbourne and back, bore off the palm for speed on that route. She accomplished the outward run in 77 days, the return voyage 64 days; second outward passage, 75 days, homeward, 65 days; the shortest passage on record being 63 days. She is owned by the proprietors of Baine's Line of Liverpool and Australian packets, and her performances indicate a profitable model, beyond the mark of steamships, upon the route to which she has been eminently adapted.

The dimensions and calculations of the "Lightning" will be found as follows:

		Feet.
Length on the load-line for calculations...................		227.50
Height of load-line, above base line......................		15.
Breadth on load-line, at dead flat.........................		43.12
Breadth extreme..		44.30
Area of load water plane, sq. feet........................	3383.17	
Exponent of the same...................................	0.654	
Centre of gravity of same abaft mid-length................		3.34
Area of greatest transverse section, sq. feet................	572.6	
Exponent of the same...................................	0.885	
Location, abaft mid-length, of load-line...................		8.
Moulded displacement, in cubic feet......................	57.227	
Moulded displacement, in gross tons.....................	1635.	
Exponent of the same...................................	0.524	
Centre of gravity below load-line.........................		5.89
Centre of gravity abaft mid-length of do..................		2.24
Moment of stability, S. ⅔d x =........................	775744.	
Height of *meta centre* above centre of buoyancy..........		13.53

From the above data, as well as from the draught, it may be seen that no timid hand, or hesitating brain, gave form and dimensions to the "Lightning." Very great stability, acute extremities, full, short, midship body, comparatively small dead-rise, and the longest end forward, are points in the excellence of this ship.

By European naval authorities such a model would be repudiated on account of the centre of gravity of displacement being found abaft of mid-length of load line, but such authors have little weight with the independent modellers of America. And although the mechanical advisers of her owners have accomplished their purpose, by filling out the bow of the vessel to suit their crude notions of science, it will be found that some modification in the distribution of the propulsory power was all that was necessary (as we shall show in connection with her spar draught in our next issue) to make her all that could be desired by the fogyistic advocates of full bows in the Old World.

It having been laid down by Chapman, the celebrated Swedish Naval Architect, that the centre of buoyancy should be determined *forward* of the mid-length of the load-line within certain arbitrary limits, because, from an analysis of the bodies of vessels which bore good characters at sea, he found this point so situated, more than half a century ago, that *naval* and marine architects of the Old World have never ventured to risk an experiment to test the value of this stale dogma. In England "experimental *fleets* have been built, none of which have ever established any marked distinction for their constructors, most of them having reached the *ultima thule* of scientific men, so called, because they have systematized hereditary knowledge, and trammelled themselves with formulas drawn from the *half revealed mysteries* of ship-building. The moderate dead rise of this remarkable ship is also at variance with *naval* learning. In fact, some builders are to be found in every part of the world, who, by this time, are awaking to the belief, that the *bow* of a ship is the seat of life and motion, nay, intelligence itself may seem almost developed in this part of the body under the hand of the artistic delineator of form. In the "Lightning" the fuller end is the posterior, as it should be, for speed. But the strongest point is her *stability*, her depth of hold being chosen without regard to a violation of "tonnage" laws. This need no longer be done in vessels for British markets. The "Lightning" is a worthy example of an improving art.

Construction and Finish of the Ship LIGHTNING
from *The U.S. Nautical Magazine and Naval Journal*

REFERENCE may be had to page 188, for the draught, calculations, and a few remarks concerning this ship. We now give additional particulars, with her spar draft.

Her keel is of white oak, sided 15, moulded 30 inches. Its scarfs are 12 feet long, bolted with copper, and its parts were also bolted together before the frames were raised. The floor timbers are sided from 12 to 14 inches, and moulded 19; and the frames are chocked with oak above and below every joint, and bolted together fore and aft. She has three tiers of midship keelsons, each tier 15 inches square, and double sister keelsons of the same size on each side, one above the other. The whole of these keelsons are bolted through the timbers and keel with inch-and-a-quarter copper and iron, the bolts within a foot of one another. The sister keelsons are also bolted horizontally through the midship keelsons and each other. All the keelsons are scarphed and keyed, and fitted close together. Her frame, all the knees in the hold, and her hooks and pointers are of white oak, and her planking is of hard pine. The whole of her ceiling is of hard pine, and that on the floor is 5 inches thick. Over the first futtocks there are two bilge keelsons, each 15 inches square, placed alongside of each other, and these, like the other keelsons, are scarphed and keyed. They are square, fastened through the timbers, the bolts having been driven alternately from both sides and riveted, and they are also bolted together edgeways. The ceiling above the bilge keelsons up to the lower deck, is all 9 by 12 inches, all bolted together edgeways every three feet, and square fastened through the timbers. The lower deck beams are 14 by 16 inches midships, tapered an inch or two towards the ends, and the knees connected with them are of white oak. The hanging knees are sided from 10 to 12 inches, have 5½ feet bodies, 4 feet arms, are moulded about 22 inches in the angles, and have 20 volts and 4 spikes in each. Their lower ends rest upon a lap-strake or stringer of 6 inches thick by 12 inches wide, which is bolted through the ceiling and the timbers. This strake forward and aft is beamed and kneed in the angles of the ends, and forms a strong horizontal hook. The lodging knees are sided 8 inches, are scarphed together in every berth, and closely bolted. The stanchions are very stout, are clasped with iron, and are kneed to the beams above, and to the keelsons below. There are 4 massive pointers of oak forward, ranging from 20 to 50 feet in length, and two of these are filled in the angles with hooks, and the others are fayed to the keelsons below and to the beams above. They are 12 inches square, and are bolted from both sides, through the cants and timbers. Her ends are as strongly secured as those of a Davis Straits whaler. The run is secured in the same massive style as the bow.

Her between deck waterways are of hard pine 15 inches square, with a strake of 9 by 12 inches inside of them, jogged over the beams and bolted through them, and another strake of 12 by 14 inches over them. These extend her whole length, are bolted vertically through the beams, and horizontally through the timbers. The ceiling above is 5 inches thick, and the clamp under the upper deck beams is 9 by 14 inches, and, like the other ceiling, it is square fastened. The upper deck beams are 9 by 14 inches, and the knees connected with them are of hackmatack, about the same size as those below, and are fastened in the same style. The stanchions under them are of oak turned, and have bolts through their centres, which are keyed on the upper deck beams and set up with nuts and screws to the beams below, thus binding both decks together. The planking of the lower deck is of hard pine, 3½ inches thick, and the upper deck

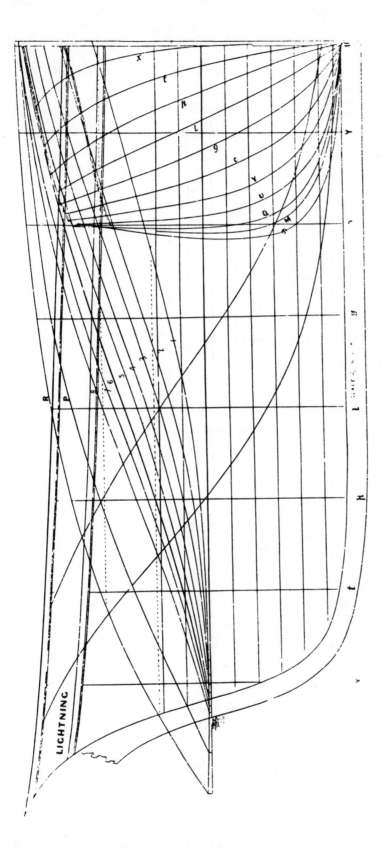

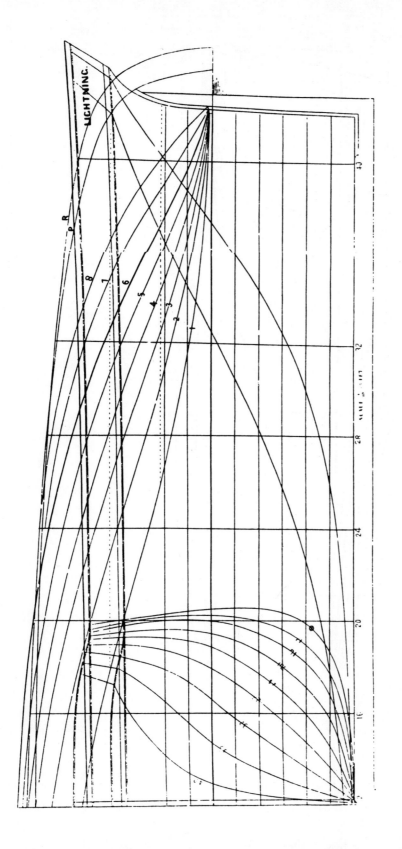

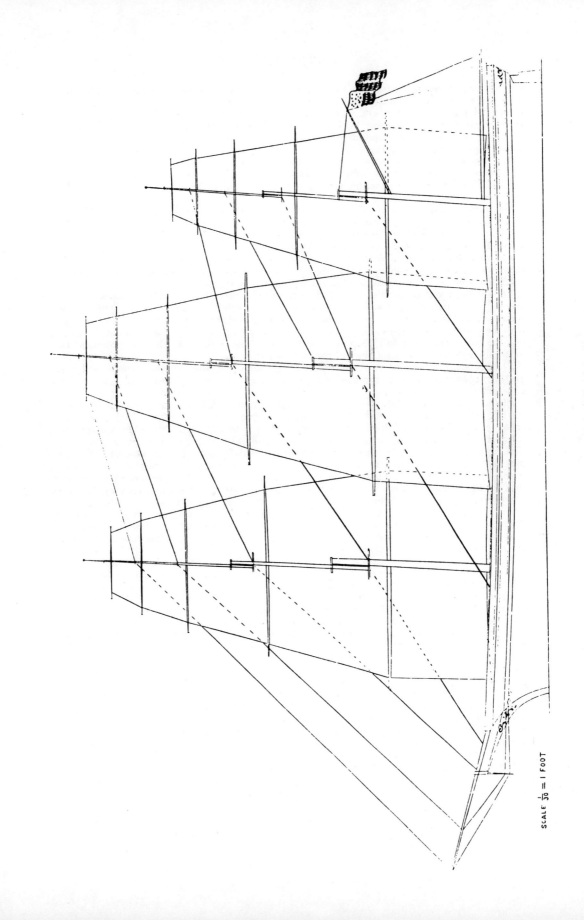

SCALE $\frac{1}{30}$ = 1 FOOT

is white pine of the same substance. In every berth, between the hanging knees, she is diagonally cross-braced with hard pine of 9 by 7 inches over the ceiling, and these braces are bolted through the ceiling and timbers. Her hooks forward and aft between decks are beamed and kneed in the same style as those below. She has 32 beams under the upper deck, and 30 under the lower deck, with a corresponding number of carlines. All the mast-partners and hatchways are strongly kneed in every angle.

The upper deck waterways are 12 by 14 inches, with a thick strake inside of them, chamfered off towards the deck; and her bulwarks, like those of a ship of war, are built solid inside and outside. The bulwarks are 5 feet high, surmounted by a monkey rail of 2 feet, which is panelled on the inside.

Her garboards are 8 by 12 inches, the second strake 7 by 12, the third 6 by 12, chamfered off to 4½ inches thick, the substance of the planking on the bottom. The wales are 5½ by 8 inches, and she is planked flush to the planksheer moulding. Outside as well as inside she is square-fastened, and is butt and bilge bolted with copper.

The mouldings of the planksheer and rail are relieved with raised strakes above and below them, which are also moulded on the edges; and outside she is polished smooth as marble, and every line and moulding is graduated in exact proportions, fore and aft.

The whole height of her bulwarks is 7 feet, and she has a full topgallant forecastle, which extends to the fore-rigging; and its deck is connected with the top of a house, which is continued aft, and is 48 feet long, and 19 wide at the after-end. The top of this house is connected with the poop by two gangways, so that the men can pass forward and aft without descending into the waist. She has a full poop-deck 90 feet long, the outline of which is protected by a mahogany rail, on turned stanchions of the same wood.

There is a spacious house over the wheel, designed, in part, for a smoking-room; and it also protects a staircase on the starboard side, which leads to the captain's state-room and the after-cabin.

The after-cabin is 34 feet long, 12 wide, and 7 high, and is wainscoted with mahogany, enamel, polished ash, and other fancy woods, relieved with rosewood pillars, paper-maché cornices, and flowered gilding. It has 4 state-rooms, 2 sofa-recesses and other apartments, a splendid sofa aft, rich carpeting, a circular marble table in each recess, and a mahogany extension table amidships. All the state-rooms are furnished differently, for the sake of variety, we suppose, and their furniture is of the choicest kind, arranged with consummate skill. Every state-room has a square window in the side, and a perforated ventilator between the beams; so that, for light and air, all has been done that could be desired. There are 4 stern windows, and a large, oblong-square skylight in the after-cabin, and similar skylights over the dining-saloon, which is connected with the after-cabin. The skylights are set on mahogany frames, and nearly all the windows are of stained glass. In the recesses and partition of the after-cabin are plate-glass mirrors, which give reflected views of every part of the cabin. A more beautiful cabin, or one more richly furnished, is seldom seen.

The dining-saloon, which leads from the cabin, is also wainscoted—is painted pure white, like enamel, and is tastefully relieved with gilded mouldings and flower-work. It is 48 feet long, 13 feet wide aft, and 14 forward, and has a large mahogany table its whole length, with settees along its sides. It has spacious state-rooms and other apartments on each side its whole length, and these rooms are admirably designed for the accommodation of families. In richness of furniture, light, and ventilation, they are equal to those of the after-cabin. At the forward partition there is a costly side-board of marble, and rising from it is a large mirror. Another mirror and sofa ornament the after part, so that the saloon is reflected from both ends.

The chief-officer's state-room is on the starboard side forward, and the pantry opposite; and between them are two doors, which lead to the quarter-deck. The front of the poop-deck projects about five feet, and shelters the entrances to the saloon.

The accommodations for her second-cabin passengers are in the house before the main hatchway, which has an entrance amidships, aft. It is 36 ft. long, and has a passage amid-ships 5 feet wide, which leads to six state-rooms on each side; and these rooms are well lighted and ventilated, and tastefully furnished. The forward part of this house contains the galley, and before it, on each side, are staircases which lead to the between-decks. Her crew's accommodations are under the topgallant forecastle, and are neatly fitted up.

The between-decks are designed for the accommodation of passengers, and have 10 plate-glass air-ports on each side, skylights and ventilators along the sides of the house above; so that they are well supplied with light and ventilation, and will be fitted up in superior style when the ship arrives in Liverpool.

As the top of the house projects three feet on each side, a waterproof awning will be spread from it to the rails, so as to shelter the waist, that the passengers may always have an opportunity of coming on deck without exposure to wet weather.

Her accommodations forward and aft are upon a liberal scale, and are most admirably designed for health, comfort, and safety.

The ship herself is amply found in the best of ground tackle, has a good, substantial windlass, three capstans, a patent steering apparatus, and copper-chambered pumps; and below she has an iron water-tank of 5,000 gallons capacity.

This magnificent ship is owned by Messrs. James Baines & Co., of Liverpool, designed for their line of Liverpool and Australian packets, and is commanded by Captain James N. Forbes, who superintended her outfits. Captain Forbes is well known as the former commander of the famous ship Marco Polo, built in St. John's, New Brunswick, in which he made two successive voyages from Liverpool to Australia, in less than twelve months, including detention in port. Her builder, Donald McKay, has a world-wide reputation. His ships, for beauty, strength and speed, have no superiors on this side of the Atlantic; and as the Lightning is the first ship ever built in the United States, for an English house, he has done his best to make her perfect in every detail.

She is the largest ship belonging to Liverpool, and has proved herself one of the fleetest sailers ever built on either side of the Atlantic.

VOYAGE OF THE CLIPPER SHIP "LIGHTNING" FROM ENGLAND TO AUSTRALIA AND BACK.

Having furnished the draught and particulars of this Boston built ship, it is only fair to place on record some of her remarkable performances, an account of which we quote as follows from a Liverpool commercial paper:

Extraordinary run of the "Lightning."

LIVERPOOL, *Oct.* 23, 1855.

A few days ago we recorded the extraordinary run of the clipper ship Red Jacket, Reed, commander, belonging to the White Star line of Australia packets, which made the passage hence to Melbourne in 69½ days, and homeward in 73½ days. We have now the pleasure of chronicling the still more extraordinary performance of the rival clipper Lightning, Forbes (late of the Marco Polo) commander, belonging to the Black Ball line. This vessel, on her recent passage to Melbourne, was delayed by light and head winds, and, consequently, made a comparatively long run of nearly 78 days; but, on the passage home, Captain Forbes has shown what the Lightning is capable of doing under moderately favorable circumstances, by making the run in the unparalleled short space of 63 days—thus regaining the supremacy which had been snatched from him by Captain Reed.

The Lightning has brought upwards of 80 passengers and 40,000 ounces of gold, besides a large amount in the hands of passengers. She also brings answers to letters taken out by the Great Britain, making the course of post 132 days.

The Lightning sailed hence on the 14th day of May, and has made the voyage out and home, including the detention of 20 clear days at her anchors in Hobson's Bay, in 5 months 8 days and 21 hours, mean time, from passing the Rock Light till she was back in the river again; thus performing the voyage in upwards of three days less time than the Red Jacket, notwithstanding that she was at anchor in Hobson's Bay for a period of five days more than that vessel.

The Lightning anchored opposite Sandridge, three miles from Melbourne, on the afternoon of the 31st of July, and her mails were delivered, after she had anchored at the Post-office, Melbourne, at half-past five o'clock in the afternoon of that day.

The time occupied by the Lightning in making the round voyage to Australia and back,, considering her detention in port, is unprecedentedly short, notwithstanding that the outward voyage, from the nature of the winds experienced, occupied longer than might have reasonably been expected from the well known qualifications of the ship and the ability of her commander. Her run from the Mersey to the Equator occupied 25 days, and from the parallel of the Cape to Port Phillip Heads 30 days; indeed, such was the nature of the winds, that the topgallantsails never had occasion to be furled during the entire passage, neither was there occasion to reef the topsails. With the exception of five days, when the ship logged 332, 348, 300, 311, and 329 knots respectively per day, no extraordinary distances were logged. Cape Otway Light was made on the night of the 29th of July, Port Phillip Heads on the 30th, and she cast anchor, as above stated, in Hobson's Bay, on the 31st, her run having occupied 77½ days, mean time.

On the 20th of August, the mails and passengers being embarked, and everything ready for sea, the anchor was hove up, and the Lightning was taken in tow by the steamer Washington as far as the Heads, which she passed at 4 P.M., a smart north-west breeze blowing at the time, and by noon of the 21st, 268 miles were logged, Swan Island Light, Banks' Straits, having been passed at 11 A.M. On the 24th, at 4 A.M., she passed a large ship supposed to be the Mermaid, which sailed two days previously for Liverpool; and at 10 P.M. same day, passed the Auckland Islands. Thence to the 28th, when the ship was in lat. 57.20 S., long. 164 W., fresh westerly and south-westerly breezes were experienced, and the ship went nobly along, seldom logging less than 14, and frequently 18½ and 19 knots an hour.

At 11 P.M. on the 28th, while under a heavy press of canvas, a violent squall from the south-west caught the ship, and carried away the foretopmast studdingsail-boom, the foretop, foretop-gallant, and foreroyal yards, and blowing all the sails to pieces, and the ship was obliged to go under easy canvas for the succeeding four days until the yards and sails had been replaced. From the first to the 8th of September fine westerly winds were experienced, and the ship averaged close upon 300 miles per day, as per log. On the 8th, at 3 A.M., Cape Horn bore north-west, distant 50 miles, being a run of only 19 days mean time from Port Phillip Heads, by far the fastest ever recorded either under canvas or steam. On the 10th, 11th, and 12th, north-east, east, and south-east winds were experienced, and but moderate distances were logged, the ship having to be frequently tacked to make a fair-way course. On the 13th and 14th, strong and south-west winds were experienced, and she ran 351 and 354 miles per day respectively. From the 15th to the 20th light and head winds were met with, and only from six to seven knots per hour were averaged. On the 20th she was in lat. 29.13 S., long. 31.40 W., and thence to Pernambuco, which port was passed at a distance of six miles, on the morning of the 28th, nothing but light north-east and north-north-east winds were experienced.

The Equator was crossed at 9 A.M. on the 30th, in long. 34.30 W., the ship at the time being only out a little over 40 days mean time from Port Phillip—an extraordinary achievement, considering the adverse winds encountered after rounding Cape Horn. For the first five days after crossing the Equator light winds and calms were met with, accompanied by heavy torrents of rain, and the ship made little or no progress. On the 5th, in lat. 10 N., long. 34 W., gentle north-east trade winds were experienced, which continued until the 10th, in lat. 30 N., long. 37 W. On the 11th and 12th she had moderate south-east winds, and at noon of the latter day was in the latitude of St. Michael's and long. 30 W., being only 4 months and 29 days out from the time of leaving Liverpool. From the 12th to the 19th the winds were east-north-east and north-east, very light, and during the intervening seven days the ship reached lat. 46.15 N., long. 28 W., and at 10 P.M. on the 19th a strong northerly breeze sprang up, which continued until her arrival off the Old Head of Kinsale, at 4 A.M., yesterday. At 10 A.M., off Mine Head, signals were exchanged with the Royal Mail steamship Arabia, hence for New-York; at 3.30 P.M. Tuskar Light was passed; at 8.30 P.M. Holyhead Light was passed; and at 10.30 P.M. the ship was abreast Point Lynas, where she received a pilot. The ship was kept under easy sail during the night, waiting a sufficiency of water to cross the bar, and arrived in the river 9.30 this morning.

Notwithstanding the performance of this vessel, there existed in the minds of the nautical fraternity a positive denial of the principles of construction developed in her model; and while it had been made quite manifest to her constructor that even a better distribution of the propulsory power might have been made, it was quite sufficient for the English builders to know this, when they had a pretext for endeavoring to cripple the original design, and succeeded in persuading the owners to fill out those hollow lines on the bows, so much at variance with their notions of propriety; accordingly the bow was filled out until a convex line was obtained, and this was done in a manner which is not mechanical, the fillings being of soft pine, and the connection being such as to leave the vessel leaky; and now, before the vessel had established a reputation, the English mechanics were quite willing to attribute any subsequent performance worthy of note to their modification of the fineness of her lines on the anterior part, which is but an incubus at best, as the spar draft, in connection with the lines, will prove, and abundantly pay for the investigation, and show the centre of propulsion to be too far forward of the centre of buoyancy.

Clipper Ship HERALD OF THE MORNING
from *The U.S. Nautical Magazine and Naval Journal*

THE clipper ship "Era" will not soon be forgotten by the careful observer of the progress of ship-building in the United States. While it is a cherished notion with many, that nothing has been done toward the advancement of the art, it is the settled conviction of quite as many, that much has been gained, and we are quite willing to be classed with those who believe that something has been done. As the man who has learned to know himself, has acquired the first and most important lesson in human wisdom, in acquiring a knowledge of his proclivities to err, so the era of clipper ship-building has taught us the weakness of our ships, and should not pass unheeded. The lessons learned by damaged cargoes should be salutary and lasting. It cannot be denied that there has been more wealth wasted in clipper ships, directly traceable to an improper distribution of the materials in their construction, than by every other consideration. In the rapid race of competing interests, during the struggle for supremacy, in the size and length of clippers, owners, and not a few builders, seem to have forgotten the alienation they were cherishing between the bow and stern, by the increasing distance between them, and that, without substituting a new bond of sympathy, they would engender discord at the very spine of the fabric. We are glad to be able to present one of the exceptions to this very general rule of construction in the HERALD OF THE MORNING, the lines and spar draft of which accompany this article.

This ship was built by Messrs. Hayden & Cudworth, of Boston, too well known in the ship-building world to require a word of commendation from us. They were assisted in maturing the plans and calculations of this vessel by Mr. S. H. Pook. For her dimensions, see draft.

In materials and mechanism, this ship will compare favorably with any of her class. She has a keel of rock-maple, sided 15 inches, moulded 20 inches, and two depths of keelson, of yellow-pine, each 15 inches square. Her frame was selected with care, is of white-oak, floors sided 12 and 13 inches, diminishing to 8 inches at rail. The scantling is 17 inches at keel, 12 in. at floor heads, and 6 ½. inches at deck, with 4-inch bolts in each scarph. She has sister keelsons, 12 by 12, fastened with 1¼ iron to keelson and floors, also riders, 8 by 12 inches. Her stem and post are white-oak, the former sided 15 inches, the latter sided 15 at keel, 17 inches at main transom, and moulded 15 and 24 inches. The dead-woods are of white-oak, bolted 2 feet apart with 1¼ inch yellow metal, and also with iron, through and riveted. Ceiling of yellow-pine, bottom 4 inches, bilge 10 inches, in two thicknesses, and bolted separately; breaking joints, below lower deck, 6 inches; lower deck clamps, 5½ inches; five strakes, 12 inches wide; lower deck water-ways, 15 by 15, with sperketing; two strakes above, 10 by 10 inches, bolted to each timber with 1⅛ bolts, and to each other; thick strakes on deck, 7 by 12, let down on beams, 1 inch, and bolted to water-way, 5 feet apart, with 1⅛ iron. Main deck clamps, 5½ thick, in two strakes. Main deck water-ways, yellow-pine, 12 by 12 inches. Lower deck beams, 13 by 15, yellow-pine. Main deck beams, 9 by 13 inches; knees of white-oak, 7, 8 and 10 inches sided, bolted through, and riveted with 1⅛ iron, three knees to each end of beam, viz: lodge, lap or bosom, and hanging. Deck plank, whitepine, 3 inches thick; plank-shear and rail are each 7 inches thick, of white-oak. She has a deck hook, both forward and aft, on each deck, with three diagonal hooks, also, both forward and aft, coming up to beams, and kneed and well fastened at ends to same with through bolts, of yellow metal. She has a poop-deck, cabin extending forward of mizzen-mast, midships, and nearly to mizzen at side. She also has a top-gallant forecastle, with suitable capstan and bitts, the deck extending nearly to windlass; she also has a house on deck, about 40 feet in length, between the fore and main hatch. The pumps, aft of the main-mast, have composition chambers, and the usual rail around the mast, forward of the main hatch; she has, also, an after hatch forward of cabin, with capstan midway between hatches. The general arrangement is that of utility and convenience; while her performance is commensurate with her model and construction. Success to her.

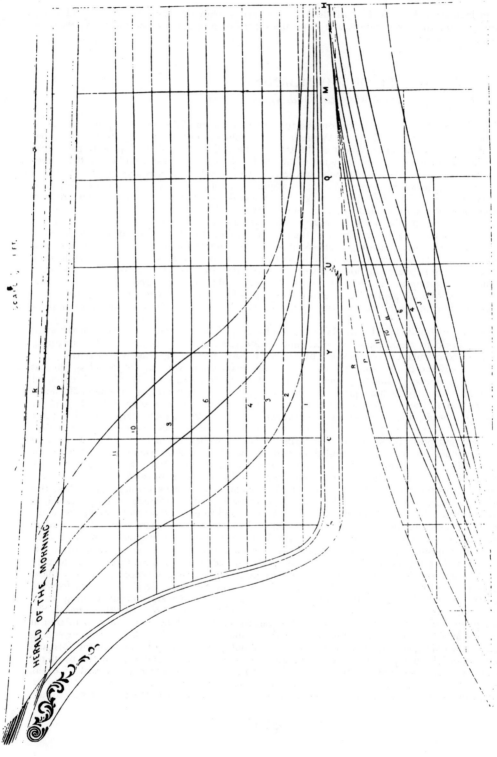

HERALD OF THE MORNING

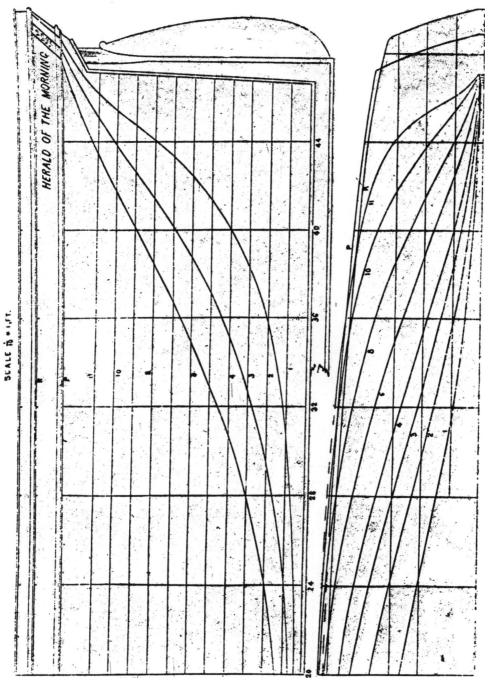

SCALE $\frac{1}{16}$ = 1 FT.

HERALD OF THE MORNING

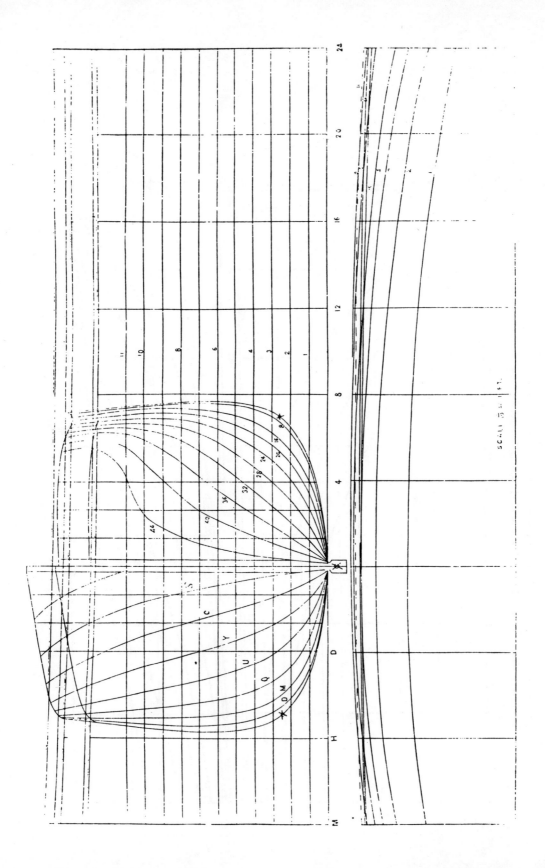

SCALE 10 1 FT.

Appendix

Clipper Ship RED JACKET from *The U.S. Nautical Magazine and Naval Journal*

THIS vessel has been regarded by many as one of the finest of her class. She was built in Rockland, Maine, by Mr. George Thomas, under the direction of Captain Isaac Taylor, of Boston, *a man of energy,—of the "live and let live" stamp*—whose ships bear the imprint of advancement; and were it not for the few there are of such men, this would be a stand-still instead of a progressive age. This vessel has proved herself to be a fine sailer, having frequently sailed 350 nautical miles in 24 hours. She is buoyant and weatherly, and withal a fine sea-boat; and we only regret that one of her logs cannot be found. Her dimensions are as follows: extreme 250 feet long, 44 feet wide, and 24 feet deep. Her design is the result of a *carte blanche* given to Mr. S. H. Pook, of Boston, by whose politeness we furnish the lines of this fine vessel.

SPARS OF CLIPPER-SHIP RED JACKET.

	Length. Ft. In.	Feet.	Ft. In.	Ft. In.
Foremast	89	head 16	Yard 80	arm 5
Topmast	50	" 10	" 63	" 5 6
Topgallant	26 6	"	" 47	" 3 6
Royal	18	"	" 37	" 2 6
Skysail	12 6	pole 5	" 28	" 1 6
Mainmast	92	head 17	Yard 90	arm 5
Topmast	54	" 11	" 70	" 5 6
Topgallant	30		" 53 6	" 4
Royal	20		" 44	" 3
Skysail	14	pole 6	" 35	" 2
Mizzenmast	82	head 14	Cross-Jack 70	arm 4
Topmast	43	" 9	Yard 56	" 4 6
Topgallant	24		" 43	" 3
Royal	17		" 32	" 2
Skysail	24	pole 4	" 23	" 1
Bowsprit	11			
Jib-boom	23 out	Spanker-boom	60	end 2
Spencer gaff	20 by 15 by 5	Gaff	45	" 5

Foremast below deck, 22 feet.   Mainmast below deck, 20 feet, 6 inches.
Mizzen "   "   " 20 " 9 inches.

Stations on Deck: Knight heads to foremast, 50 feet; Fore to main, 78 feet; Main to mizzen, 64 feet; Mizzen to taffrail, 49 feet, 6 inches;—241 feet, 6 inches.

433

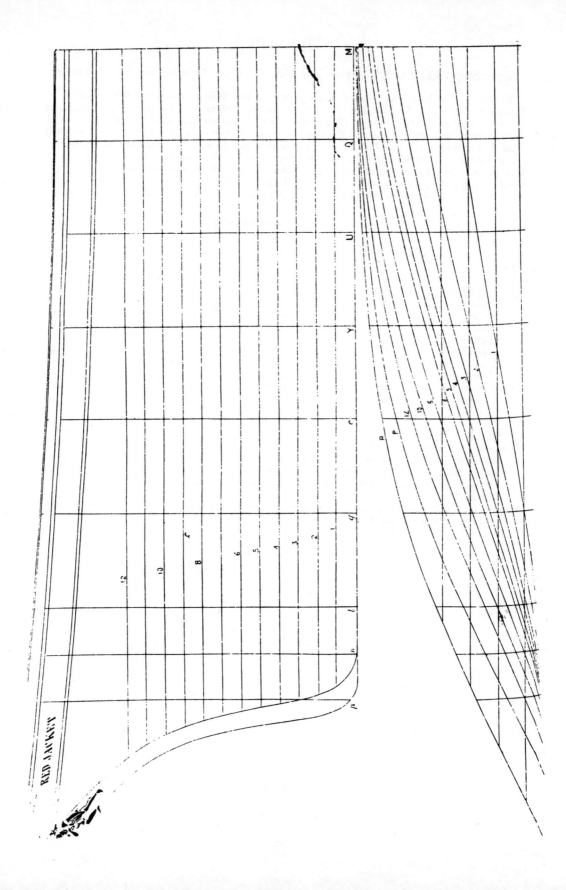
RED JACKET

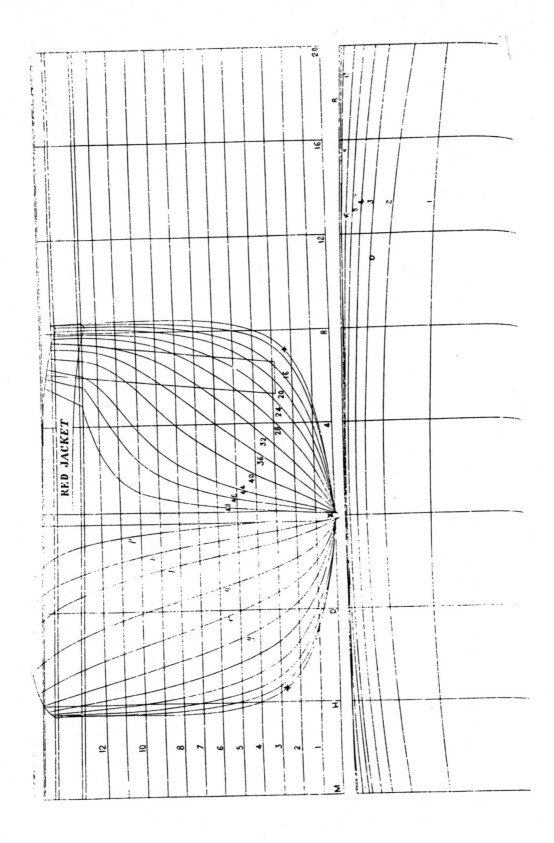

RED JACKET

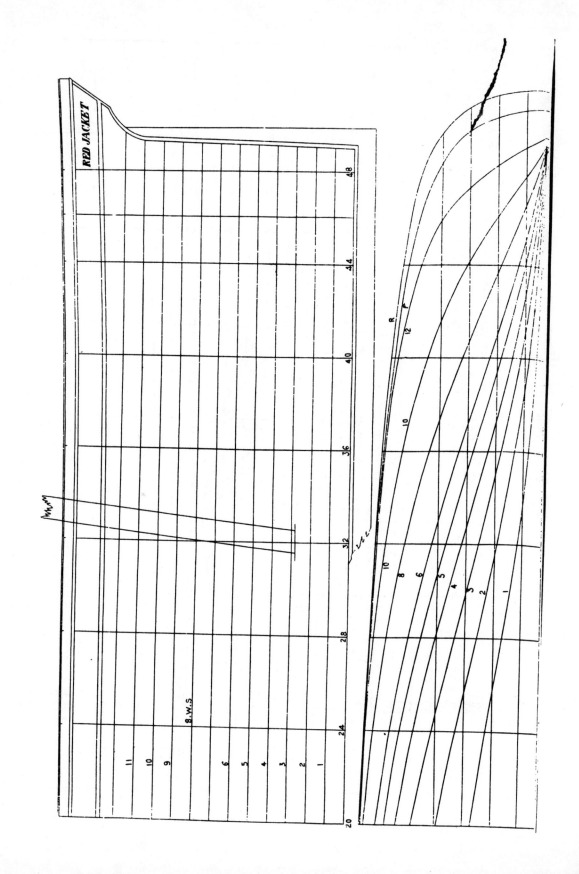

Index

INDEX

INDEX

INDEX